STRUCTURE OF MATTER SERIES

MARIA GOEPPERT MAYER
Advisory Editor

MICROWAVE SPECTROSCOPY

MICROWAVE
SPECTROSCOPY

WALTER GORDY

Professor of Physics
Duke University

WILLIAM V. SMITH

Professor of Physics, Chairman
of the Physics Department
University of Delaware

RALPH F. TRAMBARULO

Assistant Professor of Physics
Pennsylvania State College

New York · JOHN WILEY & SONS, Inc.
London · CHAPMAN & HALL, Ltd.
1953

Library of Congress Catalog Card Number: 53–6820

PRINTED IN THE UNITED STATES OF AMERICA

To

Who has helped unceasingly in the
preparation of this volume

PREFACE

Although microwave spectroscopy is a relatively new field of investigation, there are already so many research papers published in it that any new researcher must spend considerable time to become familiar with what has been done. One of the aims of this book, which is the first one written on the subject, is to provide for microwave spectroscopists, chemists, physicists, and other scientists a conveniently available source of the large amount of very precise information which has been obtained to date through microwave spectroscopy. This information is summarized in various tables. In addition, a bibliography is provided. Another objective of the book is to facilitate the analysis and interpretation of the microwave data accumulated. Pertinent formulas are given in forms most convenient for analysis. Numerical tables are provided for aid in the analysis of the spectra. A third objective is to make it easy for the beginner to become familiar with the instruments and experimental methods of microwave spectroscopy. The fundamental theory involved in the detection of microwave absorption lines is given with detailed description of significant spectrographic components.

It is readily apparent to anyone who reads this book that microwave spectroscopy is not a single subject but rather a common method which can be applied to the study of various problems in physics, chemistry, electronics, and even astronomy. The theories involved in the experimental methods and in the interpretation of the results are numerous and frequently complex. They draw upon such branches of theoretical physics as electromagnetic theory, electrodynamics, group theory, and quantum mechanics. Futhermore, a chemical background and a practical knowledge of electronics are essential to a successful microwave spectroscopist. It is obviously impossible to condense into a single volume all the information which a specialist would need, or to give a rigorous treatment of all pertinent theoretical problems. Hence, we make no pretense to either completeness or rigor. We have tried to produce a book of convenient length which will meet the needs of scientists who have an interest in the results which can be obtained from microwave spectra. The book is not written as a text, though it should prove useful for that purpose in graduate courses when it is used with specialized treatises on the various subjects involved.

Although the heterogeneous nature of microwave spectroscopy makes impossible a textbook of the conventional type, that very fact makes the subject a desirable one in which to train graduate students. In contrast to many fields of research in chemistry and physics which are narrowing in their influence on the worker, microwave spectroscopy provides a rich and varied background of experience both in its experimental and theoretical aspects, which is excellent training for teaching or for a career in pure or applied research.

Many people have contributed, either directly or indirectly, to the preparation of this volume. We are particularly indebted to Professor Walter M. Nielsen, Chairman of the Physics Department, who has constantly encouraged and supported us in this project.

This book would not have been undertaken were it not for the support we have received for the research program in microwave spectroscopy at Duke University. Although this program has been primarily supported by the U. S. Air Force Cambridge Research Laboratory, we are also indebted to the Research Corporation for a generous grant. We acknowledge a generous grant for assistance in the preparation of the book from the Duke University Council on Research.

A large number of graduate students at Duke University, both past and present, have contributed to the book. Dr. M. L. Meeks assisted much with Chapters 3 and 8 and prepared the numerical tables for analysis of Stark and Zeeman effects. Drs. John Sheridan, S. N. Ghosh, M. Mizushima, and H. G. Dehmelt, former research associates, have made suggestions. Mr. Frank Trippe, electronics technician, and the shop personnel, particularly Mr. Milton Whitfield and Mr. W. B. Francis, have at various times made helpful suggestions about the instrumental aspects. The secretaries of the Physics Department, Mrs. Sallie Wood, Miss Carolyn Daniels, Miss Emma Rose Cutts, and Miss Grace Williams, have typed different parts of the manuscript. Several of the illustrations were drawn by Mr. Colin Govan.

We are indebted to the large number of scholars at other institutions who have generously allowed us to reprint their diagrams and data, and who have supplied us with prepublication copies of their most recent results.

W. G.
W. V. S.
R. F. T.

Duke University
March, 1953

CONTENTS

INTRODUCTION

Although microwave spectroscopy had its inception in 1934 with the historic experiments of Cleeton and Williams [1] on the inversion spectrum of ammonia, no further papers on microwave spectroscopy appeared in the literature until 1946. The concentrated research on microwave radar during World War II provided the necessary instruments and the stimulus for the rapid development of the field which immediately followed the war period.

The microwave region comprises that part of the electromagnetic spectrum which lies between the far infrared and the conventional radio-frequency region. Though its boundaries are not definitely fixed, the region may be regarded as extending from about 1 mm to 30 cm in wavelength (300,000 Mc to 1000 Mc). Thus, microwaves are frequently designated as centimeter waves or millimeter waves. This region represents approximately eight octaves of the electromagnetic spectrum, whereas the visible part of the optical region covers only about one octave.

Microwave spectroscopy could be regarded as an extension of radio-frequency spectroscopy or as an extension of far infrared spectroscopy. As a consequence, it is sometimes classified under radio-frequency spectroscopy and sometimes under optical spectroscopy. There are, nevertheless, sound reasons for treating it as an independent subject. The instruments for generating, measuring, and transmitting microwaves are different from the conventional components—triodes, pentodes, coils, resistors, and capacitors—used in the longer-wave radio region. They also differ in a fundamental way from the essentially optical instruments used in the far infrared region.

The microwave region may also be defined on the basis of the type of spectral studies for which it is best adapted, although its boundaries cannot be definitely fixed in this way. Bearing in mind a number of outstanding exceptions, we may say that in the visible and ultraviolet regions the transitions between electronic energy states are directly measurable, and that vibrational and rotational energies of molecules are observed only as perturbation effects. In the infrared region the vibrational spectra are observed directly, with the rotational energies usually observed as perturbations of the vibrational spectra. In the

1

microwave region the transitions between rotational energies of molecules are in turn observed directly, with nuclear effects appearing as first-order perturbations; whereas, in the radio-frequency region the nuclear effects are directly observable.

As illustrations of the exceptions mentioned above, there are differences between certain electronic energy states which fall within the microwave region. The most notable example of this is the Lamb-Retherford [2] shift in the spectrum of the hydrogen atom. In some cases the nuclear effects might be observed directly in the microwave region. There are a few outstanding examples of certain light molecules such as hydrogen chloride and ammonia for which pure rotational lines have been measured in the far infrared region. Nevertheless, by far the greater proportion of the pure rotational spectra of molecules for practical reasons are measurable in the microwave region only.

Stark and Zeeman effects in rotational spectra have been observed only in the microwave region. Likewise, in this region only have nuclear quadrupole perturbations of pure rotational spectra been resolved. Thus, microwave spectroscopy has caused a new interest in Stark and Zeeman effects as well as in hyperfine structure of molecular spectra. New information on intermolecular interactions is obtained through measurements of the widths and shapes of spectral lines in the microwave region. In addition to the more precise testing of previously developed theories of these subjects, the accurate evaluation of such important molecular and nuclear properties as bond angles, interatomic distances, molecular dipole and molecular quadrupole moments, atomic masses, nuclear spins, nuclear magnetic and nuclear quadrupole moments has been made possible.

In addition to that of pure rotational spectra, there is another energy transition which is most conveniently observed in the microwave region. This is commonly termed paramagnetic resonance absorption. In these experiments the paramagnetic substance is placed in a magnetic field. The precession of the electronic momentum vector about the field then takes place. As is well known, the interaction energy of the magnetic moment of the ion or molecule with the external field is quantized. Transitions between the different Zeeman levels (different orientations of the electronic momentum vector in the external field) give rise to absorption in the microwave region when the external field is of the proper value. This paramagnetic absorption can be observed in the microwave region with magnetic fields of the order of a few kilogauss. The experiments are closely analogous to those of nuclear resonance absorption observed in the radio-frequency region. From such paramagnetic measurements important information can be obtained about crystal structures and in some instances about chemical bonding and the nature of the electronic state of ions in crystals. In several instances nuclear hyperfine structure has been observed in paramagnetic resonance absorption, and unknown nuclear moments have been determined therefrom.

Many liquids and solutions have broad absorption peaks occurring in the microwave region. These are associated with anomalous dispersion caused by orientation of molecular dipoles in the field of radiation. Such absorption peaks occur at frequencies of $\dfrac{1}{2\pi\tau}$, where τ is the relaxation time of the molecular dipole. Using microwave measurements with the theory of Debye[3] and others,[4] one can calculate such properties as relaxation time, dipole moment, and dielectric constant of complex organic and inorganic compounds. Information about the important problem of intermolecular interaction in liquids and solutions can thus be obtained.

Many industrial applications of microwave spectroscopy are already apparent. Eventually the largest and most important of these no doubt will be the qualitative and quantitative analysis of chemical compounds. The wide use of infrared spectroscopy for such analysis is an example of what can be expected. In general, the substance to be analyzed must be polar, and the analysis must be made of the vapor state. Despite these limitations there are large classes of compounds to which microwave analysis is applicable. Whenever it can be applied, the enormously greater resolution makes it superior to infrared analysis. For the first time, there are available for identification of complex organic compounds sharp line spectra similar to those of the isolated elements. Indeed, microwave absorption spectroscopy can provide for hundreds or even thousands of molecules the same certainty of identification as the line emission spectra provide for identification of the elements. A similar application is quantitative isotopic analysis of compounds in which rare isotopes have been artificially concentrated.

In the now famous atomic clock, developed by Lyons and his group at the National Bureau of Standards, microwave spectral lines provide a new standard of time which promises to be more accurate than that based on the rotation of the earth. The frequencies of electronic oscillators can be stabilized to better than 1 part in 10 million by coupling them to sharp absorption lines. Crystals used to stabilize the frequencies of oscillators at radio broadcast frequencies are ineffective at ultra-high frequencies. A natural substitute is a sharp, unchangeable spectral line.

Accurately measured microwave absorption lines provide excellent secondary frequency standards for checking the calibration of wavemeters. Precise measurements have now been made on lines as high as 130,000 Mc. Magnetic fields can be measured and flux meters calibrated by means of the sharp paramagnetic absorption ($\sim$1 gauss in width) of organic free radicals. Likewise, it is possible to stabilize magnetic fields with these lines.

Doubtless many other applications will be developed in this important spectral region which links optical and radio waves.

REFERENCES

[1] C. E. Cleeton and N. H. Williams, *Phys. Rev. 45*, 234 (1934).
[2] W. E. Lamb, Jr., and R. C. Retherford, *Phys. Rev. 72*, 241 (1947).
[3] P. Debye, *Polar Molecules* (Dover Publications, New York, 1929).
[4] H. Frohlich, *Nature 157*, 478 (1946).

1. INSTRUMENTS AND EXPERIMENTAL METHODS

1.1. TYPES OF MICROWAVE SPECTROGRAPHS

Although optical and microwave spectrometers perform the same general function—the measurement of the difference in the quantized energy states of material particles—the microwave spectrometer differs in a fundamental way from the optical spectrometer. The core of an optical spectrometer is the element of dispersion, prism or grating. This core is not found in the microwave spectrometer, which is a completely electronic instrument. No dispersive component is needed because the source is essentially monochromatic and because its frequency can be varied at will and measured electronically with high precision.

Reduced to its simplest form, the microwave spectrometer consists of: (1) a radiation source, (2) an absorption cell, (3) a device for measuring frequency or wavelength, (4) a detector of the microwave radiation, (5) an amplifier of the detected power, and (6) an indicator. The usual spectrograph has several auxiliary components such as attenuators, couplers, and modulators. The choice and arrangement of the components depend upon the nature of the problem to be investigated and upon the type of components available. Hence, the microwave spectrograph has no fixed form. There are many different types in current use. Diagrams of some common forms are shown in Figs. 1.1–1.4. In this section the more frequently used types of spectrographs will be described. Details of the components and a discussion of sensitivities will be given in later sections.

The semi-optical spectrograph used by Cleeton and Williams [1] has been replaced by more effective ones. Nevertheless, it is of historical interest because this first microwave spectroscope was a hybrid instrument employing in a fundamental way both optical and electronic methods. The source was electronic, being a split-anode magnetron. An optical collimating system of parabolic mirrors was used with an echelette grating for measurement of wavelength. No electronic amplification was employed. The radiation was detected by an iron pyrite phosphor-bronze crystal which was connected directly to a sensitive galvanometer. Their absorption cell was simply a rubber cloth bag.

5

1.1a. Fixed-Frequency Spectrometers. In the measurement of the attenuation of gases at high pressure where the lines are extremely broad, point-by-point plotting is employed. This method permits the use of high-power, fixed-frequency sources such as magnetrons. Both cavity and waveguide cells have been used. With this method the attenuation of the cell at a fixed frequency is measured with and without the gas in the cell. The oscillator frequency is set at a new frequency, and the process is repeated. Highest sensitivity and resolving power are obtained with a frequency-stabilized oscillator and a lock-in amplifier. Care must be taken to prevent variations in standing waves from producing errors. However, if a waveguide cell is shorted at one end, the difference in standing-wave ratio with and without the gas in the cell may be used as a measure of the gas attenuation. Point-by-point measurements have been made in a number of investigations.[2]

1.1b. Frequency-Sweep Spectrometer with Crystal Video Receiver. One of the simplest types of microwave spectrometers in current use employs a simple video or a narrow-band audio amplifier with

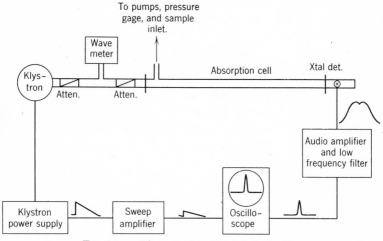

Fig. 1.1a.   Diagram of a video spectrograph.

a relatively sharp cut-off on the low-frequency side.[3] This is connected directly to the crystal detector. The klystron source is frequency modulated by a slow saw-tooth wave which is synchronized with the cathode-ray oscilloscope used to display the absorption lines. During the search for spectral lines the klystron frequency is varied manually. A long waveguide absorption cell (~100 ft for K-band waves) is used. The cell and other components are made with care so that no sharp reflections caused by impedance mismatch occur. The pressure of the gas is adjusted to make the absorption line sharp as compared to any unavoidable reflections. The rate of frequency sweep of the klystron is then adjusted so that the major Fourier components of the reflections and the mode contours occur below the low-frequency cut-off of the receiver. When the width of the absorption line is of the order of $\frac{1}{10}$ that of the sharpest reflection, this filtering can be achieved with only slight loss of signal. For best results the saw-tooth wave used to sweep the frequency of the klystron should be adjustable both in recurrence rate and in slope. The rate of sweep is adjusted for optimum results by observation of the pattern on the cathode-ray scope. Actually, the reflections should not be completely filtered since they are useful in adjusting the optimum rate of search. For a given spectrometer the optimum gas pressure is determined by the line-breadth parameter of the gas under study. The pressure is not particularly critical, however; for most cases 10^{-2} mm of Hg is satisfactory. See Fig. 1.1a for an arrangement of the spectrograph.

The sensitivity [4] of the simple, rapid, video system compares favorably with the more complicated sweep spectroscopes described below when the available power is limited to a few microwatts, as it is in the region below 5-mm wavelength or when one must operate with the gas at such low pressures that molecular saturation limits the power to a few microwatts. A quantitative discussion of its sensitivity is given in Sec. 1.4.

1.1c. Frequency-Sweep Spectrometer with Radio-Frequency Receiver. Receivers which amplify the signal at frequencies of 100 kc or higher avoid the excessive low-frequency noise generated in crystals when milliwatt powers are detected. Other low-frequency disturbances, such as flicker noise in tubes, are also avoided. The sensitive heterodyne receivers developed for radar reception are difficult to use because the local oscillator must be swept synchronously with the source sweep in the search for absorption lines. The automatic frequency control circuits used in radar can serve to couple the oscillators together over a limited range of sweep. Thus a radar receiver may be useful in special cases where lines are difficult to resolve. A spectrometer employing a radar receiver has been described by Strandberg, Wentink, and Kyhl.[5] Although the heterodyne receiver is more sensitive than the crystal video receiver, the enormous advantage of heterodyne detection over square-law or video detection of a positive pulse of power such as a radar signal is not retained in the detection of an absorption line.[4,6] See Sec. 1.4 for a discussion of its sensitivity.

Source-frequency modulation. A number of researchers [7] have successfully used source-frequency modulation at radio frequencies with a sensitive radio receiver in order to avoid the excessive low-frequency noise which occurs when powers of the order of milliwatts are used. The absorption line acts as a discriminator to convert the frequency modulation into an amplitude modulation at the detector. Thus, an a-m radio receiver can be used. When the degree of modulation is adjusted to maximize a sharp absorption line, there is discrimination against broad reflections. Low-frequency filtering in the audio stage can be used to reduce further the effects of reflections.

The modulation can be achieved conveniently by superimposing the voltage from an r-f generator upon the slowly varying saw-tooth wave used to sweep the klystron over its mode. The adjustment of the amount of modulation is critical, and considerable distortion may occur. When small modulation voltages are used, the receiver detects the first derivative of the absorption line contour. Tests made at Duke University show that a gain in sensitivity by a factor of 10 or more over the video system can be obtained in the 1-cm region but that little if any gain over the video system can be achieved in the shorter millimeter wave region where the available power is seriously limited. However, source modulation with a narrow-band lock-in amplifier can greatly increase the sensitivity in the latter region.

To prevent excessive distortion of the line and a consequent lowering of sensitivity, the modulation frequency should be somewhat less than the line breadth. For modulation frequencies greater than the line width, side bands produced by the modulation will be resolved. Also, the range of frequency sweep of the modulation should be greater than the line breadth. When the modulation range is small compared with the modulation frequency and the latter small compared to the line breadth, the receiver detects the first derivative of the line contour.

Stark-modulation. An ingenious method of increasing sensitivity was introduced by Hughes and Wilson.[8] They placed an electrode in the waveguide absorption cell and imposed a low r-f alternating voltage to modulate the absorption line. An intensity modulation of the microwave energy is thus produced when the source frequency is in the vicinity of an absorption line, since the Stark components of the line are shifted relative to the source frequency. Hence, a radio receiver tuned to the modulating frequency can be used to detect the absorption line. A sine wave may be used for the modulation. More information is obtained, however, if a square-wave voltage is employed since the individual Stark components can then be resolved and studied. A block diagram of a Stark-modulation spectrometer is given in Fig. 1.1b.

In searching for lines, just as with other methods where a cathode-ray display of the line is used, a slow saw-tooth voltage synchronized with the cathode-ray trace is employed to sweep the klystron over its mode. If an absorption line of sufficient intensity, which is sharp as compared with the frequency span of the klystron mode, is passed over, it will show up as a pip on the scope. With square-wave modulation of sufficient intensity for their resolution, the Stark components appear as separate pips. In the search for lines the klystron is tuned manually.

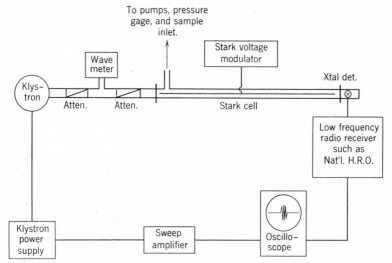

Fig. 1.1b.   Diagram of a Stark-modulation spectrograph.

The amount of voltage needed for best detection depends upon: (1) the width of the line and hence the gas pressure; (2) the dipole moment of the molecule; and (3) the nature of the Stark effect, i.e., whether of first or second order and whether high or low rotational states are being observed. For a molecule with an average dipole, ~ 1 debye, at pressure of the order of 10^{-1} mm of Hg, modulating fields of the order of 10 volts per cm are adequate for first-order Stark effects. For lines exhibiting only the second-order effect, several hundred volts per centimeter are needed.

The principal advantage of the Stark-modulation method for increasing sensitivity is that it allows detection of the absorption line without detection of power variations caused by reflections in the microwave line, even when the absorption line is as broad as, or broader than, the reflections. An additional advantage is that it allows the use of an r-f receiver to avoid low-frequency noise without the complication of heterodyne detection.

The first advantage is very significant. The previously described methods of minimizing reflections are applicable only when the line can be made sharp as compared with the reflections. This requires operation at low pressures ($\sim 10^{-2}$ mm of Hg) where molecular saturation seriously limits the power that can be used. In addition, there are large groups of molecules, such as $CHCl_3$, which because of unresolved hyperfine structure have very broad absorption lines even at low pressures. There are also certain symmetric-top molecules which do not have hyperfine structure but do have broad lines caused by rotational transitions of different quantum number K which are slightly separated by centrifugal distortions.

Equation 1.32 can be used in estimating the sensitivity obtainable with a Stark-modulation spectrograph provided that: (1) the power employed is in the milliwatt range so that the crystal operates as a linear detector; (2) the modulating voltage and gas pressure are adjusted so that efficient modulation is achieved; (3) the cell is so constructed that molecular saturation is avoided. One can, of course, include in the noise figure F the estimated losses caused by these various factors. If the modulation frequency is small compared with the line breadth, negligible distortion is produced. For a square-wave modulation frequency ν_m which is of the order of the line breadth $\Delta\nu$, the line intensity will be lowered by a factor [9b] of about $[1 - (\frac{3}{8})(\nu_m/\Delta\nu)^2]$ and the line breadth increased by $[1 + (\frac{1}{4})(\nu_m/\Delta\nu)^2]$, approximately, when as is customary the receiver is tuned to the fundamental modulation frequency.

Because crystal noise decreases with increasing frequency, it would seem that a very high r-f modulation would be most desirable when crystal detectors are employed. For practical reasons this is not true. Since the capacitive admittance across the Stark cell increases with frequency, higher and higher currents are required to charge the electrodes to a given voltage as the modulation frequency is increased, unless the capacity of the cell is correspondingly decreased. This means that a compromise between cell size and modulating frequency must be made. For square-wave modulation of lines exhibiting only second-order Stark effect it is difficult to use the optimum cell length with modulating frequencies over 100 kc. In addition, the lines are seriously broadened by very high-frequency modulation.[9] Most researchers use modulating frequencies of about 100 kc. Description of absorption cells, electronic components, and methods of measuring frequencies are given in later sections. Further details may be found in articles on the method.[10]

A device which facilitates recognition of absorption lines was introduced by J. Q. Williams, at Duke. To test a signal he imposed a bias so that the alternating Stark voltage would swing above and below ground rather than from ground to maximum value. For reasons readily apparent, this bias causes the line to disappear but leaves unchanged the signals arising from oscillator pickup or other sources.

In addition to the aids to detection mentioned, Stark modulation is useful in identification of lines and in measurement of molecular dipole moments.

1.1d. Automatic Recording Spectrometers with Phase-Sensitive Lock-In Amplifier. Equations 1.32 and 1.33 indicate that the sensitivity of a spectrograph improves markedly with a decrease in bandwidth. If the bandwidth is to be decreased, however, the rate of sweep must be made correspondingly slower so that the major Fourier components of the absorption line still fall within the bandwidth of the receiver. Thus, to achieve the highest sensitivity, one must abandon the very desirable cathode-ray display for the slower pen-and-ink recorder.

Commercially available recorders such as the Brown, the Leeds and Northrup Speedomax, and the Esterline Angus are satisfactory. The klystron frequency is usually swept slowly by an electric motor coupled through step-down gears to the mechanical tuner. In the observation of sharp lines, frequency stability of the oscillator is usually the limiting factor. A well-stabilized power supply should be used for the klystron. One can stabilize the oscillator by coupling it to an external cavity by the Pound method (Art. 1.3b) and can then sweep its frequency by tuning the external cavity. However, this method is extremely slow and tedious for a search spectrograph.

Use of the phase lock-in principle makes possible an amplifier with an exceptionally narrow bandwidth ($\sim$1 cps) and one which discriminates against noise out of phase with the signals. The lock-in detector with its associated filter responds only to incoming signals which have the frequency and phase of the reference voltage on which the detector is made to lock. Hence incoming signals are modulated at the phase and frequency of the reference voltage used to lock the amplifier.

This modulation can be achieved in several ways. Among them are: (1) amplitude modulation of the source power (this may be achieved by mechanical chopping of the beam, by square-wave modulation of the klystron voltage, or by reflection of the power from a crystal the impedance of which is varied by an alternating voltage); (2) frequency modulation of the source; (3) Stark modulation of the absorption line; (4) Zeeman modulation of the absorption line; and (5) interruption of a molecular beam.

Method 1 is most adaptable to fixed-frequency measurements. It is not very useful with automatic recorders because it does not discriminate against reflections or other causes of power variations. The other methods are very useful with the sweep spectrograph employing automatic recording. Modulating frequencies usually employed with methods 2 and 3 range from a few kilocycles to about 100 kc, although

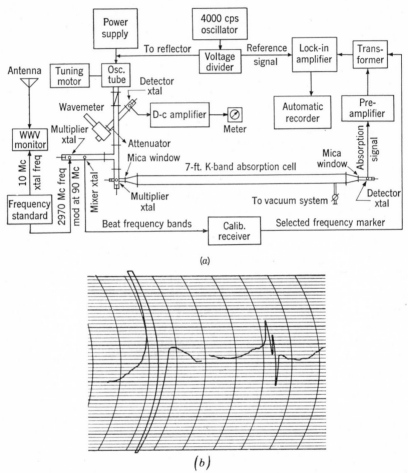

(a)

(b)

FIG. 1.2. (a) Diagram of a millimeter-wave spectrometer employing a phase-sensitive amplifier with source modulation and automatic recording. (b) Tracings of ICN lines at 2.32-mm wavelength employing this spectrograph. (From Gilliam, Johnson, and Gordy.[11])

they can extend to much higher frequencies. In practice it is difficult to achieve high-frequency Zeeman modulation although fields of several gauss at a few thousand kilocycles can be obtained. Molecular beam modulation is limited to the order of 100 cps.

Stark modulation is the most frequently used method, since it is more effective than source modulation in coping with reflections and is applicable to a wider range of molecules than is Zeeman modulation. A spectrograph employing a lock-in amplifier with Stark modulation is described by McAfee, Hughes, and Wilson.[10]

The source-frequency modulation method offers advantages in the shorter millimeter wave region where the available power is low and where the high losses in the usual Stark cell are serious. With the short cells which must be used in this region, reflections can usually be made broad as compared with the signal. Noise is generally a greater limitation than are reflections. Gilliam, Johnson, and Gordy[11] have used source-frequency modulation with a lock-in amplifier and recorder to obtain much greater sensitivity in the wavelength region from 2 to 5 mm than is possible with the video receiver. Figure 1.2a shows a diagram of their spectrograph, and Fig. 1.2b shows an ICN line at 2.29-mm wavelength recorded with it. The modulation frequency was 5 kc.

Zeeman modulation can serve to aid detection of absorption lines of paramagnetic substances in a way similar to that by which Stark modulation serves to detect the absorption of substances with an electric dipole. A spectrograph employing magnetic modulation with automatic recording has been developed by Burkhalter, Anderson, Smith, and Gordy.[12a] A similar arrangement has been used by Shimoda and Nishikawa[12b] for observing the hyperfine spectrum of atomic sodium. See also the experiment of Roberts, Beers, and Hill.[22] (Art. 1.1g.)

1.1e. Atomic and Molecular Beam Methods. Atomic and molecular beam methods have specialized applications in microwave spectroscopy. Descriptions of the techniques are available in the literature.[13] An outstanding example of the use of atomic beams in the microwave region is the experiment by Lamb and Retherford[14] on hydrogen. They used a detector which was sensitive only to atoms in excited states. Atoms in the metastable $2\,{}^2S_{1/2}$ state were used to energize the detector. When these were passed through microwave radiation of the proper frequency some were lifted to the $2\,{}^2P_{3/2}$ state from which they could decay rapidly to $1\,{}^2S_{1/2}$ ground state. Consequently, fewer atoms in the excited state arrive at the detector, and a drop in the indicator current results. No doubt there will be other, similar applications of atomic beams. Already Lamb and Skinner[15] have performed a like measurement on ionized helium.

It may be possible to use molecular beams to advantage for the study of the rotational spectra of heavy molecules which must be heated several hundred degrees before they have a significant vapor pressure. By use of such a method the necessity of heating the entire absorption cell to high temperatures can be avoided. The molecular beam can be directed at right angles to the radiation path so that Doppler broadening is avoided. A cavity, a waveguide, or a free-space cell may be used.

While the beam is being passed through the cell the absorption lines can be measured in the usual way by the sensitive detecting methods already described. A parallel plate cell with Stark modulation of the molecular beam may be used. Also, mechanical interruption of the molecular beam by a rotating or vibrating shutter at the order of 100 times a second makes possible modulation of the intensity of the absorption lines. Such systems equipped with lock-in amplifiers are being constructed at Duke.[16]

1.1ƒ. Paramagnetic Resonance Spectrographs. In paramagnetic resonance experiments it is necessary to impose a magnetic field of a few thousand gauss upon the sample since the observations are made upon transitions between Zeeman components. The usual practice is to set the oscillator at a fixed frequency and sweep the absorption line through this frequency by varying the magnetic field. Thus the troublesome problems caused by variations in oscillator power and reflections are avoided.

It is easy to superimpose upon the strong external field a small alternating field of low frequency so as to vibrate the absorption frequency relative to that of the source. This produces an intensity modulation of the microwave power in the region of an absorption line. A narrow-banded lock-in detector, which is made to lock in on the same alternating voltage, is then employed. Either automatic recording or point-by-point plotting can be used.

Very sharp lines such as are sometimes obtained with free radicals or paramagnetic gases can be displayed with a cathode-ray oscilloscope. In this case the magnetic field is swept so that the line passes completely over the source frequency several times a second. The cathode-ray trace is synchronized with the magnetic sweep. On the other hand, if the magnetic field is sufficiently stable it can be left fixed and the oscillator can be swept through the line. In either case an amplifier of appropriate bandwidth to include the signal components must be employed. When the oscillator frequency is left fixed it is advantageous to use the sensitive heterodyne radar receivers.

Both cavity and waveguide cells have been employed. The cavity cell has the advantage of the longer effective path for a sample of a given size. Also, with a cavity cell it is possible to reduce dielectric losses greatly by placing a crystal sample under study at a point where the magnetic component of the radiation is strongest and the electric component weakest. It should be remembered that paramagnetic absorption is caused by coupling of the magnetic dipole to the magnetic component of the radiation field.

With waveguide cells it is easier to impose a high external field since one dimension of the waveguide can be reduced, if necessary, to a small fraction of a centimeter. Hence, a magnet with a very small gap can be used. This is important for the millimeter wave region where the fields required are of the order of 20 kilogauss. Waveguide techniques are probably more convenient for substances in the powder or gaseous form. A balanced waveguide bridge for measuring paramagnetic resonance has been described.[17]

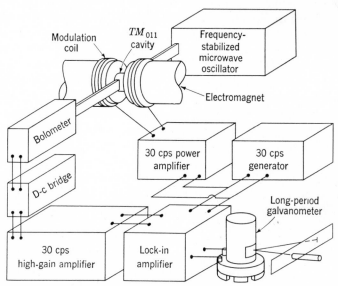

FIG. 1.3.   Diagram of a microwave-magnetic-resonance spectrometer.   (From Beringer and Castle.[18])

For the study of magnetic resonance absorption in gases Beringer and Castle [18] have designed the extremely sensitive spectrometer shown in Fig. 1.3. As indicated in the diagram, it employs a frequency-stabilized source, a cavity absorption cell, and a bolometer as a detector. The narrow-banded, phase-sensitive amplifier is locked in on the 30 cps power used to modulate the spectral line. Although designed for gases, this spectrometer can be used with equal effectiveness for the investigation of paramagnetic solids or solutions. The bolometer allows the detection of powers in the milliwatt range without the excessive low-frequency noise found in crystals. Thus the need for a balanced microwave bridge is avoided. A bolometric detector has particular advantages in paramagnetic resonance studies where the usable power is not seriously limited by saturation effects.

For the broad paramagnetic lines usually encountered in solids an ordinary electromagnet with a d-c generator power supply is adequate, and a commercial fluxmeter is satisfactory for measuring the field strength. Sharp lines such as are found in gases, free radicals, or diluted salts at low temperatures justify more elaborate equipment. A well-regulated power supply capable of being varied in small steps is necessary, and an accurate fluxmeter such as the proton resonance meter is desirable. High-quality magnets as well as proton resonance fluxmeters are now available commercially.[19]

1.1g. Zeeman Spectrograph for Gases. The problem of observing the Zeeman splitting of rotational lines is different from that of observing paramagnetic resonance absorption, although the magnetic field requirements are similar. The line components in many Zeeman studies are not sufficiently sensitive to the field to be swept through a fixed source frequency or to be modulated efficiently by an alternating magnetic field. One of the detecting methods described in the preceding sections is usually employed. The only remaining problem is the construction of an absorption cell so that a strong, uniform magnetic field can be imposed. The compact resonance cavity cell has advantages. This type of cell has been used in several measurements by Jen,[20] who employed source-frequency modulation to aid detection. Figure 1.4 shows a diagram of Jen's spectrometer, together with a spectrum obtained with it.

For measuring the nuclear magnetic moments of radioactive iodines, Gordy, Gilliam, and Livingston [21] used a waveguide cell coiled in such a way that it could be placed between the poles of an electromagnet. Also, it was coiled so that only π components were observed. The proton resonance cell used to measure the magnetic field was placed at the center of the coil, and the entire cell was enclosed within a Bakelite flask for cooling to dry-ice temperature. The crystal video receiver was used for some measurements, and for others the lock-in amplifier was combined with source modulation.

Roberts, Beers, and Hill [22] observed the Zeeman effect in an ingenious manner in the hyperfine structure of Cs vapor in the 3-cm wave region. Their method, which is applicable to other paramagnetic substances, employs a Pound stabilizer to couple a microwave oscillator to the resonant frequency of an external tunable cavity which contains the vapor at low pressure, about 10^{-2} mm of Hg. The anomalous dispersion of the vapor in the region of an absorption line alters slightly the resonant frequency of the cavity. When an absorption line occurring at the cavity frequency is modulated, it will in turn modulate the cavity frequency and that of the oscillator to which it is coupled. An f-m receiver connected to the oscillator and tuned to the modulating frequency will then detect the absorption line. The oscillator frequency is pre-set near the absorption line, and the Zeeman components are pulled through the cavity frequency by an external magnetic field. The modulation is produced by superimposing a weak alternating field.

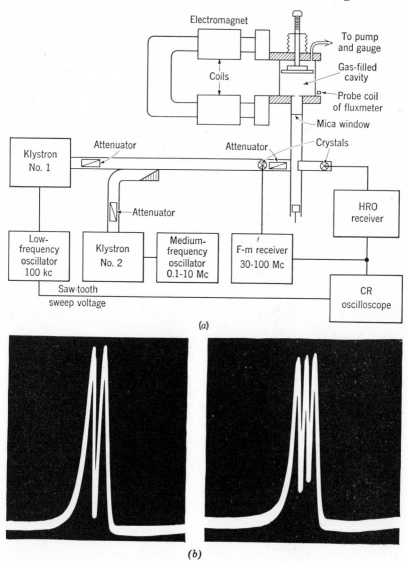

(a)

(b)

Fig. 1.4. (a) Diagram of spectrometer for studying the Zeeman effect in gases. (b) Cathode-ray tracing of an NH_3 absorption line superimposed upon the cavity mode without (left), and with (right) the magnetic field. (From Jen.[20])

1.2. MICROWAVE COMPONENTS

Various types and arrangements of microwave components are used by different workers in microwave spectroscopy. In fact, one seldom sees two spectrometers with identical arrangements of these parts. There are common functions, however, which must be performed by the microwave components of any spectrometer. They are: (1) generation of microwave power, (2) measurement of frequency or wavelength, (3) guidance of the radiation through the absorbing substance under

FIG. 1.5. Possible arrangements of microwave components: (a) one of the simplest spectrometers, (b) spectrometer which provides for accurate frequency measurements, (c) spectrometer which employs a crystal multiplier as a source and also provides for accurate frequency measurements.

investigation, and (4) detection of power or variations in power. In addition to these basic functions, a monitoring of the microwave power and a regulation of its flow by proper attenuation are usually necessary.

Figure 1.5 shows three possible arrangements of components for these functions. The first (a) is one of the simplest. For measurements where the accuracy of a cavity wavemeter is sufficient and for regions for which klystron generators are available, this diagram shows all the necessary components. Figure 1.5b gives an arrangement which provides for coupling in precision frequency markers. Figure 1.5c represents a still more complicated design which assumes that the radiation source is a crystal multiplier driven by a klystron.

In addition to these components, the precision frequency standard often employs a microwave klystron multiplier. If a superheterodyne radar receiver is used, a microwave mixer and local oscillator are required in the receiver. In special applications numerous other micro-

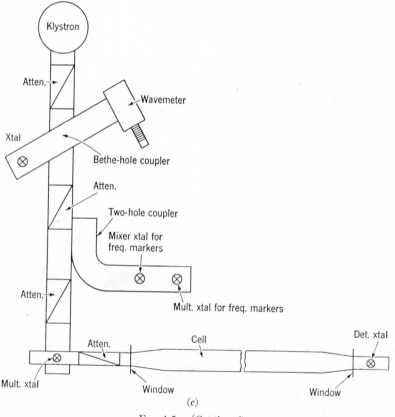

(c)

FIG. 1.5. (Continued)

wave instruments may be needed, such as thermistor bridges, standing-wave detectors, microwave switches, line tuners, mode filters, focusing horns, and spectrum analyzers. Furthermore, there are many different designs for each component. It is impossible in a volume of this length to give details of these components. Extensive treatments are available in the *Radiation Laboratory Series* [23] and other reference books. Volumes 6–12 and 14–16 of the *Series* deal specifically with microwave components. To one unfamiliar with microwaves, the maze of information presented in these lengthy volumes can be confusing. The reader of these books should bear in mind that the requirements of microwave radar are different in many respects from those of microwave spectroscopy.

Because the spectroscopist does not, in general, deal with high powers and because his measurements are usually made in the laboratory where size, shape, weight, ruggedness, resistance to weather, etc., are of secondary concern, many of the transmission line components designed for radar are needlessly complicated and expensive for his use. On the other hand, the spectroscopist must place more emphasis on frequency coverage or broad-bandedness of the components since a microwave spectroscope, unlike a radar set, is not operated at a fixed frequency. Also, when adapting radar instruments for microwave spectroscopy, one should remember that practically all the radar sets of World War II operated at wavelengths of 3 cm or longer, whereas the region of most interest to the microwave spectroscopist is at wavelengths shorter than 3 cm. For this reason, waveguide components are used almost exclusively in microwave spectroscopy, whereas coaxial lines as well are used extensively in radar. Much more emphasis is placed on precision frequency measurement in spectroscopy than in radar work. There is also a fundamental difference in the requirements of detection: in absorption spectroscopy a decrement in the normal flow of power is detected, whereas in radar the signal to be detected is a positive pulse of power.

A condensed description of the individual microwave components most often needed in spectroscopy follows.

1.2a. Waveguide. Rectangular waveguide is used extensively in making components such as attenuators, absorption cells, crystal detectors, and mounts, as well as for microwave transmission. For most purposes the guide must have such dimensions that it will propagate only the lowest or dominant mode. One important exception is the waveguide absorption cell, which can usually be constructed so that undesirable higher modes are not excited.

The longer wavelength limit for a given mode is determined by the cut-off wavelength given in terms of the inside dimensions of the guide,

a and b, by the equation

$$\lambda_c = 2/[(m/a)^2 + (n/b)^2]^{1/2}, \tag{1.1}$$

where m and n designate the particular mode. This formula applies for both TE (transverse electric) and for TM (transverse magnetic) modes. For the TE modes either m or n can be zero, provided of course that both are not zero; but for the TM modes neither m nor n can be zero.

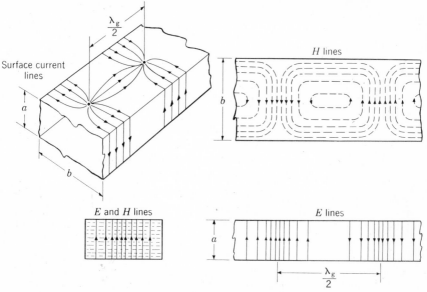

FIG. 1.6. Direction of surface currents and patterns of electric and magnetic fields for the TE_{01} mode in rectangular guide. Upper left, current lines; upper right, H lines; lower right, E lines; lower left, E and H lines, end view.

Hence, the lowest or dominant mode is a TE mode, and the guide dimensions can be chosen so as to cut out all but the dominant TE_{01}. It is seen from Eq. 1.1 that the longest wavelength which can be propagated by a rectangular guide is

$$\lambda_c = 2b, \tag{1.2}$$

where b is the longer dimension of the cross section of the guide. Thus the lower as well as the higher limits of the frequency coverage are determined by Eq. 1.1. Since the attenuation increases rapidly as the cutoff wavelength is approached, the effective bandwidth is somewhat different from that defined by this equation.

Figure 1.6 shows the pattern of the electric and magnetic field in the guide for the TE_{01} mode. The direction of flow of the surface currents is at right angles to the lines of the magnetic field at the surface. It is useful to know the direction of flow of these currents since it is possible to cut narrow slots in the guide without causing significant losses or reflections, provided that these slots are cut along the lines of current flow. Slots are sometimes needed for such purposes as measuring standing waves or for interrupting eddy currents when magnetic modulation is employed.

The wavelength in the guide, λ_g, longer than in free-space propagation, is given by the formula

$$\lambda_g = \lambda/[1 - (\lambda/\lambda_c)^2]^{\frac{1}{2}}, \tag{1.3}$$

where λ is the corresponding free-space wavelength and λ_c is the cut-off wavelength defined by Eq. 1.1.

The attenuation of the dominant TE_{01} mode in rectangular pure silver guide for wavelengths much shorter than cut-off ($\lambda < \lambda_c$) is

$$\alpha = \frac{0.0107}{b^{\frac{3}{2}}} \left\{ \frac{b/2a(\lambda_c/\lambda)^{\frac{3}{2}} + (\lambda_c/\lambda)^{-\frac{1}{2}}}{[(\lambda_c/\lambda)^2 - 1]^{\frac{1}{2}}} \right\} \quad \text{db/ft}, \tag{1.4}$$

where a and b are in inches, and where a represents the smaller and b the larger dimension of the guide. Attenuation for copper guide may be obtained by multiplying this expression by 1.03; for brass, by 2.08; and for gold-plated guide, by 1.23. For wavelengths longer than cut-off ($\lambda > \lambda_c$), the impedance is a pure resistance, and the attenuation

$$\alpha = 54.6[1/\lambda_c^2 - 1/\lambda^2]^{\frac{1}{2}} \quad \text{db/unit length} \tag{1.5}$$

or when $\lambda \gg \lambda_c$

$$\alpha \approx (54.6/\lambda_c) \quad \text{db/unit length}. \tag{1.6}$$

Waveguide and hence waveguide components of many different sizes are required to cover the workable microwave region. The region of most interest to the spectroscopist is that from about 1 mm to 2 cm in wavelength. Figure 1.7 shows the sizes of guide † necessary for coverage of this region, with the losses at the limits of the recommended bands for the dominant mode in silver guide. The radar band of highest frequency employed during World War II is that designated as the K band. For spectroscopic work at Duke the guide sizes and band designations for the millimeter wave region have been adopted as given in this chart. The sizes are chosen so as to require a minimum number of waveguide components with only slight overlapping of the recommended bands.

† Waveguide in all these sizes of coin silver or of other material is obtainable from Horton-Angell Company, Attleboro, Massachusetts.

They do not exactly coincide with the sizes of the output guide of the Raytheon millimeter wave tubes.† The mismatch is not great, however, and a satisfactory matching taper can be made simply by filing the inside of the guide.

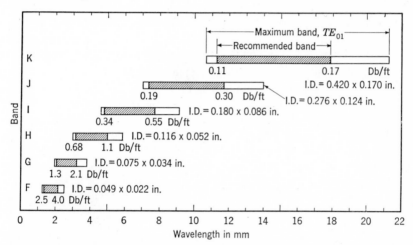

Fig. 1.7. Dimensions and losses for coin-silver waveguide covering the region from 1.3 mm to 18 mm. The designation F, G, H, I, J is that adopted at Duke for the sub-K bands as indicated. (From Gilliam, Johnson, and Gordy.[11])

1.2b. Waveguide Bends, Connectors, and Tapers. Bends, in E or H plane, and twists can be put in waveguide without objectionable mismatch if they are gradual and uniform. To prevent the walls of the guide from collapsing, it is advisable to fill the guide with Wood's metal or some such material which can be melted out after the bend is made. Frequently waveguide cells are made into circular coils with a radius of the order of a few inches. This makes a very convenient cell for cooling or heating or for Zeeman studies. However, when coils of such small radius are used, the guide should be of such size as to support only the dominant mode.

For most purposes in microwave spectroscopy the simple butt joint is to be preferred over the choke and flange joint commonly used in radar.

† Neither do these sizes and designations correspond to present R.M.A. standards. The Duke waveguide sizes have been chosen so that a minimum number would be required to cover the millimeter wave region beginning with the K-band components developed during World War II. For convenience the band designations were chosen in alphabetical sequence, starting with the previously established K-band designation. It may be noted that there are 30 R.M.A. guide sizes (WR 12– WR 42) covering the four bands H, I, J, K, listed here. Furthermore, to our knowledge, there are no standard sizes smaller than 0.100 x 0.050 in.

The butt joint is not frequency sensitive, and, if it is carefully made, reflections which it produces will be as low as, or lower than, those of the choke joint. The two surfaces forming the butt joint should be clean and well matched, and they should be pulled together tightly. Most of the waveguide components can be made of a single piece of guide so that few joints are necessary. Choke coupling is perhaps desirable only at the entrance and the exit of the absorption cell, where it is necessary to interpose a dielectric seal. Thin mica windows, however, are frequently inserted within a butt joint with no choke coupling.

In making transitions from guide of one size to another, tapered sections are used. The length of the taper for a satisfactory matching

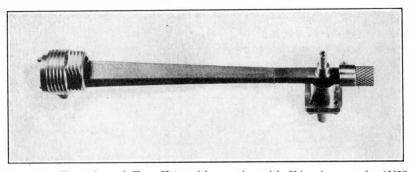

FIG. 1.8. Electroformed K to H transition section with H-band mount for 1N53 crystal.

depends upon the relative sizes of the guide to be matched. The length is not critical, however. A taper angle of the order of 3° is usually satisfactory. Good transitions can be made by milling out two halves from a block of metal such that the seam where the halves are joined occurs in the center of the broad side of the guide. They can be made more satisfactorily by the electroforming process.† The waveguide for the output crystal mount can be electroformed with the transition sections so that a junction is eliminated. See Fig. 1.8. These and many other high-frequency millimeter wave components are now electroformed.

1.2c. Attenuators. The most commonly used waveguide attenuator is the simple flap attenuator similar to that in Fig. 1.9. Though the dimensions are not critical, the more gradual the taper of the attenuating material, the better is the impedance match. Usually the attenuating strip is of I.R.C. resistance card (carbon-coated card about $\frac{1}{32}$ in. thick).

† Detailed directions for electroforming microwave components are given by R. J. Coates and S. F. Rogers (*Report* 3673, Naval Research Laboratory, Washington, June 8, 1950).

When carefully constructed with a suitable dial, these attenuators can be calibrated. Calibrated waveguide attenuators are available commercially † for the wavelength regions longer than 1 cm.

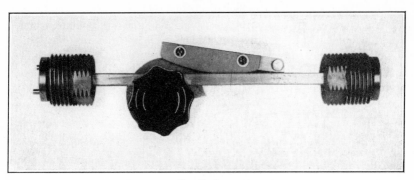

Fig. 1.9. Simple flap attenuator.

1.2d. Impedance-Matching Devices. The subject of impedance measurement and impedance matching is too extensive for the present discussion. The few remarks given here are intended to help the reader to apply the information on the subject available in the volumes already mentioned.[23]

In microwave spectroscopy the necessity for impedance-matching devices should be avoided wherever possible by careful design and construction of components. Line tuners and other narrow-banded devices are to be avoided in sweep spectroscopes. Whenever an intolerable and unavoidable reflection occurs at some point in the line, it should be canceled by a broad-banded device which would of necessity be placed near the point of reflection. Most of the accessory components are between the absorption cell and the generator. Reflections from them are not serious since attenuating pads can be interposed at any point to reduce resonances. An attenuator should not be placed beyond the cell because it attenuates the absorption line signal. It is desirable to place the final detector as near the cell as possible. When this is done, the tuners used to match the detector to the waveguide can also reduce the reflections from the output cell window. Wherever possible, broadbanded, non-resonant cell windows should be used. These are commonly of thin mica.

1.2e. Directional Couplers. It is necessary to couple out a fraction of the power from the main transmission line for such purposes as measuring frequency, monitoring power, or measuring standing waves.

† Polytechnic Research and Development Company, Inc., **202 Tillary Street**, Brooklyn 1, N. Y.

Since the usual klystron generator provides several milliwatts of power, only about $\frac{1}{100}$ of this is needed for monitoring or for making frequency measurement with a cavity wavemeter. This division of power requires a coupler with a coupling coefficient of the order of 20 db. A simple and adequate coupler for this purpose is the Bethe-hole directional coupler [24] described below. In making precision frequency measurements, it is customary to measure with a calibrated receiver the beat note of the source oscillator with a standard frequency marker obtained by multiplying the signal from a relatively low-frequency oscillator which is

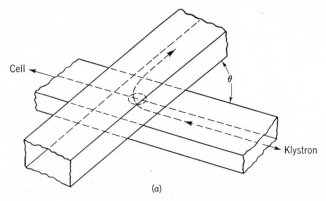

FIG. 1.10a. Schematic of Bethe-hole coupler.

monitored by comparison with station WWV. Since the frequency marker is ordinarily very weak at frequencies of K band or higher, it is necessary to use a sizable fraction of the source power for beating with the marker signal in order to obtain good reception. Line dividers such as T or Y sections are satisfactory when half the source power can be spared. When this is not the case, two-hole directional couplers which have coupling coefficients of 6–12 db are satisfactory.

In the Bethe-hole coupler a section of auxiliary guide (see Fig. 1.10a) is placed over the main transmission guide, broad side to broad side as shown, with a small coupling hole in the center. By treating the coupling hole as polarizable, Bethe [25] has shown that the coupling into the auxiliary guide will take place through an induced magnetic as well as an induced electric dipole. The radiation coupled through the induced magnetic dipole is out of phase with that coupled through the induced electric dipole for the forward direction but reinforces it in the backward direction, i.e., in the direction opposite to the power flow in the main line. Hence, the Bethe-hole coupler is a directional coupler. However, for complete cancellation of the forward radiation the magnitude of the coupling through the magnetic vector must be equal to that coupled through the electric vector. Usually the former is slightly larger. When this is true, the two can be made equivalent by a rotation of the auxiliary guide with respect to the main guide.

Bethe's theory gives the coefficient of coupling, C, which represents the relative power in db in the two guides as

$$C = 20 \log_{10} \left\{ \frac{\pi d^3}{3ab\lambda_g} [\cos \theta + \tfrac{1}{2}(\lambda_g/\lambda)^2 F_E/F_H]F_H \right\}, \qquad (1.7)$$

where θ is the angle between the guides, a and b are the guide dimensions, d is the diameter of the coupling hole, λ is the wavelength in free space, and λ_g that in the guide. The attenuation factors of the hole for electric coupling, F_E, and for magnetic coupling, F_H, are:

$$F_E = e^{-2\pi t[(1.31d)^{-2} - \lambda^{-2}]^{1/2}} \qquad (1.8)$$

and

$$F_H = e^{-2\pi t[(1.71d)^{-2} - \lambda^{-2}]^{1/2}}, \qquad (1.9)$$

where t is the thickness of the hole. When the angle θ is such that the two couplings are equivalent,

$$\cos \theta = \tfrac{1}{2}(\lambda_g/\lambda)^2 F_E/F_H, \qquad (1.10)$$

which for a hole of small t becomes

$$\cos \theta \approx \tfrac{1}{2}(\lambda_g/\lambda)^2. \qquad (1.11)$$

These formulas allow one to design a Bethe-hole coupler for any wavelength or guide size. It should be remembered that the Bethe theory assumes that the diameter of the hole is small as compared with the wavelength. Also, if the hole is made larger, objectionable reflections in the main guide will result. Coupling coefficients as low as 15 db are nevertheless feasible. Design curves for K and X bands are given by Kyhl.[24] For $\lambda = 1.25$ cm in standard K-band guide a hole 0.21 in. in diameter and 0.040 in. thick gives a coupling of 20 db and requires for maximum directivity an angle of 55°.

The Bethe-hole coupler is not particularly frequency sensitive and is excellent for monitoring power or for measuring frequency with a cavity wavemeter. It is convenient to put the wavemeter on the end of the auxiliary guide in the direction of flow of maximum power and a detector on the opposite end. Sufficient power is reflected from the wavemeter into the detector to give a reading at all times. When the wavemeter is tuned to resonance, it reflects less power, and this decrease is indicated by the detector. For power monitoring the detector should be put in the direction of the power flow in the auxiliary guide, and a matched load should terminate the opposite end.

Figure 1.10b shows a design for a broad-banded, two-hole coupler which can be used to couple out $\frac{1}{10}$ or more of the power from the main transmission line. Here the narrow sides of the guide are placed together. The two coupling holes are separated along the guide by about $\frac{1}{4}$ wavelength. In this type of coupler, the direction of power flow in the auxiliary guide is the same as that in the main guide. It is easy to see that the power coupled through the two holes will be out of phase for the reverse direction since the path difference is then $\frac{1}{2}$ wavelength, and that the power will be reinforced in the forward direction because the path difference for this direction is zero.

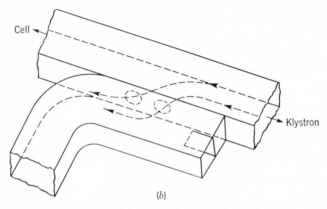

Cell

Klystron

(b)

Fig. 1.10b.   Schematic of a two-hole coupler.

A table of experimentally determined couplings for slots of different sizes and for wavelengths above 1 cm is given by Kyhl.[24] A coupling of 8.5 db for $\lambda = 1.25$ cm in the K-band guide is obtained with slot separations of 0.152 in. and slot dimensions as follows: length, 0.166 in.; width, 0.062 in.; and thickness, 0.080 in. These dimensions can be scaled down according to wavelength for making a suitable coupler for millimeter wave bands. For two round holes spaced $\frac{1}{4}$ wavelength apart, the amount of coupling can be calculated with the formula

$$C = 20 \log_{10}\left(\frac{\pi d^3 \lambda_g}{6a^3 b}\right) - 32.0\left[1 - \left(\frac{1.71d}{\lambda}\right)^2\right]^{\frac{1}{2}} \frac{t}{d}, \qquad (1.12)$$

derived by Bethe.[25] The symbols here have the same significance as defined above for the single Bethe-hole coupler. In general the two-slot coupler is to be preferred since it is more broad-banded and can be used to produce a stronger coupling than that of the coupler with two round holes.

1.2f. The Magic Tee. An extremely useful device is the so-called magic tee shown in Fig. 1.11. In microwave spectroscopy it is used, among other things, as a power divider or directional coupler in precision

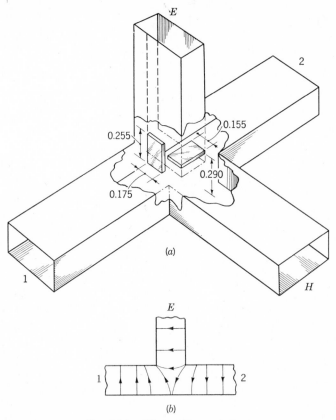

FIG. 1.11.   Waveguide magic tee.

frequency measurement, as a standing wave detector, as a bridge for balancing microwave power, and as part of a discriminator for oscillator stabilization. The magic tee is a waveguide junction of four arms. These are commonly described as the E and H arms and two side arms as designated in Fig. 1.11a. The H arm is so designated because it couples to the two side arms through the magnetic components of the field. The E arm is so designated because it couples to the side arms through the electric components. There is no direct coupling between the E and H arms because they are "crossed" waveguide. An ideal tee is electrically symmetrical: the impedance looking into each arm is matched. There is then no cross coupling between E and H or between 1 and 2. Power passed into the H arm divides equally between the side arms, with none entering arm E except that which is reflected from the side arms. Power entering either side arm divides equally between the E and H arms with only reflected power entering the other side arm. The phase relations of the radiation in the different arms are of consequence. These can be followed by observation of the electric component of the field. For the H coupling there is no change in the direction of the vibration of the E vector, and energy passing into the two side arms from the H arm will be in phase. For coupling from the E arm the electric vector swings around as indicated in Fig. 1.11b, and the radiation passing into the two side arms is 180° out of phase. Conversely, if phase-coherent energy is fed into arms 1 and 2, it will be out of phase in the E arm.

Various methods have been proposed for matching the impedance of the magic tee. Perhaps the simplest is the use of two irises, the positions and dimensions of which are determined experimentally. For K band they are given in Fig. 1.11a, as taken from Vol. 16 from the *Radiation Laboratory Series*.[23] For some purposes it is possible to use the unmatched tee. However, there is then some cross coupling and a large standing-wave ratio.

1.2g. Waveguide Mounts for Crystal Mixers and Detectors. The crystals most commonly used in microwave spectroscopy for detection and frequency multiplication are the 1N26, 1N31, or 1N53 silicon crystals. In construction these crystals are mounted along the inner conductor of a coaxial line shorted at one end. See Fig. 1.15. Thus the waveguide mounts must provide a waveguide-to-coaxial transition. Figure 1.12 shows a cross section of a simple, tunable waveguide mount for the use of the 1N26 or 1N31 crystals as detectors. This design can be adapted to the 1N53 by a simple alteration of the size of the coaxial mount holding the crystal cartridge. Because of the smaller size of the 1N53, it is advisable to fit the prongs which hold the crystal to the outside rather than to the inside of the crystal cartridge. This type of mount can be made for all sizes of millimeter waveguide shown in Fig. 1.7. Figure 1.8 shows an H-band waveguide mount electroformed with the output tapered section which connects it to a cell of K-band guide. It has two tuning adjustments. One adjustment consists of sliding the crystal in and out so as to change the length of the terminated coaxial line containing the crystal. To make this adjustment possible, the inner and outer conductors of the coaxial connector are constructed so that frictional contact is made by spring fingers with the inner and outer conductors of the crystal container. (Alternately, the crystal can be mounted in a fixed position and the tuning screw placed on the guide immediately before the crystal.) The inner connector extends across the guide at the center, where the E field is strongest, and connects to the center conductor of a dielectric cable which transmits detected energy. Preceding the cable connector is a choke-and-by-pass condenser which

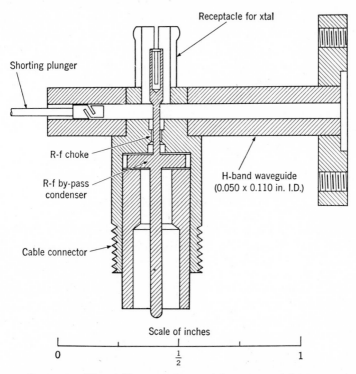

FIG. 1.12. Waveguide mount for coaxial type crystal detector.

prevents leakage of the microwave power into the dielectric cable. A second tuning adjustment is the movable shorting plunger in the end of the guide which has the usual $1/4$-wave chokes.

In the higher-frequency millimeter-wave region the performance of a crystal detector can often be improved if the crystal is removed from its cartridge and mounted directly in the guide. This has been tried by C. M. Johnson and others with good results. Crystal mounts of the types described here are usually employed with the various modulation spectrographs like the Stark spectrograph, as well as with the simple video type of detection.

Superheterodyne detection is commonly employed in fixed-frequency spectrometers such as those designed for the study of paramagnetic resonance. It is often used with frequency-sweep spectroscopes for detecting the markers of the secondary frequency standard. In this

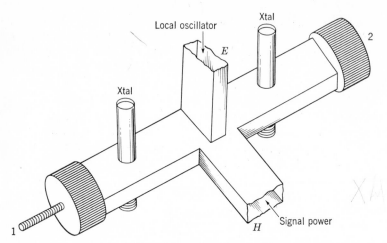

FIG. 1.13.   Balanced magic-tee mixer.

type of detection the same crystal acts as a mixer and as a detector. Provision must be made for superimposing both the local-oscillator power and the signal power upon the crystal. A relatively simple, and

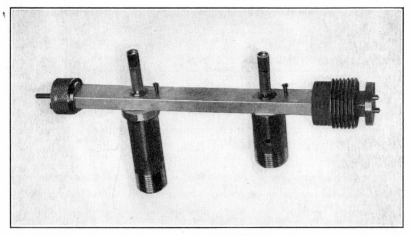

FIG. 1.14.   Crystal mixer and multiplier for standard frequency markers.

perhaps the most effective, way of doing this is with a magic tee. Figure 1.13 illustrates how this is done in the balanced magic-tee mixer. Crystal mounts, which may be of the type described above, are connected to the side arms 1 and 2. The signal power is fed in through either the E or H arm, and the local-oscillator power is coupled in through the remaining arm. The output from the two crystals is then coupled in push-pull to the amplifier.

The balanced magic-tee mixer has several advantages, the most important of which are the suppression of local-oscillator noise and the good coupling of both the local oscillator and the signal power to the crystals with a negligible inter-action between the local oscillator and the signal cir-cuits. The reason for the latter is apparent from the discussion of the magic tee already given. For a thorough discussion of this and other types of mixers, see Vol. 16, by Pound, in the *Radiation Laboratory Series.*[23]

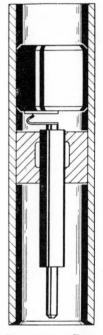

When strong frequency markers are available, as is usually the case for K-band or longer waves, a satis-factory mixer-detector can be made for frequency-standard measurements by simply mounting the crystal on a straight waveguide section, as indicated in Fig. 1.14. Here the marker power is passed into the crystal from one direction, and a sample of the source power is superimposed from the other direc-tion. In this application the interaction of the two circuits is not serious. Tuning screws can be pro-vided for matching the crystal to the guide. However, the tuning provided by sliding the crystal in and out is usually adequate if it is placed near the multiplier crystal, as indicated in Fig. 1.14, so that the tuning adjustment of the latter can help to match the mixer crystal.

FIG. 1.15. Cross section of coaxial crystal cartridge. (Courtesy Sylvania Electric Products Company.)

1.2h. Detectors. *Crystals.* A silicon crystal mounted in a coaxial cartridge, as shown in Fig. 1.15, is the most commonly used detector. The 1N26 crystal, developed for K-band radar, is of this type. This ver-satile crystal is used in mixers, detectors, and frequency multipliers. The 1N53 for millimeter waves is similar except that it is mounted in a smaller cartridge. The ceramic type, 1N23, was developed primarily for 10-cm waves and is not often used in microwave spectroscopy. Selected 1N26 types are used as video detectors. Although special crystal video detectors, such as the Sylvania 1N31 and 1N32, are available, these are designed primarily for frequencies of 10,000 Mc and lower. Tests by C. M. Johnson, however, indicated that the 1N31 performs very well in crystal video spectrometers at K band and even in the millimeter-wave region. A comprehensive treatment of these and other crystal rectifiers is given by Torrey and Whitmer in Vol. 15 of the *Radiation Laboratory Series*.[23] See also Vol. 16, by Pound.[23] The Sylvania 1N53 crystal is designed for frequencies above 30,000 Mc. Its characteristics are not now available for publication. Our tests indicate that it is superior to the 1N26 for all millimeter-wave spectroscopy.

The characteristics of these rectifiers vary from crystal to crystal. There are, however, general characteristics which are qualitatively alike for all. Figure 1.16 shows how the conversion loss and noise

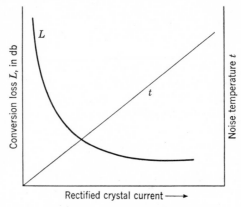

FIG. 1.16. Characteristic variations of noise temperature and conversion loss with rectified crystal current.

temperature depend upon the rectified crystal current. These are the most important properties for crystal detectors in Stark or similar spectroscopes. (See Sec. 1.4.) Combined with the noise figure of the amplifier, they determine the optimum operating power level for the spectrometer. In terms of rectified r-f current, this is the minimum point of the curve in Fig. 1.17. Beyond a certain minimum, the power level is not critical, as can be seen by the flattened bottom of the curve. If the power level (or rectified current) falls below a certain miminum, however, the performance drops rapidly with further decrease in power. In the Stark and other modulation spectrometers, the power supplied to the absorption cell also acts as local-oscillator power in the simulated heterodyne receiver. It is important that this power be kept above a certain minimum (usually of the order of $\frac{1}{10}$ mw) to prevent excessive conversion loss. For the typical radar receiver with a microwave local oscillator and an intermediate frequency of 30 Mc the optimum local-oscillator power level is of the order of $\frac{1}{2}$ mw. Because of the much greater noise temperature generated by the rectified current at low frequencies, the optimum power level for a modulation spectrograph operated at 100 kc would be lower than that of the radar receiver, probably about $\frac{1}{10}$ mw or lower. In practice, one optimizes the power level for a given crystal on a known absorption line.

In addition to the conversion loss and noise temperature, the crystal impedance, both input and output, varies with the power level. For

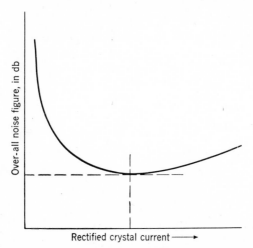

FIG. 1.17. Effective over-all noise figure as a function of rectified crystal current. The optimum current (indicated by the dotted line) is usually the order of $\frac{1}{2}$ milliamperes. Note the variation is not critical in the vicinity of the optimum current. The form of the curve is determined primarily by the L and t curves of Fig. 1.16.

optimum performance one must tune the crystal at the power level at which it is to operate.

In video receivers the crystal operates as a square-law detector; i.e., the detected voltage or current is directly proportional to the input power. For silicon detectors this is true only for powers lower than about 10 μw. Figure 1.18 illustrates the behavior of the Sylvania 1N32 video crystal. It indicates, in a general way, the behavior of other crystals operated as square-law detectors. It is seen that, below 10^{-5} watt, the detected current and voltage are linear functions of the power and that the video resistance is relatively constant. Note that, in the region between 10^{-5} and 10^{-4} watt, the video resistance changes rapidly with power. A video amplifier matched to the crystal at 10^{-5} watt will definitely not be matched at 10^{-4} watt. For a definition of the figure of merit of a video crystal, see Art. 1.4d.

A property of considerable importance to microwave spectroscopists is the variation of crystal noise temperature with frequency. For detected microwave power of the order of a milliwatt, this noise is hundreds of times greater at 100 kc than at 30 Mc. Miller and Green-

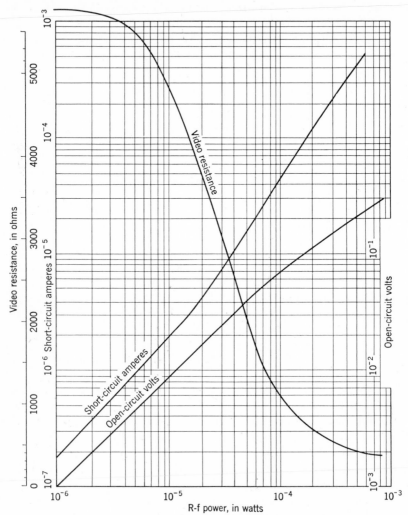

FIG. 1.18. Characteristic curves for Type 1N32 Sylvania silicon crystal. (Courtesy Sylvania Electric Products Company.)

blatt [26] found that the noise in excess of the Johnson noise generated by a crystal varies inversely with frequency. In assessing the relative importance of this excess noise, one should consider the power level at which the crystal operates. For power levels below about 5 μw, with no bias other than that of the rectified microwave power, the excess noise is relatively unimportant even at audio frequencies. Under these conditions the noise is essentially the Johnson noise which does not vary with frequency. With the small power now available from generators (excepting magnetrons) for the wavelength region below 5 mm, one may as well amplify the signal at audio frequencies as at radio frequencies. However, in the centimeter region, where milliwatts of power are available, considerable gain in sensitivity can be obtained by the use of the higher power and by the amplification of the signal at radio frequencies to avoid the low-frequency noise generated in the crystal by this power.

No quantitative data are available for publication on crystals designed for performance at millimeter-wave frequencies. Silicon crystals have been used with success at Duke both as multipliers and as detectors in spectrographs operating in the 2- to 5-mm wave range.

Thermal detectors. Thermal detectors have not been used widely in microwave spectroscopy and will not be discussed in detail here. They have the disadvantage that they cannot be used with rapid modulation methods. Certain types, however, can respond to modulation frequencies of the order of 100 or more cycles per second. Wherever it is necessary to use low-frequency modulation, as is the case with Zeeman or molecular-beam modulation, they are probably superior to crystals because microwave power does not generate in them the low-frequency noise which it generates in crystals. Beringer and Castle [18] made use of this advantage of thermal detectors in their studies of the paramagnetic resonance of gases. Details of thermistors and bolometers with their associated circuits are given in Vol. 11 of the *Radiation Laboratory Series*.[23] A discussion of their sensitivities for microwave spectroscopes is given by Beringer and Castle [18] and by Gordy.[4]

1.2i. Absorption Cells. Like other microwave components, absorption cells can be, and are, made in a variety of ways. A few of the more common types are described here. The simplest cell, commonly used, is a section of waveguide sealed at each end by thin dielectric windows (usually mica). The optimum length for these cells depends upon the waveguide losses as well as upon the type of detection. For a square-law detector it is α_c^{-1} and for linear detection it is $2\alpha_c^{-1}$, where α_c is the coefficient of attenuation of the guide. The effective absorbing length of a waveguide cell depends upon the wavelength in the guide and is

$$l_{\text{eff}} = l(\lambda_g/\lambda), \qquad (1.13)$$

where l is the measured length, λ_g is the wavelength in the guide, and λ is the corresponding free-space wavelength. Molecular saturation may be avoided by the use of oversized waveguide. A tapered transition section is then used at each end to match the impedance of the cell to the smaller guide of the transmission line. These transition sections are usually included in the cell with the cell windows at the smaller ends of the transition. If the windows are placed across the larger guide, there

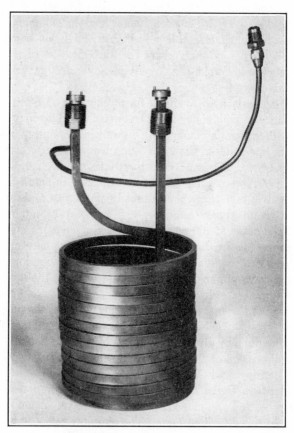

Fig. 1.19.   Coiled waveguide absorption cell.

is danger of inducing higher modes which can be transmitted in the larger guide. Also, the larger the area of the window, the thicker it must be to withstand atmospheric pressure, and it is desirable to have the window as thin as possible in order to reduce reflections. Round holes are made in the guide for evacuation of the cell and for introduction of the gas. The diameter of these holes should be small as compared with the wavelength in the guide. For K-band waves they can be of the order of $\frac{1}{32}$ in. To increase the pumping rate, several of these small holes can be bored without adverse reflections, provided that they are properly staggered to prevent resonance at any given wavelength. For studies of the Zeeman effect, a solenoid can be conveniently placed around a waveguide cell. When not made of oversized guide, the cell can be tightly coiled so that it can be placed between the poles of a permanent magnet or an electromagnet. Figure 1.19 shows a cell of J-band guide coiled for placement in a cooling flask.

A resonant cavity provides a compact cell which is very effective for special studies. However, because it must be tuned to a particular wavelength, it is not very suitable for a search spectrometer. The effective absorbing path, l_{eff}, is

$$l_{eff} \approx \left(\frac{\lambda^2}{\pi \lambda_g}\right) Q_L, \tag{1.14}$$

where Q_L is the Q of the loaded cavity, λ_g the wavelength in the guide, and λ the corresponding wavelength in free space. Thus, for a high-Q cavity, the effective absorbing path is equivalent to a very long waveguide cell. It can be shown [4] that the absorption coefficient of a gas, α_g, at the cavity resonant frequency ν is

$$\alpha_g = (2\pi\nu/c)(1/Q_L - 1/Q), \tag{1.15}$$

where Q is for the unloaded cell and Q_L represents the value after the gas is admitted. Thus, from measurement of the Q of the cavity before and after the gas is admitted, α_g can be calculated. Bleaney and Penrose [27] initiated the method of detecting with a loosely coupled detector the power at the peak of the cavity response curve with and without the gas in the cavity. Then,

$$(d_L/d)^{1/2} = Q_L/Q, \tag{1.16}$$

and it follows from Eq. 1.15 that

$$\alpha_g = (2\pi\nu/cQ)[(d/d_L)^{1/2} - 1]^{1/2}. \tag{1.17}$$

Here d_L and d represent the indicator responses with and without the gas in the cavity. For best sensitivity, a high-Q cavity with a frequency-stabilized source should be used.

A convenient way to construct a Stark-modulation cell is to place a conducting strip down the center of a waveguide section as indicated in the cross sections of Fig. 1.20. This method, originally described by Hughes and Wilson,[8] is frequently employed. The conducting strip is held in the center, perpendicular to the E lines, by a dielectric material such as Teflon which also insulates it from the waveguide walls. Usually

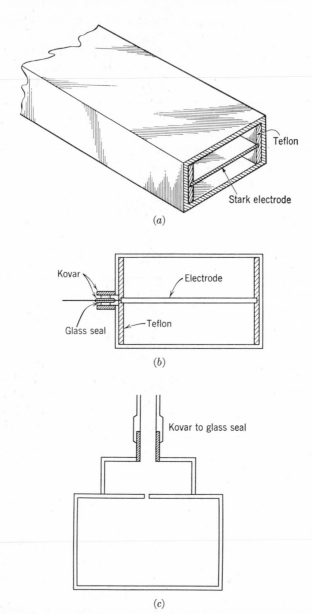

FIG. 1.20. Details of Stark cell construction: (a) placement of Stark electrode; (b) Stark voltage connection; (c) connection to vacuum system.

the waveguide is grounded and the modulating voltage applied to the inner conducting strip. For other Stark-cell designs, see reference 28.

Cell windows which are usable over a wide temperature range can be made by squeezing a thin sheet of mica with a lead gasket between two flanges or between a choke and a flange coupling. After some practice, very satisfactory seals can be made with a relatively low impedance mismatch. If the opening in the lead gasket is too small or if too much pressure is applied, the lead will protrude into the waveguide opening. When finished, the window should be examined visually or by a standing-wave measurement to make sure that the lead does not protrude.

1.2j. Cavity Wavemeters. Wavelength measurements accurate to a few megacycles can be made with coaxial or hollow cylindrical cavity wavemeters. The coaxial type is used principally for wavelengths of 3 cm or longer; the cylindrical cavity type, for waves of 3 cm or shorter.

The standing-wave patterns set up in a cylindrical cavity have modes in θ, r, and z dimensions. Two types of waves are possible: those for which E_z is zero throughout the cavity (transverse electric or TE modes), and those for which H_z is zero (TM modes). The resonant frequencies of the cavity are then given by

$$(fD)^2 = [(cx_{lm})/\pi]^2 + (cn/2)^2(D/L)^2, \tag{1.18}$$

where x_{lm} is the mth root of the Bessel's function, $J'_l(x) = 0$ for TE modes, or $J_l(x) = 0$ for TM modes; l, m, and n are integers representing the number of nodes along θ, r, and z, respectively; and c is the velocity of light. Solutions of Eq. 1.18 are plotted in Fig. 1.21, where f is expressed in megacycles per second and D and L are in inches. In normal usage L is varied until resonance occurs for successive values of n. The interval ΔL is measured with a micrometer. The solution of Eq. 1.18 for the $\Delta n = 1$ condition is

$$2\Delta L = c/\sqrt{f^2 - (cx_{lm}/\pi D)^2}, \tag{1.19}$$

which may be plotted on a large scale for the appropriate mode used. Such a wavemeter chart is usually calibrated on known lines or crystal harmonics for most accurate results.

It is evident from examination of Fig. 1.21 that for a particular value of fD several modes cross unless operation is restricted to TE_{11n} modes with $(fD/10^4)^2$ less than about 0.82. If this were the only design criterion, all cavity wavemeters would be designed to operate in TE_{11n} modes, and, indeed, such wavemeters are used for frequencies less than 25,000 Mc. Unfortunately, the quality factor Q is not highest for TE_{11n} but for TE_{01n} modes. Q is a measure of the sharpness of tuning and can be expressed as $Q = f_0/\Delta f$, where f_0 is the resonant frequency

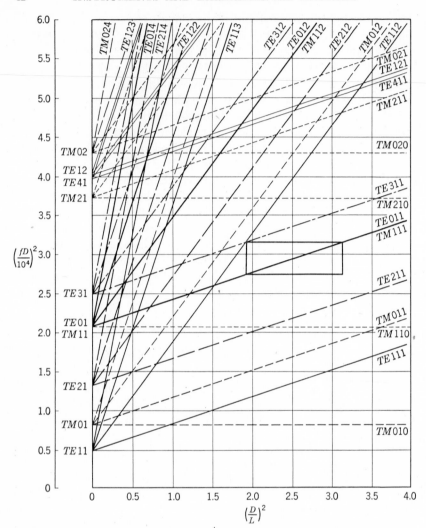

Fig. 1.21. Mode chart for cylindrical resonant cavity. (From Wilson, Schramm, and Kinzer, *Radar Systems and Components*, Bell Laboratories Staff, D. Van Nostrand Company, New York, 1949, p. 912.)

and Δf is the width of the response curve measured between the half-power points. The ultimate accuracy of the cavity meter is determined by Q. For a silver cavity TE_{111} mode, $D/L = 1$, $f = 25{,}000$ Mc, the Q is 8000. By comparison, the Q of a spectral line may be as high as 250,000. Thus it is desirable to use higher-Q cavity designs, particularly at frequencies above 25,000 Mc.

The TE_{0mn} modes have particularly high Q-values. Furthermore, no axial currents flow in these modes so that it is not necessary to furnish the cavity plunger with an r-f choke. Indeed, this feature can be used to damp out unwanted modes if a loose-fitting piston is made and a ring of polyiron is inserted behind the piston to absorb any radiation leaking past the piston. To have a TE_{01n} wavemeter cover a 20 per cent frequency band (about half the recommended band of the associated waveguide size), for $n = 1$ and 2, the meter should be designed to operate in the region $2.8 \leq (fD/10^4)^2 \leq 3.9$ approximately. It is evident from Fig. 1.21 that in this range spurious resonances can occur. As these are highly damped by the polyiron, however, they are easily distinguishable from the desired modes. Since there is no crossing of modes in the operating region, the experimental tuning curves agree well with the theoretical ones. Adaption of standard micrometer heads makes the maintenance of the necessary tolerance easy, and at the higher frequencies the larger diameter of these wavemeters makes them easier to construct than the TE_{11n} type. The Q of a TE_{011} silver wavemeter at 25,000 Mc with $D/L = 2$ is 17,000, over twice that of a TE_{111} mode. When the wavemeter is operated in the TE_{012} mode, the Q is 24,000. Narrower-band wavemeters of still higher Q using higher TE_{0mn} modes can be constructed with the aid of Fig. 1.21.

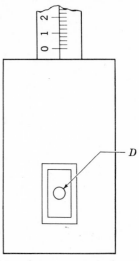

Band	Diameter of Coupling Hole in Inches
K	0.110
J	0.083
J–I	0.067
I	0.055

FIG. 1.22. Coupling iris for TE_{01n}-mode cylindrical cavity wavemeter.

A peculiar feature of the TE_{01n} modes is that they are identically degenerate with TM_{11n} modes which excite axial currents and hence are highly damped. A properly designed coupling iris does not excite the TM_{11n} modes, but they may be excited by "cross coupling" if the cavity is not perfectly symmetrical, i.e., if the piston face is not accurately perpendicular to the cavity axis, and if the gap surrounding the piston is not uniform. Cross coupling obviously lowers the Q of the TE_{01n} modes.

A complete wavemeter circuit requires provisions for coupling energy carried by waveguides into and, if used as a transmission type wavemeter, out of the cavity. Coupling is generally attained by means of round irises as in Fig. 1.22. The iris dimensions are adjusted so that the power dissipated in the cavity is about equal to that dissipated in the waveguide loads (assumed matched).

Design details for wavemeters covering the K-, X-, and S-band regions are given elsewhere.[29] Meters for these regions are also available commercially. Figure 1.23 gives a diagram of a TE_{01n} cylindrical cavity

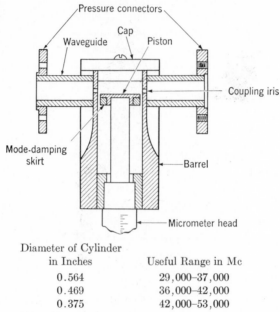

Diameter of Cylinder in Inches	Useful Range in Mc
0.564	29,000–37,000
0.469	36,000–42,000
0.375	42,000–53,000

FIG. 1.23.   Cross section of TE_{01n} cavity wavemeter.

meter with a table of the critical dimensions for coverage of the 5- to 11-mm region. Approximate calibration curves can be calculated with Eq. 1.19. These should then be checked on accurately measured spectral lines or on standard frequency markers.

1.2k. Sources of Radiation. *Klystrons.* The reflex klystron is used almost exclusively as a primary source of radiation in microwave spectroscopy. When not used as a direct source, it usually serves to drive a crystal harmonic generator which is a secondary source. The klystron was invented shortly before World War II and was rapidly developed during the war period. It is now a familiar instrument to many physicists and radio engineers. For those unfamiliar with its operation, detailed treatments are now available.[30] Several different types of reflex klystrons are manufactured. They differ in constructional details or operating voltages, frequency range, etc. Table 1.1 lists operating characteristics of Raytheon klystrons which cover the frequency range of most interest from 22,000 Mc to 60,000 Mc.

Table 1.1.   Characteristics of some Raytheon klystron oscillators †

Tube Type	Frequency Range (kmc)	Typical Power Output (milli-watts)	Typical Cathode Potential (volts)	Maximum Cathode Current (ma)	Inner Dimensions of Wave-guide Output (inches)
RK-2K33	22–25	40	−1800	10	0.210 × 0.460
QK-289	27.27–30	18	−2250	15	0.140 × 0.280
QK-140 QK-290	29.7–33.52	18	−2250	15	0.140 × 0.280
QK-141 QK-291	33.5–36.3	18	−2250	15	0.140 × 0.280
QK-142 QK-292	35.1–39.7	10	−2500	15	0.140 × 0.280
QK-226 QK-293	37.1–42.6	5	−2500	18	0.112 × 0.224
QK-227 QK-294	41.7–50	5	−3000	20	0.112 × 0.224
QK-295	50–55 54–60	—	−3500	20	0.074 × 0.148

† Raytheon Manufacturing Company, Tube Power Division, Waltham, Massachusetts.

Reflex klystrons operate on the principle of velocity modulation of an electron beam by a resonant cavity.   The velocity-modulated electrons form bunches and are reversed by a reflector voltage and sent back through the cavity in such phase as to give up energy to the oscillating field.   The two-cavity klystron employs one cavity for velocity modulation and another for the generation of power.   Some of the power generated in the second cavity is coupled back to drive the modulating cavity.   A drift space is provided between the cavities, and no reflector is required.   Because of difficulty of tuning, the two-cavity klystron is not used as a primary source in microwave spectroscopy, but it has found an important application in the multiplier chain of one type of frequency standard.

Though the usual reflex klystron generates relatively low power, only a few milliwatts as compared with a few megawatts peak power available from magnetrons, there are several features which make it a very satisfactory radiation source for spectroscopy. Among these are the purity of its spectrum and the ease of tuning. For all practical purposes, it is a monochromatic source, the frequency of which can be varied mechanically over about a 15 per cent range or electrically over a range of about $\frac{1}{10}$ per cent. Its frequency can be swept electrically at any desired rate, by simply imposing a modulating voltage on the reflector. Also, its output can be stabilized at a given frequency by coupling it electrically to an external cavity or to a spectral line. Because of the saturation effect in spectroscopy and because the most sensitive detectors are damaged by power beyond a few milliwatts, the power limitation of klystrons is seldom a disadvantage.

The operation of a klystron depends strongly upon the load impedance. A highly frequency-sensitive load can cause sharp cusps or discontinuities in the oscillator mode which under some circumstances might be mistaken for spectral lines. Also, within the mechanical tuning range of a given klystron operating into a given load, gaps or frequency bands in which the tube refuses to oscillate frequently occur. A high-Q wavemeter, when closely coupled, can cause frequency-pulling of the klystron which results in error in the wavelength measurement. To minimize these difficulties, a matched attenuating pad of about 10 db should be placed between the oscillator and load whenever the power can be spared. Frequently, there is insufficient power for optimum operation of the spectrograph with the attenuating pad. This is usually true where the klystron is used to drive a crystal frequency multiplier. When this is so, frequent tuning of the load and substitution of oscillator tubes are necessary to obtain complete coverage of a significant band of frequencies. When standing waves are present and little or no attenuating pad is used, it is desirable to insert a line squeezer so that the electrical length of the load line can be varied. Sometimes discontinuities in the output power occur even when the output load is properly terminated. These depend on the internal properties of the tube and originate largely in the electron beam. This type of behavior is designated electronic hysteresis.

Of considerable interest to the spectroscopist is the noise generated in reflex klystrons. Whenever the klystron is used as a local oscillator for a superheterodyne receiver, this noise can be largely canceled with a balanced mixer, filtered with a resonant cavity, or avoided by an i-f amplifier of high frequency. However, when the klystron is used as a primary radiation source, the noise cannot be so easily disposed of. Noise at microwave frequencies arises from random modulations of the cavity oscillation by irregular fluctuations in the beam current. Since the noise is generated in the oscillator cavity, it might be expected to have a frequency distribution similar to the response curve of the cavity.

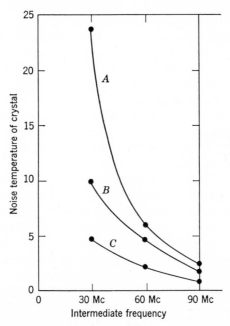

FIG. 1.24. Noise generated in crystal by 2K33 local oscillator plotted as a function of i-f frequency. Points represent data of Kuper and Waltz.[31] Curve A is for half-power point on high-voltage side of reflector mode; B is for half-power point on low-voltage side of reflector mode; C is for center or highest-power point of reflector mode.

Thus the greatest amount of noise should occur at the resonant frequency, and the noise should fall to an insignificant amount at 50 to 100 Mc on either side of this frequency. The measurements of Kuper and Waltz [31] show that this is approximately true but that the noise is not entirely symmetric about the resonant frequency. Their studies also reveal that the noise depends upon the reflector-voltage mode chosen and upon the point of operation of the reflector voltage in a given mode. Within a given mode the noise is least when the reflector voltage is adjusted for maximum power. The noise is lowest for the 170-volt mode, which is next to the highest employed. The noise is in general higher on the high-voltage side of the mode. Figure 1.24 gives a plot of the data of Kuper and Waltz,[31] which shows how the noise of a 2K33 klystron falls off as the frequency separation from the cavity-resonant frequency increases.

The microwave noise components beat with the coherent microwave power to produce low-frequency noise in the video or i-f regions. Most Stark-modulation spectrographs are operated at 100 kc or lower. Spectrographs employing crystal video or bolometer detection operate in the a-f region. A consideration of Fig. 1.24 as well as the cavity-oscillator response curve indicates that the noise increases as the resonant frequency is approached. Hence, low-frequency noise from the source is no doubt appreciably greater than the 30-Mc i-f noise. This consideration alone would suggest the use of a high i-f superheterodyne receiver in microwave spectroscopy. However, the advantages thereby gained do not for most purposes offset the advantages of simplicity offered by the Stark-modulation or video spectrographs.

Klystron power supplies, sweep generators, and frequency stabilizers are discussed in later sections.

Magnetrons. The early work of Cleeton and Williams was done with split-anode magnetrons. During World War II important measurements were made on the centimeter-wave absorption of water vapor with magnetrons as sources. Nevertheless, because of the purer spectrum and the greater ease of tuning and frequency modulation of the klystron, magnetrons are seldom used in present-day spectroscopy. Theoretically, the sensitivity of a spectrometer increases with power. Factors such as molecular saturation and the inability of sensitive detectors to handle high power usually prevent realization of the advantages of the higher power available from magnetrons. In the shorter millimeter-wave region where power generation is difficult, the magnetron is likely to prove of most advantage. Already the Columbia University group [32] has detected 1.4-mm-wave harmonic power from a magnetron operating near 4 mm. Considerable improvement in the purity of the magnetron spectrum must be made, however, before this type of source can be used to detect sharp line spectra. For details on magnetron construction and operation, the reader should consult Vol. 6, reference 23, also reference 33.

Crystal harmonic generators. Harmonic generation in rectifier crystals results from their non-linear response to the input power. Crystal multipliers are frequently used as radiation sources and are invariably used in the multiplier chain of a frequency standard.

Of the several reasons for employing harmonic generators as sources the most important is that with harmonic generators one can work in regions of the spectrum for which no satisfactory oscillator tubes have yet been developed. They greatly increase the frequency range that can be covered by a given number of oscillator tubes. By doubling or tripling the frequency of a primary source, one can frequently cover a given region with a less expensive klystron. Although klystrons are now produced to cover the region from 5 to 7 mm, their outputs are quite low, and almost as good results can be obtained in this region with crystal multipliers driven by the klystrons available for the region from 1.0 to 1.4 cm. If desirable, the K-band region can be satisfactorily covered by doubling or tripling the frequency of X-band klystrons. Another advantage of using a harmonic generator as a source is that all frequency measurements can be made in the region of the lower-frequency fundamental energy where it is easier to obtain strong frequency markers.

The wartime measurements of Beringer [34] in the 5-mm region were made with a crystal frequency doubler driven by a klystron. Since the war, many spectral measurements have been made at Duke [35] in the wavelength region from 2 to 7 mm with silicon crystals as doublers, triplers, quadruplers, and even quintuplers. Although no spectral measurements have yet been made below 2 mm with crystal multipliers, power generated in this way has been detected at 1.96 mm, with a signal-to-noise ratio of about 10. At this point, crystals appear to be very satisfactory both as multipliers and as detectors. The present difficulty in extending the method to higher frequencies appears to be the low power of the klystron driver. If klystrons with output powers of about 30 mw were available for the 4.5-mm wave region, it appears that satisfactory energy for spectral measurements at 1.5 mm could be obtained with crystal triplers.

No quantitative data are available on the amount of millimeter-wave power available from multipliers. Rough measurements at Duke indicate that at least a milliwatt can be obtained in the region of 6 mm with selected 1N26 silicon crystals driven by selected 2K33 klystrons. This indicates that the harmonic power in the most favorable cases is down only about 10 db from the fundamental power. Individual crystals differ considerably in their multiplying properties. The harmonic output depends greatly upon the input power to the crystal. Satisfactory results can be obtained with 25 mw or more of input power, whereas it is very difficult to obtain usable harmonic power when less than 10 mw of fundamental power is available. Multiplying chains of standard frequency markers sometimes employ harmonics as high as the fiftieth from silicon crystals. Data have been obtained which indicate that welded germanium crystals are superior to silicon crystals for harmonic generation,[36] but we are unaware of any present commercial source of them.

The simple crossed-waveguide design [35a] of Fig. 1.25 allows easy construction and easy tuning of harmonic generators. In addition to generators of second and third harmonics, from this design very satisfactory X- to I-band and K- to G-band multipliers have been made which operate on the fourth and fifth harmonic energy.† The multiplier has three tuning adjustments: those of moving the shorting plungers in each

FIG. 1.25a.   Photograph of a K- to F-band multiplier.   (K-band quintupler.)

of the guides and those of sliding the coaxial crystal in and out or twisting it on its mount. The crystal is mounted on the small guide in exactly the same manner as that described in Art. 1.2g. The inner conductor of the coaxial crystal mount is then extended as shown in Fig. 1.25 and joined to the inner conductor of a dielectric cable connector which is mounted on the larger guide exactly as the indicator connector is mounted on the crystal mounts of Art. 1.2g. This coaxial outlet is provided so that the fundamental energy falling on the crystal can be observed. The output guide serves as a filter as well as a transmission line and must be of the proper dimensions to transmit the desired harmonic and to eliminate all lower harmonics.

† See Fig. 1.7 for the frequency coverage of the various bands, G, H, I, etc.

A reasonably efficient harmonic generator can be made by coupling the multiplier crystal directly across the primary waveguide, as shown in Fig. 1.26a, with appropriate tuning screws to match the crystal to the guide. This design was suggested by C. M. Johnson.[37] Only one

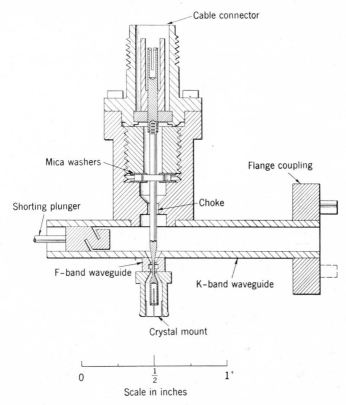

FIG. 1.25b.   Cross-section details of a K- to F-band multiplier. (K-band quintupler.)

screw is necessary if additional tuning action is provided by making the probe connector for the crystal adjustable in length. The crystal is followed by a tapered transition section which matches the primary guide to a smaller guide which transmits only the desired harmonic power. An extremely simple millimeter-wave spectrometer can be made with the multiplier by placing the absorption cell between the crystal multiplier and the transition section, as shown in Fig. 1.26b. The waveguide mount for the crystal detector is made of such size that it filters all harmonics lower than the desired one. A minimum of microwave components is needed with this arrangement which, at Duke, has been found to operate almost as well in the short millimeter-wave region as do the more complicated systems already described.

C. M. Johnson [37] initiated the practice of slotting the coaxial crystal cartridge on both sides at the place where the crystal and the cat whisker are mounted (Fig. 1.15) and of mounting the slotted cartridge so that the slots act as windows into the smaller guide. One window is the output to the cell; the other opens to a tunable shorting plunger. The

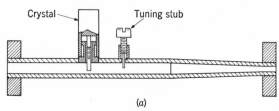

(a)

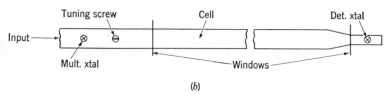

(b)

Fig. 1.26.   (a) Simple "straight through" crystal harmonic generator. (b) Illustration of the use of this generator in a spectrometer.

open end of the coaxial cartridge is then connected to the larger guide so as to pick up the fundamental power. Usually the slots are made of the same size as the inner section of the smaller guide. Some tuning is allowed by the possibility of moving or twisting the crystal cartridge. Additional tuning can be provided by the usual screws.

In a late development at Duke (W. C. King and W. Gordy, details to be published) a silicon crystal greatly reduced in size over commercial types is mounted directly in one edge of the output guide of a crossed waveguide mount with the cat whisker extending across both guides. The point of the cat whisker (2-mil tungsten wire) is sharpened by electrolytic etching. Pressure of the whisker on the crystal is critically adjusted by a differential screw mechanism. With this multiplier and a detector of similar construction spectral lines have been measured at wavelengths as short as 1.3 mm with harmonic power from 2K33 klystrons. The system is remarkably broad-banded and appears to be superior in every respect to the earlier types.

In all harmonic generators there must be a filter section which cuts out the fundamental power and other harmonics of lower frequency than the desired one. This necessary filtering action is usually provided by the smaller waveguide used to make the output transmission line of the multiplier, or by the waveguide mount for the crystal detector, or by both. The formulas given in Sec. 1.2 can be used in designing the filter. Also, Fig. 1.7 is useful for this purpose. Obviously, the higher the harmonic employed, the more stringent are the requirements for the filter. Because of the larger losses in the smaller guide, no more of it should be used than is necessary. The advantage of the assembly of Fig. 1.26 is that it uses a minimum of the smaller guide.

With only slight modification the crystal mount of Fig. 1.2 can be used as a crystal multiplier, as in Fig. 1.14, for the secondary frequency standards. In this case, the dielectric coaxial cable is used to feed the lower-frequency energy from the standard onto the crystal from which higher harmonics are generated and reflected down the guide. The tuning adjustments are used to maximize the power of the desired harmonic. The dielectric cable and its connector must then be such as to transmit the relatively high frequency fed to the crystal, usually of the order of 2700 Mc.

1.3 ELECTRONIC COMPONENTS

1.3a. Klystron Power Supplies. Klystron oscillators most commonly used in microwave spectroscopy are listed in Table 1.1. Operation of these tubes requires the following d-c sources: -1400 to -3600 volts at 7 to 20 ma for the electron beam and 0 to -300 volts with respect to the cathode for the focus grid and for the reflector. So that the klystron cavity and associated waveguide may be at ground potential, the cathode, reflector, and focus must be operated well below ground. A 6.3-volt at 0.67 amp source, either a-c or d-c, supplies the heater filament. For stable oscillator operation, it is essential that the beam, reflector, and focus supplies be well regulated, particularly for fixed-frequency or recording techniques. It is desirable that the supplies be continuously variable between the limits listed above.

Figure 1.27 shows the circuit diagram of a power supply which has been used successfully at Duke. It was designed by W. Bennett [39] and modified by G. F. Crable and R. S. Anderson. A conventional bridge full-wave rectifier followed by a low-pass filter serves as the supply for an electronic voltage regulator. The output voltage of the unregulated supply is adjusted by a variable autotransformer in the primary of the high-potential supply transformer.

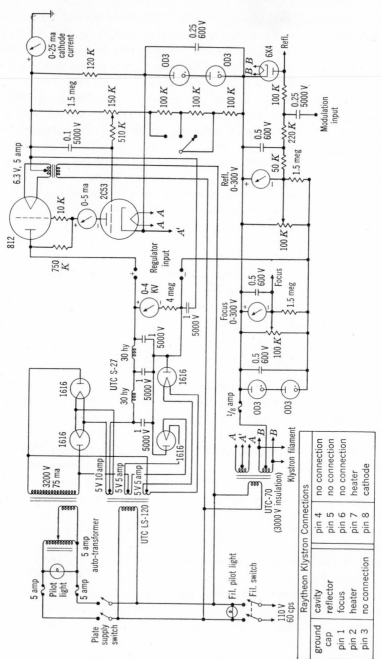

Fig. 1.27.   Circuit diagram of a power supply for Raytheon klystrons listed in Table 1.1.

Stabilization of the supply is achieved by electronic voltage regulation. Vacuum tube 812 serves as the regulator with the 2C53 as the amplifier tube. Type 2C53 is a vacuum tube developed for use in high-voltage regulator circuits. Under proper operating conditions, the 2C53 draws 1 ma of plate current. Two OD3 voltage regulator tubes in series provide the focus and reflector potentials. Diode 6X4 in the reflector circuit prevents the reflector from becoming positive with respect to the cathode, a condition leading to reflector current which can damage the klystron.

Since the reflector and focus circuits are highly negative with respect to ground, they must be well insulated. The modulation input capacitor to the reflector should have a 5000-volt insulation rating. Filament transformers supplying the klystron, the 2C53, and the 6X4 should be insulated for 7000 volts as well.

A klystron power supply which will operate the oscillators listed in Table 1.1 is available commercially.†

Power supplies in which high frequencies are substituted for 60 cps are used to some extent. The output voltage from a power oscillator operating at several hundred kilocycles is stepped up to several thousand volts, rectified, and filtered. The output is regulated by amplitude control [40] of the oscillator. At these frequencies the sizes of transformers and filter components are greatly reduced and the supplies are quite compact.

Low-voltage klystrons for K, X, or S band can be operated with batteries or electronically regulated supplies. Descriptions of some of these tubes and supplies are found in Chapter 2, Vol. 11, of the *Radiation Laboratory Series*.[23]

Saw-tooth sweeps which provide the linear time bases in oscilloscopes such as the DuMont 208 or 304 ‡ may be used to sweep the klystron oscillators. The saw-tooth oscillation should be taken directly from the oscillator in the oscilloscope so that the klystron sweep amplitude will be independent of the oscilloscope gain settings. Since the output from the saw-tooth oscillator will sweep the klystron over only a small part of its mode, it is desirable to use an amplifier with an output variable from zero to about 100 volts.

1.3b. Pound Frequency Stabilizer for Klystrons. Methods for stabilizing the frequency of a klystron by coupling it electrically to an external cavity are described by Pound and others.[41] A high-Q cavity with an associated magic tee acts as a discriminator. An error signal resulting from frequency drift is amplified and applied to the klystron

† Polytechnic Research and Development Company, Inc., 202 Tillary Street, Brooklyn 1, N. Y.

‡ Allen B. DuMont Laboratories, Inc., Passaic, New Jersey.

reflector, bringing the oscillator back to the desired frequency. Long-term stabilities of less than 10 kc have been obtained. For details, the reader is referred to the articles cited.

1.3c. Stark-Modulation Oscillators. Two forms of Stark modulation are commonly employed, sine wave and square wave. The sensitivities obtainable with the two forms are comparable. Sinusoidal modulation sacrifices detail in line and Stark component structure for simplicity in equipment. Square-wave modulation allows greater resolution of line structure and Stark components. The chief problem in the design of either modulator is that of charging and discharging the capacity of the

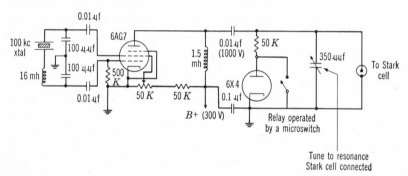

Fig. 1.28. Circuit diagram for a 100-kc sinusoidal oscillator for Stark modulation.

Stark cell at the required rate. This capacity may range from several hundred to several thousand micromicrofarads, depending upon the cell dimensions. First-order Stark effect requires only 10 to 100 volts per cm; however, for the second-order Stark effect up to 1000 volts per cm or more may be necessary. The cell capacity may be made part of a parallel resonant circuit for sinusoidal modulation, and the capacity charged and discharged by the large circulating current. For square-wave modulation the peak currents are of the order of several amperes if the cell is charged in a time which is small relative to the square-wave period.

The circuit for a 100-kc sinusoidal oscillator is shown in Fig. 1.28. Because the oscillator is crystal controlled and electron coupled, frequency stability for use with a sharply tuned signal amplifier is assured. The output amplitude is varied by changing the screen-grid potential. The 6X4 diode clamps one side of the sine wave to ground so that the signal amplifier can be tuned to the modulation frequency rather than to harmonics. An absorption line is quickly identified by switching a resistor in place of the clamping diode with a microswitch-operated relay, a practice initiated by J. Q. Williams, at Duke.

High-voltage square-wave generators which operate at 100 kc have been described by Hedrick [42] and Sharbaugh.[43] Hedrick's generator, modified by J. Q. Williams, is shown in Fig. 1.29. A 100-kc crystal-controlled oscillator synchronizes pulse generators 180° out of phase. The trigger tubes (VT 127's and RK 715 B's) are biased beyond cut-off. When a positive pulse arrives at the grids of the VT 127's, they conduct and charge the cell capacity divider in the cathode circuit. One-half cycle later, the RK 715 B's conduct and discharge the cell. The cell is isolated from the output stages by a blocking capacitor, and the 8020 diode clamps the square wave on the Stark electrode to ground. The filament transformer secondary for the VT 127's must be well insulated from the primary and have low capacity to ground. Capacitors C_1, C_2, and resistor R_2 are adjusted to give optimum wave form. This generator has a maximum output of 1800 volts at 100 kc for a Stark cell capacity of 800 $\mu\mu$f.

1.3d. Low-Frequency Amplifier. A good low-frequency signal amplifier is described in the *Radiation Laboratory Series*,[38] and a similar amplifier is available commercially from Browning Laboratories.† When an oscilloscope display is used, the output is taken from the plate of the final amplifier tube.

At a high input power ($\sim$5 mw) the detector crystal operates in its linear region with an output video impedance of about 300 to 500 ohms and is matched to the first amplifier stage with a shielded input transformer. At low power levels, however, the crystal is a square-law detector with a high impedance and is more closely matched without the transformer.

1.3e. Radio-Frequency Receivers. Excessive low-frequency noise generated in crystals and flicker effects in vacuum tubes may be avoided by modulation and detection at frequencies of 100 kc or higher. Good commercial communications receivers are adequate for signal amplification. The receiver is tuned to the modulation frequency or to a harmonic and responds to noise within the bandpass. Receivers such as the National HRO-50R ‡ which are equipped with crystal filters in the i-f stages can provide a bandpass as sharp as a few hundred cycles per second. Electronic sweep techniques are possible; however, slow sweep rates should be used with narrow bandpasses. After the i-f stages, the signal may be detected and displayed on the oscilliscope or may be heterodyned with the beat-frequency oscillator, and the audio beat note displayed. The latter method appears to give slightly higher sensitivity and is commonly employed.

† Browning Laboratories, Inc., Winchester, Massachusetts.
‡ National Company, Inc., Malden, Massachusetts.

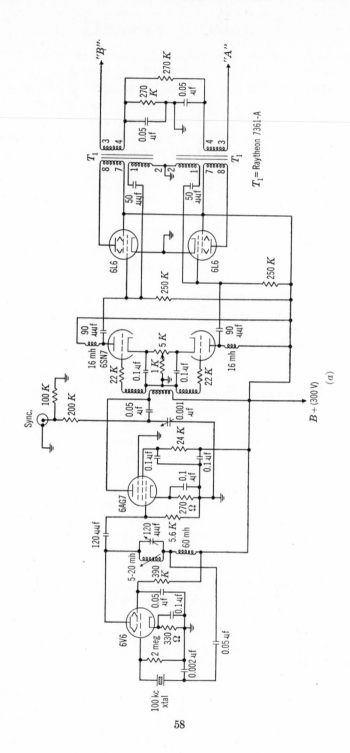

58

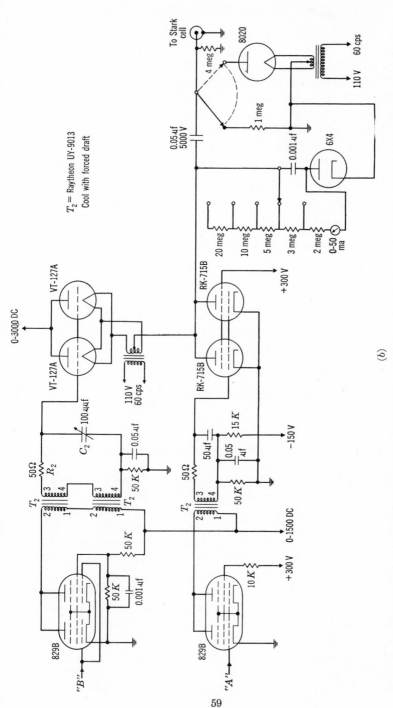

59

Fig. 1.29. A 100-kc square-wave generator for Stark modulation. All capacitors are in microfarads unless otherwise noted. The 0-1500-v and 0-3000-v d-c supplies are ganged together.

Detecting crystals are moderately well matched to the receiver input at the usual microwave power levels and may be connected directly to the antenna terminals of the receiver with a shielded cable. However, Good [44] has developed low-noise preamplifiers to match the detector crystals to a communications receiver over a wide range of crystal impedances. Diagrams of two of these preamplifiers are shown in Fig. 1.30. The input circuit is tuned to series resonance at the modu-

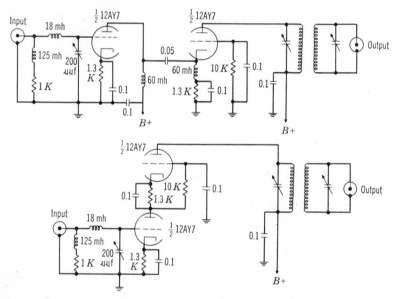

FIG. 1.30. Circuit diagrams of two 85-kc preamplifiers. (From Good.[44])

lation frequency. These circuits were designed to operate at 85 kc but can be used up to about 100 kc with the circuit constants given.

1.3f. Phase-Sensitive Lock-In Amplifiers. A selective amplifier followed by a lock-in detector and recording meter comprises a lock-in amplifier. Since a lock-in detector responds to harmonics and subharmonics of the modulation frequency, the amplifier must be selective enough to filter them. Figure 1.31 is the circuit diagram of a lock-in amplifier to operate at 100 kc, designed by J. Q. Williams and modified by R. Mockler and D. F. Trippe. In the Stark-modulation spectrographs at Duke, this unit is preceded by one of the preamplifiers of Good given in Fig. 1.30. This amplifier makes provision for visual observation of the lock-in stage output which allows rapid adjustment of the reference signal phase on an absorption line. The lock-in detector is a modification of Schuster's [45] which he used at 30 cps. A reference signal of

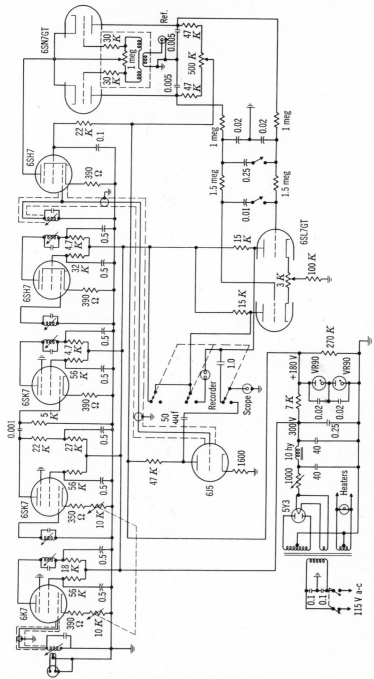

FIG. 1.31. Circuit diagram of a 100-kc lock-in amplifier.

100 volts or more is supplied by the modulation source to the grids of the 6SN7, 180° out of phase. Suitable phase-shifting devices are discussed by Terman and others.[46] The bandpass is determined by the combined time constant of the low-pass filter and vacuum-tube voltmeter which follow the detector.

1.4. SPECTROMETER SENSITIVITY

1.4a. Minimum Detectable Signal. As a result of the concentrated effort during World War II the microwave radar receiver is a highly developed instrument. It is of advantage, therefore, to carry over as much of the theory and instrumentation of radar receivers [47] as possible. To do this, one must recognize the basic differences in the types of signals which are detected and amplified. In radar the signal consists of a weak pulse of microwave power. In microwave spectroscopy, the signal is in the form of a small decrement in a relatively large amount of power. The problems can be reduced to the same form by employment of r-f balancing to cancel the power around the absorption line so that it appears as a small amount of unbalanced power. However, as has been pointed out,[4] this unbalanced power, $(\Delta P)'$, is not equal to, but is considerably less than, the actual power absorbed by the gas, (ΔP). It is, in fact,

$$(\Delta P)' \approx (\Delta P)^2/4P, \tag{1.20}$$

where P is the total power and where it is assumed that $(\Delta P) \ll P$. To get an estimate of the sensitivity obtainable when a superheterodyne receiver is used to detect $(\Delta P)'$ we set

$$(\Delta P)' = F^*kTB, \tag{1.21}$$

which, with Eq. 1.20, gives

$$(\Delta P)_{min} = \sqrt{4PF^*kTB}, \tag{1.22}$$

where F^* is the over-all noise figure of the receiver defined in Art. 1.4b, and B is the effective noise bandwidth defined by Eq. 1.38. T is the operating or room temperature, and k is Boltzmann's constant. We now need to express (ΔP) in terms of the absorption coefficient of the gas, α_g, and of the attenuation constant of the cell, α_c. If P_i is the power input to the cell, then

$$(\Delta P) = P_i e^{-\alpha_c l} - P_i e^{-(\alpha_c + \alpha_g)l}$$

$$\approx P_i e^{-\alpha_c l}(\alpha_g l). \tag{1.23}$$

Combining Eq. 1.23 with Eq. 1.22 yields (since $P = P_i e^{-\alpha_c l}$)

$$(\alpha_g)_{\min} = \frac{2}{l} \sqrt{\frac{F^* kTB}{P_i e^{-\alpha_c l}}}, \qquad (1.24)$$

which gives the minimum absorption coefficient, α_g, that can be detected with a cell length l and a spectrometer noise figure F^*. It is assumed that the power is not sufficient to saturate the molecules. To obtain the optimum cell length, we must choose the length so as to maximize $(\Delta P)'$ rather than (ΔP). We have from Eq. 1.20 and Eq. 1.23

$$(\Delta P)' \approx \frac{P_i e^{-\alpha_c l}(\alpha_g l)^2}{4}. \qquad (1.25)$$

Setting

$$\frac{\partial (\Delta P)'}{\partial l} = 0,$$

one obtains

$$l_{\mathrm{opt}} = 2\alpha_c^{-1}. \qquad (1.26)$$

With this optimum cell length Eq. 1.24 becomes

$$(\alpha_g)_{\min} = e\alpha_c \sqrt{\frac{F^* kTB}{P_i}}. \qquad (1.27)$$

The superheterodyne receiver with r-f balancing as described above is not easily used with frequency sweep spectroscopes. Most sweep spectroscopes employ some form of rapid intensity modulation of the microwave power by the absorption line with a crystal detector and a receiver tuned to the modulation frequency. Although the receivers used do not employ a microwave local oscillator, they are closely analogous to a superheterodyne radar receiver when the source power is such as to cause the crystal detector to operate as a linear detector. It is well known that an intensity-modulated wave is equivalent to the unmodulated carrier ν_c, with side-band frequencies $\nu_c - \nu_m$ and $\nu_c + \nu_m$ containing the signal power.[48] We can consider the carrier wave as the local-oscillator power and the signal as the side-band power. The crystal then detects the beat note of two microwave frequencies just as does the usual superheterodyne radar receiver. The power in each side band is $P_c(m^2/4)$, where P_c is the power in the carrier wave and m is the modulation index. Since the beat notes of the carrier with the two side bands are in phase, the total signal power P_{sig} is

$$P_{\mathrm{sig}} = P_c(m^2/2). \qquad (1.28)$$

The modulation index depends upon the type of modulation used. In the ideal case it is $(\Delta V/2)/V_c$, where V_c is the voltage amplitude of the carrier and ΔV is the change in this voltage caused by the gas absorption. Thus,

$$P_{\text{sig}} = \frac{P_c(\Delta V)^2}{8V_c{}^2} = \frac{P_i e^{-\alpha_c l}(\Delta V)^2}{8(V_i e^{-\alpha_c l/2})^2}. \tag{1.29}$$

Now

$$\Delta V = V_i e^{-\alpha_c l/2}(1 - e^{-\alpha_g l/2})$$

$$\approx V_i e^{-\alpha_c l/2}(\alpha_g l/2) \tag{1.30}$$

since $\alpha_g l \ll 1$ and $P_c = P_i e^{-\alpha_c l}$. Substituting them in Eq. 1.29 and equating to F^*kTB gives

$$P_{\text{sig}} = \frac{P_i e^{-\alpha_c l}}{8}\left(\frac{\alpha_g l}{2}\right)^2 = F^*kTB \tag{1.31}$$

or

$$(\alpha_g)_{\text{min}} = \frac{4}{l}\sqrt{\frac{2F^*kTB}{P_i e^{-\alpha_c l}}}. \tag{1.32}$$

With the optimum cell length, $l_{\text{opt}} = 2\alpha_c{}^{-1}$ which results from maximizing ΔV, this becomes

$$(\alpha_g)_{\text{min}} = 2e\alpha_c\sqrt{2F^*kTB/P_i}. \tag{1.33}$$

Here α_g and α_c are in cm^{-1}, B in cps; strictly speaking, the term under the radical should contain a factor to account for the incomplete modulation. Seldom are all components of the absorption line moved completely out of range of the source frequency during a period of modulation. Also, the receiver usually does not take in all the Fourier components of the signal. For example, when a square-wave Stark modulation is employed, the receiver is tuned to the fundamental component of the square wave. Losses caused by ineffective modulation can, however, be included in the figure F^*, which should then be regarded as the over-all noise figure for the spectrometer.

1.4b. Nature of Over-All Noise Figure. For calculating or measuring the spectrometer sensitivity it is desirable to resolve the over-all noise figure into the parts contributed by the different components. By definition, the noise figure of a network is the factor by which the ratio of *noise power to signal power* is increased by the network. Symbolically,

$$F = \frac{dN_o/S_o}{dN_i/S_i}, \tag{1.34}$$

where dN_i and dN_o are the input and output noise power for a narrow band of frequencies, df, for which F is defined, and S_i and S_o are the input and output signal power, respectively. Rearranging,

$$dN_o = F(S_o/S_i)\,dN_i = FG\,dN_i = FGkT\,df. \qquad (1.35)$$

Here we have substituted G for (S_o/S_i), which is by definition the gain of the network, and have assumed the input noise dN_i to be the Johnson noise $kT\,df$ available from a pure resistance equal in value to the input impedance. Equations 1.34 and 1.35 hold only for an infinitesimal bandwidth df. In practical situations we are concerned with the total or integrated noise at the output,

$$N_o = kT \int_0^\infty FG\,df, \qquad (1.36)$$

as compared to that $kT \int G\,df$ which would occur if only the Johnson noise from the input impedance were present. The effective or integrated noise figure F^* is therefore defined [47] as

$$F^* = \frac{kT \int_0^\infty FG\,df}{kT \int_0^\infty G\,df} = \frac{N_o}{G_{\max}kTB}, \qquad (1.37)$$

where B is the effective noise bandwidth of the network defined by

$$B = \frac{\int_0^\infty G\,df}{G_{\max}}, \qquad (1.38)$$

and where $G_{\max}$ is the maximum power gain of the network.

Consider now a signal generator connected for maximum power transfer to two networks connected in cascade. The gains of the individual networks are G_1 and G_2, and the over-all gain G equals $G_1 G_2$. The corresponding noise figures are F_1, F_2, and F. The total noise $GFkT\,df$ at the output for a narrow band df is contributed by the signal generator and different networks as follows:

$$GFkT\,df = G_1 G_2 kT\,df + G_1 G_2 (F_1 - 1)kT\,df + G_2(F_2 - 1)kT\,df,$$

| Total | From signal generator | From network 1 | From network 2 |

$$(1.39)$$

where T is the temperature of a resistance equivalent to the input impedance which would be required to give the noise $kT\,\Delta f$ equal to that from the signal generator. From Eq. 1.39 the over-all noise figure is easily obtained:

$$F = F_1 + (F_2 - 1)/G_1. \tag{1.40}$$

The effective noise figure [47] F^* is obtained by averaging F over the bandpass,

$$F^* = \frac{\int_0^\infty FG \, df}{\int_0^\infty G \, df} = \frac{\int_0^\infty [F_1 + (F_2 - 1)/G_1] G_1 G_2 \, df}{\int_0^\infty G_1 G_2 \, df} \cdot \tag{1.41}$$

In order to integrate this expression it is customary to assume the bandwidth of the second network to be sufficiently small in comparison with the bandwidth of the first so that G_1 and F_1 can be considered constant over the integration. Under these conditions

$$F^* = F_1 + (F_2^* - 1)/G_1. \tag{1.42}$$

Equation 1.40 can be generalized for n networks:

$$F = F_1 + \frac{F_2 - 1}{G_1} + \frac{F_3 - 1}{G_1 G_2} + \cdots \frac{F_n - 1}{G_1 G_2 \cdots G_{n-1}}, \tag{1.43}$$

or, if the nth network has a narrow bandwidth as compared with those preceding,

$$F^* = F_1 + \frac{F_2 - 1}{G_1} + \frac{F_3 - 1}{G_1 G_2} + \cdots \frac{F_n^* - 1}{G_1 G_2 \cdots G_{n-1}}. \tag{1.44}$$

From Eq. 1.43 or 1.44 it is apparent that, after the first high-gain stage in a receiver is reached, contributions to the over-all noise figure by the following stages are small. Thus, in improving the sensitivity of a spectrometer, one is primarily concerned with the noise arising in or before the first high-gain stage in the receiver, i.e., in the microwave generator, the detector, and the first stage or two in the amplifier.

In a spectrometer employing a crystal detector with a superheterodyne receiver or its equivalent in a modulation-type spectrometer, the crystal detector may be regarded as network 1 and the i-f or first stages in the radio receiver as network 2. The gain of the crystal is less than 1 and is usually expressed in terms of its reciprocal, the conversion loss $L = 1/G_c$. The noise figure of the crystal is usually expressed in terms of its equivalent noise temperature and conversion loss $F_c = L t_c$. The noise temperature,

$$t_c = dN_o/kT \, df, \tag{1.45}$$

is the ratio of the noise output dN_o of the crystal in a given frequency band df to that $kT\,df$ available from a pure resistor at room temperature † T. It should be pointed out that t_c is not an actual temperature but a noise ratio. The expression noise temperature has the significance that a passive resistance must have the temperature $T_c = t_cT$, if the Johnson noise is to be equivalent to the noise output of the crystal operated at temperature T. For a perfect crystal, $t_c = 1$. At 30 Mc the average crystal has $t_c = 2$ to 3. For the usual operating conditions of microwave spectrometers—amplification at $\sim$100 kc with detected power $\sim$1 mw—the crystal noise temperature $t_c \approx 100$. The extra noise from the source or local oscillator is taken into account by the addition of an appropriate amount t_s to the noise temperature of the crystal t_c. The latter procedure is justified since the local-oscillator or source noise is usually determined by measuring the extra noise available from the crystal when the microwave power is on and dividing it by that when it is heavily attenuated, or when the signal generator is replaced by a pure resistance equal to the input impedance. Thus, we set

$$F_1 = L(t_c + t_s) \qquad G_1 = 1/L \qquad F_2^* = F_{\text{i-f}}^*$$

and obtain

$$F^* = L(t_c + t_s + F_{\text{i-f}}^* - 1). \tag{1.46}$$

By various methods described elsewhere,[49] the different terms on the right side of Eq. 1.45 can be measured. It is possible with a calibrated microwave noise generator [50] to measure the combined noise figure of the detector and receiver or by measurements on a spectral line of known strength to calculate from Eq. 1.32 the over-all spectrometer noise figure F^*.

1.4c. Application to a Stark-Modulation Spectrograph. To illustrate the application of this theory, we assume a typical K-band Stark-modulation spectrograph operated at 100 kc with a receiver having a bandwidth $B = 100$ cps and $F_{\text{r-f}}^* = 2$. We assume $L = 4$ and $t = t_c + t_s = 100$. The over-all noise figure is then

$$F^* = 4(100 + 2 - 1) = 404 = 26 \text{ db.}$$

Other parameters assumed are a cell length of 500 cm, cell attenuation constant $\alpha_c = 2 \times 10^{-3}$ cm^{-1}, input power $P_i = 10^{-3}$ watt. With $T = 290°$ K, Eq. 1.32 becomes

$$(\alpha_g)_{\min} = 3.56 \times 10^{-10} l^{-1} \sqrt{\frac{F^*B}{P_i e^{-\alpha_c l}}}, \tag{1.47}$$

† In measurement or designation of a particular noise temperature, the reference temperature must be specified. The reference T is conventionally chosen as room temperature or 290°K.

where P_i is in watts, B in cps, l in cm, and α_g in cm^{-1}. With the assumed parameters, Eq. 1.47 gives

$$(\alpha_g)_{\min} = 7.5 \times 10^{-9} \text{ cm}^{-1}.$$

The value agrees well with the results usually obtained with the better spectrographs of this type. With a lock-in amplifier and an automatic recorder, the bandwidth can be reduced by about 25 times and $(\alpha_g)_{\min}$ accordingly by a factor of 5, to give

$$(\alpha_g)_{\min} = 1.5 \times 10^{-9} \text{ cm}^{-1}.$$

The power level was chosen so as to give efficient conversion by the crystal, and it was assumed that the cell volume was such that molecular saturation did not occur. Losses due to impedance mismatch and imperfect modulation were neglected.

The combined noise temperature $t = t_c + t_s$ was estimated by assuming an inverse relation of t with frequency. No measured values are available for typical crystals at 100 kc, but, from the work of Miller and Greenblatt,[26] one would expect the noise temperature of a silicon crystal when excited by microwave power of a milliwatt to be of the order of 100 times greater at 100 kc than at 30 Mc. The extra noise is largely generated in the crystal by the microwave power. A significant amount, however, originates in the source oscillator itself. In this type of spectrometer the local-oscillator power is the carrier wave of the source power, and hence the local-oscillator noise cannot be canceled with a balanced mixer as it is in the usual superheterodyne radar receiver. Whether the value estimated for t is typical or not, it is certainly true that in spectrometers operated with crystal detectors at output frequencies of 100 kc or lower with powers of the order of a milliwatt, the noise originating in the amplifier (provided that it is not inexcusably bad) is of little consequence. If the power is reduced, the noise is reduced, but the conversion loss is increased and the sensitivity reduced because of the appearance of P_i in the denominator of Eq. 1.32. The optimum power is different for different crystals, and, because of the saturation effect, it is, with cells of small volume, different for different absorbing substances. It is customary to optimize the power on known absorption lines and to tune the crystal assembly for the given power level.

1.4d. Crystal Square-Law Detector. A crystal square-law detector of a low-frequency modulation signal followed by a video or audio amplifier of the modulation frequency is commonly called a crystal video receiver. Because of its large conversion loss one might question the use of a crystal square-law detector where ample microwave power is available to cause the crystal to operate as a linear detector. For audio frequencies, however, the excess noise generated in the crystal by the higher microwave power required for linear detection in most instances probably more than offsets the gain in conversion efficiency. The degree to which this is true depends upon the individual crystal and amplifier used. It is possible that many spectrometers with a-f receivers operate best at powers intermediate between the microwatt (square-law detection) and the milliwatt (linear detection) levels.

With no d-c bias and with the microwave power of the order of a microwatt where the crystal operates as a square-law detector, the noise generated in the crystal is essentially the Johnson noise of a resistance equal in value to the d-c impedance of the crystal. Because of the high conversion loss, the input impedance of the crystal square-law detector is relatively insenstitive to the output load impedance.

Beringer [50] has shown that the rms noise voltage $\bar{N}$ from the crystal video receiver with no d-c bias can be expressed as

$$\bar{N} = G\sqrt{4kT(R + R_A)B},\qquad(1.48)$$

where R is the video resistance of the crystal and R_A is a resistance which in series with the grid of the input stage of the amplifier would generate a noise equivalent to that generated by the amplifier. G is the gain, and B the bandwidth, of the amplifier. We now need an expression for the conversion efficiency. This is usually expressed in terms of the current or voltage sensitivity. The detected signal voltage e_d is proportional to the square of the input voltage e_i:

$$e_d = Se_i^2,\qquad(1.49)$$

where S is a constant of proportionality representing the sensitivity. We assume the incoming microwave power is amplitude modulated by an a-f sine wave. Although the absorption line is not sinusoidal in shape, it can for the proper sweep rates be resolved into a number of Fourier-component sine waves, the most significant of which fall within the audio region covered by the receiver. Considering only the fundamental of these components, $mV_c \sin \omega_m t$, we have

$$e_i = V_c(1 + m \sin \omega_m t) \sin \omega_c t,\qquad(1.50)$$

where $V_c \sin \omega_c t$ represents the unmodulated carrier wave. By substituting e_i from Eq. 1.50 in Eq. 1.49, squaring, and reducing by trigonometric substitution, it is seen that there are many components in the detected output e_d. Of these, the only one of interest is the one which has the modulation frequency ω_m and which by arrangement falls within the bandpass of the receiver. It is

$$e_d = S(mV_c{}^2) \sin \omega_m t. \tag{1.51}$$

Now $m \approx (\Delta V/2)V_c$, where ΔV is the change in amplitude caused by the absorption line. The amplitude of the detected signal is therefore $SV_c(\Delta V/2)$. Substituting the value of ΔV from Eq. 1.30 and $V_i e^{-\alpha_c l/2}$ for V_c, the signal amplitude V_o at the output of the amplifier becomes

$$V_o = GSV_i{}^2 e^{-\alpha_c l}(\alpha_g l/4) = GS(2R)P_i e^{-\alpha_c l}(\alpha_g l/4). \tag{1.52}$$

We assume that, for detection, this output voltage amplitude must be equal to or greater than the rms noise voltage. From Eq. 1.48 and Eq. 1.52

$$\frac{GSRP_i e^{-\alpha_c l}(\alpha_g l)}{2} \geqq G\sqrt{4kT(R + R_A)B}. \tag{1.53}$$

Therefore,

$$(\alpha_g)_{\min} = \frac{2\sqrt{4kT(R + R_A)B}}{SRlP_i e^{-\alpha_c l}}$$

$$= \frac{8\sqrt{kTB}}{MlP_i e^{-\alpha_c l}}$$

$$= \frac{5 \times 10^{-10}\sqrt{B}}{MlP_i e^{-\alpha_c l}}, \tag{1.54}$$

where

$$M = \frac{2SR}{\sqrt{(R + R_A)}} = \frac{\beta R}{\sqrt{(R + R_A)}} \tag{1.55}$$

is the over-all figure of merit of the receiver as defined by Beringer.[50] It is assumed that the source is matched to the detector. In the last form of Eq. 1.54 P_i is in watts, α_g and α_c in cm^{-1}, l in cm, and B in cps.

A value of about 25 for M is obtainable in the 1-cm wave region. If M is assumed independent of the received power, the optimum cell length is $1/\alpha_c$. This assumption is not valid, however, for powers above the microwatt range. It is more desirable to choose l so that the received power $P_i e^{-\alpha_c l}$ equals 10^{-6} watt, with P_i equal to the available power or to that which will produce molecular saturation at the input of the cell, whichever is the smaller. With a received power of 1 μw Eq. 1.54 becomes

$$(\alpha_g)_{\min} = \frac{5 \times 10^{-4}}{Ml}\sqrt{B}. \tag{1.56}$$

When $M = 25$, $l = 20$ meters, and $B = 200$ cps, this gives $(\alpha_g)_{min} = 1.4 \times 10^{-7}$ cm^{-1}. For $\alpha_c = 10^{-3}$ cm^{-1} the input power required is $P_i = 7.3 \times 10^{-6}$ watt. Usually about half the signal is lost in filtering the spurious effects caused by r-f reflections. Sensitivities of this order of magnitude have been obtained at Duke with a video receiver and a cell of 20 meters. For example, with such a spectrometer, C^{13} in natural concentrations in methyl cyanide and methyl acetylene is easily detected in the rotational lines of these molecules which occur near the 1-cm wavelength.

1.4e. Thermal Detectors. The sensitivities of microwave spectrometers with thermal detectors are treated elsewhere.[4,18] Because these detectors are not widely used, they will not be discussed in detail here. It should be pointed out, however, that they have advantages over crystal detectors in some applications. Unlike crystal detectors, they do not have the excessive low-frequency noise (above the Johnson noise) when they are detecting moderate powers. This advantage was pointed out by Beringer and Castle,[18] who used a bolometer detector with a low-frequency modulation in detecting the paramagnetic resonance of NO.

1.5. MEASUREMENT OF LINE WIDTHS AND INTENSITIES

Typical line-shape problems in microwave spectroscopy are concerned with measurements on lines whose widths, $2 \Delta\nu$, between half-power points range from about 100 kc to 10 Mc. Sweep techniques display the entire line shape in a single oscilloscope trace or recording. Broader lines are investigated by measurements at a number of selected frequencies. The theory of line shapes of gases is deferred to Chapter 4, but, in the discussion of techniques, it is useful to know that the widths of well-resolved lines of gases are proportional to pressure over a wide range. Since the integrated intensities are also proportional to pressure, the peak intensities at the center of the absorption line are independent of pressure. This situation is in contrast to that in optical spectroscopy, where Doppler widths are of primary importance and low instrumental resolution frequently distorts the observed line contour. Except for measurements of the effect of energy density on line shape (saturation effect), it is not necessary to measure the absolute power level, since it is the fractional power absorbed per centimeter of path that is of interest. Where it is desirable, however, the absolute power level may be measured with a thermistor bridge.[29]

1.5a. Measurement of the Shapes of Narrow Lines. When the lines to be measured are sufficiently narrow ($\sim$1 Mc) and strong

$(\alpha_g \sim 10^{-4}$ cm^{-1}), their widths can be measured directly from the oscilloscope presentation of the simple video system already described in Sec. 1.1, provided that the rate of sweep, bandwidth of amplifier, etc., are such that adverse distortions of the line are not produced. Figure 1.32a is an oscilloscope presentation of a strong line obtained with a sweep spectrometer employing a crystal video receiver. The frequency

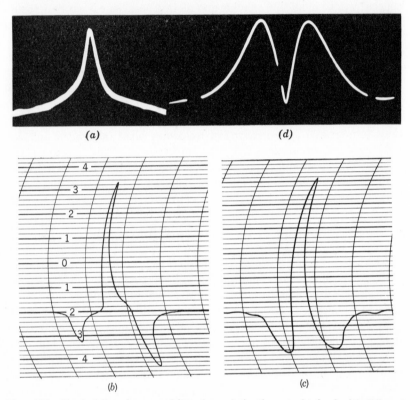

Fig. 1.32. Typical line shapes and line shape derivatives as obtained with different detection systems. (a) Video type detector. The $J = 0 \rightarrow 1$ rotational transition of CO. (From Gilliam, Johnson, and Gordy.[11]) (b) Square-wave Stark modulation (30 cps) with phase-sensitive detector and Esterline-Angus recorder. The $J = 1 \rightarrow 2$ rotational line of OCS. Stark components are pointed downward, the undisplaced line upward. (From W. C. King's Master Thesis, Duke.) (c) Sinusoidal Zeeman modulation with phase-sensitive detector and Esterline-Angus recorder. One of the 5-mm-wave oxygen lines, (13_). For the small modulations used the tracing represents the second derivative of the line shape. (d) R-f source modulation (100 kc) with radio receiver and cathode-ray-scope display. The NH$_3$ 3,3 line. With the small modulations used, the presentation represents the magnitude of the first derivative of the line shape. The blanks are frequency markers. (From Howard and Smith.[53])

scale is established by one of the marker techniques discussed in Sec. 1.6.

A square-wave Stark-modulation system followed by a lock-in amplifier is a satisfactory system for investigation of line shapes, provided that the modulation frequency is less than about one-fifth of the line width,[51] and provided that the line to be measured can be resolved from its Stark components and from the components of adjacent lines. The use of low power levels, $\sim$1 μw, simultaneously achieves a square-law crystal response [52] and avoids saturation of the gas.† A line-shape recording using a 30-cps square-wave Stark modulation is shown in Fig. 1.32b for the $J = 1 \rightarrow 2$ line of OCS. Resolution of the Stark components (these point downward) is evident, while the base line is flat and the noise level is very low as compared with the line height. To avoid distortion by the indicator, the time constant of the recording system is adjusted to be small as compared with the time required to trace out the line.

High-frequency modulation produces measurable distortions. The effects of high-frequency square-wave modulation have been treated by Townes and Merritt [9] and by Karplus.[9] If the amplifier is tuned to the modulation frequency ν_m, the apparent line breadth at half power is equal to the true line breadth $\Delta\nu$ multiplied by a factor of $1 + (\nu_m/2\,\Delta\nu)^2$.

If the modulation is sinusoidal, the line shape is further complicated but still interpretable.[12a] In a typical case, applicable to molecules with linear Stark or Zeeman effects, the sine-wave modulation is biased to zero at the minimum of the cycle. The output of a phase-sensitive detector tuned to the modulation frequency is the second derivative of the line shape, provided that the maximum shift of the line by the modulating field is much smaller than the line width. A typical picture of an oxygen line obtained with Zeeman modulation of this type is shown in Fig. 1.32c. When the shape is caused by collision broadening alone, the line width is given directly by the frequency difference between the two minima on the recording. In practice, this frequency difference is plotted against the degree of modulation and extrapolated to zero modulation to give the true line width.

It is also possible to observe line widths by a double-modulation system employing a low-frequency saw-tooth sweep and a high-frequency sine-wave sweep applied to the reflector electrode. If the detection system employs a phase-sensitive lock-in amplifier tuned to the high-

---

† If the line is very weak, as is frequently the case, the true line shape is reproduced even if the crystal is not in the region of square-law response, i.e., $\Delta P \approx nE\,\Delta E$, where ΔP is the variation in power incident on the detector; E, ΔE, the r-f field and field variation; and n, the power law of the crystal.

frequency modulation, and if both this frequency and the maximum frequency deviation are much less than the line width, the recording reproduces the first derivative of the absorption curve (Fig. 1.2b). Assuming collison broadening, the frequency separation of maximum and minimum is $3^{-\frac{1}{2}}$ times the line width 2 $\Delta\nu$. If the detection system is not phase sensitive, the detected signal is the magnitude of the derivative of the line contour (Fig. 1.32d). When the modulation frequency greatly exceeds the line width, a succession of images of the line, separated by the modulation frequency, is observed. These images reproduce the dispersion curve of the absorption line so that the separation of maximum and minimum gives the line widths directly.

In the interpretation of line-shape measurements, it is frequently desirable to correlate the data with the pressure of the gas under investigation or, in some cases, with the partial pressures of gas mixtures. In such cases the least accurate physical datum is often the pressure rather than the line width. This is particularly true with gas mixtures where preferential absorption of one component of the mixture on the walls of the absorption cell may change the composition of the mixture during the course of a data run. Under such circumstances, Stark detection systems with their relatively large surface areas and strongly absorbing dielectric supports may be undesirable, despite their high fidelity and sensitivity. For this reason, Howard and Smith [53] used a double-modulation rather than a Stark-modulation system for mixtures of ammonia with other gases.

1.5b. Measurement of Relative Intensities. Often the physical data of interest are the relative intensities of a group of lines such as those resulting from quadrupole splitting. If the lines are closely spaced, but adequately resolved, the relative intensities are given by direct comparison of the line heights. (If the line widths differ, this must be considered in comparing integrated intensities.) Often the frequency scale is so wide that appreciable variations in power and spectrometer sensitivity occur. These variations, however, can presumably be measured and corrected for. Relative intensities can be measured on both video and Stark-modulation spectrographs. The latter type is somewhat less sensitive to power variations. If spectrographs that yield line derivatives are used, it is important to note that the maximum signal response is an inverse function of the line width. (Usually it is inversely proportional to the nth power of the line widths, where n is the order of the derivative in question.)

1.5c. Measurement of Absolute Intensities. Most measurements of the absolute absorption coefficient are made on broad lines at fixed frequencies, alternately with absorbing gas in the cell and with the cell evacuated (see Art. 1.1a). If the cell is a simple waveguide, α_g is given by

$$\alpha_g = \frac{\lambda}{\lambda_g l} \ln \left(\frac{P - \Delta P}{P} \right)^{-1}, \tag{1.57}$$

where P is the square-law detector reading without gas absorption and $P - \Delta P$ the reading with gas absorption. The change in wavelength in the cell resulting from dielectric changes upon admission of the gas can cause errors when there are reflections in the cell. The magnitude of these errors can be checked by using a non-absorbing gas in the comparison run.

The requirement of a square-law detector and a linear amplifier can be avoided by the use of a calibrated microwave attenuator to restore the indicator reading after the gas is admitted to its value before the gas was admitted. In this modification a balanced detector with a null-reading indicator is usually employed. The gas absorption is then equal to the difference in attenuator settings. Beringer [34] and Strandberg, Meng, and Ingersoll [54] measured the absorption in oxygen at 50,000 Mc in this manner. Townes [55] measured the absorption in ammonia at 25,000 Mc by measuring changes in the standing-wave ratio resulting from the gas absorption in a shorted waveguide cell.

Some methods of measuring α_g employ cavities, either tuned or untuned. Knowledge of the effective cavity Q values before (Q) and after (Q_L) the gas is admitted yields α_g from Eq. 1.15. Determination of a weak absorption requires a high cavity Q, and hence a large cavity. Even for small cavities, however, an increase in sensitivity can be achieved over waveguide cells of the same volume. The disadvantages are frequency sensitivity and poor resolution (the high-energy densities in cavities require relatively high gas pressures to avoid saturation effects).

An untuned cavity is so large that its many modes cannot be resolved. Becker and Autler [56] achieved this condition at 24,000 Mc by using an 8-ft cubical copper cavity with electric fans in it to mix the large number of modes and thus to produce a uniform radiation density throughout the cavity. The oscillator spectrum is made broad by using a pulsed magnetron source. Under these conditions the response of a square-law detector coupled weakly to the cavity is proportional to the total cavity Q (rather than to the square of the Q as with a tuned cavity). The Q depends upon the losses in the cell walls as well as in the gas. Apertures in the cavity walls are used to vary the cavity Q in a calculable fashion. [57] A detection system of this sort [56] has been used to measure the absorption of water vapor at 22,000 Mc with an accuracy of about 5×10^{-9} cm^{-1}.

The poor resolution, however, requires measurements at a fairly high pressure, which is most conveniently chosen as atmospheric. In the Becker and Autler experiment thermocouples were used to detect the radiation. The 360 junctions were distributed throughout the cavity. Alternate junctions were coated with a lossy material.

1.6. PRECISION FREQUENCY MEASUREMENTS

The high resolution attainable with microwave spectroscopy implies the desirability of high-precision frequency measurements and, especially, of accurate measurements of frequency differences. The precision necessary depends on the demands of the particular physical problem under investigation. Molecular dimensions in the ground vibrational state can be determined to an accuracy of a few tenths of a per cent by cavity wavemeter measurements of the frequency of one isotopic combination together with precision measurements of the frequency differences between a number of isotopic combinations. This accuracy is usually all that is warranted by the self-consistency of solutions for the structure given by different isotopic combinations. On the other hand, the determination of certain centrifugal distortion constants of a molecule requires the comparison of widely separated frequencies and hence requires precision measurements of the absolute frequency.

If the spectral lines are well resolved, the accuracy attainable is usually determined by the relative distortions of the line and marker introduced by the spectrometer. The type of spectrometer used, in turn, depends on the many factors discussed in Sec. 1.4. With a line breadth of 100 kc, it is not difficult to estimate the center of a strong line to 10 kc. Suppose, however, that a line of this width is detected by a system using a square-wave Stark-modulation frequency, ν_m, of 100 kc. If the amplifier is tuned to the fundamental modulation frequency, the apparent line breadth is multiplied by a factor [58] $1 + (\nu_m/2 \, \Delta\nu)^2 = 1.25$. Other distortions may occur in the amplifier and in the detection systems. Furthermore, with the usual spectrograph, the optimum sensitivity occurs at comparatively high pressures where saturation effects [55] are negligible. Unresolvable fine or hyperfine structure may also prevent accurate measurements.

1.6a. Measurement of Absolute Frequencies. All the present methods of measuring absorption frequencies to accuracies of 100 kc or better are based on the use of the frequencies broadcast by the National Bureau of Standards station WWV as primary frequency standards to adjust or calibrate the frequency of a crystal-controlled oscillator used to generate the markers. The frequency of this oscillator is multiplied to the microwave region where the harmonics serve as secondary frequency standards that may be compared with spectral line frequencies. All the designs in present use are similar to the frequency standards developed by the cooperative effort of the National Bureau of Standards and the Massachusetts Institute of Technology Radiation Laboratory [29] during World War II. Details of the frequency standard design depend on the relative weighting of many criteria. It is desirable to have closely spaced crystal harmonics so that the frequency interval between a harmonic and a spectral line, measured with a calibrated radio receiver, will be as small as possible so as to minimize the error in the receiver calibration. But confusion in assigning the proper harmonic is usually avoided by means of a cavity wavemeter which is accurate only to about 5 to 15 Mc.

Frequency standard design is closely related to the sources of microwave radiation being used. At present the spectral region below 60,000 Mc is conveniently covered by the direct output of reflex klystrons; the frequencies above 60,000 Mc are best attained by multiplying the klystron frequencies by means of a crystal harmonic generator. This suggests that a frequency standard should provide coverage up to about 60,000 Mc. Frequency standards used at Duke [59] provide coverage to higher than 40,000 Mc. This coverage is adequate for most purposes since the region from 40,000 to 60,000 Mc can be investigated almost as well with harmonic generator sources as with the klystrons available.

The circuit diagram of one of the Duke frequency standards is shown in Fig. 1.33. It is crystal controlled at either 5 or 10 Mc, depending on the reception of the comparison frequencies broadcast by WWV. The crystal oscillator circuit is a modified Pierce oscillator. The resonant frequency of such an oscillator circuit is substantially independent of the operating point of the tube. The crystal is temperature controlled and may be tuned with a trimmer condenser either to exactly 5 (or 10) Mc or, more conveniently, to a few hundred cycles above or below the WWV frequency. In the latter case, the beat frequency between WWV and the local-oscillator crystal is measured by observing the Lissajous patterns with an audio oscillator. This is experimentally an easier technique than observing the null beat between WWV and the local-crystal-oscillator frequency.

In Fig. 1.33, the oscillator is followed by several stages of amplification and multiplication, using conventional tubes, and culminating in a frequency of 270 Mc. This frequency is multiplied by a klystron multiplier to 2970 Mc. The use of a klystron multiplier was dictated by the desire to reach as high a frequency as conveniently possible before generating the desired microwave standard frequencies by harmonic multiplication with silicon or germanium crystals.† It is the

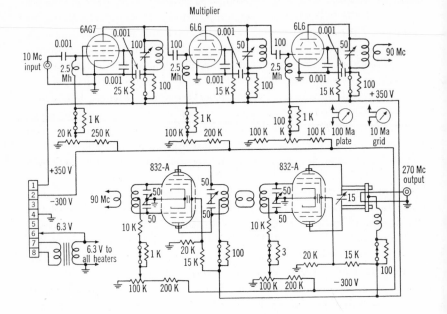

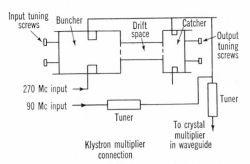

FIG. 1.33. Electronic multipliers for frequency standard. (From Unterberger and Smith.[59])

most expensive unit of the standard, and it can easily be replaced by another stage of conventional triode multiplication if standard frequencies are not needed beyond about 30,000 Mc.

† Most research workers who have used both types of crystals find the germanium ones more satisfactory in frequency standard multiplication. They are not available commercially, however, and the silicon crystals are quite adequate.

The standard microwave frequencies are generated by impressing a mixture of the 2970-Mc klystron output and 90- and 270-Mc signals from the amplifier chain onto a multiplier crystal mounted as shown in Fig. 1.14. The harmonics, f_h, of the multiplier crystal are analytically described by the relation $f_h = 2970m + 90n \pm b$ where m and n are integers and b is the multiplied beat frequency between WWV and the local crystal, with the proper sign taken. For simplicity b will be taken as zero.

Those harmonics above the cut-off frequency of the waveguide mount will be transmitted down the guide to the mixer crystal. The tuning plunger is adjusted for a maximum signal. Also incident on the mixer crystal is a fraction of the microwave energy from the reflex klystron source used to detect the particular absorption line to be measured. The differences between f_h and the klystron frequency f are present in the spectrum of frequencies generated by the mixer crystal. One of these is amplified and detected by a calibrated communications frequency receiver. When the receiver output is at a maximum, the klystron frequency is then $2970 + 90n \pm$ the receiver setting.† The integer n is determined from wavemeter measurements of the frequency.

If the upper frequency coverage of a frequency standard is limited to about 25,000 Mc, a klystron multiplier need not be employed. Conventional triode multiplication to about 500 Mc, together with crystal harmonic generation, provides adequately strong markers for the K-band region.[60] Since wavemeter calibrations below 25,000 Mc are usually good to a few megacycles, the markers can be spaced closely, 20 to 30 Mc, without danger of incorrect marker identification.

If the spectrum to be measured is above the frequency range covered by the method already described, it is possible to use as the primary marker source a stabilized klystron operating in the region of 8000 Mc, and monitored by comparison with a secondary standard of the type described in the previous paragraph. A well-designed stabilized oscillator can be maintained at a frequency constant to a fraction of a kilocycle during the measurement procedure. The output of the tunable stabilized oscillator is then multiplied by means of the usual crystal multiplier to the desired region of the spectrum and compared with an absorption line by the methods already described. Various regions can be covered by shifting the klystron frequency to different pips of the secondary frequency standard.

Details of comparing a marker frequency with an absorption-line frequency depend on the detection system used for the lines. The

† It should be noted that weak signals every 30 Mc or even 10 Mc resulting from accidental pickup are sometimes observed.

interpolation-receiver-bandpass of a few kilocycles determines the marker width at the i-f stage of the receiver—a width much less than that of the spectral line to be measured. Frequently measurements are made with sweep spectroscopes employing crystal video detection or Stark modulation. The klystron frequency is swept by a low-frequency saw-tooth voltage which is also applied to the horizontal deflection plates of an oscilloscope. The sweep must be sufficiently slow so that neither the marker pip nor the absorption line is significantly distorted or delayed by its respective amplifier. The pip and the absorption-line signal are usually mixed at the input to the broad-banded scope amplifier. The marker appears as a pip which can be superimposed on the absorption line by varying the receiver setting. In this fashion many lines have been measured to accuracies of about 50 kc at frequencies up to 40,000 Mc, and to 150 kc at frequencies above 100,000 Mc.

Markers may also be superimposed on the absorption-line signal in Stark or other modulation spectrographs which employ a lock-in amplifier with an automatic recording meter. In this case, a convenient presentation is obtained by using the receiver output to actuate a relay mechanism which drives a marker pen. The time constants of recorder and relay must be short as compared with the time of sweeping over the spectral line.

1.6b. Measurement of Frequency Differences. Often it is more desirable to know accurately the frequency difference between two spectral lines than to know accurately the absolute frequencies. For some problems, such as the measurement of quadrupole couplings, the frequency difference alone is necessary. A variety of techniques is possible for measuring these frequency differences. If the spectral lines are strong and well resolved, but not separated by more than about 50 Mc, a convenient technique is frequency modulation of the klystron source, which produces images of the spectral lines spaced from the center lines by the modulating frequency.[61] A variation of the modulating frequency can make images from adjacent lines coincide, or the image of a strong line can be made coincident with the center of a weak line. This technique is particularly suitable for measuring symmetrically placed satellites of a strong central line, such as the satellites of the ammonia inversion lines. Since the images reproduce the line shape, it is relatively easy to judge coincidence. A point to note is that, when the source of radiation for the cell is a harmonic generator, the images are still spaced by the modulation frequency rather than by a higher harmonic of the modulation frequency. This method has been used to measure the ammonia hyperfine structure with a standard deviation of about 15 kc.[62]

Often the frequencies of new spectral lines can be measured by comparison with known lines; thus the use of a crystal-controlled frequency standard is avoided. If the frequency differences are too large for use of the method described in the previous paragraph, a convenient method is to employ a calibrated receiver to measure the beat note between two oscillators, one of which is stabilized at the frequency of the known line (Sec. 1.3), while the other is used as the search oscillator. The range can be increased still further by beating a calibrated r-f oscillator against the stabilized microwave oscillator so as to produce a lattice of markers of known spacing on either side of the known spectral line. One then measures with the calibrated receiver the beat note between the search oscillator (when its frequency coincides with that of the peak of the unknown line) and the marker of the lattice which falls nearest to the unknown line. A method for using known spectral lines in the measurement of new lines has been described in detail by Rogers, Cox, and Braunschweiger.[63]

REFERENCES

[1] C. E. Cleeton and N. H. Williams, *Phys. Rev. 45*, 234 (1934).

[2] R. Beringer, *Phys. Rev. 70*, 53 (1946); B. Bleaney and R. P. Penrose, *Nature 157*, 339 (1946); *Proc. Roy. Soc. A189*, 358 (1947); W. D. Hershberger, *J. Appl. Phys. 17*, 495 (1946); C. H. Townes, *Phys. Rev. 70*, 665 (1946).

[3] (a) W. E. Good, *Phys. Rev. 70*, 213 (1946); (b) W. Gordy and M. Kessler, *Phys. Rev. 71*, 640 (1947).

[4] W. Gordy, *Revs. Modern Phys. 20*, 668 (1948).

[5] M. W. P. Strandberg, T. Wentink, and R. L. Kyhl, *Phys. Rev. 75*, 270 (1949).

[6] C. H. Townes and G. Geschwind, *J. Appl. Phys. 19*, 795 (1948).

[7] W. Gordy and M. Kessler, *Phys. Rev. 72*, 644 (1947); W. D. Hersberger, *J. Appl. Phys. 19*, 411 (1948); R. J. Watts and D. Williams, *Phys. Rev. 72*, 1122 (1947); C. K. Jen, *Phys. Rev. 74*, 1396 (1948).

[8] R. H. Hughes and E. B. Wilson, Jr., *Phys. Rev. 71*, 562 (1947).

[9] (a) C. H. Townes and F. R. Merritt, *Phys. Rev. 72*, 1266 (1947); (b) R. Karplus, *Phys. Rev. 73*, 1027 (1948).

[10] K. B. McAfee, Jr., R. H. Hughes, and E. B. Wilson, Jr., *Rev. Sci. Instr. 20*, 821 (1949); A. H. Sharbaugh, *Rev. Sci. Instr. 21*, 120 (1950).

[11] O. R. Gilliam, C. M. Johnson, and W. Gordy, *Phys. Rev. 78*, 140 (1950).

[12] (a) J. H. Burkhalter, R. S. Anderson, W. V. Smith, and W. Gordy, *Phys. Rev. 77*, 152 (1950); (b) K. Shimoda and T. Nishikawa, *J. Phys. Soc. of Japan 6*, 516 (1951).

[13] I. Estermann, *Revs. Modern Phys. 18*, 300 (1946); J. B. M. Kellogg and S. Millman, *Revs. Modern Phys. 18*, 323 (1946); H. K. Hughes, *Phys. Rev. 72*, 614 (1947).

[14] W. E. Lamb, Jr., and R. C. Retherford, *Phys. Rev. 72*, 241 (1947).

[15] W. E. Lamb and M. Skinner, *Phys. Rev. 78*, 539 (1950).

[16] C. Luck and W. Gordy, unpublished results.

[17] F. W. Lancaster and W. Gordy, *J. Chem. Phys. 19*, 1181 (1951).

[18] R. Beringer and J. G. Castle, Jr., *Phys. Rev. 78*, 581 (1950).

[19] Varian Associates, 990 Varian St., San Carlos, Calif.

[20] C. K. Jen, *Phys. Rev. 74*, 1396 (1948).

[21] W. Gordy, O. R. Gilliam, and R. Livingston, *Phys. Rev. 76*, 443 (1949).

[22] A. Roberts, Y. Beers, and A. G. Hill, *Phys. Rev. 70*, 112A (1946).

[23] *M.I.T. Radiation Laboratory Series*, L. N. Ridenour, Editor-in-Chief (McGraw-Hill Book Company, New York, 1948–1950). (1) *Radar System Engineering*, Ridenour; (2) *Radar Aids to Navigation*, Hall; (3) *Radar Beacons*, Roberts; (4) *Loran*, Pierce, McKenzie, and Woodward; (5) *Pulse Generators*, Glasoe and Lebacqz; (6) *Microwave Magnetrons*, Collins; (7) *Klystrons and Microwave Triodes*, Hamilton, Knipp, and Kuper; (8) *Principles of Microwave Circuits*, Montgomery, Dicke, and Purcell; (9) *Microwave Transmission Circuits*, Ragan; (10) *Waveguide Handbook*, Marcuvitz; (11) *Technique of Microwave Measurements*, Montgomery; (12) *Microwave Antenna Theory and Design*, Silver; (13) *Propagation of Short Radio Waves*, Kerr; (14) *Microwave Duplexers*, Smullin and Montgomery; (15) *Crystal Rectifiers*, Torrey and Whitmer; (16) *Microwave Mixers*, Pound; (17) *Components Handbook*, Blackburn; (18) *Vacuum Tube Amplifiers*, Valley and Wallman; (19) *Waveforms*, Chance, Hughes, MacNichol, Sayre, and Williams; (20) *Electronic Time Measurements*, Chance, Hulsizer, MacNichol, and Williams; (21) *Electronic Instruments*, Greenwood, Holdam and MacRae; (22) *Cathode Ray Tube Displays*, Soller, Starr, and Valley; (23) *Microwave Receivers*, Van Voorhis; (24) *Threshold Signals*, Lawson and Uhlenbeck; (25) *Theory of Servomechanisms*, James, Nichols, and Phillips; (26) *Radar Scanners and Radomes*, Cady, Karelitz, and Turner; (27) *Computing Mechanisms and Linkages*, Svoboda; (28) *Index*, Linford.

[24] An excellent treatment of directional couplers of various types is given by R. L. Kyhl, Vol. 11, reference 23. His very thorough treatment is used extensively here as most of the *Internal Rad. Lab. Reports* containing the original work are no longer available.

[25] H. A. Bethe, *Rad. Lab. Report*, quoted by R. L. Kyhl, reference 24.

[26] P. H. Miller and M. H. Greenblatt, *N.D.R.C. Report*, quoted by Torrey and Whitmer, reference 23.

[27] B. Bleaney and R. P. Penrose, *Proc. Roy. Soc. A189*, 358 (1947).

[28] R. J. Watts and D. Williams, *Phys. Rev. 72*, 980 (1947); D. Baird, R. Fristrom, and M. Sirvetz, *Rev. Sci. Instr. 21*, 881 (1950); L. J. Rueger, H. Lyons, and R. G. Nuckolls, *Rev. Sci. Instr. 22*, 428 (1951).

[29] Vol. 11, reference 23.

[30] Vol. 7, reference 23.

[31] J. B. H. Kuper and M. C. Waltz, *Rad. Lab. Report*, quoted by Pound, Vol. 16, reference 23.

[32] J. H. N. Loubser and C. H. Townes, *Phys. Rev. 76*, 178 (1949).

[33] J. B. Fisk, H. D. Hagstrum, and P. L. Hartman, *Bell System Tech. J. 25*, 167 (1946).

[34] R. Beringer, *Phys. Rev. 70*, 53 (1946).

[35] (a) A. G. Smith, W. Gordy, J. W. Simmons, and W. V. Smith, *Phys. Rev. 75*, 260 (1949); (b) O. R. Gilliam, C. M. Johnson, and W. Gordy, *Phys. Rev. 78*, 140 (1950); (c) C. M. Johnson, R. Trambarulo, and W. Gordy, *Phys. Rev., 84*, 1178 (1951).

[36] H. Q. North, *J. Appl. Phys. 17*, 912 (1946).

[37] C. M. Johnson (unpublished result).

[38] C. G. Montgomery, Vol. 11, reference 23.

[39] W. Bennett, Master's Thesis, Duke University, 1947.

[40] F. E. Terman, *Radio Engineers' Handbook* (McGraw-Hill Book Company, New York, 1943), p. 507.

[41] R. V. Pound, *Rev. Sci. Instr. 17*, 490 (1946); W. G. Tuller, W. C. Galloway, and F. P. Zaffarano, *Proc. I.R.E. 36*, 794 (1948).

[42] L. C. Hedrick, *Rev. Sci. Instr. 20*, 781 (1949); *22*, 537 (1951).

[43] A. H. Sharbaugh, *Rev. Sci. Instr. 21*, 120 (1950).

[44] W. E. Good, *Westinghouse Research Paper* 1538, 1950.

[45] N. A. Schuster, *Rev. Sci. Instr. 22*, 254 (1951).

[46] F. E. Terman, reference 40, p. 949; F. A. Everest, *Electronics 14*, Nov. 46 (1941).

[47] Vols. 15, 16, 23, and 24, reference 23.

[48] Townes and Geschwind, reference 6, have used this principle to develop a formula for the sensitivity of a microwave spectrometer. See also Gordy, reference 4.

[49] Vol. 11, reference 23.

[50] R. Beringer, *N.D.R.C. Report*, quoted by Torrey and Whitmer, Vol. 15, reference 23.

[51] R. Karplus, *Phys. Rev. 73*, 1027 (1948).

[52] Vol. 15, reference 23.

[53] R. R. Howard and W. V. Smith, *Phys. Rev. 79*, 128 (1950).

[54] M. W. P. Strandberg, C. Y. Meng, and J. G. Ingersoll, *Phys. Rev. 75*, 1524 (1949).

[55] C. H. Townes, *Phys. Rev. 70*, 665 (1946).

[56] G. E. Becker and S. H. Autler, *Phys. Rev. 70*, 300 (1946).

[57] W. E. Lamb, Jr., *Phys. Rev. 70*, 308 (1946).

[58] R. Karplus, *Phys. Rev. 73*, 1027 (1948).

[59] R. R. Unterberger and W. V. Smith, *Rev. Sci. Instr. 19*, 580 (1948).

[60] D. K. Coles, *Advances in Electronics 2* (Academic Press, Inc., New York, 1950).

[61] B. P. Dailey, R. L. Kyhl, M. W. P. Strandberg, J. H. Van Vleck, and E. B. Wilson, Jr., *Phys. Rev. 70*, 984 (1946).

[62] J. W. Simmons and W. Gordy, *Phys. Rev. 73*, 713 (1948).

[63] J. D. Rogers, H. L. Cox, and P. G. Braunschweiger, *Rev. Sci. Instr. 21*, 1014 (1950).

2. MICROWAVE SPECTRA OF GASES

With one exception the spectra discussed here were observed through absorption of radiation. Because of the rapid decrease in the coefficient of spontaneous emission with frequency, microwave emission spectra under ordinary laboratory conditions are extremely difficult to detect. The Einstein coefficients of absorption, $B_{m \to n}$, and spontaneous emission, $A_{m \leftarrow n}$, are related by the equation,

$$\frac{A_{m \leftarrow n}}{B_{m \to n}} = \frac{8\pi h \nu_{mn}{}^3 g_m}{c^2 g_n},$$

(2.1)

where ν_{mn} is the frequency involved in the transitions, and g_m and g_n are the degeneracies of the two states involved. Whereas emission spectra are easier to observe in the visible and ultraviolet regions, absorption spectra are by far the easier to detect at microwave frequencies.†

2.1. ELECTRONIC SPECTRA

2.1a. Atomic Spectra. The region of the spectrum from 0.05 cm^{-1} to 5 cm^{-1}, now covered by precise microwave spectroscopic methods, includes many transitions between fine structure levels as well as many between hyperfine levels of free atoms. For example, the electronic ground states of Na^{23}, Rb^{87}, and Cs^{113} are split into doublets with separations of 0.059, 0.228, and 0.307 cm^{-1}, respectively, by the interaction of the unpaired electron and the nuclear magnetic moment. The levels 2 $^2P_{1/2}$ and 2 $^2P_{3/2}$ in H and Li are separated by 0.365 and 0.338 cm^{-1}, respectively. Many ionized atoms have transitions falling in the microwave region. The advantages of microwave methods for measuring precisely such transitions can hardly be questioned. Nevertheless, atomic spectroscopy has not advanced so rapidly in the microwave region as has molecular spectroscopy of gases and magnetic resonance spectroscopy of solids, largely because of the difficulty of observing the microwave spectra of free atoms or ions. It is particularly hard to get

† In this book we follow the custom in microwave absorption spectroscopy (but not in optical spectroscopy) and write the lower level of a transition first—for example, $m \to n$, where m is the lower level.

enough absorbing atoms into the cell to give a detectable absorption line. New methods of producing free atoms and ions, together with further improvement in the sensitivity of microwave spectrometers should bring about considerable acceleration of the work in this field. A few important experiments have already been accomplished. Among these are the observation of transitions between hyperfine levels of Cs by Roberts, Beers, and Hill,[1a] that of transitions between hyperfine levels of Na^{23} by Shimoda and Nishikawa,[1b] the Lamb-Retherford experiment [2] on H, and the observation of emission spectra by Ewen and Purcell.[3] The theory of fine and hyperfine structure in atomic spectra is treated in such books as White's *Introduction to Atomic Spectra* and Condon and Shortley's *Theory of Atomic Spectra*, and, in view of the few applications so far made in the microwave region, will not be included here.

Lamb-Retherford experiment. In contradiction to previously established Dirac theory, Lamb and Retherford [2] found that the $2\,^2S_{1/2}$ and $2\,^2P_{1/2}$ levels of the hydrogen atom are not degenerate but are separated by about 1000 Mc. The ingenious method used by these researchers is described in Art. 1.1g. A similar experiment performed later by Lamb and Skinner [4] showed that the corresponding levels of ionized helium, which according to the Dirac theory should also be degenerate, are separated by 14,000 Mc. The latter splitting has also been detected by optical spectroscopy.[5]

The Dirac theory [6] predicts that for hydrogenlike atoms states with the same total quantum number, n, and angular momentum, j, are degenerate. Shortly after the initial Lamb-Retherford experiment showed this feature of the Dirac theory to be incorrect, Bethe [7] demonstrated that the anomaly could be caused by interaction of the electron with the radiation field. With non-relativistic quantum electrodynamics, Bethe predicted that this interaction should cause an upward shift of about 1050 Mc in the $2\,^2S_{1/2}$ level of H and a negligible downward shift in the $2\,^2P_{1/2}$ level. He predicted also, in approximate agreement with experiment, that the corresponding electromagnetic shift in He^+ should be about 13 times larger than that in H. A more precise theory for the interaction has been worked out by Kroll and Lamb,[8] and by French and Weisskopf,[9] who used relativistic quantum mechanics. The resulting formula [4] for the energy of separation of the $n\,^2S_{1/2}$ and $n^2P_{1/2}$ levels for hydrogenlike atoms is

$$\Delta W_n = \frac{8\alpha^3}{3\pi}\, Ry\, \frac{Z^4}{n^3}\left[\log\frac{1}{\bar{\epsilon}} - \log 2 + \frac{23}{24} - \frac{1}{5}\right], \qquad (2.2)$$

where α is the fine structure constant, Z is the atomic number, Ry is the ionization energy of hydrogen, and $\bar{\epsilon}$ is a calculable parameter which is proportional to an average excitation energy of the atom. With this formula the energy difference of $2\,^2S_{1/2} - 2\,^2P_{1/2}$ predicted for H is 1051 Mc and for He$^+$, 13,820 Mc. The latest measured values for these are 1062 ± 5 Mc and $14,020 \pm 100$ Mc, respectively. Although small discrepancies between theory and experiment still exist, there seems little doubt that the Lamb-Retherford shift is caused in the main by interaction of the atomic electron with the radiation field.

Emission line from interstellar hydrogen. One of the hyperfine transitions, $\nu = 1420.405$ Mc, of atomic hydrogen has been detected in galactic radiation by Ewen and Purcell.[3] The interstellar radiation was detected with a superheterodyne receiver connected to a large horn-type antenna. The beam width of the horn was 30°. The line in the vicinity of the center of the galaxy was observed in emission with a temperature of $40° \pm 5°$ C with respect to the radiation temperature of the background. It was found to have a width of 80 kc. A Doppler shift was observed which was satisfactorily accounted for by the earth's orbital motion and by the motion of the solar system. Variation of the Doppler shift during the time of observation provided evidence that the source is extended.

The Ewen-Purcell experiment represents the first observation of emission spectra in microwave spectroscopy as well as the first observation of a discrete spectral transition in microwave radiation from outer space.

2.1b. Oxygen. The microwave absorption of oxygen is of special interest because of the presence of oxygen in the atmosphere. There are two regions of the microwave spectrum in which resonant absorptions of microwaves occur,[10] the region of 5 mm and that of 2.5 mm. The 2.5-mm absorption arises from a single resonant absorption peak, whereas that in the 5-mm region consists of a large number of lines which are not resolved at atmospheric pressure. These lines spread from about 4-mm to 6-mm wavelengths with the strongest absorption occurring near 5 mm. See Fig. 2.1.†

The 5-mm absorption was first measured by Beringer[11] at atmospheric pressure during World War II and has since been remeasured at this pressure by Lamont[12] and by Strandberg, Meng, and Ingersoll.[13] Using a Zeeman-modulation spectrograph, Burkhalter, Anderson, Smith, and Gordy[14] have succeeded in detecting the 5-mm lines at low pressures where the individual lines are completely resolved. The resonant

---

† Despite the comparatively weak magnetic dipole absorption, the peak attenuation of about 15 db per kilometer in air[12] is of considerable practical importance in radar and other microwave transmission applications.

absorption at 2.5-mm wavelength was later detected by Anderson, Johnson, and Gordy.[15]

The oxygen spectrum arises through a magnetic rather than an electric coupling to the radiation field.[10] From symmetry considerations

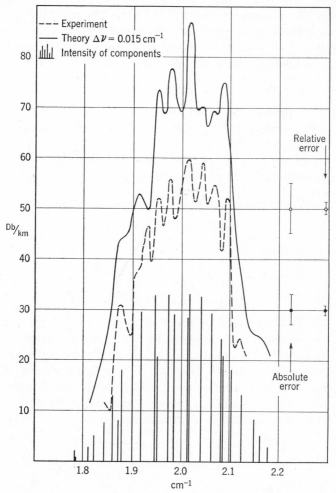

Fig. 2.1. Theoretical and observed spectrum of oxygen in the 5-mm-wave region. Pressure, 80 cm of Hg. (From Strandberg, Meng, and Ingersoll.[13])

O_2 has no permanent electric dipole moment but does have, because of its $^3\Sigma$ ground state, a permanent magnetic moment of two Bohr magnetons. The microwave spectrum of oxygen does not represent a transition between different rotational levels but rather a transition between the fine-structure components of given rotational levels. This fine structure arises from an interaction between the end-over-end rotational momentum of the molecule, defined by the quantum number N, and the total electronic spin momentum, defined by the quantum number S. The exact mechanisms involved are interpreted somewhat differently by Kramers [16] and by Hebb.[17] The resulting formulas further developed and corrected by Schlapp [18] are, however, identical.

Since in a Σ state there is no electronic orbital angular momentum, the total momentum number J is given by

$$J = N + S \qquad N + S - 1 \qquad \cdots \qquad N - S \qquad (2.3)$$

The selection rules are $\Delta J = \pm 1$ and $\Delta N = 0$. For O_2, $S = 1$ so that there are three values of J for each N. Hence, each rotational level is split into a triplet. The triplet intervals depend on the nature and magnitude of the coupling of S and N. The formulas derived from first-order perturbation theory by Schlapp [18] are

$$E_{N+1} = E_0 + (2N + 3)B - \lambda + \mu(N + 1)$$
$$- [(2N + 3)^2 B^2 + \lambda^2 - 2\lambda B]^{1/2}$$
$$E_N = E_0 \qquad\qquad\qquad (2.4)$$
$$E_{N-1} = E_0 - (2N - 1)B - \lambda - \mu N$$
$$+ [(2N - 1)^2 B^2 + \lambda^2 - 2\lambda B]^{1/2},$$

where $B = h^2/(8\pi^2 I_B c)$, $E_0 = BN(N + 1)$ are the unperturbed rotational energies, and λ and μ are coupling constants which must be determined empirically. The quantity λ is a measure of the energy of coupling which depends on the factor $[3 \cos^2 (S, N) - 1]$ in the classical Hamiltonian, and μ is a measure of the coupling energy which depends on $\cos (S, N)$. Application of the selection rules $\Delta J = \pm 1$ and $\Delta N = 0$ gives two series of microwave absorption lines,

$$\nu_+(N) = -(2N + 3)B + \lambda - \mu(N + 1)$$
$$+ [(2N + 3)^2 B^2 + \lambda^2 - 2\lambda B]^{1/2}$$
$$\nu_-(N) = +(2N - 1)B + \lambda + \mu N \qquad (2.5)$$
$$- [(2N - 1)^2 B^2 + \lambda^2 - 2\lambda B]^{1/2},$$

where $\nu_+(N)$ represents the transition $J = N + 1 \rightarrow N$, and $\nu_-(N)$ represents the transition $J = N - 1 \rightarrow N$.

Prior to accurate microwave measurements the best values of λ and μ were obtained from Babcock and Herzberg's [19] infrared measurements on atmospheric oxygen. These values ($\lambda = 1.985$ cm^{-1} and $\mu = -0.00837$ cm^{-1}) were used by Van Vleck [10] in computing the microwave atmospheric absorption of oxygen, for comparison with Beringer's high-pressure measurements.[11] At atmospheric pressure most of the absorption lines are unresolved or only partially resolved. Recent low-pressure microwave investigations [14,15] have resulted in the detection of 26 well-resolved fine-structure lines with values of N ranging from 1 to 25. These observations have resulted in a redetermination of the coupling constants as $\lambda = 1.983971$ cm^{-1}; $\mu = -0.0085114$ cm^{-1} for the ν_+ series. The accuracy of the microwave frequency measurements reveals a breakdown of Schlapp's formulas, presumably caused by neglect of higher-order perturbations. Thus the ν_- series cannot be fitted by the same value of μ, and, indeed, is best fitted by both revising μ to -0.0069497 cm^{-1} and adding a term $\alpha/[N(N+1)]^{1/2}$, where $\alpha = +0.0049345$ cm^{-1}, to the ν_- relation.[14] Other data on line breadths and Zeeman effect are discussed in Sec. 4.2 and Sec. 3.2.

Several lines of other isotopic combinations of O_2 have also been observed.[20] These have added to the knowledge of the isotopic spins. O^{16} has zero spin, resulting in zero statistical weight for even rotational levels of O_2^{16}. (Sec. 4.5.) Hence, only odd values of N are observed. Similarly, only odd values of N are observed for O_2^{18}, a result which confirms a spin of zero for this isotope.[20] Measurements on $O^{16}O^{17}$ suggest a spin [20] for O^{17} greater than $\frac{1}{2}$, in agreement with the nuclear induction value, $\frac{5}{2}$.[21]

2.1c. Free Radicals. The interaction of electronic momentum with end-over-end rotation in such light free radicals as CH, OH, and SH causes a sub-level splitting which is of the order of a microwave quantum [28] for states highly populated at room temperature. As techniques develop it seems probable that direct transitions between Λ doublets or spin multiplets (similar to those in oxygen) of many free radicals will be observed.† A promising method for their study is paramagnetic resonance.[22,23]

2.2. MOLECULAR ROTATIONAL SPECTRA

Absorption of energy by most gases in the microwave region of the electromagnetic spectrum is intimately connected with rotational motions of molecules in the gases. From rotational spectra rather precise knowledge of molecular structures may be obtained.

---

† As this book goes to press, observation of this type of spectrum in the OH free radical has been made by T. M. Sanders, A. L. Shawlow, G. C. Dousanis, and C. H. Townes (private communication).

Absorption of electromagentic energy by rotation arises from interaction of the molecular dipole moment with the electromagnetic field. Hence no pure rotational spectrum is possible if there is no permanent dipole moment in the molecule. Classically, the molecule may rotate with any angular velocity, which would result in a continuous absorption; however, discrete spectral lines are observed. This indicates that only certain rotational energies are possible—a well-known result predicted by wave mechanics. Although classical mechanics does not always lead to the correct results, it gives useful pictures of the molecular motions. In the final analysis, the use of wave mechanics becomes necessary for the correct interpretation of the spectra.

2.2a. Classical Description. Molecules may be classified dynamically as linear rotors, symmetric tops, asymmetric tops, or spherical tops, depending upon the configurations of the nuclei. More precisely, this classification is made on the basis of the momental ellipsoid.[24] The moment of inertia of a rigid molecule about any axis is defined by

$$I = \sum_i m_i r_i^2, \tag{2.6}$$

where m_i is the mass and r_i is the distance from the axis of the ith nucleus. The locus of $1/\sqrt{I}$ plotted along axes passing through the center of gravity is an ellipsoid called the momental ellipsoid with its center at the center of gravity of the molecule. Moments of inertia about the principal axes of the ellipsoid are called the principal moments of inertia. About these axes the products of inertia vanish, and the body can be dynamically balanced when rotating about a principal axis.

If a molecule has an axis of symmetry, the moment of inertia about that axis is a principal moment. Principal axes may often be found from the symmetry of the molecule. For a diatomic or a linear polyatomic molecule, the principal moment about the internuclear axis is zero; the other two are about axes perpendicular to the internuclear axis and are equal. If there is only one axis of three-or-more-fold symmetry and it is the axis of highest symmetry, the molecule (other than linear) is a symmetric top. The axis of highest symmetry is called the figure axis and is a principal axis. For example, the carbon-chlorine internuclear axis in methyl chloride is the figure axis. Moments of inertia about principal axes perpendicular to the figure axis of a symmetric top are equal. A molecule in which the moment of inertia about the figure axis is accidentally equal to the other principal moments of inertia is actually a spherical top; however, such molecules are infrequently found and have spectra characteristic of symmetric tops. Spherical tops have no preferred axes, and moments of inertia about any axes through the center of gravity are equal. The majority of molecules found in nature are asymmetric tops. In them all three principal moments of inertia are different. If a two-fold symmetry axis exists, it is a principal axis. When there are planes of symmetry, one principal axis is perpendicular to one of the planes, and the other two lie in that plane. For example, methylene chloride (CH_2Cl_2) has a two-fold symmetry axis contained in two mutually perpendicular planes of symmetry. One principal axis is the symmetry axis; each of the other two principal axes lies in one of the symmetry planes.

Most mechanical relations are compactly expressed in terms of the principal moments of inertia. The components of the angular momentum **P** of a rotating molecule are given by

$$\mathbf{P}_a = I_a\omega_a,$$

$$\mathbf{P}_b = I_b\omega_b, \qquad (2.7)$$

$$\mathbf{P}_c = I_c\omega_c,$$

where **ω** is the angular velocity, and the rotational energy is expressed as

$$E_r = \frac{P_a{}^2}{2I_a} + \frac{P_b{}^2}{2I_b} + \frac{P_c{}^2}{2I_c}. \qquad (2.8)$$

When the molecule is linear (with $I_a = 0$, $I_c = I_b$), Eq. 2.8 becomes

$$E_r = \frac{P_b{}^2 + P_c{}^2}{2I_b} = \frac{P^2}{2I_b}. \qquad (2.9)$$

Motions of a symmetric-top molecule are somewhat more complicated than are those of a linear molecule. In them there can be a component of angular momentum along the moving-figure axis. The motion can be considered to be a rotation of the molecule about the figure axis which precesses about **P**. The angular momentum **P**, which is fixed in space, is not fixed in the molecule; however, the angle between **P** and the figure axis remains constant throughout the precession. Figure 2.2 illustrates the motions of an oblate symmetric top. The molecule is rigidly attached to a right circular cone whose apex is at the molecule's center of gravity and whose axis lies along the figure axis. This cone rolls along a stationary right circular cone whose axis is the angular momentum vector **P**. If the top is prolate ($I_a < I_b = I_c$), the moving cone lies outside the fixed cone; if it is oblate ($I_a > I_b = I_c$), the moving cone is within the fixed cone as in Fig. 2.2. For a reversal of rotational direction about the figure axis the moving cones roll in the opposite direction and both **P** and **P**$_a$ are reversed. The rotational energy is the

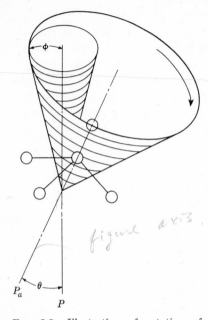

figure axis

FIG. 2.2. Illustration of rotation of oblate symmetric top.

sum of the precessional energy and the energy of rotation about the figure axis:

$$E_r = \frac{P^2}{2I_b} + \frac{1}{2}\left(\frac{1}{I_a} - \frac{1}{I_b}\right) P_a{}^2.$$

$$(2.10)$$

For all but accidental symmetric tops the dipole moment vector lies along the figure axis. Only the precessional motion involves a change in direction of the dipole. Thus, energy absorbed from an electromagnetic field is converted into precessional energy and does not speed up rotation about the figure axis.

Classical motions of an asymmetric top ($I_a \neq I_b \neq I_c$, conventionally $I_a < I_b < I_c$) are much more difficult to visualize. An asymmetric-top molecule may be considered to be attached rigidly to its momental ellipsoid. The total angular momentum vector $\mathbf{P}$ is fixed in space, and the momental ellipsoid rolls without slipping on a plane perpendicular to $\mathbf{P}$ and tangent to the ellipsoid. See Fig. 2.3. None of the ellipsoid's

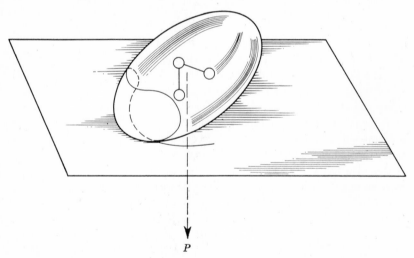

P

FIG. 2.3. Illustration of motion of asymmetric top.

axes generates a cone as does the figure axis in a symmetric top. Equation 2.8 gives the rotational energy. For a more detailed description of the behavior of an asymmetric top, the reader is referred to Winkelmann and Grammel's article in *Handbuch der Physik*.[25]

Methods of expressing the principal moments of inertia in terms of the molecular dimensions and atomic masses will be found in Sec. 8.1.

2.2b. Diatomic and Linear Molecules. For a rigid linear molecule, the quantum mechanical rotational wave equation in polar coordinates is

$$\frac{1}{\sin\theta}\cdot\frac{\partial}{\partial\theta}\left(\sin\theta\frac{\partial\psi}{\partial\theta}\right)+\frac{1}{\sin^2\theta}\cdot\frac{\partial^2\psi}{\partial\phi^2}+\frac{8\pi^2 IE}{h^2}\psi=0, \qquad (2.11)$$

where θ is the polar angle of the molecular axis with respect to a fixed direction in space (the Z axis) and ϕ is the azimuthal angle. Physically significant solutions of Eq. 2.11 are possible for certain discrete values of $E = E_J$ only, with corresponding particular wave functions $\psi = \psi_J$. Quantum mechanics texts [26, 27] give the solutions

$$E_J = \frac{h^2}{8\pi^2 I}J(J+1), \qquad (2.12)$$

$$\psi_J = N_{JM}e^{iM\phi}P_J^{|M|}(\cos\theta), \qquad (2.13)$$

$$N_{JM} = \frac{1}{\sqrt{2\pi}}\left[\frac{(2J+1)}{2}\cdot\frac{(J-|M|)!}{(J+|M|)!}\right]^{\frac{1}{2}},$$

where the rotational quantum number J may take any positive integral value, and the "magnetic" quantum number M takes the $2J + 1$ integral values

$$M = J \quad J-1 \quad J-2, \quad \cdots \quad -J \qquad (2.14)$$

$P_J^{|M|}(\cos\theta)$ is the associated Legendre function, and N_{JM} is a normalization factor whose value is such that the integral of ψ_J^2 over-all space is unity.

Comparing Eq. 2.9 and Eq. 2.12 shows that a substitution of

$$P = \frac{h}{2\pi}\sqrt{J(J+1)} \qquad (2.15)$$

in the former yields the latter. Thus the total angular momentum P is quantized. Similarly, the component of the angular momentum P_Z along the axis fixed in space is quantized and has values,

$$P_Z = \frac{h}{2\pi}M. \qquad (2.16)$$

Since all $2J + 1$ values of M give the same energy, the levels are $(2J + 1)$-fold degenerate. One way of removing this degeneracy is to split the level into $2J + 1$ sub-levels by the application of a sufficiently strong magnetic field; hence the name, "magnetic quantum number," for M.

Equation 2.12 is frequently written

$$E_J = hBJ(J + 1), \tag{2.17}$$

where $B = h/(8\pi^2 I_b)$. Centrifugal distortion in the molecule is taken into account by the addition of the small term $DJ^2(J + 1)^2$. In its more general form, the energy is

$$E_J = h[BJ(J + 1) - DJ^2(J + 1)^2]. \tag{2.18}$$

For a diatomic molecule,[28]
$$D = \frac{4B^3}{\omega^2}, \tag{2.19}$$

where ω is the fundamental vibrational frequency of the molecule. A. H. Nielsen [29] has found that for linear triatomic molecules

$$D = 4B^3 \left(\frac{\xi_3^2}{\omega_3^2} + \frac{\xi_1^2}{\omega_1^2} \right) \tag{2.20}$$

where ω_1 and ω_3 are the bond-stretching frequencies and ξ_3 and ξ_1 are weighting factors for the fundamental stretching frequencies.

The selection rules (see Chapter 4) are

$$\Delta J = \pm 1 \qquad \Delta M = 0, \pm 1. \tag{2.21}$$

Absorption of energy corresponds to $\Delta J = +1$. With Bohr's postulate,

$$E_{J'} - E_J = h\nu, \tag{2.22}$$

Eq. 2.18 yields
$$\nu = 2B(J + 1) - 4D(J + 1)^3, \tag{2.23}$$

where ν is the spectral line frequency. Here J is the quantum number for the lower state. For small values of J, the second term is negligible.

In an excited state, the value of B is in general different from that in the ground state. For diatomic molecules, the value of B in a state of vibrational quantum number v is

$$B_v = B_e - \alpha(v + \tfrac{1}{2}), \tag{2.24}$$

where B_e is the equilibrium value of B and α is a small constant (~ 0.5 to 1 per cent of B and positive). In the ground vibrational state

$$B_o = B_e - \alpha/2. \tag{2.25}$$

To determine B_e, it is necessary to know B for an excited vibrational as well as for the ground state.

The rotational constant B for linear polyatomic molecules in excited vibrational states is given by

$$B_v = B_e - \sum_i \alpha_i \left(v_i + \frac{d_i}{2} \right), \qquad (2.26)$$

where the summation extends over all modes of vibration. Quantum number v_i is the quantum number of the ith mode of vibration, and d_i is the degeneracy of that mode. A linear molecule with n atoms has $3n - 5$ modes of vibration, some of which are degenerate. For example, an XYZ molecule like HCN has two non-degenerate stretching modes and one degenerate bending mode. In order to determine B_e, it is necessary to know B_v for the ground state and for as many excited states as there are modes of vibration with each mode excited at least once.

Coupling of the rotational angular momentum with momentum resulting from excited degenerate bending vibrations leads to a symmetrical splitting of the rotational levels known as l-type doubling. The doubling of the levels gives rise to a pair of lines with separation

$$\Delta\nu = 2q(J + 1) \qquad (2.27)$$

where q is of the order $2B^2/\omega$ and ω is the vibration frequency of the degenerated bending mode.[29-33] This phenomenon is treated in more detail in Sec. 2.3.

The peak absorption coefficient of a pure rotational line of a linear molecule, with approximations and substitutions discussed in Sec. 4.6, can be expressed as

$$\alpha_{\text{Max}} = 4.94 \times 10^{-12} \left[\frac{\mu^2 \nu^3}{T^2 (\Delta\nu)_1} \right] F_v e^{\left[-4.80 \times 10^{-5} \frac{BJ(J+1)}{T} \right]}, \qquad (2.28a)$$

where α_{Max} = absorption coefficient in cm^{-1} at the resonant peak.

F_v = fraction of molecules in the particular vibration state under observation. See Sec. 4.5.

B = rotational constant in Mc.

μ = the molecular dipole moment in Debye units.

ν = the resonant frequency in Mc.

T = the absolute temperature.

$(\Delta\nu)_1$ = the line breadth in Mc at $T = 300°$ K and $P = 1$ mm of Hg.

J = the quantum number for the lower rotational state of the transition.

At room temperature (300° K) the exponential term is very close to unity, and Eq. 2.28a can be expressed

$$(\alpha_{\text{Max}})_{T=300} = 55 \times 10^{-18} \mu^2 \nu^3 F_v / (\Delta \nu)_1, \qquad (2.28b)$$

with the same units as above. For linear polar molecules $(\Delta \nu)_1$ ranges from about 6 to 24 Mc for dipole moments ranging from 0.7 to 3 Debye. See Table 4.1. Hence, very approximately $(\Delta \nu)_1 = 8\mu$, and Eq. 2.28a becomes (assuming $F_v = 1$)

$$(\alpha_{\text{Max}})_{T=300} \approx 7 \times 10^{-18} \mu \nu^3. \qquad (2.28c)$$

This last form can be used, but with caution, to estimate quickly the intensities of unknown lines of linear molecules at room temperature.

As indicated by the theory just described, the pure rotational spectrum of a linear molecule in its ground vibrational state consists in the first-order approximation (Eq. 2.17) of a series of equally spaced lines. The series originates at a frequency of $2B$ and progresses toward higher frequencies. For molecules having moments of inertia approximately as large as, or larger than, that of carbon monoxide, the series originates in the microwave region or in the still longer wave r-f region. Centrifugal distortion (Eq. 2.18) tends to make the series converge slightly in passing to higher frequencies. For molecules in excited degenerate vibrational states each line is split into a doublet with the doublet spacing increasing with the frequency of the transition (with J). The intensities of the lines increase with frequency (Eq. 2.28) until a maximum is reached somewhere in the infrared region. Figure 2.4 illustrates graphically the microwave rotational spectra of CO and SCSe. Rotational transitions for all linear molecules except the light diatomic hydrides, such as HCl, fall within the microwave region. Nevertheless, from the point of view of intensities the microwave region is not the most favorable part of the spectrum for observing rotational spectra. This can readily be inferred from Fig. 2.4 or from Eq. 2.28. However, the very high sensitivity now obtainable with microwave spectrographs makes it easy to observe the lines despite their low intensity.

The rotational spectra of a number of diatomic and linear polyatomic molecules have been measured in the microwave region. These range from the very light diatomic molecules such as CO to heavier polyatomic ones such as ICN. The rotational constants obtained by the application of the above theory to the observed spectra are listed in Table $A.4$ in the Appendix. In addition to the interatomic distances which are evaluated from these constants (see Chapter 8), considerable information is obtained from features of rotational spectra to be described in later sections. The rotational spectra of simple linear molecules are particularly useful in evaluating mass ratios of isotopes and other nuclear properties (see Chapter 6).

To obtain an accurate evaluation of the small centrifugal stretching constant D_J, it is necessary to measure rotational lines in the high-frequency millimeter region as well as in the low-frequency centimeter region. Recently, precise measurements have been made at Duke [34]

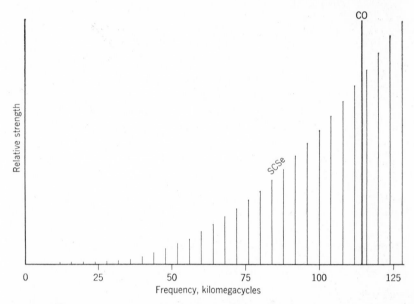

FIG. 2.4. Microwave rotational spectrum of a linear molecule with a relatively small (CO) and a relatively large (SCSe) moment of inertia. The second rotational line of CO (not shown) appears at 230 kilomegacycles.

on rotational transitions of a number of molecules in the wavelength region of 2 to 4 mm. These measurements provide a test of Eqs. 2.18 and 2.20. Equation 2.18 was found to fit the group of lines measured within the accuracy of the measurements, $\sim$3 parts in 10^6. The agreement obtained with Eq. 2.20 was only approximate.

2.2c. Symmetric-Top Molecules. The quantized rotational energies of the symmetric-top molecule were first obtained by Dennison [35] with matrix mechanical methods and later by Reiche and Rademacker [36] and by de Kronig and Rabi [36] with the Schrödinger wave equation.

The wave equation for a rigid symmetric-top rotor is most conveniently expressed in terms of Euler's angles, θ, ϕ, and χ, shown in Fig. 2.5. Axes X, Y, and Z are fixed in space, and a, b, and c, the principal axes of the momental ellipsoid, are fixed in the molecule with axis a along the

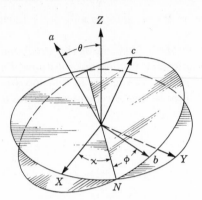

Fig. 2.5. Euler's angles.

figure axis $(I_a \neq I_b = I_c)$. In terms of Euler's angles, the wave equation is [35,36]

$$\frac{1}{\sin \theta} \frac{\partial}{\partial \theta} \left(\sin \theta \frac{\partial \psi}{\partial \theta} \right) + \left(\frac{I_b}{I_a} + \frac{\cos^2 \theta}{\sin^2 \theta} \right) \frac{\partial^2 \psi}{\partial \phi^2} + \frac{1}{\sin^2 \theta} \frac{\partial^2 \psi}{\partial \chi^2}$$

$$- 2 \frac{\cos \theta}{\sin^2 \theta} \frac{\partial^2 \psi}{\partial \phi \, \partial \chi} + \frac{8\pi^2 I_b}{h^2} E_r \psi = 0. \quad (2.29)$$

Solutions to this equation which have physical significance are

$$\psi = N_{JKM} e^{iK\phi} e^{iM\chi} (\sin \theta/2)^{|K-M|} (\cos \theta/2)^{|K+M|} F(\sin^2 \theta/2),$$

$$N_{JKM} =$$

$$\left[\frac{\left[\begin{array}{c} (2J+1)(J + \frac{1}{2}|K+M| + \frac{1}{2}|K-M|)! \\ (J - \frac{1}{2}|K+M| + \frac{1}{2}|K-M|)! \end{array} \right]}{\left[\begin{array}{c} 8\pi^2(J - \frac{1}{2}|K+M| - \frac{1}{2}|K-M|)!(|K-M|!)^2 \\ (J + \frac{1}{2}|K+M| - \frac{1}{2}|K-M|)! \end{array} \right]} \right]^{1/2}, \quad (2.30)$$

where N_{JKM} is a normalizing factor and $F(\sin^2 \theta/2)$ is the hypergeometric series.[37] Quantum numbers J, K, and M may assume the values

$$J = 0, 1, 2, \cdots$$
$$K = 0, \pm 1, \pm 2, \cdots \pm J \quad (2.31)$$
$$M = 0, \pm 1, \pm 2, \cdots \pm J$$

and have the following significance: $(h/2\pi)\sqrt{J(J+1)}$ is the total angular momentum P of Eq. 2.10, $(h/2\pi)K$ is the component of angular momentum along the figure axis corresponding to P_a, and $(h/2\pi)M$ is the component of angular momentum along the Z axis fixed in space.

The characteristic energy values for the rigid symmetrical top are given by the formula

$$E_{JK} = \frac{h^2}{8\pi^2 I_b} J(J+1) + \frac{h^2}{8\pi^2}\left(\frac{1}{I_a} - \frac{1}{I_b}\right)K^2. \qquad (2.32)$$

This formula follows as a condition for the acceptable solution of Eq. 2.29. If one assumes the quantization of angular momentum $P = (h/2\pi)\sqrt{J(J+1)}$ and its component $P_a = (h/2\pi)K$, the energy formula, Eq. 2.34, may be obtained simply by a substitution of these values in Eq. 2.10. It is to be noted that for $K = 0$ there are $2J + 1$ values of M corresponding to the same energy in the absence of an external field. For $K \neq 0$ there are $2J + 1$ values of M and two values of K $(\pm K)$ corresponding to the same energy, and each K sublevel is $2(2J + 1)$-fold degenerate when $K \neq 0$. In the usual spectroscopic notation, Eq. 2.32 is written

$$E_{JK} = h[BJ(J+1) + (A - B)K^2], \qquad (2.33)$$

where $A = h/8\pi^2 I_a$ and $B = h/8\pi^2 I_b$.

When the effects of centrifugal distortion are included as given by Slawsky and Dennison,[38] the rotational energy in the notation of Herzberg [31] is †

$$E_{JK} = h[BJ(J+1) + (A - B)K^2 - D_J J^2(J+1)^2$$
$$- D_{JK}J(J+1)K^2 - D_K K^4], \qquad (2.34)$$

where D_J, D_{JK}, and D_K are extremely small constants in comparison with A and B. The term involving D_J results from stretching which arises from end-over-end rotation of the molecule; the term in D_K arises from distortion caused by rotation about the figure axis; and the term in D_{JK} from the interaction of these two motions.

The selection rules for a symmetric rotor (see Chapter 4) are

$$\Delta J = 0, \pm 1 \qquad \Delta K = 0 \qquad \Delta M = 0, \pm 1. \qquad (2.35)$$

In the absence of external fields, the selection rule for M is unimportant. Rotational absorption spectra result for $\Delta J = +1$, and inversion spectra for $\Delta J = 0$. Applying Bohr's postulate (Eq. 2.22), one obtains the formula

$$\nu = 2B(J+1) - 4D_J(J+1)^3 - 2D_{JK}(J+1)K^2, \qquad (2.36)$$

for the rotational spectrum where J is the quantum number of the lower level of the transition.

† Note that rotational spectroscopic constants are expressed in this book in cycles per second unless otherwise mentioned. Herzberg's constants are in cm^{-1}.

No satisfactory method of calculating the distortion constants from vibrational force constants and moments of inertia, comparable with that for diatomic molecules, is available for symmetric tops. An attempt in this direction has been made by Slawsky and Dennison,[38] but the values for D_J and D_{JK} which they predict for the methyl halides do not agree well with those determined from microwave spectroscopy.[34] For symmetric tops in which the center of gravity is far removed from the atoms which do not lie on the figure axis, D_J can be approximated [34] by Eq. 2.19, where ω is now the fundamental vibrational frequency for the mode in which the atoms move away from the center of gravity during half of a vibrational cycle. For example, the observed value of D_J for methyl acetylene is 3.12 kc as compared with 3.24 kc calculated from Eq. 2.19 if the fundamental frequency used is ω_5 (C—C stretching) = 926 cm^{-1}.[31]

Although no dependence of the inversion spectrum on the quantum numbers J and K is expected from the application of the selection rules for inversion ($\Delta J = 0$, $\Delta K = 0$) to Eq. 2.34, this is not true for NH_3 discussed in Sec. 2.4. It has been explained by Sheng, Barker, and Dennison [39] as an interaction of inversion with rotation.

The peak absorption coefficient of a rotational line of a symmetric-top molecule, if it is assumed that lines of different K are resolvable, is given approximately by

$$\alpha_{\text{Max}} = 1.93 \times 10^{-14} \frac{\nu^3 \mu^2 [(J+1)^2 - K^2]}{T^{5/2}(\Delta\nu)_1(J+1)^2} F_v$$

$$\times \sigma A^{1/2} g_I g_K e^{\left[-4.80 \times 10^{-5} \left(\frac{BJ(J+1) + (A-B)K^2}{T} \right) \right]} ; \quad (2.37a)$$

or, at room temperature the exponential term is near unity, and

$$(\alpha_{\text{Max}})_{T=300} \approx \frac{1.23 \times 10^{-20} \mu^2 \nu^3 \sigma g_I g_K A^{1/2} F_v}{(\Delta\nu)_1} \left[1 - \frac{K^2}{(J+1)^2} \right], \quad (2.37b)$$

where α_{Max}, $(\Delta\nu)_1$, F_v, μ, ν, and T have the same significance and units as defined for linear molecules in Eq. 2.28, A and B are the spectral constants defined above, and σ is the symmetry number. (See Sec. 4.5.) The statistical weight factors used here are

$$g_K = 1 \quad \text{for } K = 0$$

$$\quad (2.38)$$

$$g_K = 2 \quad \text{for } K \neq 0.$$

For molecules with a threefold axis of symmetry with one set of three identical "off-axis" nuclei having spins I (C_{3v} symmetry; examples, PF_3, CH_3Cl, CH_3CCH),[†]

$$\sigma = 3,$$

$$g_I = \frac{1}{3}\left[1 + \frac{2}{(2I + 1)^2}\right] \quad \begin{array}{l} \text{for } K \text{ divisible by 3, in-} \\ \text{cluding } K = 0; \end{array}$$

$$g_I = \frac{1}{3}\left[1 - \frac{1}{(2I + 1)^2}\right] \quad \text{for } K \text{ not divisible by 3.}$$

(2.39)

For molecules with two sets of three identical "off-axis" nuclei, with spins I_1 and I_2 (C_3 symmetry; example, CH_3CF_3),

$$\sigma = 3,$$

$$g_I = \frac{1}{3}\left[1 + \frac{2}{(2I_1 + 1)^2(2I_2 + 1)^2}\right] \quad \begin{array}{l} \text{for } K \text{ divisible by 3,} \\ \text{including } K = 0; \end{array}$$

$$g_I = \frac{1}{3}\left[1 - \frac{1}{(2I_1 + 1)^2(2I_2 + 1)^2}\right] \quad \text{for } K \text{ not divisible by 3.}$$

(2.40)

The K values to which the g_I values apply are for the ground vibrational state. Excited vibrational state assignments are given in Sec. 4.5.

The rotational spectrum of a symmetric-top molecule, if hyperfine structure and centrifugal distortions are neglected, is exactly like that of a linear molecule, i.e., it consists of a series of equally spaced lines originating at a frequency of $2B$ and progressing to higher frequencies with separations of $2B$. See Fig. 2.6 for a comparison with the spectrum of an asymmetric rotor. Furthermore, one of the effects of centrifugal distortion (second term on the right in Eq. 2.36) is to make the series converge slightly with increasing frequency just as for linear molecules. Since there are $J + 1$ values of K^2 for each J, the effect of the last term in Eq. 2.36 is to split every line of a given J into $J + 1$ closely spaced components which are frequently resolvable with a microwave spectrograph. For increasing values of K, the lines in each group are progressively further apart. Figure 2.7 shows the $J = 8 \rightarrow 9$ rotational transition of CF_3CCH in which the lines for $K = 3$ to $K = 8$ are completely resolved. Because of the selection rules for K, constants A and D_K cannot be evaluated from the rotational spectrum.

The rotational spectra of a large number of symmetric-top molecules have been investigated. These include related groups of B, C, Si, and

[†] Here g_I is the reduced value. See Art. 4.5b.

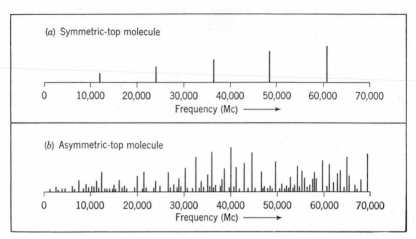

FIG. 2.6. Illustration of the general pattern of the microwave rotational spectra of symmetric- and asymmetric-top molecules. Centrifugal distortion splitting of the symmetric rotor is neglected. [From D. K. Coles, *Adv. in Elec.* II, 299 (1950).]

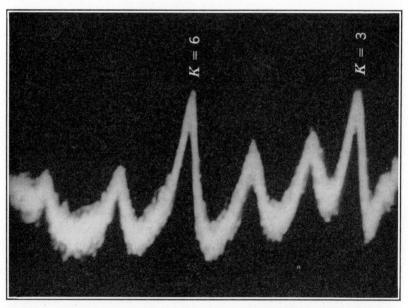

FIG. 2.7. Part of the $J = 8 \rightarrow 9$ rotational transition of CF_3CCH showing lines for $K = 3$ to 8. The lines of different K are separated by centrifugal distortion. [From Anderson, Trambarulo, Sheridan, and Gordy, *Phys. Rev. 82*, 58 (1951).]

Ge compounds, as well as compounds of N, P, As, and Sb. The information obtained is summarized in the various tables and is discussed in part in Chapters 6, 7, and 8.

Excited vibrational states. For a vibrating symmetric-top rotor, the spectroscopic constants A and B in Eq. 2.34 depend upon the vibrational state of the molecule as given by the expressions

$$A_{[v]} = A_e - \sum_i \alpha_i^A \left(v_i + \frac{d_i}{2} \right) \tag{2.41}$$

and

$$B_{[v]} = B_e - \sum_i \alpha_i^B \left(v_i + \frac{d_i}{2} \right), \tag{2.42}$$

where α_i^A and α_i^B are constants which are small in comparison with A and B. Quantum numbers v_i designate the vibrational state of the molecule, and d_i is the degeneracy of the ith mode of vibration. The summation runs over all modes of vibration with degenerate modes counted only once. A non-linear molecule containing n atoms has $3n - 6$ normal modes of vibration. Phosphorus trifluoride, for example, has six normal modes of vibration, two pairs of which are degenerate, making four fundamental frequencies and four values of α_i^A and of α_i^B in Eqs. 2.41 and 2.42. Because the selection rules do not allow quantum number K to change for a symmetric top, $A_{[v]}$ and A_e cannot be evaluated from pure rotational spectra.

The constant $B_{[0]}$ for the ground vibrational state is given by

$$B_{[0]} = B_e - \sum_i \frac{\alpha_i^B d_i}{2}. \tag{2.43}$$

To find B_e and the α_i^B's, it is necessary to know $B_{[0]}$ and at least as many values of $B_{[v]}$ as there are different normal modes of vibration with each mode excited at least once. Because of the low population of high-energy vibrational levels at ordinary temperatures, it is difficult to obtain all the α's and hence B_e.

A degenerate bending vibration which is singly excited contributes angular momentum components which couple with the angular momentum resulting from rotations of the molecule and gives rise to an interesting rotational spectrum. To explain the presence of four lines in the $J = 1 \rightarrow 2$ transition of CH_3NC and three lines (four lines with two unresolved) in the same transition of CH_3CN in the degenerate bending state for which $v_8 = 1$, H. H. Nielsen developed a general theory of l-type doubling in symmetric tops.[33] This theory has been applied successfully to interpret the rotational spectra of both CH_3CCH

and CF_3CCH in the vibrational state for which v_{10}(C—C≡C bending) = 1.[40, 41]

According to Nielsen's theory, the rotational energy of a symmetric top in a singly excited degenerate bending state is given by the formula [41a]

$$E_{JK} = h[B_{[v]}J(J + 1) + (A_{[v]} - B_{[v]})K^2 - 2A_{[v]}Kl\zeta$$

$$- D_JJ^2(J + 1)^2 - D_{JK}J(J + 1)K^2 - D_KK^4$$

$$+ 2\{(2D_J + D_{JK})J(J + 1) + (2D_K + D_{JK})K^2\}Kl\zeta$$

$$+ P(J, K, l)], \quad (2.44)$$

where

$$P = \pm\tfrac{1}{2}J(J + 1)q \quad (2.45)$$

for $K = l = \pm 1$, and

$$P = \pm \frac{\{J(J + 1) - K(K \mp 1)\}\{J(J + 1) - (K \mp 1)(K \mp 2)\}}{8(K \mp 1)\{(1 - \zeta)A_{[v]} - B_{[v]}\}} q^2$$

$$(2.46)$$

for $K \neq l = \pm 1$, and P small as compared with E_{JK}; the upper signs of Eq. 2.46 being taken when K and l have the same sign, the lower sign when K and l are of different signs. In addition to quantities already defined, $l\zeta h/2\pi$ is the angular momentum resulting from the excited degenerate vibration, with $0 \leq |\zeta| \leq 1$, q is of the order $2B_e^2/\omega$, and ω is the fundamental frequency for the degenerate vibration excited.

Selection rules resulting in a rotational spectrum are

$$\Delta J = +1 \qquad \Delta K = 0 \qquad \Delta l = 0, \quad (2.47)$$

and the frequencies of rotational transitions are

$$\nu = 2B_{[v]}(J + 1) - 4D_J(J + 1)^3 - 2D_{JK}(J + 1)K^2$$

$$+ 4(2D_J + D_{JK})(J + 1)Kl\zeta + \Delta P (J, K, l), \quad (2.48)$$

where

$$\Delta P = \pm q(J + 1) \quad (2.49)$$

for $K = l = \pm 1$, and

$$\Delta P = \pm \frac{(J + 1)\{(J + 1)^2 - (K \mp 1)^2\}}{4(K \mp 1)\{(1 - \zeta)A_{[v]} - B_{[v]}\}} q^2 \quad (2.50)$$

for $K \neq l = \pm 1$. Upper signs are taken when K and l have the same sign, and the lower signs hold when K and l have different signs. The spectrum consists of two widely spaced lines corresponding to $K = l = \pm 1$ and separated by $2q(J + 1)$. Approximately midway between these two lines lie $2J$ lines, closely but somewhat irregularly spaced.

Figure 2.8 shows diagrammatically the $J = 1 \rightarrow 2$ and $J = 2 \rightarrow 3$ transitions of CH_3CCH in the excited bending state for which $v_{10} = 1$. Although the form of Eq. 2.48 fits the data for the examples cited, abnormally large ζ values, 1.1 for CH_3CCH and 1.5 for CF_3CCH, must be assumed, but theoretically $|\zeta| < 1$.

It has been shown by Mizushima and Venkateswarlu [41b] that rotational transitions not possible in the ground vibrational state become

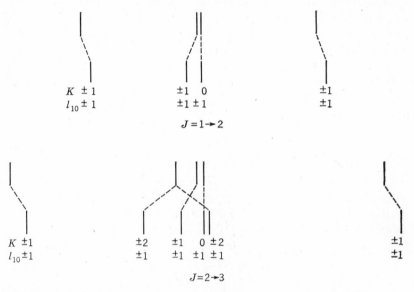

FIG. 2.8. $J = 1 \rightarrow 2$ and $2 \rightarrow 3$, $v_{10} = 1$ rotational transitions of CH_3CCH (lower patterns of each set). Outer lines of each spectrum are separated by $2q(J + 1)$. The upper patterns show the spectrum which would result if the distortion term, $4(2D_J + D_{JK})(J + 1)K\zeta l$, were not present. (From Trambarulo and Gordy.[40])

possible in some excited states of molecules of certain symmetries. The lines are expected to be weak, however, and no such absorption has yet been detected. Nevertheless, the possibility of the study of non-polar molecules with microwave spectroscopy is attractive, and it seems likely that with the sensitive spectrographs now available such spectra will be observed in the future.

Torsional oscillations and restricted internal rotations. Symmetric-top molecules which have two axially symmetric groups, for example, CH_3SiH_3 or CH_3CF_3, have the possibility of either a low-frequency torsional oscillation or a restricted internal rotation of one of the groups with respect to the other. Restricted internal rotation in this type of molecule cannot be detected directly as an absorption spectrum because the motion carries with it no change in the dipole moment. Nevertheless it can be detected indirectly through its effects on I_b. It was pointed out by Minden, Mays, and Dailey [42] that the effects on I_b of a torsional oscillation could arise from a change in the interaction of the symmetrical groups as the atoms deviate from their equilibrium positions. In addition, effects of centrifugal distortion resulting from the internal rotation could change I_b, just as does the normal rotation of the symmetric top about the figure axis. In most cases that have been studied so far, the barrier restricting rotation has been so high that the effects of torsional oscillation have been observed rather than relatively free rotation, although evidence for restricted internal rotation in CH_3SiH_3 has been found by Lide and Coles.[43]

The theory of torsional oscillation has been worked out by H. H. Nielsen [44] and by Koehler and Dennison.[45] The potential-energy function usually assumed is of the form

$$V = \frac{V_0}{2}(1 - \cos n\phi), \qquad (2.51)$$

where V_0 is the height of the barrier opposing rotation, n is the number of barriers for one complete cycle, and ϕ is the relative angle of rotation of the two groups. With this type of potential, the barrier height, V_0, in terms of the fundamental torsional oscillation frequency, ω_t, is

$$V_0 = \frac{\omega_t^2}{n^2} \frac{A}{A_1 A_2}, \qquad (2.52)$$

where A is the rotational constant associated with the total moment of inertia about the symmetry axis ($A = h/8\pi^2 I_a$), and A_1 and A_2 are the corresponding constants for the two separate parts. When the barrier height is low, the corresponding ω_t is low and hence difficult to measure in the infrared region. By measuring the intensities of the rotational lines for the excited torsional oscillation relative to that of

Table 2.1. **Torsional frequencies and barrier heights of some symmetric tops having hindered internal rotation**

Molecule	ω_t (cm^{-1})	V_0 (cm^{-1})	Ref.
CH_3CF_3	230	1200	46
CH_3SiH_3	183	460 †	43
CH_3SiF_3	140	410	42, 47
CF_3SF_5	93.5	219	46b

† Calculated using the double parabola potential of Blade and Kimball, *J. Chem. Phys.* **18**, 630 (1950).

the ground vibration state, one can obtain from the Boltzmann distribution of energies an approximate value for ω_t and hence can calculate V_0 from Eq. 2.52. By this method the barrier heights for the molecules given in Table 2.1 have been obtained from microwave spectroscopy.

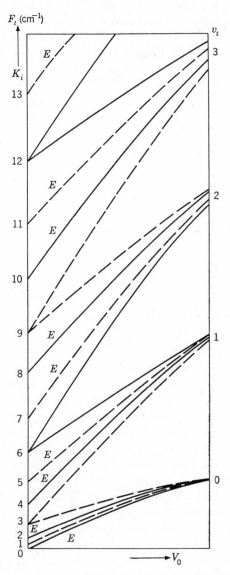

FIG. 2.9. Correlation between free rotation and torsional oscillation for C_2H_6. Solid curves refer to even, and broken curves to odd K values. (From Herzberg.[31])

A splitting of the torsional oscillation levels into sub-levels results from the atoms "tunneling through" the barriers. This splitting is larger the higher the vibrational level is, as the "tunneling frequency" is then greater. The effect is very similar to that which gives rise to the NH_3 inversion spectrum, except that there are, in general, more than two sub-levels of the torsional levels because there is more than one barrier. Evidence for these sub-levels has been found in CH_3SiH_3 by Lide and Coles [43] and in CH_3SiF_3 by Sheridan and Gordy.[47] As the

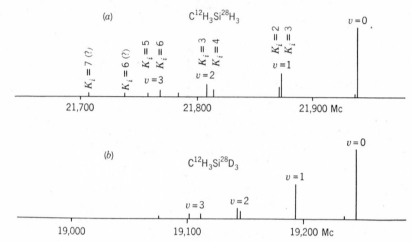

Fig. 2.10. Microwave spectrum ($J = 0 \rightarrow 1$ transition), showing evidence for torsional oscillation and restricted internal rotation in methyl silane. (From Lide and Coles.[43])

torsional vibrational levels approach the top of the barrier the splitting gets wider and goes over into restricted internal rotational levels after the barrier is transcended. This is illustrated by Fig. 2.9 for C_2H_6 which is reproduced from Herzberg,[48] and by the microwave data on CH_3SiH_3 and CH_3SiD_3 by Lide and Coles in Fig. 2.10. Such molecules as $CH_3-C\equiv C-CF_3$, not yet investigated, should prove of interest because internal rotation in them is probably less hindered than in the ones discussed here.

2.2d. Asymmetric-Top Molecules. The rigid asymmetric rotor ($I_a \neq I_b \neq I_c$) has now been treated by a number of scholars. For references to the various treatments and for a summary of the theoretical methods employed the reader should consult the review by Nielsen.[49]

The solutions are considerably more involved than are those for linear and symmetric-top molecules. They can be expressed in closed form for low-J values only. Except for specialized types of molecules, the solutions obtained apply only to J up to 12 for the rigid rotor [50] and to J up to 6 when centrifugal effects are included.[49] These solutions are given in the form of algebraic equations which increase in degree as J increases. Hence, it is possible to obtain from them explicit expressions for the levels for certain low-J values only. These expressions are, nevertheless, very useful to the microwave spectroscopist because in many cases one or more of the low-J transitions fall in the microwave region. From them alone a determination of the structure and the dipole moment of very many molecules is possible. Also, the large centrifugal distortion effects, which are in general very difficult to determine for the higher values, can usually be calculated or neglected for the low-J transitions.

Energy levels. There are $2J + 1$ sub-levels for each J of an asymmetric top. These are labeled J_τ where τ takes on the $2J + 1$ values $-J \leq \tau \leq J$, or alternately J_{K_{-1}, K_1}. See discussion below. The sub-levels are numbered in order of increasing energy, the lowest level being J_{-J}, the next J_{-J+1}, and so on to the highest level J_{+J}.

An insight into the general behavior of the characteristic rotational energies E_r can be gained from a graph of the solutions for $J = 0, 1, 2,$ and 3, plotted in Fig. 2.11 for the specific cases

(a) $A = 3$ $B = 3$ $C = 1$ $(\kappa = +1)$

(b) $A = 3$ $B = 2$ $C = 1$ $(\kappa = 0)$

(c) $A = 3$ $B = 1$ $C = 1$ $(\kappa = -1)$,

where κ is an asymmetry parameter defined by Eq. 2.55. It is seen that cases a and c correspond to the limiting oblate and prolate symmetric tops. Case b corresponds to $\kappa = 0$, which is conventionally referred to as the "most asymmetric top."

In Fig. 2.11, the energy levels for the three cases plotted are connected together in such a manner that the lowest sub-levels in each J group are connected, and immediately above them the next lowest levels are connected, and so on in order to the highest levels. Consequently, as κ is continuously varied from -1 to $+1$ the energy levels maintain their ordered sequence; there is no crossing of sub-levels for a given J. (Some of the sub-levels of one J group may cross sub-levels of another J group, however, as is the case in this example for the lower $J = 3$ and upper $J = 2$ sub-levels near the prolate rotor limit.) The non-crossing of J sub-levels is a general phenomenon, extending to all values of J. The straight lines drawn are approximations to the real E_r for intermediate values of κ. There must be $2J + 1$ of these non-intersecting lines, two from each symmetric-top level where $K \neq 0$.

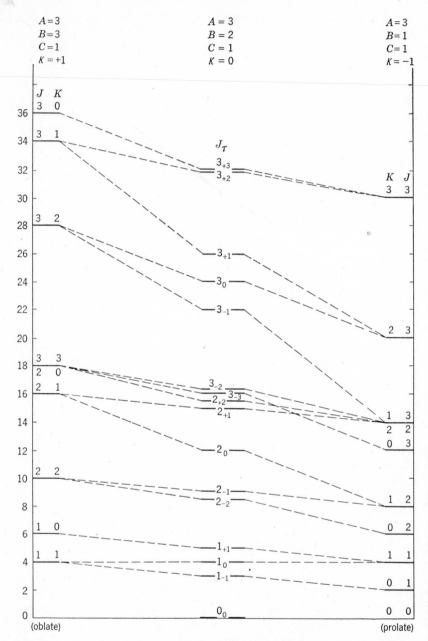

FIG. 2.11. Correlation of energy levels of an asymmetric rotor with those of the limiting symmetric tops.

It is to be noted that a given asymmetric-top level is connected to one limiting prolate K level (denoted by K_{-1}), and, in general, to a different oblate K level (denoted by K_1). This correspondence is unique, so that the sub-levels can be identified in terms of these limiting K values as subscripts, in the order listed. As an example, the 3_{-1} level can also be written $3_{1,\,2}$. It may further be shown that in general

$$\tau = K_{-1} - K_1. \tag{2.53}$$

The purpose in introducing this alternative nomenclature, proposed by King, Hainer, and Cross,[51] will become more apparent after consideration of the symmetry properties of the different sub-levels, and the resulting selection rules for dipole radiation. As this book goes to press, the alter-

Table 2.2. Asymmetric-top energy levels

(a) Exact solutions for E_r which are roots of linear or quadratic secular equations

$J_{K_{-1},\,K_1}$	Energy, E_r
0_{00}	0
1_{10}	$A + B$
1_{11}	$A + C$
1_{01}	$B + C$
2_{20}	$2A + 2B + 2C + 2\sqrt{(B-C)^2 + (A-C)(A-B)}$
2_{21}	$4A + B + C$
2_{11}	$A + 4B + C$
2_{12}	$A + B + 4C$
2_{02}	$2A + 2B + 2C - 2\sqrt{(B-C)^2 + (A-C)(A-B)}$
3_{30}	$5A + 5B + 2C + 2\sqrt{4(A-B)^2 + (A-C)(B-C)}$
3_{31}	$5A + 2B + 5C + 2\sqrt{4(A-C)^2 - (A-B)(B-C)}$
3_{21}	$2A + 5B + 5C + 2\sqrt{4(B-C)^2 + (A-B)(A-C)}$
3_{22}	$4A + 4B + 4C$
3_{12}	$5A + 5B + 2C - 2\sqrt{4(A-B)^2 + (A-C)(B-C)}$
3_{13}	$5A + 2B + 5C - 2\sqrt{4(A-C)^2 - (A-B)(B-C)}$
3_{03}	$2A + 5B + 5C - 2\sqrt{4(B-C)^2 + (A-B)(A-C)}$
4_{41}	$10A + 5B + 5C + 2\sqrt{4(B-C)^2 + 9(A-C)(A-B)}$
4_{31}	$5A + 10B + 5C + 2\sqrt{4(A-C)^2 - 9(A-B)(B-C)}$
4_{32}	$5A + 5B + 10C + 2\sqrt{4(A-B)^2 + 9(A-C)(B-C)}$
4_{23}	$10A + 5B + 5C - 2\sqrt{4(B-C)^2 + 9(A-C)(A-B)}$
4_{13}	$5A + 10B + 5C - 2\sqrt{4(A-C)^2 - 9(A-B)(B-C)}$
4_{14}	$5A + 5B + 10C - 2\sqrt{4(A-B)^2 + 9(A-C)(B-C)}$
5_{42}	$10A + 10B + 10C + 6\sqrt{(B-C)^2 + (A-B)(A-C)}$
5_{24}	$10A + 10B + 10C - 6\sqrt{(B-C)^2 + (A-B)(A-C)}$

Table 2.2. Asymmetric-top energy levels (*Continued*)

(*b*) Exact solutions for $E(\kappa)$ which are roots of cubic secular equations (from Hainer, Cross, and King, reference 56)

$$E\,(\kappa) = x - p(\kappa)$$

$$x = \mp(8/3)a(\kappa)^{1/2}\cos[(\phi/3) + 120°\,n]$$

$$\cos\phi = |\,b(\kappa)\,|a(\kappa)^{-3/2}$$

The upper sign is used in the equation for x if $b(\kappa)$ is negative, the lower if it is positive. Three roots are obtained for $n = 0$, 1, and 2. The levels are identified by the indices K_{-1} and K_1 which are obtained in two steps. Their parity is defined by the submatrix giving the secular equations, and is given in column 2. The numerical assignment is made by noting that the three roots of any one secular equation can be arranged in magnitude in the same order as their K_{-1} values, which are all different.

J	$K_{-1}K_1$	$b(\kappa)$	$a(\kappa)$	$p(\kappa)$
4	ee	$35\kappa(\kappa^2 - 9)$	$13(\kappa^2 + 3)$	$-20\kappa/3$
5	oo	$-5\kappa(7\kappa^2 - 135)$	$13\kappa^2 + 99$	$-20\kappa/3$
5	oe	$-5(16\kappa^3 \pm 9\kappa^2 - 108\kappa \pm 27)$	$2(14\kappa^2 \mp 15\kappa + 27)$	$-(35\kappa \pm 15)/3$
	eo		ditto, lower sign	
6	oo	$\kappa(143\kappa^2 - 783)$	$7(7\kappa^2 + 9)$	$-56\kappa/3$
6	oe	$80\kappa^3 \mp 63\kappa^2 - 972\kappa \mp 189$	$14(2\kappa^2 \mp 3\kappa + 9)$	$-(35\kappa \mp 21)/3,$
	eo		ditto, lower sign	
7	ee	$143\kappa(\kappa^2 - 9)$	$49(\kappa^2 + 3)$	$-56\kappa/3$

native and simpler labeling $J_{a,\,c}$ for $J_{K_{-1},\,K_1}$ has been recommended by Mulliken.†

Mention has been made of the fact that for certain low-J values the solutions for the energies of an asymmetric rotor can be expressed in closed form. Specific formulas for the energies of these levels in terms of A, B, and C are given in Table 2.2(*a*). The levels are designated according to the King-Hainer-Cross notation $J_{K_{-1},\,K_1}$ as explained above. These formulas, like the numerical solutions mentioned below, are for the rigid rotor. A discussion of centrifugal distortion is given under a separate heading.

King, Hainer, and Cross, following Ray,[52] express the characteristic energies $E_{J\tau}$ in the form

$$E_{J\tau} = \frac{(A + C)}{2}J(J + 1) + \frac{(A - C)}{2}E_\tau{}^J(\kappa). \tag{2.54}$$

This form is very useful in tabulating numerical values since, as shown by Ray, $E_\tau{}^J(\kappa) = -E_{-\tau}{}^J(-\kappa)$, and hence values for only one sign of κ

† Private communication.

need to be tabulated. In this expression κ is Ray's asymmetric parameter defined as

$$\kappa = \frac{2B - A - C}{A - C} \qquad (2.55)$$

and $E(\kappa)$ is termed the reduced energy. Values for $E(\kappa)$ are tabulated by King, Hainer, and Cross [51,53] for κ values differing by 0.1 and for J values up to 12. Although the κ intervals are in general too large to allow full use of the accuracy of microwave measurements, the tables are extremely useful in the identification of transitions and in many instances can be interpolated to obtain useful accuracy. Exact solutions for $E(\kappa)$ of a few levels are given in Table 2.2(b).

The energy levels of asymmetric-top molecules near the prolate ($\kappa = -1$) and oblate ($\kappa = +1$) symmetric rotor limits may be calculated by treating the asymmetry as a small perturbation of the appropriate prolate or oblate symmetric rotor wave functions. King, Hainer, and Cross [51] have derived expressions for the energy levels in a power series in the asymmetry parameter δ where

$$\delta = \frac{\kappa + 1}{2} = \frac{B - C}{A - C}. \qquad (2.56)$$

Also, for planar molecules, $\delta = B^2/A^2$. The expansion is directly applicable to almost-prolate rotors for which $\delta \approx 0$. The prolate rotor limit is most obviously treated by this approach, but the oblate limit [51] is also covered since

$$E_\tau{}^J(\kappa) = -E_{-\tau}{}^J(-\kappa) \qquad \text{or} \qquad E(\delta) = -E(1 - \delta). \qquad (2.57)$$

The values of $E(\kappa)$, expanded in terms of δ rather than κ, are

$$E(\kappa) = E(\delta) = \lambda_0 + \delta\lambda_1 + \delta^2\lambda_2 + \delta^3\lambda_3 + \cdots. \qquad (2.58)$$

The coefficients λ are tabulated by King, Hainer, and Cross.[51,53] The limiting case approaching the most asymmetric top ($\kappa \approx 0$) has also been solved by King, Hainer, and Cross [51,53] by expanding $E(\kappa)$ in a power series in κ similar to Eq. 2.58.

In the limit of a symmetric top, for high K, the classical motion of the top is a good first approximation to the quantum mechanical picture, so that the problem can be solved by the correspondence principle. Correspondence-principle solutions have been treated by Wang,[54] King,[55] and Hainer, Cross, and King.[56] King gives tables of the elliptic integral of the third kind that can be used for more asymmetric cases. Hainer, Cross, and King give numerical tables. They also compare the various approaches to the high-J case.

Many transitions of heavy asymmetric-top molecules are observable in the microwave region essentially because of K splitting. For these, the correspondence-principle approach is unsatisfactory. Fortunately, the limit of low K, high J, is also amenable to a perturbation treatment. Golden [57] has shown that the asymmetric-top solutions can be correlated with tabulated solutions of Mathieu's equation, providing J is large and the K of the appropriate limiting symmetric rotor is small. Accurate solutions require corrections for centrifugal distortion, which can amount to hundreds of megacycles. Golden has also treated the general high-J, low-K centrifugal distortion case.[57] The main effect is to distort the angles in the molecule, hence causing the parameter of asymmetry to vary with rotational level.

The terminology involved in expressing the solution of Mathieu's equation in a form satisfactory for both prolate and oblate symmetric-top limits necessitates reference to the original papers. A first approximation to the solution by the expansion of Mathieu's equation, expressed in a form appropriate near the limit of the prolate rotor and specialized to Q-branch transitions ($\Delta J = 0$), is

$$\nu(\theta) = \frac{A - C}{2} (2 - \delta)[\alpha(\theta) - \alpha'(\theta)], \qquad (2.59)$$

where $\nu(\theta)$ is the spectral line frequency,

$$\theta = \frac{J(J + 1)}{2} \frac{\delta}{2 - \delta}, \qquad (2.60)$$

and $\alpha(\theta)$, $\alpha'(\theta)$ are the appropriate solutions of Mathieu's equation. In Ince's notation,[58] these solutions are labeled a_0, b_1, a_1, b_2, a_2, b_3, a_3 $\cdots$ and are to be identified with $K_{-1} = 0, 1, 1, 2, 2, 3, 3 \cdots$. The importance of this method of solution may be judged from the fact that it has yielded the first microwave solutions of such molecules as formaldehyde [59] and SO_2,[60] and subsequent low-J solutions essentially served as confirmations of the high-J solutions.

Centrifugal distortion. Although the problem of centrifugal distortion is much more difficult in asymmetric rotors than in symmetric tops or in linear molecules, these distortion effects upon the microwave spectra of asymmetric rotors can be rather large, especially when any of the moments of inertia of the molecules are very small. For example, in the $12_{6,\,7} \to 12_{6,\,6}$ transition [61] at 28,842.84 Mc of HDS, an extremely light asymmetric rotor, the correction for centrifugal distortion amounts to 1008.25 Mc. This is a rather exceptional case, however; the correction amounts to only about 100 Mc for very low-J transitions of this molecule.

Wilson and Howard,[62] Nielsen,[49, 63] and others have developed theory which allows centrifugal distortion constants of asymmetric rotors to be evaluated. Nielsen gives explicit but rather cumbersome expressions for calculation of the distortion constants from the vibrational frequencies and the structural parameters.

For slightly asymmetric tops ($\kappa \approx \pm 1$) the centrifugal terms can be closely approximated by comparison with the limiting symmetric-top case. The frequencies of $\Delta J = +1$ transitions (R branch) for which $\Delta K_{-1} = 0$ or $\Delta K_1 = 0$ are hence given approximately by

$$\nu = 2(J + 1)\left(\frac{A + C}{2}\right) + \left(\frac{A - C}{2}\right)[E^{J+1}(\kappa) - E^J(\kappa)]$$
$$-4D_J(J + 1)^3 - 2D_{JK}(J + 1)K^2, \quad (2.61)$$

where K represents K_{-1} for a $\Delta K_{-1} = 0$ transition of a nearly prolate top and $K = K_1$ for a $\Delta K_1 = 0$ transition of a nearly oblate top. Compare with Eq. 2.36 for a symmetric top.

Hillger and Strandberg [61] have developed a perturbation method of calculating centrifugal distortion corrections for $\Delta J = 0$ transitions (Q branch) which involve a dipole moment either wholly along the axis of least moment of inertia ($\Delta K_{-1} = 0$) or along the axis of greatest moment of inertia ($\Delta K_1 = 0$). The method applies to any value of κ. The frequency of such a transition is given by

$$\nu = \Delta E^J(\kappa) \left[\frac{A - C}{2} + \frac{2KJ(J + 1)\delta_J}{H} \right.$$
$$+ \frac{(K - 1)J(J + 1)D_{JK}}{G - F} + \frac{2}{3}K(K^2 + 2)\left[\frac{D_K}{G - F} - \frac{2R_5}{H}\right] \cdots$$
$$+ \left[\frac{16R_6(G - F)}{H^2} - \frac{4D_K}{(G - F)}\right] \text{ for } K \text{ even}$$
$$+ \left[\frac{64R_6(G - F)}{H^2}\right] \text{ for } K \text{ odd and } \geq 3$$
$$- \left.\left[\frac{2D_K}{(G - F)}\right] \text{ for } K \text{ odd} \right] . \quad (2.62)$$

In Eq. 2.62 $\Delta E^J(\kappa)$ is the difference between the reduced energy levels; D_J, D_{JK}, D_K, δ_J, R_5, and R_6 are centrifugal distortion constants ; †

† Our notation differs from that of Hillger and Strandberg in that our distortion constants have the units of A and C, but those of Hillger and Strandberg are dimensionless.

and K has the same meaning as in Eq. 2.61. The quantities $(G - F)$ and H have the following values: for a $\Delta K_{-1} = 0$ transition, $(G - F) = -\frac{1}{2}(\kappa - 3)$ and $H = -\frac{1}{2}(\kappa + 1)$; for a $\Delta K_1 = 0$ transition, $(G - F) = -\frac{1}{2}(\kappa + 3)$ and $H = \frac{1}{2}(\kappa - 1)$. Equation 2.62 holds only in the region for which

$$\frac{H^2[J(J + 1) - (K - 1)(K - 2)][J(J + 1) - K(K - 1)]}{64(G - F)^2(K - 1)^2} \ll 1. \quad (2.63)$$

Even for a rather asymmetric molecule such as HDS ($\kappa \approx -0.5$) for which the above theory was primarily developed by Hillger and Strandberg, the above condition holds for all the transitions observed in the microwave region ranging from low-J, low-K to high-J, high-K transitions except for the $1_{1,\,1} \rightarrow 1_{1,\,0}$ transition which, nevertheless, appears to fit the theory as well as the other lines.

A fitting of the above equations to a spectrum allows the empirical determination of the distortion constants if a sufficient number of transitions lie in the microwave region. Since the observable spectra of asymmetric tops vary greatly from one molecule to another, no general rules can be stated for the process of fitting the equations to the spectra. See, however, references 61, 64, and 66. Only for a few asymmetric-top molecules—formaldehyde,[59, 64] hydrogen deuterium sulfide,[61] partially deuterated ammonias,[65] and ketene [66]—have centrifugal distortions been taken into account. For formaldehyde, Bragg and Sharbaugh [59] corrected for these effects by a method of Golden,[67] applicable for high-J transitions near the correspondence-principle limit. Their results were found to be in good agreement with those of Lawrance and Strandberg,[64] who used essentially the method given above.

In the case of HDS, distortion constants determined from the microwave rotational lines have been compared with those calculated from vibrational spectra with the theoretical expressions given by Nielsen.[68] Rather good agreement was obtained.

Selection rules and line strengths. The selection rule (see Sec. 4.4)

$$\Delta J = 0, \pm 1 \quad (2.64)$$

applies to asymmetric rotors. Since sub-levels of different J's sometimes cross in asymmetric rotors, all three changes in J may be observable in absorption spectra. In band-spectra notation, $\Delta J = 0, +1$, and -1 correspond to Q, R, and P branches, respectively.

Further restrictions are imposed by the symmetry properties of the momental ellipsoid. The momental ellipsoid is unchanged by a rotation of π about any of the principal axes; thus the probability density ψ^2 is similarly unchanged. The wave function ψ itself, however, can either remain unchanged (even $\equiv e$) or change signs (odd $\equiv o$). Since a rotation of π about any two of the axes in succession is equivalent to a rotation about the third, ψ must either be odd with respect to two axes and even with respect to the third (type B), or even with respect to all three axes (type A).† There are, thus, four different species of functions. The B wave functions are further subdivided by subscripts denoting the axis with respect to which they are even. A B_b wave function is unchanged in sign by a π rotation about axis b, and changed in sign by a π rotation about a and about c. In the King-Hainer-Cross formulation the parity is described with respect to the a and c axes in that order. With this convention, B_b is oo; B_a is eo; B_c is oe; A is ee. In the J_{K_{-1}, K_1} notation of King, Hainer, and Cross,[51] the parity of the J subscripts ‡ indicates the parity of the levels, i.e., $J_{3,2}$ is oe, and hence a $J_{3,2}$ level is symmetric with respect to a π rotation about the c axis and anti-symmetric with respect to such a rotation about the a or b axis. The symmetry with respect to b, not indicated explicitly, is obtained by adding K_{-1} and K_1. If the sum is an odd integer, the wave function is odd with respect to a π rotation about b; if an even integer, it is even.

Dennison,[35b] who first derived the symmetry selection rules for an asymmetric rotor, designated the parity of the rotational wave functions as $+$ or $-$ with respect to a rotation of π degrees about a principal axis. He designated the four different species as $++$, $-+$, $+-$, and $--$. Unfortunately, Dennison [35b] and King, Hainer, and Cross [51] did not indicate the rotational operations in the same order. In Dennison's notation the operation with respect to the c axis is indicated by the first sign and the operation with respect to the a axis by the second. Hence, confusingly, a $+-$ parity is equivalent in the King-Hainer-Cross terminology to an oe and not to an eo, as the signs seem to indicate. We shall adopt the notation of King, Hainer, and Cross.[51]

Dennison [35b] also showed that the lowest sub-level of a given J (the J_{-J} level) is even with respect to a rotation of π degrees about the a axis ($C_2{}^a$ operation), that the next two higher ones are odd, the next two even, and so on. He showed further that the highest sub-level of a given J is even with respect to a rotation of π degrees about the c axis ($C_2{}^c$ operation), that the next two lower ones are odd, the next two even, and so on. These sequences can be deduced from a consideration of the parities of the symmetric-top levels from which the asymmetric-top levels emerge. The energy of the sub-levels of a given J increase with

---

† Mulliken's notation.[69]

‡ An even subscript corresponds to an even function with respect to a π rotation about the appropriate axis, and an odd subscript to an odd function.

K for the prolate top. Therefore, the K_{-1} subscript is zero (parity even) for the lowest sub-level of a given J, and the K_1 subscript is zero (even parity) for the highest sub-level of a given J. It will be recalled that two asymmetric rotor levels emerge out of each non-zero value of K (K splitting). Hence, the next two levels above the lowest have $K_{-1} = 1$ (odd parity), the two above these have $K_{-1} = 2$ (even parity), and so on. Furthermore, the two sub-levels immediately under the highest have $K_1 = 1$ (odd parity), the next lowest $K_1 = 2$ (even parity), and so on. These properties will be obvious from a consideration of Fig. 2.11. Note that the K sub-levels of the oblate top are inverted with respect to those of the prolate top.

For the probability of an induced transition between two states J_{K_{-1}, K_1} and $J'_{K'_{-1}, K'_1}$ not to be zero, the dipole matrix elements $(J_{K_{-1}, K_1} | \boldsymbol{\mu} | J'_{K'_{-1}, K'_1})$ must not all vanish. (See Sec. 4.4.) But an integral of this form, if real and finite, must have the same value for all operations which change the system into an indistinguishable one; it cannot change signs for a rotation of π degrees about any one of the principal axes. Hence, if real, it must have an even number of odd symmetries with respect to the operations $C_2{}^a$, $C_2{}^b$, and $C_2{}^c$. Now the dipole moment components have B symmetries with respect to these operations. For a rotation of π degrees about a, $\boldsymbol{\mu}_a$ does not change, but it changes in sign for a rotation about b or c. It therefore has B_a, or eo symmetry. Similarly, $\boldsymbol{\mu}_b$, which does not change for the $C_2{}^b$ operation but changes in sign for the $C_2{}^a$ or $C_2{}^c$ operations, has B_b, or oo, symmetry. For similar reasons, $\boldsymbol{\mu}_c$ has B_c, or oe, symmetry. Considering the symmetry of $\boldsymbol{\mu}_a$, eo, it is apparent that for $(J_{K_{-1}, K_1} | \boldsymbol{\mu}_a | J'_{K'_{-1}, K'_1})$ to have an even number of odd symmetries, K_{-1} and K'_{-1} must both be even or both be odd. (Hence, $\Delta K_{-1} = 0, \pm 2 \cdots$.) Also, either K_1 or K'_1 must be odd but not both odd. (Hence, $\Delta K_1 = \pm 1, \pm 3 \cdots$.) Considering the symmetries of $\boldsymbol{\mu}_b$ and $\boldsymbol{\mu}_c$, the other symmetry selection rules listed in Table 2.3 are similarly proved. Note that the permitted

Table 2.3.   Selection rules for K_{-1} and K_1 †, ‡

Dipole Component	ΔK_{-1}	ΔK_1
$\boldsymbol{\mu}_a$	$0, \pm 2 \cdots$	$\pm 1, \pm 3 \cdots$
$\boldsymbol{\mu}_b$	$\pm 1, \pm 3 \cdots$	$\pm 1, \pm 3 \cdots$
$\boldsymbol{\mu}_c$	$\pm 1, \pm 3 \cdots$	$0, \pm 2 \cdots$

† Note that changes in $(K_{-1} + K_1)$ are limited by the selection rules in Table 2.4.

‡ In general, transitions for which ΔK_{-1} or ΔK_1 is large have very low intensities.

transitions corresponding to any one dipole component are forbidden for the two remaining components.

Stated in the King-Hainer-Cross notation, the allowed parity changes corresponding to the different dipole moment components are:

Dipole Component	Permitted Transitions
μ_a (Component along axis of least moment of inertia)	$\begin{cases} ee \leftrightarrow eo \\ oe \leftrightarrow oo \end{cases}$
μ_b (Component along axis of intermediate moment of inertia)	$\begin{cases} ee \leftrightarrow oo \\ oe \leftrightarrow eo \end{cases}$
μ_c (Component along axis of greatest moment of inertia)	$\begin{cases} ee \leftrightarrow oe \\ eo \leftrightarrow oo \end{cases}$

If the dipole moment lies entirely along one of the principal axes, it will have no components along the other two axes, and hence only the transitions corresponding to the non-zero component will be allowed. For example, if $\mu_a \neq 0$, but $\mu_b = 0$ and $\mu_c = 0$, the only parity changes allowed are $ee \leftrightarrow eo$ and $oe \leftrightarrow oo$. If none of the dipole components is zero, all the changes listed above are allowed. The only combinations then forbidden are those which have the same symmetry, i.e.,

$$ee \nleftrightarrow ee \qquad eo \nleftrightarrow eo$$

$$oe \nleftrightarrow oe \qquad oo \nleftrightarrow oo.$$

The expression of the symmetry selection rules in terms of the Dennison or the Mulliken notation will be obvious.

The symmetry selection rules have a particularly important consequence for Q-branch ($\Delta J = 0$) transitions. If the dipole moment is along the axis of the intermediate moment of inertia, the b axis, no transitions are permitted between adjacent energy levels, whereas, if the moment is along the a or the c axis, transitions are permitted between alternate pairs of adjacent levels. The magnitudes of the inertial constants are such that, in the former case, only a few low-J Q-branch transitions are observable in the microwave region, whereas, in the latter cases, both high- and low-J transitions are possible. Thus the general composition of the microwave spectrum depends strongly on the direction of the dipole moment.

In addition to the symmetry rules just stated, there is a relation between K_{-1} and K_1 arising from the manner in which these subscripts are chosen. See Fig. 2.11. The usual way of stating this relation is as follows: [70] The sum of K_{-1} and K_1 for any sub-level is equal to J for levels for which $J + \tau$ is even, and to $J + 1$ for levels for which $J + \tau$ is odd. This consideration, which may be easily verified by examining Fig. 2.11, leads to a limitation on the possible values of $\Delta(K_{-1} + K_1)$ given in Table 2.4. It is to be noted that the sum rule is automatically satisfied

Table 2.4. Allowed changes in $(K_{-1} + K_1)$

$J + \tau$	$P\ (\Delta J = -1)$	$Q\ (\Delta J = 0)$	$R\ (\Delta J = 1)$
Even	$-1, 0$	$0, 1$	$1, 2$
Odd	$-1, -2$	$0, -1$	$1, 0$

in the labeling of the levels, so that the usefulness of the rule consists in predicting possible final levels from a known initial level.

The total (coordinate) wave function of an asymmetric-top molecule, like that for a linear or a symmetric-top molecule, can be even or odd with respect to inversion, i.e., a reflection of all its particles at the origin. Only even and odd levels with this classification can combine. Except for levels of planar molecules in which the "inversion" can be accomplished by rotation, each rotational level is actually double (inversion doubling); one component is even, and the other, odd. The selection rule based on this classification, i.e., that only levels of unlike parity can combine ($e \leftrightarrow o$, $e \not\leftrightarrow e$, $o \not\leftrightarrow o$), is not as useful as rules based on the symmetry properties of the momental ellipsoid.

The total eigenfunction can also be symmetric or antisymmetric with respect to an exchange of two identical nuclei. This follows from the fact that such an exchange does not affect the probability density ψ^2. With this classification, only levels of like parity combine (symmetric $\leftrightarrow$ symmetric, antisymmetric $\leftrightarrow$ antisymmetric). This classification, however, is of significance only for symmetric molecules in which exchange of the two identical nuclei can be accomplished by a rotation of the molecule about one of the principal axes. See Sec. 4.5.

In general, the transitions involving large ΔK values are extremely weak. Those which correspond to the permitted transitions in the limiting symmetric top $\Delta K = 0, \pm 1$ (for the dipole parallel and perpendicular to the symmetry axis) are the most significant, i.e., $\Delta K_{-1} = 0, \pm 1$ and $\Delta K_1 = 0, \pm 1$. If an asymmetric rotor is near the prolate symmetric type ($\kappa \approx -1$), transitions involving $\Delta K_{-1} = 0, \pm 1$ (or $\Delta K_{-1} = 0$ if the dipole lies wholly along the a axis) will be the only important ones, but those corresponding to larger changes in K_1 might have significant intensities. If it is near the oblate case ($\kappa \approx 1$), the transitions involving $\Delta K_1 = 0, \pm 1$ (or $\Delta K_1 = 0$ if the dipole lies wholly along the c axis) will be the only ones of significant strength, but transitions involving larger changes in K_{-1} might then be important. These qualitative intensity rules follow from the selection rules governing changes in K for the limiting symmetric top. Nearly prolate tops will be so far from the oblate extreme that the oblate-top selection rules ($\Delta K_1 = 0$ or ± 1) will be violated to some extent. Likewise, for a nearly oblate top the selection rules for the prolate extreme ($\Delta K_{-1} = 0$ or ± 1) will fail to hold rigidly. For the intermediate case (most asymmetric type) the intensities will be influenced strongly by the selection rules of both extremes but will not be dominated by either. Hence, for strongly asymmetric types, lines for both ΔK_{-1} and ΔK_1 of magnitude greater than 1 might be observed, but lines corresponding to changes in either subscript by any amount greater than 1 will be weak.

The peak absorption coefficient α of any asymmetric-top spectrum line is given approximately by

$$\alpha_{\text{Max}} = 3.85 \times 10^{-14} \frac{\nu^2 \mu^2 (\lambda_{J,\,\tau;\,J',\,\tau'})}{T^{5/2}(\Delta\nu)_1} F_v \sigma (ABC)^{1/2} g_I e^{-E_{J\tau}/kT},$$

(2.65)

where all the quantities except $\lambda_{J,\,\tau;\,J',\,\tau'}$, $E_{J\tau}$, and g_I are defined as in Eq. 2.28. The reduced nuclear weight g_I is unity for molecules possessing no symmetry. Other cases are discussed in Sec. 4.5. $E_{J\tau}$ is the rotational energy of the lower state involved in the transition. The quantity $\lambda_{J,\,\tau;\,J',\,\tau'}$ is the line strength tabulated by Cross, Hainer, and King.[70] These line strengths are tabulated for all permitted $J_{K_{-1},\,K_1} \rightarrow J'_{K'_{-1},\,K'_1}$ transitions for which $J \leq 12$, excepting "high-order forbidden" branches for which $|\Delta\tau| \geq 9$. Values of $\lambda_{J,\,\tau;\,J',\,\tau'}$ for $\kappa = -1, -0.5, 0, +0.5,$ and $+1$ are listed. They are generally slowly changing functions of κ for strong transitions ($\Delta K_{-1} = 0, \pm 1$ and $\Delta K_1 = 0, \pm 1$). If the transition is forbidden for either or both symmetric rotor limits, however, the line strengths decrease rapidly near the forbidden limit. A further discussion of intensities is given in Chapter 4.

Applications. Since the spectrum of an asymmetric top is, in general, quite complicated (see Fig. 2.6.), all possible auxiliary information should be utilized in making an analysis. A major help is the Stark effect (Chapter 3). To extract maximum information from this type of data, one must measure the frequency splittings and relative intensities of the Stark components to distinguish between Q- and P- or R-branch transitions. In general, a series of Q-branch transitions is most easily analyzed since these frequencies are functions of $A - C$ and δ (or κ) only. In a typical analysis, Cunningham, Boyd, Myers, Gwinn, and Le Van [71] identified with the Stark effect the three following Q-branch transitions

($\Delta J = 0$) for ethylene oxide: $\nu = 24{,}924$ Mc, $J = 2$; $\nu = 23{,}134$ Mc, $J = 3$; $\nu = 23{,}610$ Mc, $J = 3$. Approximate magnitudes of the term values showed that the only possible $J = 2$ Q-branch transition was $2_{02} \rightarrow 2_{11}$. The two $J = 3$ transitions possible were $3_{21} \rightarrow 3_{30}$ and

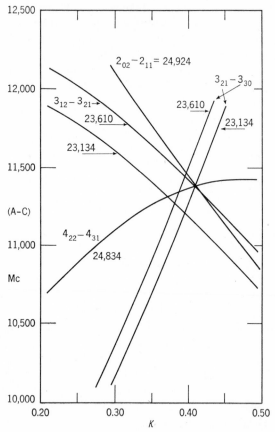

FIG. 2.12. Determination of κ and (A-C) for $C_2{}^{12}H_4O^{16}$, and demonstration of the basis of the assignment of the two known $3 \rightarrow 3$ lines as $23{,}610$ Mc $= 3_{12} \rightarrow 3_{21}$ and $23{,}134$ Mc $= 3_{21} \rightarrow 3_{30}$. (Cunningham, Boyd, Myers, Gwinn, and Le Van.[71])

$3_{12} \rightarrow 3_{21}$, but it was not known which should have the higher frequency. A simple solution was found by plotting values of κ and $A - C$ consistent with the observed frequencies for the known transition $2_{02} \rightarrow 2_{11}$, and for both possible identifications of the $J = 3$ transitions (Fig. 2.12). The correct identifications gave curves intersecting in a single point, thus determining κ and $A - C$. As a check, an identification of $4_{22} \rightarrow 4_{31} = 24{,}834$ Mc intersected the other curves in the same point. With approximate values for $A - C$ and κ thus established, an enlarged plot of the region of intersection yielded a more accurate value, and also revealed the presence of centrifugal distortions since the curves did not intersect at quite the same point. For practical

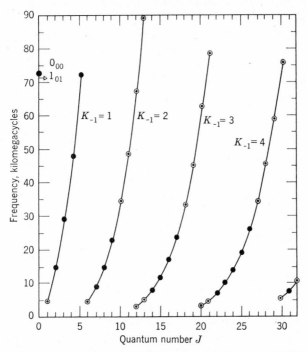

FIG. 2.13. The microwave absorption frequencies of $H_2C^{12}O$ as functions of J and K_{-1}. The solid circles represent the presently known spectrum. (From Lawrance and Strandberg.[64])

purposes, these distortions could be neglected, however. Once $A - C$ and κ were thus established, identification of any low-J, P, or R transition yielded $A + C$ and, hence, all the term values.

The general properties of slightly asymmetric-top molecules can be illustrated by the example of formaldehyde ($H_2C^{12}O$), a planar molecule investigated by Bragg and Sharbaugh [59] and Lawrance and Strandberg.[64] All the lines observed save the $J = 0 \rightarrow 1$ line correspond to $\Delta J = 0$, $\Delta K_{-1} = 0$ (Q-branch) transitions which are not observed in perfectly symmetric-top molecules. Plots of these lines are given in Fig. 2.13. The $J = 0 \rightarrow 1$ line is a $\Delta J = 1$, $\Delta K_{-1} = 0$ (R-branch) transition corresponding to the usual symmetric-top transition. Thus the introduction of a slight asymmetry into the molecule has resulted in a major change in the microwave spectrum inasmuch as all but one of the observed 18 lines would be missing for a perfect symmetric top. None the less, the asymmetry parameter δ is very small ($\delta < 0.02$).

The asymmetric-top theory is applicable to such molecules as $PCl^{35}Cl_2^{37}$ and PH_2D where deviations from the symmetric-top case arise from isotopic substitution. For the heavier isotopes, the K-splitting produced by such substitution gives rise to Q-branch transitions in the very long wavelength region which are unobservable by present techniques, although the splitting of R-branch transitions yields structural information.[72] The replacement of hydrogen by deuterium, however, frequently brings these Q-branch transitions into the observable region. This technique has been used by Loomis and Strandberg [73] to obtain a microwave confirmation of the spins of antimony isotopes and to obtain structural information on phosphine, arsine, and stibine. As the R-branch transitions (corresponding to the $\Delta J = 1$ symmetric-top transitions) occur at the extreme high-frequency end of the present microwave range, this deliberate introduction of a slight asymmetry into the molecule greatly simplifies the study of these molecules.

As indicated in the previous analysis, it is possible to subdivide the broad category of asymmetric-top molecules into many smaller groups based on such factors as the degree of asymmetry, the direction of the dipole moment with respect to the inertial axes, and the magnitude of the moments of inertia. These factors determine whether the observable transitions correspond to high J or low J; P-, Q-, or R-branches. For this reason, the nature of the data obtainable for different molecules differs widely. Often the data are expressed most accurately as combinations of term values such as $B + C$, or $A - C$, etc. The nature of the centrifugal distortion corrections vary widely among the molecular types. In Table $A.4$, an effort has been made to present the most significant data in a consistent manner despite the diversities of molecular types. The quantities chosen are the term values A, B, and C, or, for almost symmetric tops, an appropriate average of B and C or A and B. The asymmetry parameter κ is listed as an alternative or supplementary description in some cases. It will be noted that many of the molecules listed are planar, so that necessarily the dipole moment μ lies in the plane of the molecule ($\mu_c = 0$). For these planar molecules, also, the sum of the I_a and I_b equals I_c, classically. Quantum mechanically, because of zero-point vibrations, this equality no longer holds, and the deviation $\Delta = I_c - (I_a + I_b)$ is known as the quantum defect.[74] Where all three spectroscopic constants, A, B, and C, are known, Δ is easily calculated but is not tabulated.

Internal rotation. The possibilities for hindered internal rotation in complicated asymmetric-top molecules are numerous. To date, however, methyl alcohol is the only such molecule to be investigated extensively. The probability of hindered rotation of the OH group relative to the CH_3 group in CH_3OH had been well established by the theoretical analysis of Koehler and Dennison [45] as applied to the far-infrared spectrum observed by Lawson and Randall. Koehler and Dennison treated CH_3OH as a symmetric top, as discussed in Art. 2.2c, with the exception that the rotating OH group has a dipole moment, so that the effects of the internal rotation are directly observable.

The complex microwave spectrum of methyl alcohol has been observed by Hershberger and Turkevitch,[75] Dailey,[76] Coles,[77] Hughes, Good, and Coles,[78] and Edwards.[79] The first four investigators concentrated their attention on an unusual group of lines near 25,000 Mc showing a linear Stark effect [76] and a regular sequence that could be expressed as a power series in $J(J + 1)$.[80] This group of lines has been identified as resulting from internal rotation. Edwards measured lines of several isotopic combinations near 50,000 Mc tentatively identified as $J = 0 \rightarrow 1$ transitions. The microwave data have been analyzed by Burkhard and Dennison,[80] who used a model involving internal rotation about the C-O axis of the actual asymmetric top. An important internal consistency feature of their theory is that the calculated torsional frequency of 250 cm^{-1} is much lower than any of the other vibrational frequencies, the lowest of which is about 1000 cm^{-1}, as observed by Borden and Barker.[81] Thus a model treating CH_3 and OH as separate rigid entities is reasonable. In addition to calculating the barrier height of 380 cm^{-1}, B rkhard and Dennison have calculated the structure of the molecule. The results are listed in Table A.9. The barrier height determined by the microwave spectrum is somewhat lower than the earlier value of 470 cm^{-1} estimated from infrared data.[45] The structural determination is not to be regarded as final since the $0 \rightarrow 1$ transitions are yet to be identified conclusively with the Stark effect. Theoretical work on the problem is being continued by Ivash and Dennison.

2.3. TRANSITIONS BETWEEN *l*-TYPE DOUBLETS

An interesting new type of transition was observed by Shulman and Townes.[32a] While searching for rotational transitions of HCN dimers, they found instead transitions between *l*-type doublets of the excited bending vibrational states of the HCN monomer ($\Delta J = 0$ transitions with $v_2 = 1$). As a result, they were able to measure precisely the *l*-type doubling intervals for several different rotational states and to obtain a critical test of Nielsen's theory of l-type doubling.[29, 30, 32, 33]

According to Nielsen's theory, the separation of the l-type doublets of the rotational levels in a linear molecule is

$$\Delta E = hqJ(J + 1), \qquad (2.66)$$

where

$$q = q_0(v_s + 1), \qquad (2.67a)$$

in which v_s is the quantum number for the bending vibrational mode. Nielsen further predicts

$$q_0 = \frac{B^2}{\omega_s}\left[1 + 4\sum_{s'}\xi_{ss'}^2\,\frac{\lambda_s}{\lambda'_s - \lambda_s}\right], \qquad (2.67b)$$

where ω_s in the frequency of the degenerate bending mode and $\xi_{ss'}$ represents the Coriolis coupling factors.

Equation 2.66 was confirmed beautifully by the measurements of the direct transitions ($\Delta J = 0$) between the l-type doublets over a wide range by Shulman and Townes. Table 2.5 gives the results.

Table 2.5. **Observed transitions between l-type doublets in HCN** [82]

J	Frequency in Mc	$q = \text{frequency}/J(J + 1)$ Mc
6	$9,460 \pm 30$	225.2 ± 0.8
8	$16,147.67 \pm 0.1$	224.273 ± 0.002
10	$24,689.96 \pm 0.1$	224.454 ± 0.001
11	$29,650 \pm 30$	224.6 ± 0.3
12	$35,043.24 \pm 0.1$	224.635 ± 0.001

Equation 2.67a, which shows the dependence of q on the vibrational quantum number, was confirmed by Shulman and Townes,[82a] who made measurements in the usual manner of the splitting of the rotational levels of OCS molecules in two excited bending vibrational states, $v_2 = 1$ and 3. In accordance with Eq. 2.67a the q for $v_2 = 3$ was found to be twice that for $v_2 = 1$. Transitions between l-type doublets in HCN as well as DCN have been observed by Weatherly, Manring, and Williams,[82b] whose findings agree with those of Shulman and Townes. For HCN they obtain an average q of 226.2 Mc and for DCN, an average q of 183.6 Mc.

Equation 2.67b is more difficult to confirm because of the complicated nature of the Coriolis coupling factors. A. H. Nielsen has given expressions for $\xi_{ss'}$ in linear XYZ molecules.[29] H. H. Nielsen has evaluated these expressions for HCN and OCS and has shown that Eq. 2.67b agrees exactly with the results of Shulman and Townes for OCS and deviates only 2 per cent from the measured q_0 for HCN.[30] The expressions for

$\xi_{ss'}$ are rather involved. Shulman and Townes point out that all the q_0's of the several linear XYZ molecules in which l-type doubling has been measured are approximately 30 per cent greater than those calculated with $q_0 = B^2/\omega_s$. Thus, for linear XYZ molecules, $q_0 \approx 1.30B^2/\omega_2$.

The fact that transitions can be observed between the l-type doublets of a given rotational level makes it possible to observe in the microwave region internal transition in levels of high J near the peak of the Boltzmann distribution. Furthermore, it makes possible the observation of absorption spectra of gases in the low-frequency radio region. For example, the $\Delta J = 0$ transition between the l-type doublet for $v_2 = 1$ and $J = 1$ of OCS would give an absorption line at 12.68 Mc.

2.4. INVERSION SPECTRA

If the coordinates of all the nuclei of any non-planar molecule are inverted at the center of mass, the resulting configuration is also an equilibrium structure for the molecule. Consequently, every non-planar molecule has identical potential energy minima, separated by potential barriers, and corresponding to equally stable molecular structures. These structures, moreover, cannot be obtained one from another by simply rotating the molecule about any succession of axes. If the barrier is sufficiently high, the two forms are stable isomers, often separable, and often with different optical anisotropies. If the barrier is low and narrow, however, the molecule resonates between the two possible structures. The solutions to the quantum mechanical wave equation are linear combinations of the wave functions corresponding to the two structures. One of the solutions is symmetric and one antisymmetric with respect to the inversion of the coordinates. The energies of these two solutions differ by a small amount, ΔE_{inv}, which is largest for light molecules with low, narrow potential barriers. The molecule may be treated as an oscillator of reduced mass μ,† moving in a symmetrical double minimum potential well. The first such treatment was given by Hund.[83] A particularly useful analysis by Dennison and Uhlenbeck,[84] relates ΔE_{inv} to the area of the potential hill lying above the particular vibrational energy level E_v considered. Their result is

$$\frac{\Delta E_{inv}}{\Delta E_v} = \frac{1}{\pi A^2}$$

$$A = \exp\left[\left(\frac{2\pi}{h}\right)\int_0^{x_1} [2\mu(V - E_v)]^{\frac{1}{2}}dx\right],$$

(2.68)

† The appropriate reduced mass may be deduced from the observed vibrational frequencies.

where ΔE_v = the separation of vibrational levels.

x = inversion coordinate (dimensionless).

$x = 0$ at maximum of potential hill.

$x = x_1$ at $V = E_v$.

For a given molecule, the inversion splitting is least for the ground vibrational state; it increases exponentially for higher vibrational states that have energies closer to the top of the potential barrier.

Ammonia. Ammonia is unique among molecules investigated by microwaves. Since Cleeton and Williams [85] observed its spectrum in 1934 and thus began microwave spectroscopy, more experiments on this molecule have been reported than on any other molecule studied by microwave methods. It was the first molecule to show an inversion spectrum,[85] the first to exhibit a sharp microwave line spectrum,[86] first to show nuclear hyperfine structure [87, 88] and the power saturation effect,[89] first to confirm the Van Vleck-Weisskopf theory of pressure broadening at moderate pressures,[89, 90] and first to show the inadequacy of the theory at high pressures,[90] first to be used in an atomic clock,[91] and first to be used for isotope analysis.[92, 93] The obvious reason for its use in so many diverse experiments is its exceptionally strong absorption in the microwave region.

To date, experimental evidence of inversion has been found only in ammonia. Infrared data on $N^{14}H_3$ yield splittings of 0.67, 32, and 310 cm^{-1} (Manning [94]) for the ground state and the $v_2 = 1$ and $v_2 = 2$ excited vibrational states. Wright and Randall's high resolution spectrograms [95] of the pure rotational spectrum of NH_3 are particularly beautiful. The data have been analyzed by Dennison and Uhlenbeck [84] and by Manning.[94] The former authors applied Eq. 2.68 to a potential function consisting of two parabolic minima connected by a straight line; the latter used a smooth curve so chosen that exact solutions of the wave function were obtained. Manning's solution predicted a ground-state inversion of 0.8 cm^{-1} with a potential hill of 2076 cm^{-1} and a pyramidal height of 0.37 A to 0.40 A, depending on the choice of reduced mass. (The observed pyramid height is 0.38 A).

Shortly after Wright and Randall's infrared observations,[95] Cleeton and Williams [85] performed their historic microwave investigation of atmospheric pressure $N^{14}H_3$, observing a broad maximum near 0.8 cm^{-1}. The low-pressure measurements of Bleaney and Penrose,[86] Good,[87] and a number of other investigators have shown that the inversion maximum occurs at 0.7935 cm^{-1}.

The NH_3 inversion spectrum consists of a number of different lines arising from molecules in different rotational states. This rotational structure was first resolved by Bleaney and Penrose.[86] It has been explained theoretically by Sheng, Barker, and Dennison [39] as an interaction of inversion and rotation. If nuclear hyperfine structure is neglected, a total of 64 lines of $N^{14}H_3$ has been observed,[96, 97] for rotational quantum numbers up to $J = 17$, $K = 15$, and frequencies ranging from 16,800 Mc to 40,000 Mc. The strongest of these lines ($J = 3$, $K = 3$) has a peak absorption of 7.2×10^{-4} cm^{-1}. Thirty-seven lines of $N^{15}H_3$ have been found.[96, 97]

Except for lines with $K = 3$, Costain [98] has fitted all 64 $N^{14}H_3$ lines with an rms error of 2.9 Mc by a 6-constant empirical formula of a form, suggested by Eq. 2.68,

$$\nu = \nu_0 \exp\left[A'J(J + 1) + B'K^2 + C'J^2(J + 1)^2 \right.$$

$$\left. + D'J(J + 1)K^2 + E'K^4\right], \quad (2.69)$$

where $\nu_0 = 23,785.88$ Mc; $A' = -6.36996 \times 10^{-3}$; $B' = +8.88986 \times 10^{-3}$; $C' = +8.6922 \times 10^{-7}$; $D' = -1.7845 \times 10^{-6}$; and $E' = +5.3075 \times 10^{-7}$. The anomalous deviations of the $K = 3$ lines from the above formulas were first observed by Strandberg, Kyhl, Wentink, and Hillger,[99] and have been explained by Nielsen and Dennison [100] on the basis of a K splitting of these levels.

The intensities of the various ammonia lines have been calculated in the original papers. They are strongly dependent on the population of the rotational levels involved; they are also proportional to $\mu^2 K^2/J(J + 1)$, the square of the permanent component of the dipole moment. The intensities are also inversely proportional to the line breadths which vary with rotational state in a manner discussed in Chapter 4.

Deuterated ammonia. Loubser and Klein,[101] using magnetron harmonics, observed a broad resonance peak centered at 117,000 Mc in ND_3 at atmospheric pressure. This resonance is an inversion of the $\nu_2 = 1$ excited vibrational state of ND_3. The ground-state inversion of ND_3 has been observed by Lyons, Rueger, Nuckolls, and Kessler [102] in the vicinity of 2000 Mc.

Weiss and Strandberg [65] have observed and identified 20 NH_2D and 14 ND_2H lines scattered throughout the frequency range of 7500 to 75,000 Mc. These observations have been extended to 4800 Mc by Sawyer [65] who lists 16 ND_2H lines between 4800 Mc and 6500 Mc. Weiss and Strandberg have given a thorough analysis of the entire ammonia-inversion problem, with special emphasis on the asymmetric-top members of the ammonia family (NH_2D and ND_2H). They show that quite generally, for a molecule whose dipole moment is perpendicular to the inversion plane, a rotational transition must be accompanied by an inversion transition, and vice versa. For the asymmetric tops NH_2D and ND_2H, there is no K degeneracy, and each observed microwave spectral line consists of a combination of an inversion and a Q-branch ($\Delta J = 0$) rotational transition. For a given $J_\tau \to J_{\tau'}$, two

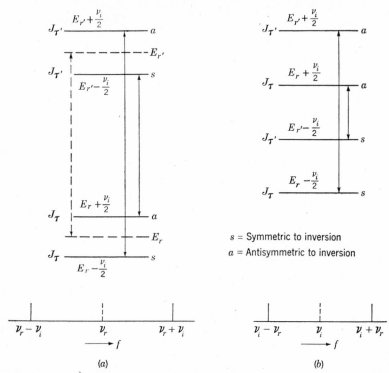

s = Symmetric to inversion
a = Antisymmetric to inversion

(a)   (b)

FIG. 2.14. Rotation inversion energy levels: (a) $\nu_r > \nu_i$, (b) $\nu_i > \nu_r$. (From Weiss and Strandberg.[65])

lines result because of the inversion splitting. The separation between the two frequencies will be equal to the sum of the inversion splittings of the two levels involved, if the pure rotational frequency ν_r is larger than the inversion splitting. If the inversion splitting is larger than the pure rotational energy difference, the separation between the two resulting absorption lines is equal to twice the pure rotation frequency. The two situations are illustrated in Fig. 2.14, where the levels are labeled to denote the symmetry with respect to inversion. Transitions are allowed only between levels of opposite symmetry.

In their analysis, Weiss and Strandberg apply the special form of Eq. 2.68 derived by Dennison and Uhlenbeck [84] for a potential well consisting of two equal parabolas connected by a straight line. In dimensionless units, the separation of the two parabola minima is $2x_0$; the length of the straight line maximum $2(x_0 - \alpha)$; and the height of the maximum V. The pertinent relations are

$$\frac{\Delta_0}{\nu_1} = \left(\frac{2\alpha}{\pi^{\frac{1}{2}}}\right) \exp\left[-\alpha^2 - 2(x_0 - \alpha)(\alpha^2 - 1)^{\frac{1}{2}}\right]$$

$$\frac{\Delta_1}{\nu_1} = \left(\frac{4\alpha^3 - 4\alpha}{\pi^{\frac{1}{2}}}\right) \exp\left[-\alpha^2 - 2(x_0 - \alpha)(\alpha^2 - 3)^{\frac{1}{2}}\right], \quad (2.70)$$

where Δ_0 = ground-state inversion splitting.

Δ_1 = inversion splitting for the excited state, $v_2 = 1$.

ν_1 = vibrational frequency corresponding to $v_2 = 1$.

$x_0 = (4\pi^2\mu\nu_1/h)^{\frac{1}{2}}q$; $V = \alpha^2 h\nu_1/2$, q = height of ammonia pyramid = 0.38×10^{-8} cm and μ = reduced mass.

By adjusting x_0 and α to the observed data for NH_3, V was calculated to be 1793.36 cm^{-1}.[†] Maintaining V constant and choosing μ proportional to ν_1^{-2}, the above authors calculated values of Δ_0 and Δ_1 which are compared with experiment in Table 2.6. The agreement

Table 2.6. Comparison of calculated and observed potential constants for NH_3 and some isotopic modifications [65]

	NH_3		NH_2D		NHD_2		ND_3	
	Calc.	Obs.	Calc.	Obs.	Calc.	Obs.	Calc.	Obs.
Δ_0 (cm^{-1})	0.7935	0.7935	0.402	0.406	0.172	0.1705	0.068	
Δ_1 (cm^{-1})	30.4	35.84	15.5	19.7	6.8	9.84	2.8	3.4
ν_1 (cm^{-1})		950.16		884		813		747.3
x_0	3.173		3.2896		3.4302		3.5778	
α	1.9429		2.0143		2.1004		2.1908	
μ (amu)	2.47		2.87		3.385		4.20	

is seen to be excellent, particularly for the ground state.

A number of NHD_2 and ND_2H lines were also observed by Lyons and co-workers.[102]

Other molecules. No inversion transitions have been observed for other molecules. A predicted PH_3 inversion line appears to have been a result of a misinterpretation of the data. The large reduced mass of PH_3 would make the ground-state line lie at very long wavelengths, if it is observable at all. It has also been suggested that H_2O_2 (nonplanar) may exhibit an observable inversion.

[†] In comparison with Manning's [94] 2076 cm^{-1}, it should be remembered that the areas, not the heights, of the two different potentials should be nearly equal. Manning's potential is best for excited vibrational states.

2.5. MAGNETIC RESONANCE SPECTRA OF GASES

A few gaseous substances, the most familiar of which are O_2, NO, NO_2, Cl_2O, and F_2O, have unpaired electrons in the ground state and hence have large magnetic moments as compared with those of most molecules which have a $^1\Sigma$ ground state. These paramagnetic gases have large Zeeman effects, also, when there is a nucleus with $I \neq 0$, large magnetic hyperfine structures.

One of the simplest ways to study paramagnetic gases in the microwave region is to observe transitions between Zeeman components of a given rotational state. This type of observation is analogous to paramagnetic resonance and nuclear magnetic resonance commonly observed in solids (Chapter 5). A field of only a few kilogauss is required to bring the resonance frequency of a free-electron spin into the microwave region. One can conveniently leave the microwave oscillator frequency fixed and "sweep" the absorption line to the desired frequency of observation by varying the magnetic field. Hyperfine structure and other effects can be studied as perturbations of the "Zeeman lines." The strong fields which must be employed break down weak magnetic couplings so that the simple theory of the Paschen-Back effect is often adequate for interpretation of the perturbations. Nevertheless, the resulting spectrum is frequently complex because of the large number of interactions usually present.

So far, the study of paramagnetic resonance spectra of gases has been concentrated at Yale, with the experimental side developed by Beringer and Castle and the theoretical aspects treated by Margenau and Henry. Three of the more common paramagnetic gases, O_2, NO, and NO_2, have been investigated. Although there are only a few more substances of this type to be studied, the possible application of the experimental method and the theory to gaseous free radicals or ions makes the subject potentially of wide interest.

The three cases already investigated illustrate fairly well the three degrees of coupling (relative to the coupling of μ and the magnetic field) between the magnetic moment μ and the molecular axis: (1) weak (NO_2), (2) intermediate (O_2), and (3) strong (NO). The first and last cases are analogous to the Paschen-Back and Zeeman effects, respectively, in atomic spectra, and, if hyperfine structure is neglected, they can be treated by the methods of Chapter 3. As in atomic spectra, the intermediate field case 2 is much more complex.

Because it is simplest, case 1 will be discussed first. In NO_2 there is a single unpaired electron which has only very weak coupling to the molecular axis. (The ground state is essentially a $^2\Sigma$ state.) This coupling is broken down by the fields required to obtain paramagnetic resonance at microwave frequencies. The frequencies observed by Castle and Beringer [103] could be explained by the simple Paschen-Back energy formula,

$$E = M_S g_S \mu_0 H + A M_S M_I + B M_S M_J, \qquad (2.71)$$

with $A = 132$ Mc and $B \approx A/2$, and the selection rules $\Delta J = 0$, $\Delta M_S = 1$, $\Delta M_I = 0$, and $\Delta M_J = 0$. In this formula the quantum numbers M_S, M_I, and M_J have their usual significance (Chapter 3). Formula 2.71, which is readily apparent from the vector model, is easily derived from first-order perturbation theory. The first term on the right is the principal term and represents the Larmor precessional energy of the electron spin. A and B represent the coupling constants in $A(\mathbf{S} \cdot \mathbf{I})$ and $B(\mathbf{S} \cdot \mathbf{J})$. It should be mentioned that, previous to the work of Castle and Beringer, McAfee [104] had measured these constants from the structure of the microwave rotational spectrum of NO_2. Because of the large number of J values for which the rotational levels are populated at room temperature, the last term causes a splitting of the main paramagnetic line into a large number of components which are not completely resolved. Since $I = 1$ for N^{14} and $I = 0$ for O^{16}, the term $A M_S M_I$ causes a splitting of the resonance line into three components. These components were resolved by Castle and Beringer. Except for the different nuclear moments, the paramagnetic resonance spectra of F_2O and Cl_2O are probably similar to that of NO_2.

The separations of the O_2 Zeeman levels observed in the experiment of Beringer and Castle [23] are only about one-third of the average separation of the spin triplets (Art. 2.1b). Therefore, the fields required for this Zeeman frequency are sufficient to cause appreciable decoupling of the magnetic vectors within the molecule, but not sufficient to break down these couplings completely. Consequently, the magnetic resonance lines observed do not agree closely with those expected from the simple vector-model treatment nor with the treatment of Schmid, Budó, and Zemplén.[105] The latter researchers assume that oxygen is an example of Hund's case (b),[106] but with S coupled weakly to the molecular axis, and they treat the Zeeman splitting as a perturbation of the spin triplet. Henry [107] introduced Zeeman perturbation into the original Hamiltonian used to calculate the spin triplet (Art. 1.1b). Because of the number of terms in the resulting Hamiltonian, the calculation of the allowed energy values is rather involved, and the resulting secular determinant whose roots yield the desired energies is cumbersome. It is sufficient to say here that Henry's treatment yielded results in good agreement with experiment for the several lines measured by Beringer and Castle.

As a result of the cancellation of the orbital and spin magnetic moments, the lowest electronic state of NO, $^2\Pi_{1/2}$, is non-magnetic. The

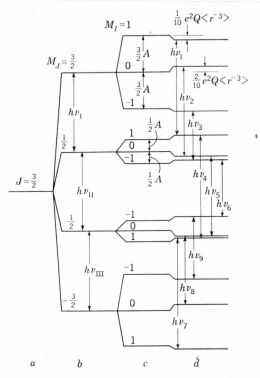

FIG. 2.15. Energy-level diagram of the $J = 3/2$ level of the $^2\Pi_{3/2}$ state of $N^{14}O^{16}$. Stage a is in the absence of magnetic field. Stage b shows the magnetic levels, considering only molecular effects. Stage c includes the nuclear magnetic and stage d the nuclear quadrupole coupling. The nine transitions $\Delta M_J = \pm 1$, $\Delta M_I = 0$ are shown in stage d. Arabic indices on the transitions correspond to the labeling of the observed absorption lines. (From Beringer and Castle.[22])

state $^2\Pi_{3/2}$, which lies only 121 cm^{-1} above and is appreciably populated at room temperature ($kT \approx 200$ cm^{-1}), is, however, magnetic and gives rise to the well-known paramagnetism of NO. In this state, the molecule has a magnetic moment of 2 Bohr magnetons which is strongly coupled to the internuclear axis [Hund's case (a)]. The resultant electronic momentum, $\Omega = |\Lambda + \Sigma|$ lies along the internuclear axis and forms with the end-over-end rotational momentum a total angular momentum J. The rotational energy is given by the symmetric-top formula, with K replaced by Ω, with the allowed values of J being $\frac{3}{2}$, $\frac{5}{2} \cdots$ for the $^2\Pi_{3/2}$ state. Since J cannot be less than its component, Ω, the lowest rotational levels for the $^2\Pi_{3/2}$ state is that for $J = \frac{3}{2}$. It was this lowest state $(J = \frac{3}{2})$ which was investigated by Beringer and Castle.[22]

If nuclear interactions are neglected, the paramagnetic resonance frequencies of NO can be calculated by the vector model treatment of Hund's case (a).[106] This treatment immediately yields a g factor of $3/J(J + 1)$ for $^2\Pi_{3/2}$. With $J = \frac{3}{2}$, the g factor is $\frac{4}{5}$. Since $M_J = J$,

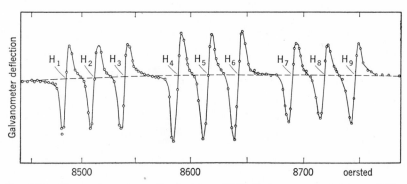

FIG. 2.16. Observed paramagnetic spectrum of $N^{14}O^{16}$ at a pressure of 1.0 mm of Hg. (From Beringer and Castle.[22])

$J - 1 \cdots -J$, there are four Zeeman levels spaced $\frac{4}{5}H\beta$ apart, where β is the Bohr magneton. With the selection rule for paramagnetic resonance spectra, $\Delta M = 1$, a triply degenerate line of frequency $\frac{4}{5}(H\beta/h)$ would be expected, if there were no nuclear perturbations. This is illustrated by stage b of the diagram by Beringer and Castle reproduced in Fig. 2.15. As a result of nuclear interactions, nine lines are actually observed, as indicated in the diagram and shown in the Fig. 2.16. An indirect result of the nuclear interaction is to cause a small decoupling in the molecule so that it is no longer a perfect example of Hund's case (a). This effect is treated by Margenau and Henry.[108]

2.6. HYPERFINE STRUCTURE

Hyperfine structure in molecular rotational spectra arises through a coupling of the nuclear spin, $\mathbf{I}$, to the molecular rotational vector, $\mathbf{J}$. This coupling may be magnetic or electric, or both. Nuclei do not have electric dipole moments but can have electric quadrupole moments which interact with the gradient of the molecular electric field at the nucleus. The unbalanced molecular fields, electric and magnetic, at the nucleus arise primarily from the valence-shell electrons which are strongly coupled to the molecular axis and which, so to speak, rotate with the molecule. When the molecular axis changes orientation with respect to the nuclear axis, the molecular field components at the nucleus in the direction of the spin axis change value, and hence the interaction energy changes. It is this change in interaction energy which must be supplied by the radiation field and which gives rise to the hyperfine structure in rotational spectra. Vectorially, I and J can be regarded as forming a resultant F fixed in space, about which both J and I precess. See Fig. 2.17. The interaction energies of J and I, and hence the rates of precession, depend upon the orientation angles as well as upon the coupling constants.

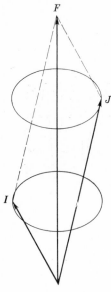

FIG. 2.17. Vector diagram showing coupling of J and I to form a resultant F about which both precess.

In atomic spectra the magnetic hyperfine structure is much more prominent than the electric quadrupole hyperfine structure. In molecular rotational spectra the quadrupole hyperfine structure is the more prominent. Most stable molecules have $^1\Sigma$ ground states and consequently only extremely small molecular magnetic moments. There are a few molecules, such as NO and ClO_2, which do not have $^1\Sigma$ ground states. These have large molecular magnetic moments and accordingly have widely spaced magnetic hyperfine structures. A very large number of molecules are found to have observable nuclear quadrupole hyperfine structure in their microwave spectra. Although both types of interactions can occur in the same molecule, most frequently one type predominates over the other. It is convenient to treat the two effects separately. One should remember, however, that if the $2I + 1$ degeneracy resulting from a given nucleus is completely lifted by one of these interactions, no further components in the hyperfine structure arising from this nucleus can be produced by the other type of interaction but only a further displacement of the existing components.

2.6a. Nuclear Quadrupole Interactions. If the electric charge of a nucleus is not spherically symmetric (which is usually the case when the spin is not zero or $\frac{1}{2}$), it has an electric quadrupole moment Q (see Chapter 6) which can couple the nuclear axis to the molecular axis through the electric field gradient of the molecule, effective at the nucleus. This resulting interaction of the nuclear spin and the molecular rotation causes a splitting of the rotational levels, which is called the nuclear quadrupole hyperfine structure. To find the splitting of the rotational levels, quantum mechanical perturbation methods (see introduction to Chapter 3) are applied to the perturbing Hamiltonian of Eq. 2.72. In most instances the transformations are involved. Only the pertinent results will be given here.

Nuclear quadrupole effects in microwave spectra were discovered by Good [87] in the inversion spectrum of ammonia and were quickly confirmed by Dailey, Kyhl, Strandberg, Van Vleck, and Wilson.[88] Figure 2.18 reproduces the original cathode-ray presentation of the 3,3 line

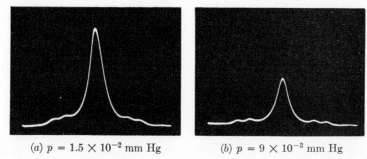

$(a)\ p = 1.5 \times 10^{-2}$ mm Hg $\qquad$ $(b)\ p = 9 \times 10^{-3}$ mm Hg

FIG. 2.18. The $N^{14}H_3$ 3,3 line showing satellites arising from N^{14} quadrupole coupling. These photographs represent the first evidence obtained for nuclear effects in microwave spectroscopy. (From Good.[87])

of $N^{14}H_3$ by Good. Note the symmetrical satellites on either side of the strong central line (undisplaced line).

Previous to the discovery by Good,[87] nuclear quadrupole effects had been found in the optical spectra of atoms [109] and in the molecular-beam r-f spectra [110] of diatomic molecules. The fundamental theory of the interaction of nuclear quadrupole moments with extranuclear electrons was developed some years ago in an important work by Casimir.[111] This theory, which had earlier been adapted to linear molecules by Nordsieck [112] and by Feld and Lamb,[113] was quickly adapted by Coles and Good [114] and by Van Vleck [115] to symmetric-top molecules to account for the hyperfine structure of $N^{14}H_3$. Bragg [116] and Knight and Feld [117] have since extended it to asymmetric rotors.

The Hamiltonian of Casimir which describes the quadrupole coupling of nuclei in a molecule is of the form

$$H_Q = \sum_i eQ_i \left\langle \left(\frac{\partial^2 V}{\partial Z^2}\right)_i \right\rangle_{Av} \left[\frac{3(\mathbf{J}\cdot\mathbf{I}_i)^2 + \frac{3}{2}(\mathbf{J}\cdot\mathbf{I}_i) - \mathbf{J}^2\mathbf{I}_i^2}{2J(2J-1)I_i(2I_i-1)} \right], \quad (2.72)$$

in which $\mathbf{J}$ refers to the total angular momentum of the molecule exclusive of the nuclear momenta, which are described by $\mathbf{I}_i$. The quantity Q_i represents the electric quadrupole moment of the ith nucleus (described in Chapter 6), and e, the electronic charge. The only term in H which differs for atoms and molecules and for various types of molecules is $\left\langle \dfrac{\partial^2 V}{\partial Z^2} \right\rangle_{\mathrm{Av}}$. In this term V is the potential at the nucleus in question which results from all the electrons, and Z is the axis fixed in space. [In the expression $(\partial^2 V/\partial z^2)$, as commonly used in microwave papers, z refers to an axis fixed in the molecule.] It is easily shown that

$$\left\langle \frac{\partial^2 V}{\partial Z^2} \right\rangle_{\mathrm{Av}} = \left\langle \sum_j e_j \left[\frac{3 \cos^2 \theta_j - 1}{r_j^3} \right] \right\rangle_{\mathrm{Av}}, \tag{2.73}$$

where $\mathbf{r}_j$ is the radius vector from the center of the ith nucleus to the jth electron, and θ_j is the angle between $\mathbf{r}_j$ and the space-fixed axis Z. The average is taken over the state with $M_J = J$.

Single nucleus with coupling. The numerator within the brackets of Eq. 2.72 has the same characteristic values for a single nucleus with quadrupole coupling in a molecule (of any type) as it has for atoms. It has been evaluated by Casimir.[111] From his result, the characteristic energy values for quadrupole coupling of a single nucleus with spin I and quadrupole moment Q is

$$E_Q = eQ \left\langle \frac{\partial^2 V}{\partial Z^2} \right\rangle_{\mathrm{Av}} \left[\frac{\frac{3}{4}C(C + 1) - I(I + 1)J(J + 1)}{2J(2J - 1)2I(2I - 1)} \right], \tag{2.74}$$

where $C = F(F + 1) - I(I + 1) - J(J + 1)$.

$F = J + I, \ (J + I - 1) \cdots \left| J - I \right|.$

The term $\left\langle \dfrac{\partial^2 V}{\partial Z^2} \right\rangle_{\mathrm{Av}}$ takes different forms for different molecular types and for different reference axes. For diatomic or linear polyatomic ones (in Σ states) it is

$$\left\langle \frac{\partial^2 V}{\partial Z^2} \right\rangle_{\mathrm{Av}} = -\frac{2J}{2J + 3} \left(\frac{\partial^2 V}{\partial z^2} \right), \tag{2.75}$$

where z is along the bond axis.

For symmetric-top molecules † with the coupling nucleus on the sym-

---

† Details of the derivation for the symmetric-top case are given by Jauch [*Phys. Rev. 72*, 715 (1947)]. The value for the linear case may be obtained from the symmetric-top form by setting $K = 0$.

metry axis it is

$$\left\langle\frac{\partial^2 V}{\partial Z^2}\right\rangle_{\mathrm{Av}} = \frac{2J}{2J+3}\left(\frac{3K^2}{J(J+1)} - 1\right)\frac{\partial^2 V}{\partial z^2}, \qquad (2.76)$$

where z is along the symmetry axis, and K is the quantum number which measures the component of J along this axis.

For asymmetric tops $\left\langle\dfrac{\partial^2 V}{\partial Z^2}\right\rangle_{\mathrm{Av}}$ has been expressed in different forms. A form given by Bragg [116] which can be conveniently evaluated from existing tables is

$$\left\langle\frac{\partial^2 V}{\partial Z^2}\right\rangle_{\mathrm{Av}} = \frac{2J}{(2J+3)(2J+1)}\sum_{\tau'}\left[\left(\frac{\partial^2 V}{\partial a^2}\right)\lambda^a{}_{J\tau;\,J\tau'}\right.$$
$$\left. + \left(\frac{\partial^2 V}{\partial b^2}\right)\lambda^b{}_{J\tau;\,J\tau'} + \left(\frac{\partial^2 V}{\partial c^2}\right)\lambda^c{}_{J\tau;\,J\tau'}\right], \quad (2.77)$$

where the reference coordinates a, b, and c are the principal axes of inertia. The values for $\lambda_{J\tau;\,J\tau'}$ are the Q-branch intensities tabulated by Cross, Hainer, and King.[70] A second very useful form, by Bragg and Golden,[118] develops $\left\langle\dfrac{\partial^2 V}{\partial Z^2}\right\rangle_{\mathrm{Av}}$ in terms of the reduced energy $E(\kappa)$ and Ray's parameter κ. For other forms, see Knight and Feld.[117]

If we designate with $Y(F)$ the part of the equation which is common to molecules of all types, then for diatomic and linear molecules (z along the molecular axis)

$$E_Q = -eQ\left(\frac{\partial^2 V}{\partial z^2}\right)Y(F) \qquad (2.78)$$

where $Y(F)$ is defined by Eq. 2.82.

For symmetric tops (z along the symmetry axis)

$$E_Q = eQ\left(\frac{\partial^2 V}{\partial z^2}\right)\left(\frac{3K^2}{J(J+1)} - 1\right)Y(F); \qquad (2.79)$$

and for asymmetric tops (a, b, and c along the principal axes of inertia)

$$E_Q = eQ\sum_{\tau'}\left[\left(\frac{\partial^2 V}{\partial a^2}\right)\lambda^a{}_{J\tau;\,J\tau'} + \left(\frac{\partial^2 V}{\partial b^2}\right)\lambda^b{}_{J\tau;\,J\tau'}\right.$$
$$\left. + \left(\frac{\partial^2 V}{\partial c^2}\right)\lambda^c{}_{J\tau;\,J\tau'}\right]\left(\frac{1}{2J+1}\right)Y(F), \quad (2.80)$$

or, alternately, in terms of Ray's parameter κ and the reduced energy $E(\kappa)$

$$E_Q = eQ \left\{ \left(\frac{\partial^2 V}{\partial a^2}\right) \left[J(J+1) + E(\kappa) - (\kappa + 1)\left(\frac{\partial E(\kappa)}{\partial \kappa}\right) \right] \right.$$

$$+ 2\left(\frac{\partial^2 V}{\partial b^2}\right)\left(\frac{\partial E(\kappa)}{\partial \kappa}\right) +$$

$$\left. \left(\frac{\partial^2 V}{\partial c^2}\right)\left[J(J+1) - E(\kappa) + (\kappa - 1)\left(\frac{\partial E(\kappa)}{\partial \kappa}\right) \right] \right\} \left(\frac{1}{J(J+1)}\right) Y(F).$$

$$(2.81)$$

Definitions of κ and $E(\kappa)$ and methods of evaluating them are given in Art. 2.2d. The a, b, and c axes are the axes of principal moments of inertia designated according to the relative magnitudes of the moments of inertia, in the order $I_a < I_b < I_c$.

Numerical values for the common term

$$Y(F) = \frac{\frac{3}{4}C(C+1) - J(J+1)I(I+1)}{2(2J-1)(2J+3)I(2I-1)} \tag{2.82}$$

for values of J up to 20 are given in the Appendix, Table $A.10$. In the same table are given relative intensities for $\Delta J = 1$. These apply to all classes of molecules as well as to atoms. Numerical values for $\left(\dfrac{3K^2}{J(J+1)} - 1\right)$ in Eq. 2.79 are given in Table $A.10$. The values in Eq. 2.80 are the Q-branch entries tabulated by Cross, Hainer, and King.[70] The summation includes values for all levels of τ that can combine with the level being analyzed. In computation of their tables advantage was taken of the fact that $\lambda^i{}_{J\tau;\,J\tau'} = \lambda^i{}_{J\tau';\,J\tau}$. Values of the reduced energies $E(\kappa)$ in Eq. 2.81 are tabulated by King, Hainer, and Cross.[51, 53]

One must not overlook the fact that the molecular-frame-reference axes used above are different for the different molecules. In the linear and symmetric-top cases only a single axis is required, whereas for asymmetric rotors three are used, although in view of the relation $\nabla^2 V = 0$ only two of these are independent. In evaluation of the quantity $\dfrac{\partial^2 V}{\partial z^2}$ from electronic structure it is frequently convenient to have the reference axis along a symmetric bond axis. For linear molecules and for certain symmetric tops such as CH_3Cl, the reference axis used above is already along a bond formed by the atom in question. In asymmetric tops none of the coordinates employed necessarily lies along a bond formed by the coupled atom. When, however, the structure of the molecule is known, the quantities $\dfrac{\partial^2 V}{\partial a^2}$, etc., can be estimated from $\dfrac{\partial^2 V}{\partial \xi^2}$, where ξ is along an axis of the bond formed by the atom, with approximate relations of the form [116]

$$\frac{\partial^2 V}{\partial x_i^2} = \frac{\partial^2 V}{\partial \xi^2} \left(\frac{3 \cos^2 \alpha_{x_i \xi} - 1}{2} \right) \qquad i = 1, 2, 3, \qquad (2.83)$$

where angles $\alpha_{x_i \xi}$ are the angles between the bond axis and the principal axes, a, b, and c, here designated as x_1, x_2, and x_3. This relation assumes that the electronic distribution near the nucleus is symmetrical about the bond. The relations are not limited to a bond axis but hold for any axis through the nucleus about which this electronic charge is symmetric. Vice versa, Eq. 2.83 can be used to resolve the coupling factors $\partial^2 V/\partial a^2$, etc., along a new set of reference axes, x, y, and z.

The field gradients $(\partial^2 V/\partial z^2)$, $(\partial^2 V/\partial a^2)$, etc., are usually abbreviated q_{zz}, q_{aa}, etc., and the quadrupole coupling eQq_{zz}, eQq_{aa}, etc., as χ_{zz}, χ_{aa}, etc., with the subscripts denoting the particular reference axis. In linear or symmetric-top molecules, where only one reference axis is involved, frequently the subscripts are dropped and the field gradient is indicated simply by q. This practice will be followed in succeeding discussions. In the general case the field gradient is a tensor and hence has nine components. However, the axes can always be chosen so that the cross terms such as $q_{xy} = \partial^2 V/\partial x\, \partial y$ vanish, leaving only the three terms with like subscripts. Assuming no electronic charge at the nucleus, Laplace's equation, $\nabla^2 V = 0$, can be used to eliminate one of the remaining terms. A further discussion of the coupling constants will be found in Chapters 6 and 7.

To obtain the hyperfine components of a given transition of J, the quadrupole perturbation energies E_Q (Eqs. 2.78–2.81) are added to the unperturbed rotational energies E_r and the Bohr relation $\Delta E = h\nu$, with the appropriate selection rules applied. In practice, one usually computes first the frequency deviations and adds them to the theoretical unperturbed frequency. The selection rules for F are

$$\Delta F = 0, \pm 1.$$

These must be used with the selection rules governing the unperturbed transition. Since the selection rules for rotational transitions in asymmetric rotors differ from those for linear and symmetric-top molecules, the combinations of hyperfine energy levels give rise to a greater variety of patterns than are found for the simpler molecular types. Since these patterns are unique for particular combinations of I and J, they can be used to identify the rotational transition as an alternative to identification by means of the Stark effect. As with all quadrupole splittings (and with the Stark effect), only moderately low-J transitions can be analyzed in this fashion. For high-J values, the splittings become smaller and the pattern approaches a type characteristic of the nuclear spin only.

Numerous examples of hyperfine structure in microwave spectra have been observed. Figure 2.19 shows one of the simplest possible

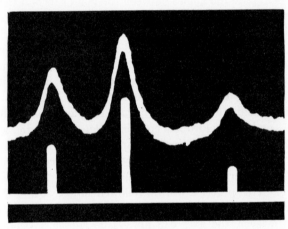

FIG. 2.19.   Theoretical and observed hyperfine structure of the $J = 0 \rightarrow 1$ rotational transition of DCN. [From Simmons, Anderson, and Gordy, *Phys. Rev.* **77**, 77 (1950).]

quadrupole hyperfine patterns, that for the $J = 0 \rightarrow 1$ transition of a linear molecule. Figure 2.20 gives the actual energy levels (first order) with the allowed transitions for the symmetric-top case, $J = 1 \rightarrow 2$, with $I = \frac{5}{2}$.

Goldstein and Bragg [119] have applied the theory of Bragg, Eq. 2.80, to the asymmetric rotor vinyl chloride (C_2H_3Cl). Figure 2.21 shows a comparison of theory and experiment. The second method by Bragg and Golden, Eq. 2.81, has been applied by Loomis and Strandberg [73] to the partly deuterated arsine and stibine. Sufficient low-J transitions were observed so that the reduced energy expression could be obtained analytically without the use of the approximate tables.

For a discussion of the nuclear and molecular information obtained from nuclear quadrupole hyperfine structure, see Chapters 6, 7, and 8.

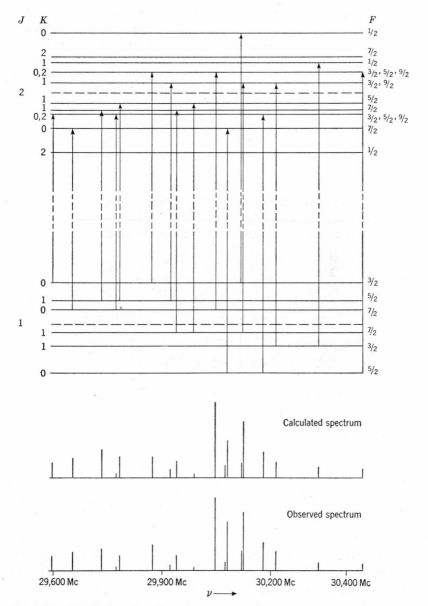

F<small>IG</small>. 2.20. Illustration of nuclear quadrupole hyperfine structure ($I = \tfrac{5}{2}$) in the rotational spectrum of a symmetric top. The $J = 1 \rightarrow 2$ transition of CH_3I^{127}. [From W. Gordy, *Rev. Mod. Phys.* *20*, 668 (1948).]

Second-order effects. The first-order treatments discussed above account very satisfactorily for the quadrupole hyperfine structure when the spacings of the rotational energy levels are large as compared with the quadrupole splitting. However, deviations from the first-order theory of a few megacycles were early found to occur for the I^{127} hyperfine structure [120, 121] in CH_3I and ICN. The quadrupole theory for

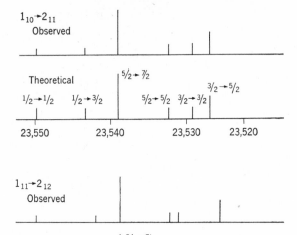

FIG. 2.21. Hyperfine structure in the spectrum of an asymmetric rotor. The Cl^{35} quadrupole effects in vinyl chloride. (From Goldstein and Bragg.[119])

linear and symmetric-top molecules, extended to the second order by Bardeen and Townes,[122] was found to account beautifully for this deviation. The second-order energy is

$$E_Q{}^{(2)} = \sum_{J'} \left[\frac{(IJFM_F|\,H_Q\,|IJ'FM_F)^2}{E_r - E_r{}'} \right], \qquad (2.84)$$

where J' can differ from J by 1 or 2. Physically, this represents an interaction between levels of different J but of the same F and M_F. The squared matrix elements in the numerator are

$$(IJFM_F|\,H_Q\,|IJ + 1FM_F)^2$$

$$= \left[\frac{3eqQK}{8I(2I-1)J(J+2)} \right]^2 \left[1 - \frac{K^2}{(J+1)^2} \right] \frac{[F(F+1)-I(I+1)-J(J+2)]^2}{(2J+1)(2J+3)}$$

$$\times (I+J+F+2)(J+F-I+1)(I+F-J)(J+I-F+1)$$

$(IJFM_F|\ H_Q\ |IJ + 2FM_F)^2$

$$= \left[\frac{3eqQ}{16I(2I - 1)(2J + 3)}\right]^2 \left[1 - \frac{K^2}{(J + 1)^2}\right]$$

$$\times \left[1 - \frac{K^2}{(J + 2)^2}\right] \frac{1}{(2J + 1)(2J + 5)} (F + I + J + 3)$$

$$\times (F + I + J + 2)(J + I - F + 2)(J + I - F + 1)(J + F - I + 2)$$

$$\times (J + F - I + 1)(I + F - J)(I + F - J - 1). \tag{2.85}$$

The expression in the denominator is the difference in the rotational energy of the molecular states J and J' with $K = K'$ for symmetric tops. For linear molecules, of course, $K = 0$. Perturbations are produced by levels above as well as below that of a given level. The squared matrix element is symmetric, however, in J and J', and the above formulas are sufficient. The matrix elements vanish when J and J' differ by more than 2. Numerical values of $E_Q^{(2)}$ are given in Table A.10c for $I = \frac{3}{2}, \frac{5}{2}$ and J up to 6.

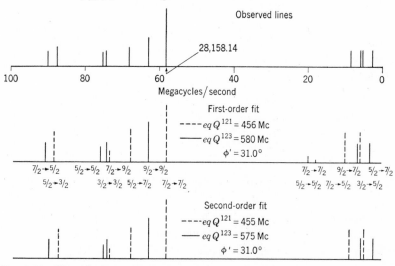

FIG. 2.22. Hyperfine structure in the $1_{01} \rightarrow 1_{11}$ rotational line of SbH_2D, showing second-order effects. (From Loomis and Strandberg.[73])

Second-order theory for quadrupole coupling in asymmetric rotors has been developed by Bragg.[116] The accidental near-degeneracy of certain rotational levels in asymmetric rotors can give rise to large second-order effects. Small but noticeable second-order effects were detected by Loomis and Strandberg [73] in the hyperfine structure of SbH_2D. See Fig. 2.22.

Two or more nuclei with coupling. The case of two or more nuclei (in a molecule) with quadrupole coupling is much more complex than that of a single-coupling nucleus. The Hamiltonian can be represented as a sum of the separate interactions as indicated in Eq. 2.72. The greatest complexity arises when different couplings are of the same order of magnitude. When one coupling is very much stronger than the others, the formulas for the coupling of a single nucleus may be applied to it, with the smaller splitting by the other nuclei treated as first-order perturbation of the resulting levels or neglected entirely.

Bardeen and Townes [123] have considered the case of two nuclei with coupling in linear molecules. They assigned the quantum numbers

$$F_1 = J + I_1 \qquad J + I_1 - 1 \quad \cdots \; \big| J - I_1 \big|,$$
$$F_2 = J + I_2 \qquad J + I_2 - 1 \quad \cdots \; \big| J - I_2 \big|,$$

(2.86)

where I_1 and I_2 are the spins of the two nuclei and represented by F the total angular momentum quantum number,

$$F = J + I_1 + I_2 \qquad J + I_1 + I_2 - 1 \quad \cdots \; \big| J - I_1 - I_2 \big|$$
$$= F_1 + I_2 \qquad F_1 + I_2 - 1 \quad \cdots \; \big| F_1 - I_2 \big|.$$

(2.87)

Thus, for $I_1 + I_2 \leqq J$ each level of J is split into $(2I_1 + 1)(2I_2 + 1)$ hyperfine levels. If E_{Q_1} and E_{Q_2} represent the characteristic coupling energy of each nucleus alone (as in Eq. 2.78), and $E_{Q_1} \gg E_{Q_2}$, then the combined energy E_Q can be written

$$E_Q = E_{Q_1}(F_1) + \sum_{F_2} C(F_1 F_2)^2 E_{Q_2}(F_2).$$

(2.88)

The transformation coefficients $C(F_1 F_2)$, which require too much space for listing here, are given by Bardeen and Townes [123] for $I_1 = 1$ and $\frac{3}{2}$, with I_2 and J arbitrary. This first-order theory has been found adequate when the coupling of one nucleus is 10 or more times that of the other.[123] The case of two nuclei with coupling is illustrated with ClCN in Fig. 2.23. Note that the top spectrum obtained with low resolution obeys well the coupling theory for the single nucleus, Cl.

The case of the three equivalent Z nuclei with coupling in symmetric molecules of the type XYZ_3, where X and Y have no coupling, is treated by Bersohn [124] and by Mizushima and Ito.[125] The large number of molecules, such as chloroform, to which this theory applies makes it of wide interest. Unfortunately, this case is extremely complex except for very low J, and the pertinent results are too lengthy to give here. Mizushima and Ito give the theoretical pattern for the $J = 0 \rightarrow 1$ transition with $I = 1$, $\frac{3}{2}$, 2, and $\frac{5}{2}$.

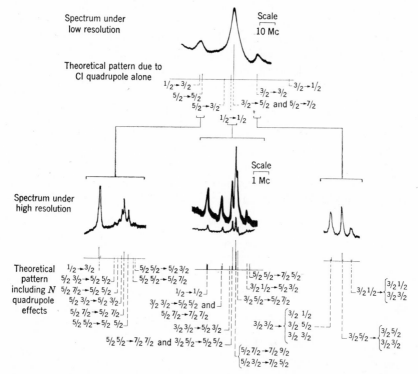

Fig. 2.23. Illustration of effects of quadrupole coupling by two nuclei on a rotational transition of a linear molecule. The hyperfine structure of the $J = 1 \rightarrow 2$ transition of $Cl^{35}CN^{14}$. [From Townes, Holden, and Merritt, *Phys. Rev.* 74, 1113 (1948).]

2.6b. Magnetic Hyperfine Structure. Magnetic hyperfine structure is pronounced only in the few molecules which are paramagnetic. Small nuclear magnetic-moment perturbations can, however, be detected in many non-magnetic molecules in $^1\Sigma$ states. These effects were found in $N^{14}H_3$ by Simmons and Gordy,[97] who noticed that the lines of the N^{14} quadrupole hyperfine structure were slightly displaced from their expected positions by N^{14} magnetic interactions with the molecular rotational moment. The theory of this interaction was worked out by Jauch[126] and by Henderson.[127] A similar, but stronger, interaction has been found by Gilbert, Roberts, and Griswold[128] in FCl. The magnetic hyperfine structure of the hydrogens in NH_3 has been partly resolved by Good [129] et al., and explained by Van Vleck.[130] In the last case, additional splitting of the NH_3 lines is observed because of the lifting of the $2I + 1$ orientation degeneracy of each hydrogen, whereas in the N^{14} interaction no additional lines are observed because the spin degeneracy of the N^{14} nucleus is completely lifted by the quadrupole interaction.

If the magnetic field generated by the molecular rotation is proportional to J, as is expected for linear molecules, the interaction Hamiltonian is $CI \cdot J$ and the characteristic energies are readily shown from first-order perturbation theory to be

$$E = \tfrac{1}{2}C[F(F + 1) - J(J + 1) - I(I + 1)], \qquad (2.89)$$

where C is a coupling constant. For FCl^{35} C was found [128] to be 0.036 Mc.

If in a symmetric top a magnetic field component $C_K K$ is generated by the rotation about the symmetry axes and a component $C_N N$ by the component of momentum normal to K, then the average field along J is

$$\mathbf{H}_J = C_N N \cos (\mathbf{N}, \mathbf{J}) + C_K K \cos (\mathbf{K}, \mathbf{J})$$

$$= \frac{C_N N^2}{\sqrt{J(J + 1)}} + \frac{C_K K^2}{\sqrt{J(J + 1)}}.$$

Since $N^2 = J(J + 1) - K^2$ and

$$\mathbf{H}_J = [C_N(J(J + 1) + (C_K - C_N)K^2]/\sqrt{J(J + 1)},$$

the interaction between $\mathbf{H}_J$ and the nuclear magnetic moment, $\mu_I = g_I \beta_I \sqrt{I(I + 1)}$, is

$$E = \mathbf{\mu}_I \cdot \mathbf{H}_J = g_I \beta_I \sqrt{I(I + 1)} \, H_J \cos (\mathbf{J}, \mathbf{I}).$$

From the law of the cosine applied to Fig. 2.7

$$\cos (\mathbf{J}, \mathbf{I}) = [F(F + 1) - J(J + 1) - I(I + 1)]/2\sqrt{J(J + 1)}\sqrt{I(I + 1)}.$$

Substituting and rearranging,

$$E = \left[a + \frac{bK^2}{J(J + 1)} \right][F(F + 1) - J(J + 1) - I(I + 1)], \quad (2.90)$$

where $a = g_I \beta_I C_N/2$ and $b = g_I \beta_I (C_K - C_N)/2$. This equation is identical to that derived by Henderson and Van Vleck.[131] It fits the $N^{14}H_3$ case with $a = 0.0057$ Mc and $b = 0.0011$ Mc. For asymmetric rotors Henderson and Van Vleck derive a similar expression with a term $cf(J, K)$ added in the first brackets as an asymmetry correction. A related treatment of molecular rotational magnetic moments is given by Jen.[132] The vector model treatment given assumes that the precession of **K** and **N** about **J** is rapid as compared with that of **J** and **I** about **F**, and that the rotational levels are widely spaced as compared with the hyperfine multiplet.

Hyperfine structure in paramagnetic gases will not be treated here because of the limited number of these gases. For a discussion of the subject, see the work of Henderson and Van Vleck,[131] Margenau and Henry,[108] and particularly that of McAfee.[104] The last researcher has observed and interpreted magnetic hyperfine structure in the rotational spectrum of NO_2. Magnetic hyperfine structure has also been detected in the microwave rotational spectrum of ClO_2 by Shawlow and Sanders,[133] and in $O^{16}O^{17}$ by Miller, Javan, and Townes.[20] See also Sec. 2.5.

2.6c. Relative Intensities. The relative intensities of the hyperfine components of a given rotational transition depend upon weights, $2F + 1$, of the upper as well as the lower state involved in the transition. They may be evaluated from the sum rules but have been derived with quantum mechanical methods by Hill.[134] The relevant formulas are

$$I_{\mp} = \left(\frac{1}{F}\right) \cdot Q(F) \cdot Q(F - 1) \qquad \Delta F = \mp 1$$

$$I_0 = \frac{(2F + 1)}{F(F + 1)} \cdot P(F) \cdot Q(F) \qquad \Delta F = 0 \qquad \left.\right\} \Delta J = \pm 1$$

$$I_{\pm} = \left(\frac{1}{F}\right) \cdot P(F) \cdot P(F - 1) \qquad \Delta F = \pm 1 \qquad (2.91)$$

$$I_0 = \frac{(2F + 1)}{F(F + 1)} \cdot R^2(F) \qquad \Delta F = 0$$

$$\left.\right\} \Delta J = 0,$$

$$I_{\pm} = \left(\frac{1}{F}\right) \cdot P(F) \cdot Q(F - 1) \qquad \Delta F = \pm 1$$

where $P(F) = (F + J)(F + J + 1) - I(I + 1)$.
$Q(F) = I(I + 1) - (F - J)(F - J + 1)$.
$R(F) = F(F + 1) + J(J + 1) - I(I + 1)$.

The larger values of J and F involved in the transition are employed. In Eq. 2.91 the upper signs are to be used together, and the lower signs are to be used together. Numerical values from Eq. 2.91 are tabulated for $\Delta J = 1$ and $J = 0$ to 20 (Table A.10 in the Appendix).

REFERENCES

[1] (a) A. Roberts, Y. Beers, and A. G. Hill, *Phys. Rev.* 70, 112 (1946); (b) K. Shimoda and T. Nishikawa, *J. Phys. Soc. of Japan 6*, 512 (1951).

[2] W. E. Lamb and R. C. Retherford, *Phys. Rev.* 72, 241 (1947); R. C. Retherford and W. E. Lamb, *Phys. Rev.* 75, 1325 (1949).

[3] (a) H. I. Ewen and E. M. Purcell, *Phys. Rev.* 83, 881 (1951); (b) C. A. Muller and J. H. Oort, *Nature 168*, 357 (1952).

[4] W. E. Lamb, Jr., and M. Skinner, *Phys. Rev.* 78, 539 (1950).

[5] For list of references, see Lamb and Skinner, reference 4.

[6] See, for example, H. E. White, *Introduction to Atomic Spectra* (McGraw-Hill Book Company, New York, 1934), Chapter 8.

[7] H. A. Bethe, *Phys. Rev.* 72, 339 (1947).

[8] N. M. Kroll and W. E. Lamb, Jr., *Phys. Rev.* 75, 388 (1949).

[9] J. B. French and V. F. Weisskopf, *Phys. Rev.* 75, 1240 (1949).

[10] J. H. Van Vleck, *Phys. Rev.* 71, 413 (1947).

[11] R. Beringer, *Phys. Rev.* 70, 53 (1946).

[12] H. R. L. Lamont, *Phys. Rev.* 74, 353 (1948).

[13] M. W. P. Strandberg, C. Y. Meng, and J. G. Ingersoll, *Phys. Rev.* 75, 1524 (1949).

[14] J. H. Burkhalter, R. S. Anderson, W. V. Smith, and W. Gordy, *Phys. Rev.* 77, 152 (1950); 79, 651 (1950).

[15] R. S. Anderson, C. M. Johnson, and W. Gordy, *Phys. Rev.* 83, 1061 (1951).

[16] H. A. Kramers, *Z. Physik 53*, 422 (1929).

[17] M. H. Hebb, *Phys. Rev.* 49, 610 (1936).

[18] R. Schlapp, *Phys. Rev.* 51, 342 (1937).

[19] H. D. Babcock and L. Herzberg, *Astrophys. J. 108*, 167 (1948).

[20] S. L. Miller, A. Javan, and C. H. Townes, *Phys. Rev.* 82, 454 (1951).

[21] F. Alder and F. C. Yu, *Phys. Rev.* 81, 1067 (1951).

[22] R. Beringer and J. G. Castle, Jr., *Phys. Rev.* 78, 581 (1950).

[23] R. Beringer and J. G. Castle, *Phys. Rev.* 75, 1963 (1949).

[24] G. Joos, *Theoretical Physics* (Hafner Publishing Co., New York, 1934), p. 137ff.

[25] *Handbuch der Physik* (Julius Springer, Berlin, 1927), Vol. 5, Chapter 8, pp. 390–397.

[26] L. Pauling and E. B. Wilson, Jr., *Introduction to Quantum Mechanics* (McGraw-Hill Book Company, New York, 1935), p. 271.

[27] H. Eyring, J. Walter, and G. E. Kimball, *Quantum Chemistry* (John Wiley & Sons, New York, 1944), p. 72.

[28] G. Herzberg, *Spectra of Diatomic Molecules* (D. Van Nostrand Co., New York, 1950).

[29] A. H. Nielsen, *J. Chem. Phys. 11*, 160 (1943).

[30] H. H. Nielsen, *Phys. Rev.* 78, 296 (1950).

[31] G. Herzberg, *Infrared and Raman Spectra* (D. Van Nostrand Co., New York, 1945).

[32] H. H. Nielsen and W. Shaffer, *J. Chem. Phys. 11*, 140 (1943).

[33] H. H. Nielsen, *Phys. Rev.* 77, 130 (1950).

[34] C. M. Johnson, R. Trambarulo, and W. Gordy, *Phys. Rev.* 84, 1178 (1951).

[35] D. M. Dennison, (a) *Phys. Rev.* 28, 318 (1926); (b) *Revs. Modern Phys. 3*, 280 (1931).

[36] F. Reiche and H. Rademacher, *Z. Physik 39*, 444 (1927); R. de Kronig and I. I. Rabi, *Phys. Rev. 29*, 262 (1927).

[37] H. Margenau and G. M. Murphy, *The Mathematics of Physics and Chemistry* (D. Van Nostrand Co., 1943), p. 72.

[38] Z. I. Slawsky and D. M. Dennison, *J. Chem. Phys. 7*, 509 (1939).

[39] H. Y. Sheng, E. F. Barker, and D. M. Dennison, *Phys. Rev. 60*, 786 (1941).

[40] R. Trambarulo and W. Gordy, *J. Chem. Phys. 18*, 1613 (1950).

[41] (a) W. E. Anderson, R. Trambarulo, J. Sheridan, and W. Gordy, *Phys. Rev. 82*, 58 (1951); (b) M. Mizushima and P. Venkateswarlu, *J. Chem. Phys.*, in press.

[42] H. T. Minden, J. M. Mays, and B. P. Dailey, *Phys. Rev. 78*, 347 (1950).

[43] D. R. Lide and D. K. Coles, *Phys. Rev. 80*, 911 (1950).

[44] H. H. Nielsen, *Phys. Rev. 40*, 445 (1932).

[45] J. S. Koehler and D. M. Dennison, *Phys. Rev. 57*, 1006 (1940).

[46] (a) B. P. Dailey, H. T. Minden, and R. G. Shulman, *Phys. Rev. 75*, 1319A (1949); (b) P. Kisliuk and G. A. Silvey, *J. Chem. Phys. 20*, 517 (1952).

[47] J. Sheridan and W. Gordy, *J. Chem. Phys. 19*, 965 (1951).

[48] G. Herzberg, reference 31, pp. 225, 495.

[49] H. H. Nielsen, *Revs. Modern Phys. 23*, 90 (1951).

[50] H. H. Nielsen, *Phys. Rev. 38*, 1432 (1931); H. M. Randall, D. M. Dennison, N. Ginsburg, and L. R. Weber, *Phys. Rev. 52*, 160 (1937).

[51] G. W. King, R. M. Hainer, and P. C. Cross, *J. Chem. Phys. 11*, 27 (1943).

[52] B. S. Ray, *Z. Physik 78*, 74 (1932).

[53] R. M. Hainer, P. C. Cross, and G. W. King, *J. Chem. Phys. 17*, 826 (1949).

[54] S. C. Wang, *Phys. Rev. 34*, 243 (1929).

[55] G. W. King, *J. Chem. Phys. 15*, 820 (1947).

[56] R. M. Hainer, P. C. Cross, and G. W. King, *J. Chem. Phys. 17*, 826 (1949).

[57] S. Golden, *J. Chem. Phys. 16*, 78 (1948).

[58] E. L. Ince, *Proc. Roy. Soc. Edinburgh 52*, 355 (1951).

[59] J. K. Bragg and A. H. Sharbaugh, *Phys. Rev. 75*, 1774 (1949).

[60] B. P. Dailey, S. Golden, and E. B. Wilson, Jr., *Phys. Rev. 72*, 871 (1947).

[61] R. E. Hillger and M. W. P. Strandberg, *Phys. Rev. 83*, 575 (1951).

[62] E. B. Wilson, Jr., and J. B. Howard, *J. Chem. Phys. 4*, 260 (1936).

[63] H. H. Nielsen, *Phys. Rev. 59*, 565 (1941).

[64] R. B. Lawrance and M. W. P. Strandberg, *Phys. Rev. 83*, 363 (1951).

[65] M. T. Weiss and M. W. P. Strandberg, *Phys. Rev. 83*, 567 (1951).

[66] H. R. Johnson and M. W. P. Strandberg, *J. Chem. Phys. 20*, 687 (1952).

[67] S. Golden, *J. Chem. Phys. 16*, 250 (1948).

[68] H. H. Nielsen, *Phys. Rev. 60*, 794 (1941).

[69] R. S. Mulliken, *Phys. Rev. 59*, 873 (1941).

[70] P. C. Cross, R. M. Hainer, and G. W. King, *J. Chem. Phys. 12*, 210 (1944).

[71] G. L. Cunningham, Jr., A. W. Boyd, R. J. Myers, W. D. Gwinn, and W. I. Le Van, *J. Chem. Phys. 19*, 676 (1951).

[72] G. Matlack, G. Glockler, D. R. Bianco, and A. Roberts, *J. Chem. Phys. 18*, 332 (1950).

[73] C. C. Loomis and M. W. P. Strandberg, *Phys. Rev. 81*, 798 (1951).

[74] B. T. Darling and D. M. Dennison, *Phys. Rev. 57*, 128 (1940).

[75] W. D. Hershberger and J. Turkevitch, *Phys. Rev. 71*, 554 (1947).

[76] B. P. Dailey, *Phys. Rev. 72*, 84 (1947).

[77] D. K. Coles, *Phys. Rev. 74*, 1194 (1948).

[78] R. H. Hughes, W. E. Good, and D. K. Coles, *Phys. Rev. 84*, 418 (1951).

[79] H. D. Edwards, Ph.D. Thesis, Duke University (1950).

[80] D. G. Burkhard and D. M. Dennison, *Phys. Rev. 84*, 408 (1951).

[81] A Borden and E. F. Barker, *J. Chem. Phys. 6*, 553 (1938).

[82] (a) R. G. Shulman and C. H. Townes, *Phys. Rev. 77*, 421 (1950); (b) T. L. Weatherly, E. R. Manring, and D. Williams, *Phys. Rev. 85*, 717 (1952).

[83] F. Hund, *Z. Physik 43*, 805 (1927).

[84] D. M. Dennison and G. E. Uhlenbeck, *Phys. Rev. 41*, 313 (1932).

[85] C. E. Cleeton and N. H. Williams, *Phys. Rev. 45*, 234 (1934).

[86] B. Bleaney and R. P. Penrose, *Nature 157*, 339 (1946).

[87] W. E. Good, *Phys. Rev. 70*, 213 (1946).

[88] B. P. Dailey, R. L. Kyhl, M. W. P. Strandberg, J. H. Van Vleck, and E. B. Wilson, Jr., *Phys. Rev. 70*, 984 (1946).

[89] C. H. Townes, *Phys. Rev. 70*, 665 (1946).

[90] B. Bleaney and R. P. Penrose, *Proc. Phys. Soc. (London) 59*, 418 (1947).

[91] H. Lyons, *National Bureau of Standards Tech. Report* 1320, January, 1949.

[92] A. L. Southern, H. W. Morgan, G. W. Keilholtz, and W. V. Smith, *Oak Ridge National Laboratory Report* Y-546, Y-621 (1950).

[93] J. Weber and K. J. Laidler, *J. Chem. Phys. 19*, 381 (1951).

[94] M. F. Manning, *J. Chem. Phys. 3*, 136 (1935).

[95] N. Wright and H. M. Randall, *Phys. Rev. 44*, 391 (1933).

[96] W. E. Good and D. K. Coles, *Phys. Rev. 71*, 383 (1947).

[97] J. W. Simmons and W. Gordy, *Phys. Rev. 73*, 713 (1948); A. H. Sharbaugh, T. C. Madison, and J. K. Bragg, *Phys. Rev. 76*, 1529 (1949).

[98] C. C. Costain, *Phys. Rev. 82*, 108 (1951).

[99] M. W. P. Strandberg, R. L. Kyhl, T. Wentink, and R. E. Hillger, *Phys. Rev. 71*, 326 (1947).

[100] H. H. Nielsen and D. M. Dennison, *Phys. Rev. 72*, 1101 (1947).

[101] J. H. N. Loubser and J. A. Klein, *Phys. Rev. 78*, 348A (1950).

[102] H. Lyons, L. J. Rueger, R. G. Nuckolls, and M. Kessler, *Phys. Rev. 81*, 630 (1951).

[103] J. G. Castle, Jr., and R. Beringer, *Phys. Rev. 80*, 114 (1950).

[104] K. B. McAfee, Jr., *Phys. Rev. 78*, 340A (1950); *82*, 971 (1951).

[105] R. Schmid, A. Budó, and J. Zemplén, *Z. Physik 103*, 250 (1936).

[106] G. Herzberg, reference 28, pp. 219–226.

[107] A. Henry, *Phys. Rev. 80*, 396 (1950).

[108] H. Margenau and A. Henry, *Phys. Rev. 78*, 587 (1950).

[109] H. Schüler and T. Schmidt, *Z. Physik 94*, 457 (1935); *98*, 430 (1935).

[110] J. M. B. Kellogg, I. I. Rabi, N. F. Ramsey, and J. R. Zacharias, *Phys. Rev. 57*, 677 (1940).

[111] H. B. G. Casimir, *On the Interaction between Atomic Nuclei and Electrons* (Teyler's Tweede Genootschap, E. F. Bohn, Haarlem, 1936).

[112] A. Nordsieck, *Phys. Rev. 58*, 310 (1940).

[113] B. T. Feld and W. E. Lamb, *Phys. Rev. 67*, 15 (1945).

[114] D. K. Coles and W. E. Good, *Phys. Rev. 70*, 979 (1946).

[115] J. H. Van Vleck, *Phys. Rev. 71*, 468 (1947).

[116] J. K. Bragg, *Phys. Rev. 74*, 533 (1948).

[117] G. Knight and B. T. Feld, *Phys. Rev. 74*, 354 (1948).

[118] J. K. Bragg and S. Golden, *Phys. Rev. 75*, 735 (1949).

[119] J. H. Goldstein and J. K. Bragg, *Phys. Rev. 75*, 1453 (1949).

[120] O. R. Gilliam, H. D. Edwards, and W. Gordy, *Phys. Rev. 73*, 635 (1948).

[121] C. H. Townes, F. R. Merritt, and B. D. Wright, *Phys. Rev. 73*, 1334 (1948).

[122] J. Bardeen and C. H. Townes, *Phys. Rev. 73*, 627, 1204 (1948).

[123] J. Bardeen and C. H. Townes, *Phys. Rev. 73*, 97 (1948).

[124] R. Bersohn, *J. Chem. Phys. 18*, 1124 (1950).

[125] M. Mizushima and T. Ito, *J. Chem. Phys. 19*, 739 (1951).

[126] J. M. Jauch, *Phys. Rev. 74*, 1262 (1948).

[127] R. S. Henderson, *Phys. Rev. 74*, 107 (1948).

[128] D. A. Gilbert, A. Roberts, and P. A. Griswold, *Phys. Rev. 76*, 1723 (1949).

[129] W. E. Good, D. K. Coles, G. R. Gunther-Mohr, A. L. Shawlow, and C. H. Townes, *Phys. Rev. 83*, 880 (1951).

[130] J. H. Van Vleck, *Phys. Rev. 83*, 880 (1951).

[131] R. S. Henderson and J. H. Van Vleck, *Phys. Rev. 74*, 106 (1948).

[132] C. K. Jen, *Phys. Rev. 81*, 197 (1951).

[133] A. L. Shawlow and M. Sanders, quoted by C. H. Townes, *Physica 17*, 354 (1951).

[134] E. L. Hill, *Proc. Natl. Acad. Sci. 15*, 779 (1929).

3. STARK AND ZEEMAN EFFECTS

In atomic spectra, the Zeeman effect is generally more important than the Stark effect. The reverse is true in molecular spectroscopy since most molecules have $^1\Sigma$ ground electronic states; i.e., they have no unpaired electrons, no electronic angular momentum or spin, and hence no electronic magnetic moment. With a few significant exceptions (such as O_2, NO) the magnetic moments are only of the order of a few nuclear magnetons ($\sim 10^{-23}$ emu). The electric dipole moments, however, are of the order of a Debye unit (10^{-18} esu). Whereas magnetic fields of many thousands of gauss often cause line shifts and splittings of less than the line width, electric fields of a few hundred to a few thousand volts per centimeter may completely resolve the individual line components.

The fundamental property of the Stark or the Zeeman effect is that it removes the spatial (M) degeneracy of the energy levels. If there is a uniform electric or magnetic field in the space-fixed Z direction, the angular momentum $\mathbf{J}$ can assume $2J + 1$ orientations with respect to Z corresponding to integral values of M_J from $-J$ to $+J$. If there is a permanent electric or magnetic moment $\boldsymbol{\mu}$ which has a component in the $\mathbf{J}$ direction, there will be $2J + 1$ values of $\boldsymbol{\mu} \cdot \boldsymbol{\mathcal{E}}$ or $\boldsymbol{\mu} \cdot \mathbf{H}$, giving rise to a linear Stark or Zeeman effect. If there is only an induced moment proportional to the field, a quadratic effect results, with $J + 1$ different energy values. Precise measurements of the frequency splittings of the line components frequently yield measurements of electric dipoles more accurate than those measured by any other technique. Because the magnetic splitting is smaller, the magnetic dipole measurements are generally less accurate.

The similarity of Stark and Zeeman effects makes it possible to develop the theory of both effects simultaneously.[1] The approach presented here, however, is first to indicate the general method used in the calculations and then to discuss each effect separately.

The Stark and Zeeman effects in rotational spectra might be treated by including the energy of orientation of the dipole in the external field with the total energy used in setting up the wave equation for the rotor. This approach, however, is needlessly complicated. Because the Stark and Zeeman energies are usually small as compared with the rotational energies, the simpler approach of the quantum mechanical perturbation theory is usually employed. This type of treatment is used not only for the Stark and Zeeman effects but also for nuclear hyperfine structure, centrifugal distortion, collision broadening, and many other phenomena encountered in microwave spectroscopy.

The elements of the perturbation theory are given in quantum mechanics texts and need not be elaborated here. It suffices to recall the pertinent results.

The first-order perturbation energies (except for certain degenerate states which are too involved for discussion here but are treated in all standard quantum mechanics texts) are obtained from an average of the perturbing term $H^{(1)}$ in the Hamiltonian

$$H = H^{(0)} + H^{(1)} \cdots \tag{3.1}$$

over the unperturbed state, i.e.,

$$E_J{}^{(1)} = \int \psi_J{}^{(0)} H^{(1)} \psi_J{}^{(0)*} \, d\tau, \tag{3.2}$$

where the $\psi_J{}^{(0)}$ for the present purpose would be the wave functions of the unperturbed rotor, and $H^{(1)}$ the potential energy of the molecular dipole in the external field. These zeroth-order wave functions are obtained from the solution of the wave equation

$$H^{(0)} \psi^{(0)} = E^{(0)} \psi^{(0)} \tag{3.3}$$

for the unperturbed rotor. $H^{(0)}$ is the Hamiltonian operator for the field-free rotor. For a molecule with the permanent dipole perpendicular to J (as in linear molecules) the first-order effects are readily shown from Eq. 3.2 to be zero.

The second-order energies (again excepting certain degenerate states) are

$$E_J{}^{(2)} = \sum{}' \frac{\left[\int \psi_J{}^{(0)} H^{(1)} \psi_{J'}{}^{(0)*} \, d\tau \right] \left[\int \psi_{J'}{}^{(0)} H^{(1)} \psi_J{}^{(0)*} \, d\tau \right]}{E_J{}^{(0)} - E_{J'}{}^{(0)}}. \tag{3.4}$$

The prime on the summation indicates omission of terms for $J = J'$. When, as is usually the case, $H^{(1)}$ is a first-degree function of the coordinates, the integrals in the numerator of the last term reduce to the matrix elements of the dipole moments (since the perturbing field is maintained constant and can be factored out). Therefore, only those neighboring states to which transitions are allowed by the selection rules enter into the summations. Also, if the dipole-moment matrix elements have been calculated for other purposes (see Sec. 4.4)—in predicting line intensities, for example—these can then be used for calculating Stark splitting. This is the basis of the method suggested by Golden and Wilson [2] for using the line-strength tables for asymmetric rotors of Cross, Hainer, and King [3] for Stark-effect calculations. For linear and symmetric-top molecules the characteristic Stark energies can be expressed in convenient formulas.

In the following discussions we use the abbreviations $(J| H |J')$ for integrals like those in Eq. 3.4, and correspondingly for the dipole-moment matrix elements $\int \psi_J \mu \psi_{J'}^* \, d\tau$ we use the abbreviations $(J| \mu |J')$.

Actually, more quantum numbers are usually required to designate the particular eigenstates, but for simplicity we employ only one in the above discussion.

If the perturbing $H^{(1)}$ contains no differential operators, as in the Stark and Zeeman effects as well as in nuclear interactions with the molecular rotation, the two integrals in Eq. 3.4 are identical, and the second-order interaction energy becomes (if the term in $H^{(2)}$ is neglected) in the abbreviated notation

$$E_J^{(2)} = \sum{}' \frac{\left| (J| H^{(1)} |J') \right|^2}{E_J^{(0)} - E_{J'}^{(0)}}, \qquad (3.5)$$

where again the prime on the summation indicates $J \neq J'$. This "non-degenerate" theory does not exclude the $2J + 1$ degeneracy arising from the space orientation (M degeneracy) nor the $\Pi(2I_i + 1)$ nuclear orientation degeneracy.

3.1. EFFECTS OF ELECTRIC FIELDS

3.1a. Stark Effect of Molecules without Hyperfine Structure.
Symmetric-top molecules. A discussion of the Stark effect in rotational spectra logically considers first the case of a symmetric top with a permanent dipole μ directed along the axis of symmetry. Since this class of molecule has an electric dipole component $\mu K / \sqrt{J(J + 1)}$ in the direction of the angular momentum $\mathbf{J}$, it has, except when $K = 0$, a simple first-order Stark effect. The energy of μ at angle θ in an external field $\mathcal{E}$ is $-\mu \mathcal{E} \cos \theta$. Quantum mechanically, the angle θ between μ and $\mathcal{E}$ assumes the $2J + 1$ quantized values $\cos \theta = M_J / \sqrt{J(J + 1)}$.

The corresponding first-order splittings $E^{(1)}{}_{JKM_J}$ of the Jth energy level are therefore

$$E^{(1)}{}_{JKM_J} = -\frac{\mu\mathcal{E}KM_J}{J(J+1)}. \tag{3.6}$$

$$E^{(1)}{}_{000} = 0$$

Note that Eq. 3.6 is independent of the inertial constants of the molecule.

For a transition $J \to J + 1$, with the microwave electric vector parallel to the Stark field $\mathcal{E}$, as is the usual experimental case, selection rules are $\Delta K = 0$, $\Delta M_J = 0$. These conditions yield the frequency displacements from the unperturbed rotational line frequency ν_0 as

$$\Delta\nu = 2\left(\frac{\mu\mathcal{E}}{h}\right)\frac{KM_J}{J(J+1)(J+2)}. \tag{3.7}$$

For ν in megacycles, μ in Debye units, and $\mathcal{E}$ in volts per centimeter, the factor $2/h$ is to be replaced by 1.0064. The maximum splitting, which occurs when $K = M_J = J$, is approximately inversely proportional to J. Typical values of $\mu = 1$ Debye unit and $\mathcal{E} = 1000$ volts/cm yield a maximum splitting of about $1000/J$ Mc, so that this linear Stark effect is easily observable even for high J.

Debye and Manneback [4] in 1927 first suggested using the first-order Stark effect for measuring dipole moments. Only with the advent of microwave spectroscopy has this become feasible, however. Microwave dipole-moment determinations are discussed in Chapter 7.

The above first-order Stark effect was derived on the assumption that μ is independent of the electric field. Actually the field perturbs the rotational motion, giving rise to an additional component of dipole moment proportional to the electric field. The resulting expression for $E^{(2)}{}_{JKM_J}$ from Eq. 3.5 is

$$E^{(2)}{}_{JKM_J} = \mathcal{E}^2 \sum{}' \frac{\left|(JKM_J|\,\mu\,|J'KM_J')\right|^2}{E_{JK} - E_{J'K}}, \tag{3.8}$$

where the summation is over all states for which $J' \neq J$.

The dipole matrix element in Eq. 3.8 is the same matrix element as that involved in the emission of electric dipole radiation. The only non-vanishing terms in Eq. 3.8 are from energy levels connected with the level in question (JKM_J) by dipole radiation, for which the selection rules (parallel electric fields) are $\Delta K = 0$, $\Delta M_J = 0$, $\Delta J = \pm 1$. Hence, two terms only contribute to $E^{(2)}{}_{JKM_J}$. If the squared matrix elements $(J, K, M|\,\mu\,|J-1, K, M)^2$ from Eq. 4.32 and $(J-1, K, M|\,\mu\,|J, K, M)^2$

(which may be obtained from Eq. 4.32 by substitution of $J - 1$ for J) are substituted in Eq. 3.8 with the corresponding rotational energy differences from Eq. 2.32 in the denominator, the second-order Stark energies are obtained as follows [4,5,6]

(a) $E^{(2)}_{JKM_J}$
$(J \neq 0)$

$$= \frac{\mu^2 \mathcal{E}^2}{2hB} \left[\frac{\{3K^2 - J(J+1)\}\{3M_J^2 - J(J+1)\}}{J^2(J+1)^2(2J-1)(2J+3)} - \frac{M_J^2 K^2}{J^3(J+1)^3} \right]$$

(3.9)

(b) $$E^{(2)}_{000} = \frac{-\mu^2 \mathcal{E}^2}{6hB},$$

where $B = h/8\pi^2 I_B$. In general, the second-order effect is completely negligible as compared with the first-order effect when the first-order effect does not vanish. Examination of Eqs. 3.6 and 3.9 shows, however, that for $K = 0$ there is only a second-order effect. Nevertheless, the $K = 0$ component of a symmetric-top transition is frequently used in determining dipole moments from the Stark effect. Furthermore, a linear molecule is equivalent to a $K = 0$ level of a symmetric top.

The relative intensities of the component lines, $\Delta M = 0, J \to J + 1$, are given by [7]

$$I_{M_J} = Q(J, K)[(J + 1)^2 - M_J^2],$$

(3.10)

The M_J dependence of Eq. 3.10 is particularly important and applies to all molecular types for $\Delta J = +1$ transitions. Unfortunately, the line with the greatest frequency shift ($M_J = J$) is also the weakest one. It will subsequently be shown that, when quadrupole effects are considered, simplicity of theoretical interpretation generally dictates the use of maximum M_J.

The Stark effect of the inversion doubling of NH_3 represents a rather special case. Although ammonia is a symmetric top, its dipole moment is only "semi-permanent," because of inversion splitting. Hence it possesses a second-order Stark splitting given by [8a,9]

$$\Delta \nu = 0.5065 \frac{\mu^2 \mathcal{E}^2}{\nu_0} \left[\frac{KM_J}{J(J+1)} \right]^2,$$

(3.11)

with ν in megacycles, μ in Debye units, $\mathcal{E}$ in volts per centimeter. Coles and Good [9] observed the Stark splitting of ammonia shortly after their observations on OCS. Their dipole measurement of 1.5 Debye units for ammonia has since been remeasured as 1.468 ± 0.009.[10] Complications introduced into the problem by quadrupole splitting are discussed by Jauch.[11] The transition probabilities [12] are proportional to

$$I_{M_J} \propto \mu^2 \left[\frac{KM_J}{J(J+1)} \right]^2. \tag{3.12}$$

Hence, in this case the intensity ratios of the components are the same as their relative frequency displacements from the undisturbed line. This coincidence arises from the fact that in this case the summation indicated in Eq. 3.5 contains only the one term corresponding to the line being observed.

Linear molecules. A linear molecule can be considered as a special case of a symmetric top with $K = 0$. Alternatively, the second-order Stark effect can be evaluated for linear molecules directly from Eq. 3.5 by use of the wave function of the rigid rotor. The energy-level splittings are given by

(a)

$$E^{(2)}{}_{\substack{JM_J \\ J \neq 0}} = - \frac{\mu^2 \mathcal{E}^2}{2hB} \left[\frac{3M_J{}^2 - J(J+1)}{J(J+1)(2J-1)(2J+3)} \right]$$

(b)

$$E^{(2)}{}_{00} = - \frac{\mu^2 \mathcal{E}^2}{6hB}$$

$$\tag{3.13}$$

and the frequency differences from the unsplit "zero field" lines ν_0 for $\Delta J = 1$, $\Delta M = 0$ by

(a) $(\Delta\nu)_{J \neq 0}$

$$= \frac{2\mu^2 \mathcal{E}^2}{h^2 \nu_0} \left[\frac{3M_J{}^2(8J^2 + 16J + 5) - 4J(J+1)^2(J+2)}{J(J+2)(2J-1)(2J+1)(2J+3)(2J+5)} \right]$$

(b)

$$(\Delta\nu)_{J=0} = \frac{8}{15} \frac{\mu^2 \mathcal{E}^2}{h^2 \nu_0},$$

$$\tag{3.14}$$

where J is for the lower rotational level. For ν_0 and $\Delta\nu$ in megacycles, μ in Debye units, and $\mathcal{E}$ in volts per centimeter, the factors $2/h^2$ and $8/15h^2$ in (a) and (b) are to be replaced by 0.5065 and 0.1351, respectively. The relative intensities are given by Eq. 3.10.

The greatest displacements occur for $M_J = J$, being, except for $J = 0$,

$$(\Delta\nu)_{\max} = \frac{2(5J + 8)\mu^2 \mathcal{E}^2}{(J+2)(2J+3)(2J+5)h^2 \nu_0}. \tag{3.15}$$

Converting to ν in megacycles, μ in Debye units, and $\mathcal{E}$ in volts per centimeter, Eq. 3.15 for high J is approximately equal to $\frac{5}{8}(\mu^2 \mathcal{E}^2)/(\nu_0 J^2)$. If ν_0 is 25,000 Mc, μ is 1 Debye unit, and $\mathcal{E}$ is the rather large value of 5000 volts/cm, the resulting displacement is $625/J^2$ Mc. This rapid decrease in Stark splitting with J limits accurate measurements to relatively light molecules, particularly if the dipole moment is low. For example, N_2O, whose dipole moment is only 0.166 Debye unit, has been accurately measured [13] by using the $J = 0 \rightarrow 1$ transition; a molecule

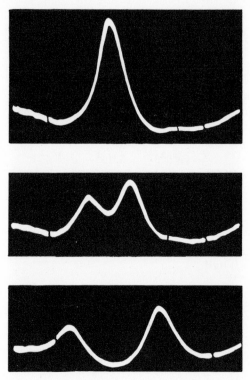

Fig. 3.1. Stark splitting of the $J = 1 \rightarrow 2$ rotational line of OCS. Upper curve, no field; middle curve, 750 volts/cm; lower curve, 1070 volts/cm. (From Dakin, Good, and Coles.[15])

of the same dipole moment with a moment of inertia ten times as large probably could not have been measured by the same.techniques.†

The first molecule whose microwave Stark effect was investigated was the linear molecule OCS. The photograph obtained by Dakin, Good, and Coles [15] is shown in Fig. 3.1. A rough value of 0.72 Debye unit obtained as the first Stark-effect dipole determination has since

---

† Transitions of SCSe, which is heavier than N_2O and presumably has a smaller dipole moment, have been observed, but the Stark splitting has not been well resolved.[14]

been remeasured with higher precision by several experimenters (Table A.5).

For a linear molecule, the Stark effect of excited stretching vibrational states may be treated in the same way as for the ground state. In a bending vibration, however, the molecule is very nearly a symmetric top. The slight asymmetry, in the absence of field, yields a doublet called the l-type doublet, where l has essentially the same significance as K for a symmetric top. In the first excited bending vibration $l = \pm 1$ are the only possible values.

Penney [16] has calculated the case of the Stark effect of an almost symmetric top. If the l-type doublet energies in the absence of electric field are $E_1{}^{(0)}$ and $E_2{}^{(0)}$, they become in the presence of a field $\mathcal{E}$

$$E_1 = \frac{1}{2}\left[E_1{}^{(0)} + E_2{}^{(0)} + \sqrt{(E_1{}^{(0)} - E_2{}^{(0)})^2 + 4\left\{\frac{\mu\mathcal{E}lM_J}{J(J+1)}\right\}^2}\, \right]$$

(3.16)

$$E_2 = \frac{1}{2}\left[E_1{}^{(0)} + E_2{}^{(0)} - \sqrt{(E_1{}^{(0)} - E_2{}^{(0)})^2 + 4\left\{\frac{\mu\mathcal{E}lM_J}{J(J+1)}\right\}^2}\, \right].$$

Strandberg, Wentink, and Hill [17] have applied this relation to OCSe showing that the Stark effect here is quadratic for low fields (asymmetric-top approximation, $\left|\dfrac{2\mu\mathcal{E}lM_J}{J(J+1)}\right| \ll \left|\,E_1{}^{(0)} - E_2{}^{(0)}\,\right|$) and linear for high fields (symmetric-top approximation, $\left|\dfrac{2\mu\mathcal{E}lM_J}{J(J+1)}\right| \gg \left|\,E_1{}^{(0)} - E_2{}^{(0)}\,\right|$). The resulting Stark splittings for the $J = 2 \rightarrow 3$ l-doublet of OCSe are shown in Fig. 3.2. It is interesting to note that the Stark components of the two l-type doublets approach each other as the field increases and intersect at a field given by [17]

$$\mathcal{E} = \frac{hJ(J+1)(J+2)}{4\mu M_J}\,\Delta\nu',$$

(3.17)

where $\Delta\nu'$ is the absorption frequency difference of the unperturbed l-doublet. This gives a convenient means of measuring the dipole moment for l-type doublets.

Asymmetric-top molecules. Golden and Wilson [2] have calculated the Stark effect of rigid asymmetric rotors by second-order perturbation theory. For cases where the Stark splitting is small compared with the separation of the unperturbed energy level from its nearest neighbor (non-degenerate case) they derive the expression

$$[E_g^{(2)}]_{J,\,\tau,\,M_J} = \frac{2\mu_g^2\mathcal{E}^2}{(A+C)h}\,[A_J(\kappa,\,\alpha) + M_J^2 B_J(\kappa,\,\alpha)]. \qquad (3.18)$$

Here μ_g is the component of dipole moment along the gth principal axis of the molecule, $[E_g^{(2)}]_{J,\,\tau,\,M_J}$ is the corresponding second-order energy

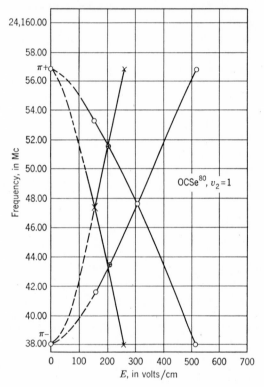

FIG. 3.2. Observed l-doublet Stark pattern for $OCSe^{80}$. (From Strandberg, Wentink, and Hill.[17])

shift for the M_J component of the J_τ energy level, and κ and α are asymmetry parameters of the molecule. (Note that the total energy shift is $\sum_{g=1}^{3} E_g^{(2)}$.) Values of A_J and B_J have been tabulated [2] for $J = 0, 1,$ and 2. When the microwave electric field is parallel to the Stark field, the selection rules are $\Delta M_J = 0,\ \Delta J = 0, \pm 1$. There are $(J+1)$ Stark components of a completely resolved spectrum line, where J is the smaller of the two J's involved in the transition.

Quite generally, Golden and Wilson showed that Eq. 3.18 could be put in a form utilizing Cross, Hainer, and King's [3] tabulated line strengths $\lambda(J, \tau; J', \tau')$ between levels whose unperturbed energy differences are $E^{(0)}{}_{J, \tau}$ and $E^{(0)}{}_{J', \tau'}$ where $J' = J - 1, J$, or $J + 1$. The resulting relation is

$$[E_g{}^{(2)}]_{J, \tau, M_J} = \mu_g{}^2 \mathcal{E}^2 \left[\frac{J^2 - M_J{}^2}{J(2J - 1)(2J + 1)} \sum_{\tau'}' \frac{\lambda(J, \tau; J - 1, \tau')}{E^{(0)}{}_{J, \tau} - E^{(0)}{}_{J-1, \tau'}} \right.$$

$$+ \frac{M_J{}^2}{J(J + 1)(2J + 1)} \sum_{\tau' \neq \tau}' \frac{\lambda(J, \tau; J, \tau')}{E^{(0)}{}_{J, \tau} - E^{(0)}{}_{J, \tau'}}$$

$$\left. + \frac{(J + 1)^2 - M_J{}^2}{(J + 1)(2J + 1)(2J + 3)} \sum_{\tau'}' \frac{\lambda(J, \tau; J + 1, \tau')}{E^{(0)}{}_{J, \tau} - E^{(0)}{}_{J+1, \tau'}} \right]. \quad (3.19)$$

The prime over the summation indicates that the summation is to extend only over those values of $J'\tau'$ for which $E^{(0)}{}_{J', \tau'}$ is not near $E^{(0)}{}_{J, \tau}$. This formidable-looking array actually contains only terms connected by dipole radiation to the particular energy level under consideration (see discussion following Eq. 3.8). The energy differences may be observed spectroscopic values or, where these are not available, may be computed from King, Hainer, and Cross's energy level tables.[18]

The absolute intensities of the component lines depend upon J, τ, and M_J as well as upon the asymmetry parameter of the molecule. We are concerned here with the relative intensities of the Stark components of a given line, the M_J dependence of the intensities. These are readily obtained from the dipole matrix elements and are [2]

$$I_{M_J} = P(J, \tau, \kappa)M_J{}^2 \qquad \Delta J = 0 \qquad \Delta M = 0$$

$$\quad (3.20)$$

$$I_{M_J} = Q(J, \tau, \kappa)\{(J + 1)^2 - M_J{}^2\} \qquad \Delta J = \pm 1 \qquad \Delta M = 0,$$

where J is the smaller of the two quantum numbers involved in the transition. Equation 3.20 is particularly useful in distinguishing $\Delta J = 0$ from $\Delta J = \pm 1$ transitions. Intensities for transitions in which $\Delta M = \pm 1$ (electric field not parallel to Stark field), if they are needed, can be obtained from Eqs. 3.44–3.46 since the Stark and Zeeman components have the same intensities.

The general nature of Stark splittings in asymmetric-top molecules is illustrated in Fig. 3.3, where, to the same scale, patterns for the $0_{00} \rightarrow 1_{11}$, $2_{02} \rightarrow 2_{11}$, $3_{13} \rightarrow 4_{04}$, and $4_{04} \rightarrow 4_{13}$ transitions of SO_2 are shown. Note the characteristic difference in the intensity pattern for $\Delta J = 0$ and $\Delta J = 1$ transitions. Note also that the Stark patterns may be on one side or both sides of the main line; frequency may increase or decrease with increase in M_J.

In their paper, Golden and Wilson [2] point out the possibilities of accidental degeneracy of levels for asymmetric-top molecules (even for

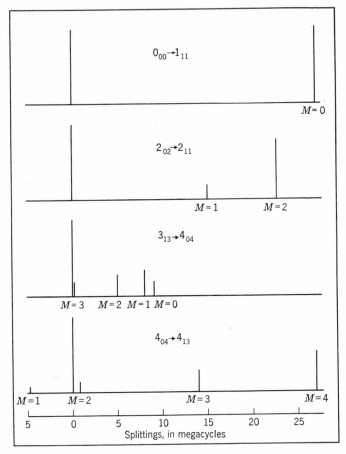

FIG. 3.3. Stark pattern for low-J transitions of the asymmetric rotor, SO_2. (From G. Crable, Ph.D. Thesis, Duke.)

low-J number) and analyze this case in some detail. Here a linear Stark effect may appear giving rise to $2J + 1$ component lines. Also transitions with $|\Delta J| > 1$ become possible. It should be pointed out, however, that, although such degeneracies are possible, coincidences to within, say, 50 Mc are rare. Quadratic Stark effects as large as this are seldom observed because of the large fields necessary. The well-known linear Stark effect in a series of methyl alcohol lines [19, 20] is ascribed to the hindered internal rotation of the OH group. For this type of molecule, rigid rotor analysis is not satisfactory and must be replaced by a consideration of the internal rotation,[21] as well as the over-all rotation of the molecule. Figure 3.4 illustrates the first-order Stark effect. It is a recorded tracing of an internal rotational transition corresponding to $J = 6$ in methyl alcohol.

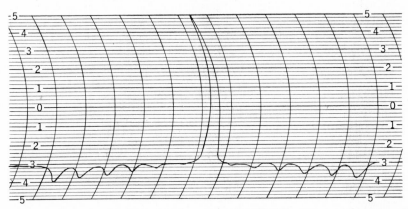

FIG. 3.4.   First-order Stark effect in the spectrum of CH_3OH. The restricted internal rotational line at 25,018 Mc ($J = 6$). The pattern was obtained with a phase-lock-in detector followed by an Esterline-Angus recorder. With this system the Stark components point downward; the zero-field line points upward. A 40-volt, square modulation at 100 kc was employed. (By John Cox, of Duke.)

3.1b. Stark Effect of Molecules with Nuclear Quadrupole Coupling.

The problem of the Stark effect in linear molecules having a nucleus with quadrupole coupling has been solved by Fano.[22] Extensions to symmetric-top rotational spectra have been made by Low and Townes,[23] and by Coester.[1] The extension to asymmetric rotors is straightforward although, in general, tediously involved because of the nature of asymmetric wave functions. The Stark effect in the $N^{14}H_3$ inversion spectrum has been worked out by Jauch.[11] The weak-field case for asymmetric rotors has been treated by Mizushima.[8b]

The Hamiltonian for a rotor in an external field having quadrupole coupling is

$$H = H^{(0)} + H_Q + H_{\mathcal{E}}, \qquad (3.21)$$

where $H^{(0)}$ is the Hamiltonian for the unperturbed rotor, solutions of which are given in Chapter 2. H_Q is the quadrupole-coupling Hamiltonian of Eq. 2.72, and $H_{\mathcal{E}}$, the energy in the electric field $-\mu\mathcal{E}\cos\theta$, where θ is the angle between $\mathbf{\mu}$ and $\mathbf{\mathcal{E}}$. It is convenient to divide the problem into three parts: the weak-field case, in which $H_\varepsilon \ll H_Q$; the intermediate-field case, in which $H_\varepsilon \sim H_Q$; and the strong-field case, in which $H_\varepsilon \gg H_Q$.

Symmetric-top molecules: weak-field solution. We consider the single nucleus with coupling. When $\boldsymbol{\mu} \cdot \boldsymbol{\mathcal{E}} \ll eQq \ll B, F, M_F, J, K,$ and I are good quantum numbers, but M_J is not. The Stark effect can now be regarded as a correction upon the quadrupole splitting. The level characterized by $E_r + E_Q$ is regarded as the principal state and $\boldsymbol{\mu} \cdot \boldsymbol{\mathcal{E}}$ treated as a perturbation. There are then $2F + 1$ Stark components of a given F level. The first-order Stark perturbation energies may then be obtained from

$$E_\varepsilon^{(1)} = (FM_FJKI| \boldsymbol{\mu} \cdot \boldsymbol{\mathcal{E}} |FM_FJKI), \qquad (3.22)$$

in which the required wave functions are obtained from an expansion of the normalized, orthogonal wave functions of the unperturbed rotor and the nuclear spin function.

$$\psi_{FM_FJKI} = \sum_{M_J} C(FM_FJIM_J)\psi_{JKM_J} \cdot \psi_{IM_I}. \qquad (3.23)$$

The substitution of this wave function in Eq. 3.22 yields, upon integration,[23]

$$E_\varepsilon^{(1)} = -\frac{\mu\mathcal{E}K}{J(J+1)} \sum_{M_J} |C_{M_J}(FM_FJI)|^2 M_J. \qquad (3.24)$$

The summed expression is just the average of M_J over the wave function, ψ_{FM_FJI}, which when evaluated [24] gives for the first-order energy

$$E^{(1)}_{FJKM_F} = -\frac{\mu\mathcal{E}KM_F}{J(J+1)} \frac{[F(F+1) + J(J+1) - I(I+1)]}{2F(F+1)}$$

$$= -\frac{\mu\mathcal{E}KM_F\alpha_J}{J(J+1)}. \qquad (3.25)$$

The quantity α_J is numerically evaluated in Table $A.11$ for low values of J. To obtain the total energy of the perturbed rotor, $E_\varepsilon^{(1)}$ must be added to $E_r + E_Q$, as given in Chapter 2.

Equation 3.25 can also be derived from the vector-model treatment. Since this treatment gives more physical insight into the problem, it will also be summarized. The characteristic Stark energy for a given state is the product of the field $\boldsymbol{\mathcal{E}}$ and the average component of the electric dipole moment which lies along $\boldsymbol{\mathcal{E}}$ for the particular energy state of the molecule. In a symmetric-top molecule the dipole moment lies along $\mathbf{K}$ and has a component $\mu_J = \mu K/\sqrt{J(J+1)}$ along $\mathbf{J}$. In the weak-field case considered, $\mathbf{J}$ and $\mathbf{I}$ form a resultant about which they both precess. The dipole component then has a component along $\mathbf{F}$ which is $\mu_F = \mu_J \cos (\mathbf{F}, \mathbf{J})$, where $(\mathbf{F}, \mathbf{J})$ denotes the angle between $\mathbf{F}$

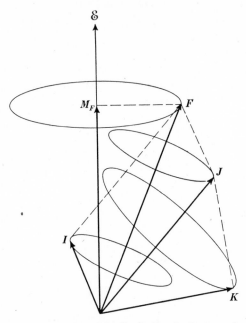

FIG. 3.5. Vector model of the weak-field Stark effect in the hyperfine structure of the rotational spectrum of a symmetric-top molecule.

and $\mathbf{J}$. Because of the interaction of μ_F with the field, $\mathbf{F}$ will precess about $\mathcal{E}$ as indicated in Fig. 3.5. The component of $\boldsymbol{\mu}$ along $\mathcal{E}$ is then

$$\mu_\mathcal{E} = \mu_F \frac{M_F}{\sqrt{F(F+1)}} = \frac{\mu K M_F \cos (\mathbf{F} \ \mathbf{J})}{\sqrt{J(J+1)F(F+1)}}.$$

With

$$\cos (\mathbf{F}, \mathbf{J}) = \frac{F(F+1) + J(J+1) - I(I+1)}{2F(F+1)J(J+1)},$$

determined from the cosine law, this expression for $\mu_\mathcal{E}$ substituted in $E_\mathcal{E} = -\mu_\mathcal{E}\mathcal{E}$ yields Eq. 3.25.

In the vector model treatment it is assumed that F, J, K, I, and M_F are good quantum numbers. It is apparent that, if this treatment is to apply, the precession of $\mathbf{K}$ about $\mathbf{J}$ must be rapid as compared with that of $\mathbf{J}$ about $\mathbf{F}$ and that the precession of $\mathbf{J}$ about $\mathbf{F}$ must be rapid as compared with that of $\mathbf{F}$ about $\mathcal{E}$. These conditions are inherent in the first-order perturbation treatment of this case which holds only when $B \gg eQq \gg \mu_\varepsilon\varepsilon$.

It is interesting to note that for the largest values of F and M_F, i.e., when $F = J + I = M_F$, Eq. 3.25 reduces to

$$E^{(1)} = -\mu\varepsilon K/(J + 1), \qquad (3.26)$$

and hence for this case $E_\varepsilon^{(1)}$ is independent of the nuclear quadrupole effects. Note also that the first-order energy is zero for $K = 0$.

The second-order effect for a symmetric top can be expressed as

$$E_\varepsilon^{(2)} = \sum_{\substack{F \\ F' \neq F}} \sum_{\substack{J \\ J' \neq J}} \frac{\left| (FM_FJKI \left| \boldsymbol{\mu} \cdot \boldsymbol{\varepsilon} \right| F'M_FJ'KI) \right|^2}{E^{(0)}_{FM_FJKI} - E^{(0)}_{F'M_FJ'KI}}. \qquad (3.27)$$

The needed wave functions are again obtained by expansions in terms of those of the unperturbed rotor and nuclear spin function. The transformations, which are too involved to give here, lead to the second-order energies,[23,1]

$$E^{(2)}_{\substack{FJKM_F \\ (J \neq 0)}} = \frac{\mu^2\varepsilon^2 K^2}{eQq[3K^2 - J(J + 1)]J(J + 1)}$$

$$\left[\frac{R(F)(F^2 - M_F^2)}{Y(F) - Y(F - 1)} - \frac{R(F + 1)\{(F + 1)^2 - M_F^2\}}{Y(F) - Y(F + 1)} \right]$$

$$- \frac{\mu^2\varepsilon^2[3M_F^2 - F(F + 1)][3D(D - 1) - 4F(F + 1)J(J + 1)]}{hB2J(J + 1)(2J - 1)(2J + 3)2F(F + 1)(2F - 1)(2F + 3)} \qquad (3.28)$$

where

(a) $$R(F) = \frac{[F^2 - (I - J)^2][(I + J + 1)^2 - F^2]}{4F^2(2F - 1)(2F + 1)}$$

(b) $$Y(F) = \frac{\frac{3}{4}C(C + 1) - I(I + 1)J(J + 1)}{2(2J + 3)(2J - 1)I(2I - 1)}$$

(c) $$C = F(F + 1) - I(I + 1) - J(J + 1)$$

(d) $$D = F(F + 1) - I(I + 1) + J(J + 1).$$

The function $Y(F)$, giving the quadrupole splitting at zero field, is tabulated in A.10 of the Appendix. When $J = 0$, E_Q is also zero, and $E_\varepsilon^{(2)}$ is given by Eq. 3.13b.

The second-order correction Eq. 3.28 appears formidable. It is also of limited usefulness except for $K = 0$, when the first-order effect vanishes. This may be seen by referring to Fig. 3.6, where the weak-

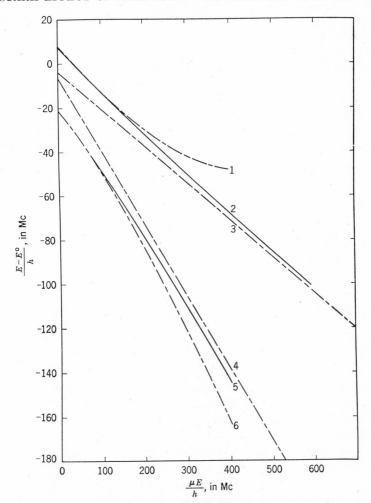

FIG. 3.6. Stark splitting of the $J = 2$, $K = 1$ level of AsF$_3$ as a function of $\mu\mathcal{E}/h$. Curve: (1) for $F = \frac{7}{2}$, $M_F = \frac{5}{2}$, weak-field approximation; (2) accurate solution; (3) $M_J = 1$, strong-field approximation.   Curve: (4) $M_J = 2$, strong-field approximation; (5) accurate solution; (6) $F = \frac{5}{2}$, $M_F = \frac{5}{2}$, weak-field approximation. (For As, $I = \frac{3}{2}$, $eQq = -235$ Mc.)

field solutions for AsF$_3$, $J = 2$, $K = 1$, $M = \frac{5}{2}$, $F = \frac{5}{2}$, $\frac{7}{2}$, are plotted as curves 1 and 6. The accurate intermediate-field solutions that connect weak- and strong-field solutions are also plotted (curves 2 and 5), and will be discussed later. It is clear, however, that the quadratic Eq. 3.28 cannot bridge much of the gap between the strong- and weak-field solutions.

Symmetric-top molecules: strong-field solutions. If the electric field interaction is very strong, ($| \mu\varepsilon | \gg | eQq |$), the nuclear spin **I** and angular momentum **J** are uncoupled and precess separately about the field direction. Thus the appropriate quantum numbers are J, K, I, M_J, and M_I. As the nucleus has no electric dipole moment, its orientations in the electric field have identical energies so that the strong-field Stark effect, if quadrupole interactions are neglected, is still given by Eqs. 3.6 and 3.9. The quadrupole interaction may now be treated as a small perturbation upon the Stark levels, except when $| M_J | = 1$. The appropriate representation is JKM_JM_I, and the first-order quadrupole perturbation energy in this case is

$$E_Q{}^{(1)} = (JKIM_JM_I| \, H_Q \, |JKIM_JM_I)$$

$$= eQq \left\{ \frac{3K^2}{J(J+1)} - 1 \right\} \frac{[3M_J{}^2 - J(J+1)][3M_I{}^2 - I(I+1)]}{4I(2I-1)(2J-1)(2J+3)}.$$

(3.29)

This correction is to be added to the Stark levels determined for the molecule without quadrupole coupling (Art. 3.1a). If there are two quadrupole moments one adds the coupling of the second nucleus determined in the same way.

The strong-field solution when $| M_J | = 1$ cannot always be obtained by the above method, although it can when $| M_J | = 1$ if $M_J = 1$ and $M_J + M_I = I, I + 1$. In general, when $M_J = 1$ and $M_J + M_I = 1$, the energy must be obtained from the solution of the appropriate secular equation which is given by Low and Townes.[23]

Symmetric-top molecules: intermediate-field solution. The intermediate-field solution for which $H_\varepsilon \sim H_Q \ll H^{(o)}$ is generally complex. Low and Townes [23] give the secular equations and matrix formulation from which the energies can be obtained. The evaluations are straightforward though laborious.

For $F = I + J$ and $M_F = F$ it has been shown (Eq. 3.26) that weak-, strong-, and intermediate-field solutions are identical. If the d-c field is perpendicular to the r-f electric field, the selection rule $\Delta M_F = 1$ holds so that this simple theory is applicable. In most experimental set-ups the d-c and r-f fields are parallel, however, and $\Delta M_F = 0$. In this case the M_F value of the upper level is 1 less than its maximum value when $M_F = F$ for the lower level. Fortunately, a simple, accurate solution is also possible for this case. From the results of Low and Townes it can be shown that the general solution for $F = I + J$ or $I + J - 1$ and $M_F = I + J - 1$ is of the form

$$E_{I+J, J, K, I+J-1} = \frac{E_Q \, (F = I + J) + E_Q \, (F = I + J - 1)}{2}$$

$$+ B(\mu\mathcal{E}) \pm \left[\frac{\{E_{(Q)} \, (F = I + J) - E_Q \, (F = I + J - 1)\}^2}{4} \right. $$

$$\left. + C(\mu\mathcal{E}) + D^2(\mu\mathcal{E})^2 \right]^{\frac{1}{2}}, \quad (3.30)$$

where the zero-field splittings E_Q are obtainable from Table $A.10$. The other constants may be evaluated most simply by expanding Eq. 3.30 in power series appropriate in the strong- and weak-field approximations and comparing with Eqs. 3.6 and 3.25 or, for $F = I + J$, with Eq. 3.26. The intermediate-field solution so obtained is plotted in Fig. 3.6 for comparison with strong- and weak-field solutions. It is to be noted that the above method of calculation does not require calculation of the exact intermediate-field wave functions. In this example the weak-field solution is satisfactory up to $\mu\mathcal{E}/h = 10$ Mc (a frequency shift of 30 Mc for the $F = \frac{5}{2} \rightarrow \frac{7}{2}$ line), whereas the strong-field solution is satisfactory only off the range of the graph at about $\mu\mathcal{E}/h = 1000$ Mc (a frequency splitting of 200 Mc for the $M_J = 1 \rightarrow 1$ line). The molecule AsF$_3$ was chosen as a fitting illustration since many molecules have either much larger or much smaller quadrupole couplings so that either strong- or weak-field approximation is easily realizable physically. Furthermore, for high-J values (and therefore high F) there is much less difference between strong- and weak-field cases. For example, for $J = 10$, $I = 1$, $F = J + I = 11$, $M_F = F - 1 = 10$, $M_J = (J - 1)$, the ratio of strong- to weak-field values of $\dfrac{d(E^{(1)})}{d(\mu\mathcal{E})}$ is $\dfrac{(J - 1)F}{J(F - 1)} = 0.99$.

Linear molecules. The Stark effect in quadrupole hyperfine structure for a linear molecule is quite similar to that for a symmetric top and the energies may be obtained if K is set equal to 0 in the various symmetric-top formulas given. In the strong-field case the energy levels are given by Eq. 3.13, with the added (small) quadrupole splitting by Eq. 3.29 with $K = 0$. Examples are N_2O and ClCN.[13] The relation for the weak-field case [22] is obtained if K is replaced by 0 in Eq. 3.28. It is

$$E^{(2)}_{\substack{FJM_F \\ (J \neq 0)}} = - \frac{\mu^2 \mathcal{E}^2}{hB} [3M_F^2 - F(F + 1)]$$

$$\times \frac{3D(D - 1) - 4F(F + 1)J(J + 1)}{2J(J + 1)(2J - 1)(2J + 3)2F(F + 1)(2F - 1)(2F + 3)}, \quad (3.31)$$

where $D = F(F + 1) + J(J + 1) - I(I + 1)$.

Again the case $F = J + I$ is the simplest. For it, Eq. 3.31 becomes

$$E^{(2)}{}_{J+I, J, M_F} = -\frac{\mu^2 \mathcal{E}^2}{hB}\left[\frac{3M_F{}^2 - F(F + 1)}{(J + 1)(2J + 3)(2F)(2F - 1)}\right]. \quad (3.32)$$

For the largest value of $M_F = F$, this reduces to

$$E^{(2)}{}_{J+I, J, J+I} = -\frac{\mu^2 \mathcal{E}^2}{2hB(J + 1)(2J + 3)} \quad (3.33)$$

which is identical to Eq. 3.13 for $M_J = J$. Thus no quadrupole effects exist for the $M_F = F = J + I$ level.

The intermediate-field solution for linear molecules with quadrupole coupling for $F = J + I$, $M = F - 1$ is also quite analogous to that for symmetric top.

Asymmetric rotors. The general method of approach for the asymmetric-top molecules with one nucleus having quadrupole coupling is the same as that outlined for symmetric tops. For the weak-field case one chooses the representation FM_FJI which will diagonalize H_Q, and then one uses the corresponding wave functions (obtained by expansion of the rotor and nuclear spin functions) to calculate the Stark perturbation energies of the hyperfine levels.

In the strong-field case the quadrupole interaction is treated as perturbation on the Stark levels with the latter obtained as for molecules without hyperfine structure (Art. 3.1a). The term in the brackets $[3(\mathbf{J}\cdot\mathbf{I})^2 + \frac{3}{2}(\mathbf{J}\cdot\mathbf{I}) - \mathbf{J}^2\mathbf{I}^2]$ of the quadrupole interaction Hamiltonian of Eq. 2.72 has diagonal elements $\frac{1}{2}[3M_J{}^2 - J(J + 1)][3M_I{}^2 - I(I + 1)]$ when evaluated in the $M_J M_I$ representation. The quadrupole perturbation to be added to the Stark levels in the strong-field case is therefore

$$E_Q = eQ\left\langle\frac{\partial^2 V}{\partial Z^2}\right\rangle_{Av} \frac{[3M_I{}^2 - I(I + 1)][3M_J{}^2 - J(J + 1)]}{8J(2J - 1)I(2I - 1)}, \quad (3.34)$$

where the value of $\left\langle\dfrac{\partial^2 V}{\partial Z^2}\right\rangle_{Av}$ given in Eq. 2.77 can be used, or if preferable it can be obtained in other terms if Eq. 2.81 is divided by $\dfrac{2J + 3}{2J} Y(F)$.

When, as is usual, the rotational energy levels are widely spaced as compared with the hyperfine splitting of these levels, one can obtain the weak-field solution by replacing $M_J{}^2$ in Eq. 3.19 by its quantum mechanical average in the $FJIM_F$ representation. This average, already obtained by Fano,[22] is

$$\overline{M}_J{}^2 = \frac{[3M_F{}^2 - F(F + 1)][3D(D - 1) - 4F(F + 1)J(J + 1)]}{6F(F + 1)(2F - 1)(2F + 3)}$$

$$+ \frac{J(J + 1)}{3} \quad (3.35)$$

where $D = F(F + 1) - I(I + 1) + J(J + 1)$.

One important case $F = J + I$, $M_F = F$ is simple. Here the Stark splitting is not affected by the quadrupole coupling. Since it is generally possible to observe $\Delta J = 0$ transitions for asymmetric tops, it is possible to select transitions for which $F = J + I$, $M_F = F$ for both levels of the transition. For such transitions the observed frequency shifts in the presence of an electric field are not affected by the quadrupole coupling, so that dipole moments may be computed directly from Eq. 3.19. Loomis and Strandberg [25] have used $\Delta J = 0$, $F = J + I$, $M_F = F$ transitions to measure the dipole moments of deuterated arsine and stibine.

Intensities. In the weak-field case the relative intensities (M_F dependence) are:

$$I_{M_F} = Q[(F + 1)^2 - M_F{}^2] \quad \text{for } \Delta F = \pm 1,\ \Delta M_F = 0$$

$$I_{M_F} = PM_F{}^2 \quad \text{for } \Delta F = 0,\ \Delta M_F = 0, \quad (3.36)$$

where F is the smaller value involved in the transition and P and Q are parameters, independent of M_F, which depend upon the strength of the unsplit line. The M_F dependence in the strong-field representation is given by Eq. 3.36 with F replaced by J and M_F by M_J, where P and Q are parameters independent of M_J. The intensities for intermediate fields can be approximated by extrapolation from the strong- to the weak-field case.

3.2. EFFECTS OF MAGNETIC FIELDS

3.2a. Molecules in $^1\Sigma$ States. Practically all molecules have "nonmagnetic" $^1\Sigma$ ground states. The average molecule in the $^1\Sigma$ state does have, however, a very small molecular magnetic moment (of the order of a nuclear magneton) which arises from molecular rotations or from slight contributions from excited "magnetic" states. In addition, some of the nuclei usually have magnetic moments which are of the same order of magnitude as the molecular moment. When the spins of these nuclei are strongly coupled to the molecular frame via the nuclear quadrupole moment, their magnetic moments contribute to the over-all magnetic moment of the molecule. These small moments are suffi-cient to cause observable Zeeman effects in the microwave rotational spectra of most molecules. This was first shown in the inversion spec-trum of NH_3 by Coles and Good [9] and has been amply verified by Jen [26] with a number of significant observations. Fields of several kilogauss are usually required to produce resolvable Zeeman splittings of the microwave lines of molecules in $^1\Sigma$ states.

Molecular rotational effects. The small magnetic moment associated with molecular rotation can be represented by

$$\mu_J = g_J \beta_I \mathbf{J}, \qquad (3.37)$$

where g_J is the molecular gyromagnetic ratio which is a function of the rotational state, β_I is the nuclear magneton, and $\mathbf{J}$ is the angular mo-mentum vector. For a molecule in a $^1\Sigma$ state containing only nuclei of zero spin, Eq. 3.37 represents the sole contribution to the magnetic moment. The energy of interaction with the field $\mathbf{H}$ is then $-g_J\beta_I\mathbf{J}\cdot\mathbf{H}$, and the allowed energy values (first order) are

$$E_H{}^{(1)} = -g_J\beta_I M_J H, \qquad (3.38)$$

where $M_J = J, J - 1 \cdots - J$. Equation 3.38 with the Bohr condition gives the Zeeman splitting of a rotational line $J \to J'$ as

$$\Delta\nu = [-g_J' \Delta M_J + (g_J - g_J')M_J] \frac{\beta_I H}{h} \qquad (3.39)$$

$$\approx \frac{-g_J\beta_I \Delta M_J H}{h} = -762 g_J \Delta M_J H, \qquad (3.40)$$

where the latter form assumes $g_J \approx g_J'$ and gives $\Delta\nu$ in cycles per second when H is in gauss. This assumption has been found to hold in all cases studied except ozone. M_J and g_J refer to the lower state and g_J' to the upper. The selection rules are

$$\Delta M_J = 0 \quad \text{for } \pi \text{ transitions,}$$

$$\Delta M_J = \pm 1 \quad \text{for } \sigma \text{ transitions.}$$

When H is parallel to the electric vector of the radiation field, the π components ($\Delta M = 0$ transitions) are observed. With the approxima-tion $g_J = g_{J+1}$, a single undisplaced π component is observed. When H is perpendicular to the E vector of the radiation field, the σ com-ponents are observed. These are spaced $(g_J\beta_I H)/h$ above and below the undisplaced line. These conditions apply to electric dipole coupling to the radiation field, as is the case for pure rotational spectra. When the coupling is through the magnetic vector, the conditions are reversed; i.e., the σ components are observed when H is perpendicular to the magnetic vector of the radiation, and the π components are observed when H is parallel to the magnetic vector. With $g_J = 1$, a field of 5000 gauss yields a splitting of only 4 Mc. Since the g_J's usually observed (see Table 3.1) are less than unity, relatively high fields are re-

Table 3.1. Rotational g factors (From Jen.[26d])

Molecule	Transition	g Value (average) †
H_2O	5_{-1} —— 6_{-5}	0.586 ± 0.012
NH_3	Inversion	$+0.477 \pm 0.030$
HDO	5_0 —— 5_1	0.439 ± 0.009
N_2O	$0 \to 1$	0.086 ± 0.004
SO_2	$7_{2,\,6}$ —— $8_{1,\,7}$	0.084 ± 0.010
OCS	$1 \to 2$	0.029 ± 0.006

† Sign uncertain unless specified.

quired to resolve the simple Zeeman pattern of Eq. 3.40. It appears from Eq. 3.39 that the Zeeman effect might be useful in identifying the rotational transition in asymmetric tops. In practice, however, the structure dependent on M_J, indicated by the last term, is not resolvable with available field strengths. A rather large dependence of the rotational g_J factor in ozone has been found by Trambarulo, Ghosh, Burrus, and Gordy,[28a] who obtained $| g_J | = 0.15$ for the 2_{02} state and 1.54 for the 1_{11} state.

When the molecule is non-linear, the g_J of Eq. 3.37 may be a function of inner quantum numbers. Let us suppose, for example, that the molecule is a symmetric top with a component of magnetic moment $g_K \beta_I K$ along the symmetry axis and a component $g_N \beta_I N$ (where $N = \sqrt{J(J+1) - K^2}$) perpendicular to this axis. Then it may be readily proved from the vector diagram of the precessing top that

$$g_J = \left[g_N + (g_K - g_N) \frac{K^2}{J(J+1)} \right].$$

For a further discussion of molecular g factors, see Chapter 7.

Although, strictly speaking, Eq. 3.39 or Eq. 3.40 applies only to molecules having all nuclear spins of zero, it applies in a practical sense to all molecules which do not have a resolvable hyperfine structure. Since the interaction of the largest known nuclear magnetic moment with the largest known μ_J of a $^1\Sigma$ state can barely produce a resolvable magnetic hyperfine structure, this theory applies approximately to all molecules which have no observable nuclear quadrupole interaction.

This includes nuclear spins of $\frac{1}{2}$ as well as of zero, and certain cases with $I > \frac{1}{2}$ when the eQq is very small. Figure 1.4 shows the Zeeman splitting of one of the NH_3 lines by Jen. The field polarization was such that only σ components were observed.

Because of the symmetry of the Zeeman pattern, the measurements do not yield the sign of g_J directly. However, Jen has pointed out that the sign of g_J may be determined by the use of circularly polarized radiation. One or the other of the σ components can then be made to disappear, according to the sense of the rotation. Jen [26c] has also pointed out that the sign of g_J can be determined when there is coupling by a nucleus of known moment.

Zeeman effect in hyperfine structure. The Zeeman effect in nuclear quadrupole hyperfine structure is important because, among other things, it can be used to evaluate nuclear magnetic moments of rare or radioactive nuclei. In the present treatment we assume only one nucleus with coupling, and this coupling sufficiently strong so that it is not broken down by the fields applied. For this important case the Zeeman effect in the hyperfine structure of molecules is completely analogous to the atomic hyperfine spectra. F and J are good quantum numbers, and the simple vector-model treatment [27] yields the characteristic energies,[26]

$$E_H^{(1)} = -(\alpha_J g_J + \alpha_I g_I)\beta_I' M_F H, \tag{3.41}$$

where

$$\alpha_J = \frac{F(F + 1) + J(J + 1) - I(I + 1)}{2F(F + 1)},$$

$$\alpha_I = \frac{F(F + 1) + I(I + 1) - J(J + 1)}{2F(F + 1)},$$

where

$$F = J + I, J + I - 1 \cdots |J - I|$$

$$M_F = F, F - 1 \cdots - F,$$

and the selection rules

$$\Delta M_F = 0, \pm 1$$

apply. For electric dipole radiation (rotational spectra) the π components, $\Delta M_F = 0$, are observed when the E vector of the microwave radiation is parallel to the external H, and the σ components, $\Delta M_F = \pm 1$, are observed when this vector is perpendicular to H. The energies of Eq. 3.41 are to be added to the zero-field quadrupole energies of a given F. For convenience, numerical values of α_J and α_I are given in Table $A.11$.

When the nuclear g_I factor and the spin I are known, Eq. 3.41 can be used to evaluate g_J. This application has been made by Jen on methyl chloride. See Fig. 3.7. He showed that g_J in this case is very small in comparison with g_I. When the g_J is thus determined with a

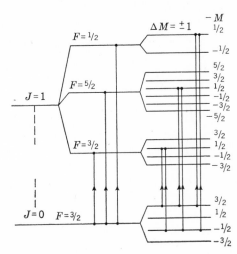

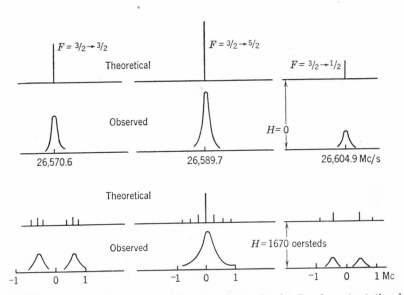

FIG. 3.7. Energy-level diagram and Zeeman splitting for the $J = 0 \rightarrow 1$ rotational transition of CH_3Cl^{35}. $I(Cl^{35}) = \frac{3}{2}$, $g_I(Cl^{35}) = 0.547$, and $g_J \ll g_I$ (Cl^{35}). [From Jen, Phys. Rev. 74, 1396 (1948).]

known isotope, this factor can be assumed to a good approximation to hold for other isotopes of the same element. Equation 3.41 can then be applied to determine the g_I of the other isotopes which may be unknown. This application was made by Gordy, Gilliam, and Livingston [28] to determine the magnetic moment of the radioactive element I^{129}. The μ_J for methyl iodide was first shown to be negligible by measurements with I^{127}. Figure 3.8 shows the pattern which they obtained for one of the hyperfine lines. In a similar application, Eshbach, Hillger, and

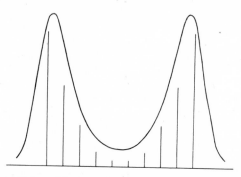

FIG. 3.8.   Zeeman splitting of the hyperfine structure of the $J = 2 \rightarrow 3$ transition of CH_3I^{129}. $F = \frac{9}{2} \rightarrow \frac{9}{2}$. $\Delta M_F = 0$. Separation of the observed peaks is 2.25 Mc. $H = 3700$ gauss.   Bars represent calculated lines; curve represents the observed spectrum. (From Gordy, Gilliam, and Livingston.[28])

Jen [29] measured the magnetic moment of the stable but rare isotope S^{33}. They established the sign of the magnetic moment by employing circularly polarized microwaves as suggested by Jen. (See above.)

The nuclear quadrupole coupling of I^{127} is so strong that the Zeeman splitting with fields of a few kilogauss is small in comparison. Hence, the first-order theory of Eq. 3.41 should apply in the experiment of Gordy, Gilliam, and Livingston.[28] They obtained, however, an anomalous splitting of the $F = \frac{5}{2} \rightarrow \frac{7}{2}$ transitions at low fields for CH_3I^{127}. This anomaly has been explained by Jauch [30] on the basis of perturbations of neighboring levels.

The relative intensities of the various Zeeman components of a given hyperfine transition are the same as those for the Stark components. They can be obtained from Eqs. 3.44–3.46.

Paschen-Back effect in hyperfine structure.†   Here we consider only nuclear quadrupole hyperfine structure with sufficiently small spacing so that the coupling can be broken down completely with attainable

† This is sometimes referred to as the Back-Goudsmit effect since the strong-field case was first observed for hyperfine structure by these observers.

magnetic field strengths. (No treatment of the involved intermediate-field case will be given, since in measuring g_I or g_J one can usually adjust the field to give either the weak-field or strong-field case.) This includes quadrupole coupling of a large number of nuclei such as B^{10}, B^{11}, N^{14}, O^{17}, and S^{33}, which have small, but not negligible, quadrupole moments. Some nuclei, such as deuterium, have such small quadrupole coupling that their perturbations can be neglected entirely. The nuclear magnetic hyperfine structure can likewise be neglected for molecules in $^1\Sigma$ states. Although the nuclear magnetic moments interact strongly with the imposed field, this interaction cannot observably perturb the spectral lines with which we are concerned, unless the nuclear spin is sufficiently coupled to the molecular frame to produce an observable zero-field hyperfine structure. Direct transitions between the Zeeman components M_I can, of course, be detected in the lower radio-frequency region (nuclear magnetic resonance spectra) with no coupling between I and the molecular frame.

The Paschen-Back effect in the quadrupole hyperfine structure of NH_3 and N_2O has been observed and analyzed by Jen.[31] The analysis is relatively simple. The quadrupole perturbation energies in the strong-field representation are added to the characteristic $\mathbf{J \cdot H}$ and $\mathbf{I \cdot H}$ energies to obtain the total splitting of the rotational energy state as

$$E_H = -g_J M_J \beta_I H - \beta_I H \sum_i g_{I_i} M_{I_i} -$$

$$\sum eQ_i \left\langle \left(\frac{\partial^2 V}{\partial Z^2}\right) \right\rangle_{i/\mathrm{Av}} \frac{\{3M_J^2 - J(J+1)\}\{3M_{I_i}^2 - I_i(I_i+1)\}}{8(2J-1)I_i(2I_i-1)}, \quad (3.42)$$

where $\left\langle \dfrac{\partial^2 V}{\partial Z^2} \right\rangle_{\mathrm{Av}}$ for various molecular types is given by Eqs. 2.75, 2.76, and 2.77. The summation is taken over the nuclei with quadrupole couplings, all of which are assumed to be decoupled by the external field.

The Paschen-Back spectrum of a given rotational transition can be obtained from Eq. 3.42 by application of the Bohr condition with the selection rules

$$\Delta M_J = 0, \pm 1 \qquad \Delta M_{I_i} = 0.$$

The selection rule $\Delta M_{I_i} = 0$ means physically that the nuclear orientation does not change in an observable electric-dipole transition. The relative orientation of I and J does change, however, because of the change allowed in the molecular orientation. The latter change accounts for the quadrupole splitting in the strong-field case. Because of the selection rule $\Delta M_{I_i} = 0$ the term in $\mathbf{I \cdot H}$ (second term on the right side of Eq. 3.42) is of no consequence here. Small terms in $M_J M_{I_i}$ are neglected.

The Paschen-Back effect in quadrupole hyperfine structure is illustrated by the spectrum of N_2O in Fig. 3.9. Note that the σ and π components of the Zeeman triplet are evident with the smaller splittings

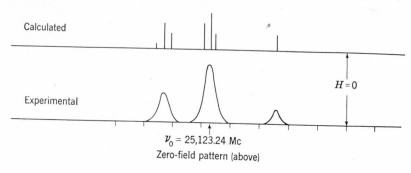

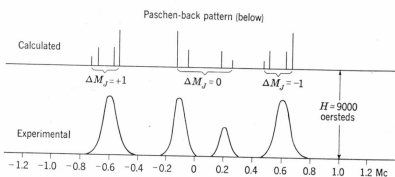

Fig. 3.9. Theoretical and experimental zero-field and Paschen-Back patterns for $N^{14}N^{14}O$, $J = 0 \rightarrow 1$, rotational transition. (From Jen.[31])

caused by the nuclear perturbations superimposed. The gross triplet results from the molecular g_J factor and is accounted for by the first term of Eq. 3.42, which is seen to be of the same form as Eq. 3.38. The quadrupole couplings of both N^{14} nuclei were broken down by fields of 8000 gauss. A further increase of field made no change in the observed pattern.

For a discussion of relative intensities in the Paschen-Back effect, see the paper by Jen.[31]

3.2b. Paramagnetic Molecules. A few molecules, O_2, NO, etc., have paramagnetic ground states. These have magnetic moments of the order of a Bohr magneton (~ 1800 times the nuclear magneton) as a result of unpaired electrons. When this magnetic moment is strongly coupled to the molecular frame, as it always is when there is an uncanceled electronic orbital moment (for example, in the $^2\Pi_{3/2}$ state of NO), its rotational spectrum is very sensitive to a magnetic field, and resolvable splitting can be obtained with only a few gauss. Even when the paramagnetic molecule has no orbital moment ($^2\Sigma$ as in NO_2 or $^3\Sigma$ as in O_2) the electron-spin magnetic moment will be coupled to the molecular rotational axis by interaction of the spin moment with the weak molecular rotational moments of the types mentioned above for $^1\Sigma$ states. Because of the large value of the electron spin moment, this coupling is sufficient to allow observation of a weak-field (Zeeman) splitting of the microwave spectral lines. The Zeeman splitting of this type has been observed in the microwave spectrum of oxygen.[32] Fields of the order of a kilogauss break down the internal couplings in paramagnetic molecules in a Σ state, either wholly or in part, so that an intermediate-field case or even a Paschen-Back effect might be observed. Evidence for a partial breaking down of the coupling in O_2 has been obtained by Beringer and Castle.[33]

If there are nuclei with magnetic moments in paramagnetic substances, these will couple to the electronic moment. This coupling will usually be of the same order of magnitude as the electron spin to molecular momentum coupling ($\mathbf{S} \cdot \mathbf{J}$ coupling) for paramagnetic Σ states ($^2\Sigma$ or $^3\Sigma$) and about 1800 times greater than the nuclear spin to molecular momentum coupling ($\mathbf{I} \cdot \mathbf{J}$) for $^1\Sigma$ states.

The interaction of the external field with the electron spin or the nuclear-spin magnetic moment cannot perturb the rotational energies unless these spin moments are in some way coupled to the molecular rotational axis. Therefore, the small μ_J ($\sim$ a nuclear magneton) of molecules in non-singlet Σ states which arises from molecular rotation is of significance in molecular Zeeman effects of paramagnetic molecules because it provides a means of coupling J with S and, indirectly, J with I through the $\mathbf{S} \cdot \mathbf{I}$ coupling. This coupling, with μ_J and the nuclear quadrupole coupling, is the only mechanism through which the $\mathbf{H} \cdot \mathbf{I}$ or the $\mathbf{H} \cdot \mathbf{S}$ interactions can perturb the rotational energies of molecules in Σ states.

Because of the small number of possible applications in the microwave region and the diversity of treatments required for them, the Zeeman effect of paramagnetic substances will not be treated quantitatively here. Nitric oxide, the only known stable molecule with orbital electronic momentum not zero, has no rotational transitions occurring in the microwave region. A few molecules in $^2\Sigma$ and $^3\Sigma$ states have absorption frequencies in the microwave region. The most important of these is perhaps O_2. Exclusive of nuclear effects (which do not occur in O_2 [16]) the Zeeman splitting of the spin doublet or triplet of the rotational levels is

$$E_H = -g\beta H M_J,$$ (3.43)

in which

$$g = \frac{J(J+1) + S(S+1) - N(N+1)}{J(J+1)}$$

and

$$\beta = \text{Bohr magneton.}$$

The selection rules $\Delta M_J = 0, \pm 1$ apply. Here N is the number quantizing the angular momentum of the molecule exclusive of the electron spin S, and J is the total momentum quantum number.

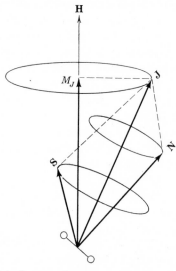

Fig. 3.10. Vector model of oxygen in a magnetic field. S represents the electronic spin momentum; N, the end-over-end molecular rotational momentum; J, the total angular momentum; M_J, the component of J along the external field. Ellipses indicate the precession of the various vectors.

Equation 3.43 is easily derived from the vector model of Fig. 3.10. The vectors S and N with magnitudes $\sqrt{S(S+1)}$ and $\sqrt{N(N+1)}$ are coupled through the interaction of the spin and rotational magnetic moments and precess about their resultant J (magnitude $\sqrt{J(J+1)}$), while J precesses at a much slower rate (weak-field case) about H. The spin magnetic moment $\mu_S = 2\beta\sqrt{S(S+1)}$ is along S and has a component $\mu_J = \mu_S \cos(S,J)$ along J. In comparison with μ_S, the rotational moment can be neglected in the Zeeman energy. Hence, $\mu_H = \mu_J$

$\cos (\mathbf{H,J}) = 2\beta\sqrt{S(S+1)} \cos (\mathbf{S,J}) \cos (\mathbf{H,J})$. From the geometry of

Fig. 3.10, $\cos (\mathbf{S,J}) = \dfrac{J(J+1) + S(S+1) - N(N+1)}{2\sqrt{J(J+1)}\sqrt{S(S+1)}}$ and $\cos (\mathbf{H,J})$

$= M_J/\sqrt{J(J+1)}$. Substitution of these values in the energy formula $E_H = \mu_H H$ yields Eq. 3.43.

The weak-field splittings of the oxygen line have been studied by Hill and Gordy.[32b] The g factors observed for the various levels were found to be in agreement with those predicted from the above formula. The theory of the Zeeman effect in oxygen which allows for decoupling within the molecule has been worked out by Henry.[33b]

Hyperfine structure can complicate the Zeeman effect greatly, as has been shown by the work of Margenau and Henry [34] on NO. However, the Zeeman effect in paramagnetic hyperfine structure might be relatively simple in some instances where the ratios of the various couplings are such that the vector-model treatment can be applied. The Zeeman effect in the hyperfine structure of a rotational line of NO_2 has been observed by McAfee [35] but has not yet been interpreted.

3.2c. Relative Intensities. The relative intensities of Zeeman components are

$$\left.\begin{aligned}I_{M_J \to M_J} &= PM_J{}^2 \\ I_{M_J \to M_J \pm 1} &= (P/4)(J \mp M_J)(J \pm M_J + 1)\end{aligned}\right\} J \to J, \qquad (3.44)$$

$$\left.\begin{aligned}I_{M_J \to M_J} &= Q[(J+1)^2 - M_J{}^2] \\ I_{M_J \to M_J \pm 1} &= (Q/4)(J \pm M_J + 1)(J \pm M_J + 2)\end{aligned}\right\} J \to J+1, \qquad (3.45)$$

$$\left.\begin{aligned}I_{M_J \to M_J} &= Q(J^2 - M_J{}^2) \\ I_{M_J \to M_J \pm 1} &= (Q/4)(J \mp M_J)(J \mp M_J - 1)\end{aligned}\right\} J \to J-1 \qquad (3.46)$$

where P and Q are parameters independent of M_J. The same rules apply either to Stark or Zeeman effects of nuclear hyperfine structure weak-field cases) if J is replaced by F and M_J by M_F.

REFERENCES

[1] F. Coester, *Phys. Rev.* 77, 454 (1950).

[2] S. Golden and E. B. Wilson, Jr., *J. Chem. Phys.* 16, 669 (1948).

[3] P. C. Cross, R. M. Hainer, and G. W. King, *J. Chem. Phys.* 12, 210 (1944).

[4] P. Debye and C. Manneback, *Nature 119*, 83 (1927).

[5] P. Debye, *Polar molecules* (Chemical Publishing Co., New York, 1929), Chapter IX; J. H. Van Vleck, *Theory of Electric and Magnetic Susceptibilities* (Clarendon Press, Oxford, 1932), Chapter VI.

[6] R. de L. Kronig, *Proc. Natl. Acad. Sci. 12*, 608 (1926).

[7] H. B. G. Casimir, *Z. Physik*, *59*, 623 (1930).

[8] (a) M. Mizushima, *Phys. Rev. 74*, 705 (1948); (b) *J. Chem. Phys.*, in press.

[9] D. K. Coles and W. E. Good, *Phys. Rev. 70*, 979 (1946).

[10] D. K. Coles, W. E. Good, J. K. Bragg, and A. H. Sharbaugh, *Phys. Rev. 82*, 877 (1951).

[11] J. M. Jauch, *Phys. Rev. 72*, 715 (1947).

[12] P. W. Anderson, *Phys. Rev. 76*, 656 (1949).

[13] R. G. Shulman, B. P. Dailey, and C. H. Townes, *Phys. Rev. 78*, 145 (1950).

[14] B. Bak, R. Sloan, and D. Williams, *Phys. Rev. 80*, 101 (1950).

[15] T. W. Dakin, W. E. Good, and D. K. Coles, *Phys. Rev. 70*, 560 (1946).

[16] W. G. Penney, *Phil. Mag. 11*, 602 (1931).

[17] M. W. P. Strandberg, T. Wentink, Jr., and A. G. Hill, *Phys. Rev. 75*, 827 (1949).

[18] G. W. King, R. M. Hainer, and P. C. Cross, *J. Chem. Phys. 11*, 27 (1943).

[19] B. P. Dailey, *Phys. Rev. 72*, 84 (1947).

[20] D. K. Coles, *Phys. Rev. 74*, 1194 (1948); R. H. Hughes, W. E. Good, and D. K. Coles, *Phys. Rev. 84*, 418 (1951).

[21] D. G. Burkhard and D. M. Dennison, *Phys. Rev. 84*, 408 (1951).

[22] U. Fano, *J. Research Natl. Bur. Standards 40*, 215 (1948).

[23] W. Low and C. H. Townes, *Phys. Rev. 76*, 1295 (1949).

[24] E. U. Condon, and G. H. Shortley, *The Theory of Atomic Spectra* (The Macmillan Co., New York, 1935), pp. 76–77.

[25] C. C. Loomis and M. W. P. Strandberg, *Phys. Rev. 81*, 798 (1951).

[26] C. K. Jen (a) *Phys. Rev. 74*, 1396 (1948); (b) *76*, 471 (1949); (c) *81*, 197 (1951); (d) *Physica 17*, 379 (1951).

[27] H. E. White, *Introduction to Atomic Spectra* (McGraw-Hill Book Company, New York, 1934), Chapter 18.

[28] (a) R. F. Trambarulo, S. N. Ghosh, C. A. Burrus, and W. Gordy, to be published; (b) W. Gordy, O. R. Gilliam, and R. Livingston, *Phys. Rev. 76*, 443 (1949).

[29] J. R. Eshbach, R. E. Hillger, and C. K. Jen, *Phys. Rev. 80*, 1106 (1950).

[30] J. M. Jauch, private communication.

[31] C. K. Jen, *Phys. Rev. 76*, 1494 (1949).

[32] (a) R. S. Anderson, C. H. Johnson, and W. Gordy, *Phys. Rev. 83*, 1061 (1951); (b) R. M. Hill and W. Gordy, to be published.

[33] (a) R. Beringer and J. G. Castle, Jr., *Phys. Rev. 75*, 1963 (1949); (b) see also, A. Henry, *Phys. Rev. 80*, 396 (1950).

[34] H. Margenau and A. Henry, *Phys. Rev. 78*, 587 (1950).

[35] K. B. McAfee, *Phys. Rev. 82*, 971 (1951).

4. SHAPES AND INTENSITIES OF ABSORPTION LINES OF GASES

4.1. THE MICROWAVE ABSORPTION COEFFICIENT

A straightforward development of the intensity formula for microwave absorption can be made from the Einstein transition coefficients. Consider non-degenerate quantum states J and J' in absorbing particles. The probability $p_{J \to J'}$ that a transition $J \to J'$ will be induced in unit time from the lower state J to the higher one J' by radiation of frequency $\nu_{JJ'}$ and density $\rho(\nu_{JJ'})$ is represented by the product

$$p_{J \to J'} = B_{J \to J'}\rho(\nu_{JJ'}), \tag{4.1}$$

where $B_{J \to J'}$ is the Einstein coefficient of induced absorption. The number of particles per cubic centimeter $N_{J \to J'}$ undergoing such transitions in unit time is

$$N_{J \to J'} = N_J p_{J \to J'} = N_J B_{J \to J'}\rho(\nu_{JJ'}), \tag{4.2}$$

where N_J is the total number of particles per cubic centimeter in the lower state J. The number undergoing the reverse transition in unit time similarly is

$$N_{J \leftarrow J'} = N_{J'}[A_{J \leftarrow J'} + B_{J \leftarrow J'}\rho(\nu_{JJ'})]$$

$$\approx N_{J'}B_{J \leftarrow J'}\rho(\nu_{JJ'}), \tag{4.3}$$

in which $B_{J \leftarrow J'}$ is the Einstein coefficient of induced emission, $A_{J \leftarrow J'}$ is the Einstein coefficient of spontaneous emission, and $N_{J'}$ is the number of particles in the upper state J'. At microwave frequencies the coefficient $A_{J \leftarrow J'}$ is extremely small in comparison with $B_{J \leftarrow J'}$ and can be neglected in laboratory experiments.† (The coefficient A increases as the cube of frequency and becomes of significance at optical frequencies.) Since the induced emission as well as the induced absorption is coherent

---

† Emission spectra have been observed, however, in an extended astronomical source.[1]

with the radiation $\rho(\nu_{JJ'})$, the net loss of energy density of frequency $\nu_{JJ'}$ in time Δt is

$$-\Delta\rho(\nu_{JJ'}) = h\nu_{JJ'}(N_{J \to J'} - N_{J \leftarrow J'}) \, \Delta t$$

$$= h\nu_{JJ'}(N_J B_{J \to J'} - N_{J'} B_{J \leftarrow J'})\rho(\nu_{JJ'}) \, \Delta t$$

$$= h\nu_{JJ'}(N_J - N_{J'})B_{J \to J'}\rho(\nu_{JJ'}) \, \Delta t. \tag{4.4}$$

In the last form, use has been made of the fact that $B_{J \to J'} = B_{J \leftarrow J'}$. The absorption of radiation at a given frequency therefore depends upon the difference in the populations of the upper and lower states as well as upon the Einstein coefficient of absorption and the radiation density. The absorption coefficient α is defined as $-(1/P)(dP/dx)$ where P is the power and $-dP/dx$ is its rate of loss with distance. Since $P = \text{const.} \times \rho$ and $dx = c \, dt$, α can be expressed as $-(1/c\rho) \times (d\rho/dt)$. Hence, from Eq. 4.4

$$\alpha_{J \to J'} = \frac{h\nu_{JJ'}}{c} (N_J - N_{J'})B_{J \to J'}. \tag{4.5}$$

In this expression c represents the velocity of propagation. If thermal equilibrium is maintained (radiation density sufficiently low to avoid the saturation effect), the Boltzmann distribution law requires

$$(N_{J'}/N_J) = e^{\frac{-h\nu_{JJ'}}{kT}}. \tag{4.6}$$

Hence,

$$N_J - N_{J'} = N_J(1 - e^{\frac{-h\nu_{JJ'}}{kT}}) \approx N_J \frac{h\nu_{JJ'}}{kT}. \tag{4.7}$$

The last approximation holds very well, since at microwave frequencies $h\nu \ll kT$ except at temperatures near absolute zero. Frequently, however, the thermal equilibrium is upset by excessive microwave power. This saturation effect will be discussed later. It can be shown from quantum mechanical perturbation theory (see, for example, Pauling and Wilson [2]) that for plane-polarized radiation

$$B_{J \to J'} = \frac{8\pi^3}{h^2} (J| \, \boldsymbol{\mu} \, |J')^2. \tag{4.8}$$

For isotropic radiation a factor of 3 must be inserted in the denominator. Here the expression in the parenthesis represents the matrix elements of the components of the dipole moment $\boldsymbol{\mu}$ which gives rise to the transition. See Sec. 4.4. Substitution of Eqs. 4.7 and 4.8 in Eq. 4.5 yields

$$\alpha_{J \to J'} = \frac{8\pi^3\nu_{JJ'}{}^2N_J}{ckT} (J| \, \boldsymbol{\mu} \, |J')^2. \tag{4.9}$$

Thus far it has been assumed that $\nu_{JJ'}$ is a single, discrete frequency. In actuality this is, of course, not true. Because the line has a natural width and is also broadened by the Doppler effect, collisions, and other phenomena to be discussed later, the transition $J \to J'$ results in absorption over a band of frequencies. Hence, the absorption coefficient α_ν for any frequency ν in the band will be less than the $\alpha_{J \to J'}$ indicated by Eq. 4.5. Therefore, to obtain α_ν one must multiply $\alpha_{J \to J'}$ by a function $S(\nu, \nu_0)$ which depends upon the shape of the absorption line. The frequency for maximum absorption $(E_{J'} - E_J)/h$ is now represented by ν_0. The absorption coefficient α_ν is then

$$\alpha_\nu = \frac{8\pi^3 \nu^2 N_J}{ckT} (J| \, \boldsymbol{\mu} \, |J')^2 S(\nu, \nu_0). \tag{4.10}$$

Equations 4.9 and 4.10 apply to plane-polarized radiation, usually employed in microwave spectroscopy.

Equation 4.10 is a general expression which applies to any type of absorption line in the microwave region, induced either by an electric or by a magnetic dipole coupling. The three factors, N_J, $(J| \, \boldsymbol{\mu} \, |J')^2$, and S, however, vary in form for different substances and for different conditions. In the following sections helpful information will be given for evaluating them for the absorption of gaseous molecules. Equation 4.51 is a specialized form for rotational lines of gases at moderately low pressures. Still more specific forms are given in Chapter 2 for particular molecular types.

The total microwave power of frequency ν absorbed in a given length x can be readily obtained from the absorption coefficient by integration, as follows:

$$\int_{P_0}^{P} \frac{dP}{P} = -\int_0^x \alpha_\nu \, dx \quad \text{or} \quad \log_e \frac{P}{P_0} = -\alpha_\nu x.$$

Therefore

$$P = P_0 e^{-\alpha_\nu x}, \tag{4.11a}$$

or, if the loss in the cell walls, with loss coefficient α_c, is included,

$$P = P_0 e^{-(\alpha_\nu + \alpha_c)x}, \tag{4.11b}$$

where P_0 is the input power to the cell and P is that remaining after transmission of x distance through the absorption cell. In the derivation of the absorption coefficient it was assumed that the propagation in the cell travels at the velocity of light c. When this is not true, corrections must be made accordingly. Usually this is done by an adjustment of the effective length, according to the difference of the wavelength in the cell from the wavelength in free space. See Eq. 1.13.

4.2. LINE SHAPES

The shapes of spectral lines have long been a subject of theoretical interest, a subject intimately connected with the development of both classical and quantum mechanical radiation theory. Theoretical treatments usually start with the concept of a single isolated radiating oscillator with a "natural" line breadth determined classically by radiation damping and quantum mechanically by the probability of spontaneous emission of radiation. This natural line breadth is proportional to the cube of the frequency. Although the natural width is important at X-ray frequencies, it is completely negligible—only a fraction of a cycle—at microwave frequencies. In observations on gases, the Doppler effect usually sets the lower limit to the observable width of microwave lines.† For widths greater than the Doppler widths ($\sim$50 kc) collisions with other molecules (pressure broadening) become the principal factor for determining line widths in the microwave region. At very low pressures where the mean free path becomes comparable with the dimensions of the absorption cell, collisions with the cell walls increase the line width. With the usual cell, these wall collisions contribute less to the line width than does the Doppler effect. Line breadths in solids are treated in Chapter 5.

4.2a. Doppler Broadening. Doppler broadening is a consequence of the motions of the absorbing molecules relative to the detector. If the molecular velocity in the direction of observation is v, the molecular frequency ν_0 appears to an observer as $\nu = \nu_0(1 + v/c)$, where c is the velocity of light. A Maxwellian distribution of velocities for molecules of molecular weight M at absolute temperature T gives a line shape proportional to $e^{-(Mc^2/2RT)[(\nu-\nu_0)/\nu_0]^2}$ where R is the gas constant per mole. The line width $2\Delta\nu$ at half-maximum power is given by

$$\frac{2\Delta\nu}{\nu_0} = 7.15 \times 10^{-7} \left(\frac{T}{M}\right)^{\frac{1}{2}} = 1.48\frac{\bar{v}}{c}. \tag{4.12}$$

For NH_3 and ICN, with $\nu_0 = 24{,}000$ Mc and $T = 300°$ K, the Doppler widths are 70 kc to 30 kc, respectively.

4.2b. Collision Broadening. Pressure broadening is a general term covering the various possible contributions to line breadth arising from molecular interactions in a gas. At low pressures these interactions are best described through the concept of binary collisions. Although the word "collision" often has the connotation of a hard-sphere impact, as between two billiard balls, measured collision cross sections are functions

---

† Special techniques permit one to circumvent this limit (see Sec. 9.1).

of the velocities of the colliding molecules, and of the particular molecular property disturbed by the collision. Most kinetic theory tables of molecular cross sections are derived from viscosity measurements involving the momentum transfer at a collision, whereas line widths are directly connected with energy transfer. Hence, observed differences in these cross sections are not surprising.

Line shape functions. Certain aspects of collision broadening may be treated without any knowledge of the details of the intermolecular forces responsible for the collisions, provided only that the collision duration is small as compared with the mean time τ between collisions. Classical [3] and quantum mechanical [4] derivations are equivalent. Lorentz [5] and Van Vleck and Weisskopf [3] assume an assemblage of harmonic oscillators whose frequency is ν_0. The oscillators are interrupted momentarily at random times about a mean time τ. The conditions immediately after the collision differ in the two theories. Lorentz assumes random oscillator energies, whereas Van Vleck and Weisskopf assume a Boltzmann distribution of energies. Experiment has substantiated the latter form of the theory. The Van Vleck-Weisskopf expression for the line-shape function is

$$S(\nu, \nu_0) = \frac{\nu}{\pi \nu_0} \left[\frac{\Delta \nu}{(\nu_0 - \nu)^2 + \Delta \nu^2} + \frac{\Delta \nu}{(\nu_0 + \nu)^2 + \Delta \nu^2} \right] \quad (4.13)$$

where

$$\Delta \nu = \frac{1}{2\pi\tau}. \quad (4.14)$$

τ = the mean time between collisions.

ν_0 = the peak resonant frequency.

The Van Vleck-Weisskopf shape function, Eq. 4.13, also depends upon the condition, valid in microwave spectroscopy, that the duration of the collision ($\sim 10^{-12}$ second) is short as compared with the period of oscillation ($\sim 3 \times 10^{-11}$ second) of the microwave radiation. This condition is reversed in the optical region, where many periods of oscillation are executed in the duration of a single collision. For relatively sharp lines such as are commonly observed in the microwave region and where $\nu \approx \nu_0$, the last term of Eq. 4.13 becomes negligible as compared with the first, and the equation reduces to the Lorentzian shape function,

$$S(\nu, \nu_0) = \frac{1}{\pi} \left[\frac{\Delta \nu}{(\nu_0 - \nu)^2 + \Delta \nu^2} \right]. \quad (4.15a)$$

At the resonant peak $(\nu = \nu_0)$ Eq. 4.15 becomes simply

$$S = \frac{1}{\pi \Delta \nu}.$$ (4.15b)

From Eqs. 4.10 and 4.13 it is evident that for low pressures where the second term of Eq. 4.13 can be neglected, $2\Delta\nu$ is the line width between the half-power points. It is to be noted that the contour of Eq. 4.13 is higher in the wings of the line than is the contour arising from Doppler broadening, Eq. 4.12. When the resonant frequency ν_0 approaches zero, the line shape reduces to the Debye non-resonant absorption curve.[6] The adequacy of Eq. 4.13 at medium and low pressures may be judged by the agreement between theory and experiment in Fig. 4.1.

Over a wide range of pressures it is experimentally observed that $\Delta\nu$ is proportional to pressure, in agreement with considerations of kinetic theory, Eq. 4.16, and that ν_0 is independent of pressure. In the low-pressure region where Eq. 4.15a is valid, these conditions on $\Delta\nu$ and ν_0 result in a pressure-independent peak absorption at the center of the line. Equation 4.13 is valid for O_2 for pressures ranging from a fraction of a millimeter[9] of Hg to atmospheric pressure.[10] The fine structure line widths at low pressure yield an average of 0.04 cm^{-1}/atm (if line width is assumed proportional to pressure), whereas those on the integrated absorption at one atmosphere by Strandberg, Meng, and Ingersoll[10] and by Lamont[10] yield for $\Delta\nu$ 0.015 and 0.02 cm^{-1}/atm, respectively. The earlier work of Beringer[10] at atmospheric pressure, however, gave $\Delta\nu$ in the range of 0.02 to 0.05 cm^{-1}/atm. For ammonia the proportionality of $\Delta\nu$ to pressure and also the constancy of ν_0 holds only up to a pressure of about 30 cm of Hg. Above this pressure the data can be fitted to a curve of the form of Eq. 4.13 if $\Delta\nu$ is assumed to become nearly constant, with allowed variations from 15,000 Mc to 21,000 Mc in the pressure range of 60 to 380 cm of Hg. In the same range the apparent resonant frequency drops rapidly from 13,000 Mc to zero.[8, 11, 12, 13]

Margenau[14] and Anderson[15] give a semi-quantitative explanation of the pressure variations for NH_3, particularly of the shift in resonant frequency. They find that as a result of mutual interactions the system of two stationary NH_3 molecules has two inversion frequencies, displaced, one above and one below the unperturbed frequency. As the perturbation is increased the low-frequency inversion approaches zero frequency and also becomes more intense than the high-frequency inversion. High pressures with small free paths correspond to strong perturbations; hence the observed shift in resonant frequency with pressure. Other theories involve consideration of multiple collisions.[8, 11, 12]

Bleaney and Loubser [11] have investigated the broadening of inversion resonances in CH_3Cl and CH_3Br. These resonances occur at essentially zero frequency but cause absorption at high pressures in the microwave

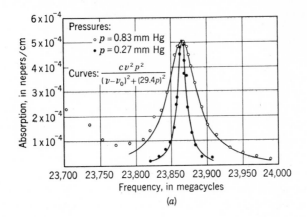

$$\text{Curves: } \frac{cv^2p^2}{(v-v_0)^2+(29.4p)^2}$$

(a)

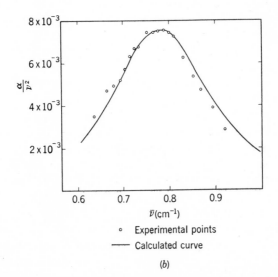

○ Experimental points

—— Calculated curve

(b)

FIG. 4.1. Comparison of observed and theoretical line shape of the 3,3-NH₃ line (a) at pressures of 0.27 and 0.83 mm of Hg (from Townes [7]) and (b) at 10 cm of Hg (from Bleaney and Penrose [8]).

region since the line widths are comparable with the frequency. The only other line for which extensive data are available is the $6_{1,6} \rightarrow 5_{2,3}$ transition of H_2O measured by Becker and Autler.[16] This line is well isolated from other H_2O lines, but, if its center is fitted by Eq. 4.13, the intensity in its wings is too great. This anomaly has not yet been explained.

Line widths and collision diameters. The mean collision time τ may be related to the molecular diameter b and the collision cross section $\sigma = \pi b^2$ by the kinetic theory relations,

$$\tau = \frac{1}{N\bar{v}_{1,2}\sigma} \qquad 2\Delta\nu = N\bar{v}_{1,2}b^2, \qquad (4.16)$$

where N is the molecular density and $\bar{v}_{1,2}$ is the mean relative velocity of the colliding molecules. For a fixed temperature, $\bar{v}_{1,2}$ and σ are constant while N is proportional to the pressure. This accounts for the observed proportionality of $\Delta\nu$ to pressure, already mentioned. The temperature dependence is more complicated, as N, $\bar{v}_{1,2}$, and even σ are temperature dependent.

Observed line widths and collision diameters for self-broadening of various gases are listed in Table 4.1. Collision diameters for the 3,3 line of NH_3 in mixtures with different gases, and for the $J = 8 \rightarrow 9$ line of O_2 in gas mixtures, are listed in Table 4.2. Table 4.3 shows the

Table 4.1. Line-breadth parameters and collision diameters for self-broadening at room temperature

Gas	Transition	Static Dipole Moment (Debye units)	$\Delta\nu$ (Mc/mm of Hg) Observed	b (Angstroms) Micro-wave	b (Angstroms) Kinetic Theory [18]	Ref.
NH_3	$J = 3, K = 3$	1.44	27 ± 2	14	4.43	7, 8
	$J = 5, K = 1$	1.44	11.5 ± 2	9	4.43	8
ICl	$J = 3 \rightarrow 4$					
	$F = 11\frac{1}{2} \rightarrow 13\frac{1}{2}$	0.65	5.5 ± 1	11		19
OCS	$J = 1 \rightarrow 2$	0.71	6.0 ± 1	9		20
HCN	$J = 0 \rightarrow 1$	2.96	25	15		21
ClCN	$J = 1 \rightarrow 2$	2.80	25 ± 4	19		20
BrCN	$J = 2 \rightarrow 3$	2.94	21 ± 3	20		20
ICN	$J = 3 \rightarrow 4$	3.71	20 ± 3	21		20
PF_3	$J = 1 \rightarrow 2$	1.03	16	16		22
CHF_3	$J = 1 \rightarrow 2, K = 1$ $K = 0$	1.59	18 ± 1	16		22
CH_3F	$J = 0 \rightarrow 1$	1.83	20	14		22
H_2O	$J = 5_{-1} \rightarrow 6_{-5}$	1.84	14 ± 1.5	10		23
CH_2O		2.31	10.3 ± 1	10		24
O_2	$K = 1(-)$	0	2.53	5.0		33a
	$K = 3(+)$	0	1.71	4.1	3.61	27
	$K = 7(+)$	0	2.05	4.5	3.61	27
	$K = 21(-)$	0	1.26	3.5	3.61	27

large variations of line width with rotational state that occur in the ammonia inversion spectrum. These line widths arise from intermolecular forces and are calculable in simple cases. They show good agreement with observed values for ammonia self-broadening,[30] but poorer agreement in certain other cases.

Table 4.2. Collision diameters for mixtures of various gases with $NH_3(J = 3, K = 3)$ and with $O_2(J = 8 \rightarrow 9)$ at room temperature

Colliding Molecule	μ_2 (Debye units)	$\bar{\mu}_2$ † (Debye units)	b (Angstroms)				
			NH$_3$			O$_2$	
			Micro-wave [25]	Anderson's Theory [26]	Kinetic Theory [18]	Micro-wave [27]	Kinetic Theory [18]
NH$_3$	1.44	0.78	13.8 [28]	14.0 [30]	4.43	4.3	4.02
He	0	0	2.00	2.15	3.31		
A	0	0	3.73	3.42	4.04	3.6	3.63
H$_2$	0	0	2.95	2.57	3.59		
N$_2$	0	0	5.54	3.39	4.09	3.8	3.68
O$_2$	0	0	3.86	3.35	4.02	3.4 to 4.6	3.61
CO$_2$	0	0	7.59		4.51		
OCS	1.71	0	7.56				
CS$_2$	0	0	7.72				
N$_2$O	0.25	0	7.32 [29]			4.35	4.4	4.15
HCN	2.96	0	10.0				
ClCN	2.80	0	11.9				
CH$_3$Cl	1.87	0.47	11.3				
CH$_2$Cl$_2$	1.59	0	10.3				
CHCl$_3$	0.95	0.57	13.7				
CCl$_4$	0	0	7.20				
SO$_2$	1.7	0	10.4				

† An average, weighted according to population of rotational states.

Examination of the tables shows that many microwave collision diameters greatly exceed kinetic theory values. A rough correlation with the static dipole moment is also apparent; large dipoles yield large diameters and broad lines. For a given static dipole moment, a symmetric-top molecule generally has a larger line width than has a linear molecule. Microwave collision diameters of O_2 generally more nearly approximate kinetic theory values than do those of NH_3.

The detailed derivation of line widths from intermolecular forces is a complicated problem which has attracted the attention of many theo-

rists. The general nature of the problem, however, is straightforward.
A molecule in an ideally sharp energy state is disturbed by the force field
of a passing molecule which may shift the energy state by a Stark effect
interaction, or may induce a transition to some other energy state. Both
the energy shift and the transition probability may be calculated by
time-dependent perturbation theory, and both contribute to the observed line breadth. The Stark perturbation broadens the line in an
obvious manner, whereas the induced transitions decrease the lifetime
in the energy state and produce a broadening based upon the uncer-
tainty principle. This principle may be stated in the form $\tau \cdot \Delta E \approx h/2\pi$.
Hence, $\Delta \nu = \Delta E/h \approx 1/2\pi\tau$, when τ is the lifetime in the state.

Line-width calculations are most reliable when there are only a few
important interactions and when the collision diameter is much greater
than the kinetic theory diameter so that the molecules may be assumed
to travel in straight-line paths undeflected by the microwave "collision."
Symmetric-top molecules possess permanent dipole moments directed
along their figure axes; hence they have strong, long-range interactions
and large collision diameters. It is only for this class of molecule that
calculations of line widths are in a satisfactory state. However, approximate analyses of the fairly long-range dipole-quadrupole moment interactions have led to determinations of quadrupole moments [25, 29] which
hitherto had been measurable only for H_2 and D_2 (by molecular-beam
techniques).[31] Other intermolecular forces, such as the quadrupole-
quadrupole,[17] the dipole-induced dipole,[30] and the quadrupole-induced
dipole,[26] have also been investigated.

Variation of line breadth with rotational state. Oxygen and ammonia,
because of the special origin of their spectra, are the only molecules
having microwave spectral lines in the entire range of significantly
populated rotational states. The line breadths of most of the NH_3 lines
have been measured accurately by Bleaney and Penrose.[28] It was
found empirically that the J and K dependence can be expressed by
the simple formula, $\Delta \nu \propto [K^2/J(J + 1)]^{1/3}$. P. W. Anderson [30] has
given a theoretical explanation for the observed breadths. He showed
that the significant matrix elements in the interacting Hamiltonian
(dipole-dipole interaction) which do not vanish correspond (1) to the
first-order "Stark effect" interaction ($J \rightarrow J$ matrix elements) and (2)
to rotational resonance effects involving $J \rightarrow J \pm 1$ matrix elements
(collisions of absorbing molecules in state J with perturbing neighbors in
state $J \pm 1$). Table 4.3 compares his calculated values with those
measured by Bleaney and Penrose.

R. S. Anderson, Smith, and Gordy,[27] who measured the individual
oxygen lines as a function of the rotational quantum number N, also

found evidence for broadening caused by rotational resonance (interactions involving $N \rightarrow N \pm 2$ matrix elements). Their plot of the O_2 line breadth shows a slight maximum in the region of the most densely populated states. The plot of the data was found to fit the semi-empirical relation,

$$\Delta\nu/c = C_1 + C_2 N^{-\frac{1}{2}} + C_3[f(N-2) + f(N+2)],$$

with the constants $C_1 = 0.033$, $C_2 = 0.010$, and $C_3 = 0.050\text{cm}^{-1}/\text{atm}$. The rather large constant C_1 can arise from short-range interactions of

Table 4.3. Illustration of the variation of line-breadth parameter with rotational state: the NH_3 inversion spectrum

		$\Delta\nu$ (Mc/mm Hg)	
J	K	Observed [28]	Theoretical [30]
2	1	15.5	15.5
3	1	14.5	14
3	2	19	20
3	3	27	27
4	4	27	27.5
5	1	11	11
5	2	15.5	15
5	3	20	20
5	5	28	29
6	3	18.5	17
6	4	21.5	21
6	6	28	29
7	5	24.5	22
7	6	23.5	26
8	7	24.5	26
10	9	25	27
11	9	17.5	24.5

different types, including polarizability. The second term includes the quadrupole-quadrupole interaction terms calculated by Mizushima.[17] The third term, which is proportional to the fraction of molecules $f(N-2)$ and $f(N+2)$ in the neighboring states, $N+2$ and $N-2$, evidently results partly from rotational resonance. Oxygen line widths have been measured by several researchers.[31a] All the data are not in agreement.

Johnson and Slager [31b] measured the breadths of pure rotational lines of the linear molecule OCS for transitions ranging from $J = 1 \rightarrow 2$ to $7 \rightarrow 8$. They found the line breadths to increase with J in the region from about 6 to 11 Mc per mm of Hg. This increase probably results partly from rotational resonance.

Temperature dependence of line widths. Over the pressure range in which line breadth is directly proportional to pressure, $\Delta\nu$ can be expressed as

$$\Delta\nu = (\Delta\nu)_1 P_{\mathrm{mm}}(300/T)^x, \qquad (4.17)$$

where $(\Delta\nu)_1$ is the line breadth at one millimeter of Hg pressure and room temperature ($300°$ K), and T is the absolute temperature at which $\Delta\nu$ is measured. There is some uncertainty as to the temperature dependence of the line breadth. "Hard sphere" kinetic theory indicates that the exponent x should be $\frac{1}{2}$, whereas a single experiment by Howard and Smith [32] suggests that it should be near unity for dipole-dipole collision broadening. This result is in agreement with the theories of Anderson [30] and of Margenau [33] which predict that the collision cross section should vary inversely as the impact velocity and hence that $\Delta\nu$ should vary inversely with temperature. (Since $\Delta\nu = N\sigma\bar{v}/2\pi$ and $N \propto P/T$, $\bar{v} \propto T^{\frac{1}{2}}$.) The temperature dependence of $\Delta\nu$ will vary somewhat with the nature of the interacting forces of the colliding molecules.

Johnson and Slager [31b] have found the rotational lines of OCS to vary in width approximately as $T^{-\frac{3}{2}}$. Beringer and Castle [31a] observed that the width of paramagentic resonance lines of O_2 varied as $T^{-\frac{3}{4}}$ to T^{-1}. The measurements of Hill and Gordy [34a] on several O_2 lines indicate a variation as T^{-1}, approximately. In the various intensity formulas in this book we have assumed a T^{-1} variation of line breadth, which at present seems most probable. More work on this subject is needed, particularly on the experimental phase.

Broadening by collisions with cell walls. When any dimension of the cell is comparable with the mean free path in the gas, collisions with cell walls become significant in the determination of line breadths. For a waveguide cell of dimensions a and b the line width between half-power points, $2\Delta\nu$, resulting from collisions with cell walls alone is

$$2\Delta\nu \approx 10 \left(\frac{a+b}{ab}\right)\left(\frac{T}{M}\right)^{\frac{1}{2}} \quad \text{kc}, \qquad (4.18a)$$

where T is the absolute temperature, M is the molecular weight, and a and b are the cross-section dimensions of the cell in centimeters. When only one dimension is so small as to be comparable with the mean free path, as is usually the case with Stark cells, this expression reduces to

$$2\Delta\nu \approx \frac{10}{a}\left(\frac{T}{M}\right)^{\frac{1}{2}} \quad \text{kc}. \qquad (4.18b)$$

For the light molecule HCN, at room temperature, with $T = 300$ and $M = 27$, in a typical x-band Stark cell $a = 0.50$ cm, the broadening produced by collisions with cell walls is about 65 kc. For AsF$_3$ under the same conditions the cell broadening would be about 30 kc.

The form of relation 4.18 follows simply from the width factor $\Delta \nu$ $= \dfrac{1}{2\pi\tau}$ (Eq. 4.14) if τ, the mean lifetime in the state, is taken as the mean time for collision with the cell walls. Rather tedious integrations are required for establishment of the exact scale factor. The scale factor used here is that calculated by Johnson and Strandberg.[34b]

4.3. SATURATION EFFECT

The absorption of monochromatic radiation by a gas is a process that tends to destroy thermal equilibrium among the various energy states. In optical spectroscopy the interchange of energy between states is sufficiently rapid in comparison with the rate of absorption of light that departures from thermal equilibrium are unobservably small. In the microwave region, however, at low pressures and high energy densities the departure from thermal equilibrium is so pronounced that the rate of absorption of energy becomes independent of the density of incident energy, rather than directly proportional to it as is the usual case. This effect is appropriately termed the saturation effect.† It was first noticed in the microwave region by Townes [7] and by Bleaney and Penrose.[8] A simple treatment follows, only transitions from a non-degenerate lower state J to the upper state J' being considered. A combination of Eqs. 4.7, 4.10, and 4.15 yields

$$\alpha(\nu) = \frac{8\pi^2\nu}{hc} (J|\,\mathbf{\mu}\,|J')^2 (N'_J - N'_{J'}) \frac{\Delta\nu}{(\nu - \nu_0)^2 + \Delta\nu^2}, \qquad (4.19)$$

where N'_J is the population of the lower state, and $N'_{J'}$ is the population of the upper state. For thermal equilibrium (no primes on N) N_J and $N_{J'}$ are related by Eq. 4.6.

If P is the power density incident on the gas in erg sec^{-1} cm^{-2}, multiplication of $\alpha(\nu)$ by $P/h\nu$ yields the rate of removal of molecules per cubic centimeter from state J to J' by absorption of radiation. This rate must be equal to the rate of restoration of the population to that for thermal equilibrium by collisions. It is approximately $\dfrac{N'_{J'} - N_{J'}}{2\tau} - \dfrac{N'_J - N_J}{2\tau}$ so that

$$\frac{\alpha(\nu)P}{h\nu} = \frac{1}{2\tau}[(N_J - N'_J) - (N_{J'} - N'_{J'})]. \qquad (4.20)$$

† The phenomenon is similar to saturation in nuclear induction.

Here τ is the mean time between non-elastic collisions resulting in transitions to different states for the molecules participating and is assumed to be the same for molecules in both states J and J'. This equality is indicated for ammonia, the only molecule thoroughly investigated. In the limit of complete saturation $N'_{J'} = N'_J$, and Eq. 4.20 becomes

$$\alpha(\nu)P = \frac{h\nu}{2\tau}(N_J - N_{J'}) \approx \frac{h^2\nu^2}{2\tau}\left(\frac{N_J}{kT}\right). \tag{4.21}$$

Thus the maximum power absorbed is one quantum per molecule per collision multiplied by the excess probability of finding the colliding molecule in the lower state after the collision. This maximum power increases with the square of the frequency, and hence the effect is unobservable in the optical region.

At complete saturation the loss in power density per centimeter of length at the resonant frequency is given by

$$\Delta P_0 = \frac{ch^2(\Delta\nu)^2\alpha(\nu_0)}{8\pi(J|\,\mu\,|J')^2}$$

$$= 0.51 \times 10^{-43}\frac{(\Delta\nu)^2\alpha(\nu_0)}{(J|\,\mu\,|J')^2} \qquad \text{erg/sec/cm}^3. \tag{4.22}$$

Here $\alpha(\nu_0)$ and $\Delta\nu$ refer to the condition of no saturation. For ΔP_0 in milliwatts per square centimeter per centimeter of length, μ in Debye units, and $\Delta\nu$ in megacycles, the coefficient of proportionality becomes 5.1. For incident power densities less than that required for complete saturation, α decreases faster with increasing P at low incident power levels than near complete saturation, and the product αP for partial saturation is always less than its value at complete saturation.

For low pressures and incomplete saturation, Karplus and Schwinger [4] show that the shape factor of Eq. 4.15 should be altered to the form

$$S = \frac{1}{\pi}\left[\frac{\Delta\nu}{(\nu - \nu_0)^2 + (\Delta\nu)^2 + B_{J \to J'}P/c\pi^2}\right], \tag{4.23}$$

where B is the Einstein absorption coefficient, Eq. 4.8, and P is the power density. The shape factor, Eq. 4.23, reduces to Eq. 4.15, when P is zero. Bleaney and Penrose,[35] and Carter and Smith,[36] working with ammonia, have experimentally confirmed the validity of Eq. 4.23, suitably modified from its plane-wave form above to the forms for cavity and waveguide systems, respectively. The observed saturation for the 3,3 line of NH_3 is shown in Fig. 4.2. Conditions were adjusted so that figures a and b would be identical in the absence of saturation.

The center line of b is saturated while the satellites, with smaller transition probabilities, remain unsaturated. Confirmatory data were earlier obtained by Townes,[7] and by Pond and Cannon.[37] The latter workers investigated the saturation effect at still lower pressures where the Doppler broadening is important. Originally the data seemed to indicate that τ was not identical to $1/(2\pi\Delta\nu)$, but Karplus and Schwinger [4, 38, 39] showed that the apparent discrepancy was due to neglect of the Zeeman degeneracy of the transition; i.e., for the 3,3 line of NH_3 in question,

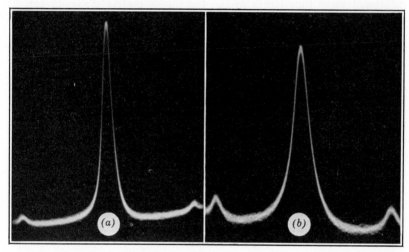

Fig. 4.2. Illustration of saturation broadening. The 3,3 line of NH_3 with gain adjusted for approximately constant height and pressure held constant. (a) Input to cell is 1.5×10^{-6} watt; (b) input to cell is 150×10^{-6} watt. (From Carter and Smith.[36])

the absorption coefficient is the sum of three components corresponding to $M_J = 1$, 2, and 3. Saturation of each of these must be computed separately and then averaged. When this is done, τ is found to be identical with $1/(2\pi\Delta\nu)$, within the experimental error of 10 to 20 per cent. This fact may be interpreted by saying that "collision" contributions to impact broadening are identical with "collisions" redistributing among molecules the energies corresponding to the microwave transitions.

4.4. DIPOLE-MOMENT MATRIX ELEMENTS

From Eq. 4.10 it is seen that the absorption coefficient has a factor

$$(J|\,\mu\,|J')^2 = (J|\,\mu_X\,|J')^2 + (J|\,\mu_Y\,|J')^2 + (J|\,\mu_Z\,|J')^2, \qquad (4.24)$$

where μ_X, μ_Y, and μ_Z are the components of the dipole along the space-fixed axes. This factor is the basis of selection rules governing the transitions. When all components of the dipole matrix element are zero for a given transition, the transition is "forbidden"; when any components remain, the transition is "allowed." It is also apparent from Eq. 4.10 that the line intensities are proportional to the square of the nonvanishing matrix elements.

In the general case in which the molecule has permanent dipole components μ_a, μ_b, and μ_c along each of the principal axes of inertia, and the rotational wave function is $\psi_{J,i,M}$, the dipole matrix elements can be expressed as

$$(J, i, M| \mu_f |J', i', M') = \mu_a \int \psi_{J,i,M} \cos \alpha_{fa} \psi^*_{J',i',M'} \, d\tau$$

$$+ \mu_b \int \psi_{J,i,M} \cos \alpha_{fb} \psi^*_{J',i',M'} \, d\tau + \mu_c \int \psi_{J,i,M} \cos \alpha_{fc} \psi^*_{J',i',M'} \, d\tau, \quad (4.25)$$

where $f = X$, Y, or Z represents a space-fixed axis. The angles α_{fa}, α_{fb}, and α_{fc} are the angles between the space-fixed axis and the axes a, b, and c in the molecule.

In a linear molecule the dipole moment must of necessity be along the bond axis. The components along the space-fixed axes are then

$$\mu_X = \mu \sin \theta \cos \phi,$$

$$\mu_Y = \mu \sin \theta \sin \phi,$$

$$\mu_Z = \mu \cos \theta.$$

With the rotational wave function of a rigid linear rotor (see Chapter 2) the dipole matrix elements are found to vanish except when $J = J' \pm 1$ and $M = M'$ or $M' \pm 1$. The only components of interest here are the $J' = J + 1$ components which correspond to the absorption of radiation. These are

$$(J, M| \mu_Z |J + 1, M) = \mu \sqrt{\frac{(J + 1 + M)(J + 1 - M)}{(2J + 1)(2J + 3)}}, \quad (4.26)$$

$(J, M| \mu_X + i\mu_Y |J + 1, M - 1)$

$$= \mu \sqrt{\frac{(J + 1 - M)(J + 2 - M)}{(2J + 1)(2J + 3)}}, \quad (4.27)$$

$(J, M| \mu_X - i\mu_Y |J + 1, M + 1)$

$$= \mu \sqrt{\frac{(J + 1 + M)(J + 2 + M)}{(2J + 1)(2J + 3)}}. \quad (4.28)$$

The first expression corresponds to the absorption of the component of the radiation which lies along the reference Z axis. It is readily apparent that

$$\mu_X + i\mu_Y = \mu \sin \theta \, e^{i\phi},$$

$$\mu_X - i\mu_Y = \mu \sin \theta \, e^{-i\phi}.$$

The $M \to M \pm 1$ transition corresponds therefore to absorption of radiation which is circularly polarized in the XY plane. The two components are equal in amplitude. They arise from dipole components which have the same amplitude ($\mu \sin \theta$) but which rotate in opposite directions (ϕ and $-\phi$).

If non-polarized radiation is employed and no external field is imposed, the total absorption is proportional to the sum of the squares of the matrix elements summed over all values of M and all directions of space. The result is

$$\sum_{M=-J}^{M=J} (J, M| \, \mu_Z \, |J + 1, M)^2 + \tfrac{1}{2} \sum_{M=-J}^{M=J} (J, M| \, \mu_X + i\mu_Y \, |J + 1, M - 1)^2$$

$$+ \tfrac{1}{2} \sum_{M=-J}^{M=J} (J, M| \, \mu_X - i\mu_Y \, |J + 1, M + 1)^2 = \mu^2(J + 1) \quad (4.29)$$

Since plane-polarized radiation is generally used in microwave spectroscopy, only one of these components is observed, and the "microwave line strengths" are proportional to

$$\sum_{M=-J}^{M=J} (J, M| \, \mu_Z \, |J + 1, M)^2 = \tfrac{1}{3}\mu^2(J + 1). \qquad (4.30)$$

When the M degeneracy is lifted by an external electric field, the squared matrix elements to be used in Eq. 4.10 to obtain the absorption coefficients of each component (if plane-polarized radiation is assumed with the alternating electric vector parallel to the external $\mathcal{E}$) are

$$(J, M| \, \mu_Z \, |J + 1, M)^2 = \mu^2 \frac{(J + 1)^2 - M^2}{(2J + 1)(2J + 3)}. \qquad (4.31)$$

The dipole matrix elements for a symmetric-top molecule may be obtained from the wave functions of Eq. 2.30. When, as usual, the dipole moment lies wholly along the symmetry axis, the only non-vanishing components [40] correspond to $\Delta J = 0, \pm 1, \Delta K = 0, \Delta M = 0, \pm 1$. Only the squared $M \to M$ components [40] are given here since these are the ones generally needed in microwave spectroscopy. The appropriate formulas are

$$(J, K, M| \mu_Z |J + 1, K, M)^2 = \mu^2 \frac{[(J + 1)^2 - M^2][(J + 1)^2 - K^2]}{(J + 1)^2(2J + 1)(2J + 3)}$$

(4.32)

and

$$\sum_{M=-J}^{M=J} (J, K, M| \mu_Z |J + 1, K, M)^2 = \tfrac{1}{3}\mu^2 \frac{(J + 1)^2 - K^2}{(J + 1)}.$$

(4.33)

The latter expression is to be used for the squared dipole matrix element in Eq. 4.10 when plane-polarized radiation is employed with no field applied. The former is used when the $M \rightarrow M$ components are resolved by an external field.

Sometimes the K components of a symmetric top are unresolved. The integrated intensity is then proportional to the squared matrix elements summed over K,

$$\sum_{M=-J}^{M=J} \sum_{K=-J}^{K=J} (J, K, M| \mu_Z |J + 1, K, M)^2 = \mu^2 \frac{(2J + 1)(2J + 3)}{9}.$$

(4.34)

Equation 4.34 is particularly convenient to use since no nuclear statistical weight factors enter the final intensity formula.

For an inversion transition of a symmetric-top molecule the squared matrix elements are

$$(J, K^-, M| \mu_Z |J, K^+, M)^2 = \mu^2 \left[\frac{KM}{J(J + 1)}\right]^2$$

(4.35)

$$\sum_{M=-J}^{M=J} (J, K^-, M| \mu_Z |J, K^+, M)^2 = \mu^2 \frac{(2J + 1)K^2}{3J(J + 1)}.$$

(4.36)

The symbols $+$ and $-$ represent the two inversion states.

The matrix elements for an asymmetric rotor cannot be expressed in closed formulas except for very low J values. They can be obtained for certain asymmetries for J up to 12 from the line-strength tables of Cross, Hainer, and King.[41] The most frequently needed $M \rightarrow M$ components are

$$(J, \tau, M| \boldsymbol{\mu}_g |J + 1, \tau', M)^2$$

$$= \mu_g^2 \frac{(J + 1)^2 - M^2}{(J + 1)(2J + 1)(2J + 3)} \lambda_g(J, \tau; J + 1, \tau'), \quad (4.37)$$

$$(J, \tau, M| \, \mu_g \, |J, \tau', M)^2 = \mu_g^2 \frac{M^2}{J(2J+1)(J+1)} \lambda_g(J, \tau; J, \tau'), \quad (4.38)$$

$$(J, \tau, M| \, \mu_g \, |J-1, \tau', M)^2$$

$$= \mu_g^2 \frac{J^2 - M^2}{J(2J-1)(2J+1)} \lambda_g(J, \tau; J-1, \tau'). \quad (4.39)$$

When no field is applied, the expression to be used for polarized microwave radiation is

$$\sum_{M=-J}^{M=J} (J, \tau, M| \, \mu_g \, |J', \tau', M)^2 = \tfrac{1}{3}\mu_g^2 \lambda_g(J, \tau; J', \tau'). \quad (4.40)$$

The $g = a$, b, or c designates the dipole components along the three principal axes of inertia. The λ_g's represent the "line strengths" $\Sigma| \, \Phi \, |^2$ tabulated by Cross, Hainer, and King.[41] and are the squared direction-cosine matrix elements summed over the three directions of space and over-all values of M and M'.

The effects of nuclear hyperfine structure are neglected in the calculation of the matrix elements given above. When there is resolvable hyperfine structure, the absorption coefficients of the individual components are proportional to squared matrix elements of the form $(J, i, F, M_F| \, \mu \, |J, i, F, M_F)^2$. However, it is customary, and easier, to calculate the integrated intensity of a given hyperfine multiplet with the matrix elements given above (which ignore nuclear splitting) and then to divide this integrated intensity among the different hyperfine components in proportion to their relative intensities as given by Eq. 2.91. (These are tabulated numerically in the Appendix, Table $A.10$.) A similar procedure is often followed for the Stark and Zeeman components; nevertheless, the M dependence of the matrix elements is given above, since they are useful in the calculation of the Stark splittings in Chapter 3.

4.5. POPULATION OF ENERGY STATES

For a system in thermal equilibrium, the population of each energy state is proportional to a statistical weight factor g_n multiplied by the Boltzmann factor $e^{-E_n/kT}$. The sum over all states $\sum_n g_n e^{-E_n/kT}$ is designated as the partition function Q.

In pure rotational spectra commonly observed in the microwave region, one makes observations on molecules in a particular vibrational state, usually the ground vibrational state. For most molecules studied, however, vibrational states other than the one considered have significant populations. Hence, in calculating intensities one must know the fractional number of the molecules which are in the particular vibrational state for which the measurement is made, as well as the number in the lowest rotational state of the transition. In almost all studies of microwave rotational spectra, one can assume that all the molecules are in the ground electronic state. For a molecule which has a total rotational quantum number J and an inner quantum number i, the population per cubic centimeter of the lower rotational state J, i is

$$N_{J, i} = N \frac{F_v g e^{-E(J, i)/kT}}{Q_r}, \tag{4.41}$$

where N = total number of molecules per cubic centimeter.

= 9.68×10^{18} (P_{mm}/T), where P_{mm} is the pressure in millimeters of Hg.

F_v = fraction of molecules in the vibrational state considered.

Q_r = the rotational partition function defined in Art. 4.5a.

$E(J, i)$ = rotational energy of the state J, i (given in Chapter 2).

g = weight factor for degeneracies associated with the inner and outer quantum numbers. (See Art. 4.5b.)

T = absolute temperature.

k = Boltzmann's constant = 20,840 Mc/degree = 0.6951 cm^{-1}/degree.

In Eq. 4.41, the fractional population F_v of the vibrational quantum state is given by

$$F_v = \frac{g_v e^{-E_v/kT}}{Q_v}, \tag{4.42}$$

where g_v is the statistical weight ($g_v = 1$ for non-degenerate levels; $g_v = d$ for d-fold degenerate levels).

$E_v = (n_v h \omega_v)$, the energy relative to the ground vibrational state.

n_v is the vibrational quantum number.

ω_v is the vibrational frequency.

Q_v is the vibrational partition function defined in Art. 4.5a.

If the lowest vibrational frequency is more than 1000 cm^{-1}, F_v is unity to within one per cent for the ground vibrational state at room temperature.

Equation 4.42 is useful in deducing unknown vibrational frequencies from the measured intensities of microwave spectra. For example, Strandberg, Wentink, and Hill [42] determined the vibrational frequency ω_2 of OCSe from relative intensity measurements.

4.5a. The Partition Functions. The vibrational partition function for a molecule is

$$Q_v = \sum_{n=0}^{\infty} e^{-h(n_1\omega_1 + n_2\omega_2 + \cdots)/kT}, \tag{4.43}$$

where the vibrations are assumed to be harmonic, the vibrational energy is relative to the ground vibrational energy, and each member of a degenerate set of frequencies is counted separately. The infinite sum in Eq. 4.43 may be expressed as the finite product

$$Q_v = \prod_v (1 - e^{-h\omega_v/kT})^{-1}.$$

Here, again, the product is taken with each mode of vibration counted separately. If there are g_v frequencies, ω_v, which are identical, the partition function may be written as

$$Q_v = \prod_v (1 - e^{-h\omega_v/kT})^{-g_v}, \tag{4.44}$$

where, now, each different frequency is counted only once.

For a linear molecule the rotational partition function is

$$Q_r = \sum_{J=0}^{\infty} \frac{g_I(2J+1)}{\sigma} e^{-hBJ(J+1)/kT}. \tag{4.45}$$

Here g_I is the reduced nuclear statistical weight, and σ is the symmetry number, defined to be unity for non-linear molecules having no axis of symmetry and p for those with a p-fold axis of symmetry. For electrically polar linear molecules both σ and g_I are unity. An expansion of Eq. 4.45 for this case gives

$$Q_r = \frac{kT}{hB} + \frac{1}{3} + \frac{1}{15}\left(\frac{hB}{kT}\right) + \frac{4}{315}\left(\frac{hB}{kT}\right)^2 + \cdots. \tag{4.46}$$

For the lightest linear molecule for which a microwave rotational transition has been observed (CO), B is 2 cm^{-1} and hB/kT at room temperature is 10^{-2}. Hence, for most purposes Eq. 4.46 may be replaced by its classical value

$$Q_r = 20,840T/B, \tag{4.47}$$

where B is in megacycles.

For a symmetric-top molecule Q_r becomes

$$Q_r = \sum_{J=0}^{J=\infty} \sum_{K=-J}^{K=J} g_I(2J+1)e^{-h[BJ(J+1)+(A-B)K^2]/kT}. \tag{4.48}$$

Although g_I depends on the spins of the identical nuclei and on the rotational states, its average value over adjacent states is unity. Consequently, g_I is replaced by its average in the expansion of Eq. 4.48, which then becomes

$$Q_r = \frac{e^{Bh/4kT}}{\sigma} \left[\frac{(kT)^3 \pi}{h^3 A B^2} \right]^{\frac{1}{2}}$$

$$\times \left[1 + \frac{1}{12} \left(1 - \frac{B}{A} \right) \frac{hB}{kT} + \frac{7}{480} \left(1 - \frac{B}{A} \right)^2 \left(\frac{hB}{kT} \right)^2 + \cdots \right] \quad (4.49)$$

or, approximately, with the rotational constants in megacycles,

$$Q_r = \frac{5.335 \times 10^6}{\sigma} \left[\frac{T^3}{B^2 A} \right]^{\frac{1}{2}}. \quad (4.50)$$

Since the rotational energies of an asymmetric-top molecule cannot be expressed in closed form, it is not possible to obtain an accurate analytical expression for Q_r for this molecular type. However, Eqs. 4.49 and 4.50 also apply to an asymmetric top (to a close approximation) if $B^2 A$ is replaced by ABC, and if B in the exponent and series expansion is replaced by the geometric mean of the most nearly equal rotational constants, with the remaining constant replacing A in the series expansion.

4.5b. Statistical Weights. In principle, the weight factor g_i in Eq. 4.51 is a product of the statistical weights associated with all the different internal quantum numbers. For a symmetric top, for example, $g_i = g$ (nuclear) $\times g$ (K degeneracy) $\times g$ (inversion), and it may include a degeneracy with respect to internal rotation. When no field is applied, the $2J + 1$ degeneracy associated with the outer quantum M is taken care of by the definition of Q_r and by the summation over M. The g_i factors also occur in the partition function. In many cases each term in the partition function has the same statistical weight factors. This is true, for example, for unresolved inversion doubling. Hence the common factor cancels in the ratio g_i/Q_r of Eq. 4.41 and can be ignored. Statistical weight factors arising from internal rotational degeneracies also cancel from the ratio g_i/Q_r. The K degeneracy of symmetric-top molecules, $g_K = 2$ for $K \neq 0$, $g_K = 1$ for $K = 0$, does not cancel, however.

Nuclear statistical weights have been treated by Dennison,[40] Wilson,[43] and others.[44, 45] The present analysis treats a nuclear hyperfine multiplet as a single integrated line. For molecules possessing no symmetry, g (nuclear) $= \prod (2I_i + 1)$ for all states, and hence cancels in the ratio

g_i/Q_r. Here I_i is the spin of the ith nucleus, and the product is taken over all nuclei in the molecule. We employ in place of the true g (nuclear) a reduced nuclear statistical weight g_I, which is defined as the total g (nuclear) divided by $\prod_i (2I_i + 1)$. For molecules with no symmetry g_I is unity.

To determine the reduced nuclear statistical weight g_I of a level for a molecule containing two or more such identical nuclei, the symmetry of the over-all wave functions as well as the statistics of the identical nuclei must be considered. If the identical nuclei follow Bose-Einstein statistics (integral spin), the over-all wave functions must be symmetric (even) under a transformation of coordinates which exchanges two such nuclei, but, if the identical nuclei obey Fermi-Dirac statistics (spins which are an odd multiple of one-half), the over-all wave functions must be antisymmetric (odd) for an exchange of these nuclei. The symmetry of the over-all wave function is the product of the symmetries of the electronic, vibrational, rotational, and nuclear-spin wave functions, $(\psi = \psi_e \psi_v \psi_r \psi_n)$.

In the well-known case of homonuclear diatomic molecules there are in all $(2I + 1)^2$ nuclear-spin functions of which $I(2I + 1)$ are antisymmetric (odd) and $(I + 1)(2I + 1)$ are symmetric (even) for an exchange of the nuclei. The only homonuclear diatomic molecule so far investigated in the microwave region is oxygen. For the ground electronic state which is $^3\sum_g^-$ the electronic wave function is antisymmetric in the coordinates of the nuclei; the vibrational ground state is symmetric, and the rotational states are symmetric when N (the quantum number for end-over-end rotation) is even and antisymmetric when N is odd. Only symmetric nuclear-spin states exist in $O^{16}O^{16}$ since $I = 0$. Only rotational levels for odd values of N can exist because $O^{16}O^{16}$ obeys Bose-Einstein statistics and the over-all wave function must be symmetric. The case of $O^{18}O^{18}$ is identical.

When $I \neq 0$, both even and odd nuclear spin functions exist for homonuclear diatomic molecules. The even correspond to total spins, $T = 2I, 2I - 2, \cdots, 1$ or 0, and the odd to $T = 2I - 1, 2I - 3, \cdots, 1$ or 0. Therefore either even or odd coordinate wave functions can combine with one of the two species of nuclear spin functions to give a symmetric or an antisymmetric over-all wave function, and, hence, satisfy either Bose-Einstein or Fermi-Dirac statistics. Thus, there are no missing rotational levels when $I \neq 0$, but there is a difference in the weights of the even and odd levels. Each of the states corresponding to the $(2I + 1)$ values of T is $(2T + 1)$-fold degenerate $(M_T = T, T - 1, \cdots, -T)$. The sum of the degeneracies for all odd functions is $I(2I + 1)$ and of all even, $(I + 1)(2I + 1)$. These are the total symmetric and antisymmetric weights already mentioned. The corresponding reduced g_I values are $I(2I + 1)/(2I + 1)^2 = I/(2I + 1)$ and $(I + 1)(2I + 1)/(2I + 1)^2 = (I + 1)/(2I + 1)$. When $I = 0$, these are 0 and 1, respectively, and, when $I = 5/2$, as in $O^{17}O^{17}$, the respective values are $5/12$ and $7/12$. For $O^{17}O^{17}$ all rotational levels occur but with alternating weights of 5 to 7. This variation should show up (but would be difficult to measure) in the relative intensities of the even and odd N lines of the microwave spectrum of $O^{17}O^{17}$.

The treatment of symmetric tops closely follows that of Wilson.[43] The figure axis of the majority of symmetric-top molecules is a threefold symmetry axis (molecules such as CH_3CF_3 and PF_3 which belong to point groups C_3 and C_{3v}, respectively). There are one or more sets of three identical atoms which can be interchanged by rotation of $2\pi/3$ or $4\pi/3$ about the figure axis. Consider first only one set of three identical nuclei. The above rotations are equivalent to an even number of exchanges of similar nuclei so that the over-all wave function must be symmetric for these rotations, whether the identical nuclei obey Bose-Einstein or Fermi-Dirac statistics. Wave functions for the point groups C_3 and C_{3v} can be constructed which fall into one of two categories: (1) they are symmetric for rotations of $2\pi/3$ or $4\pi/3$ about the figure axis or (2) they change by phase factors for these rotations and occur in pairs. In group-theory notation [40] a wave function belonging to the first category is designated by symmetry A, and a pair of functions belonging to the second have symmetry E. These symmetries multiply in the following manner: $A \times A = A$, $A \times E = E \times A = E$, and $E \times E = A + A + E$. In the last product two pairs of wave functions are involved from which two product functions are formed in which the phase factors have compensated $(A + A)$ and two in which they have not (E). Molecules with $^1\Sigma$ ground states have electronic ground-state functions which have symmetry A. The ground vibrational wave function has symmetry A. Rotational states for which K (the quantum number for rotation about the figure axis) is zero or a multiple of 3 have symmetry A; but for K not a multiple of 3 they have symmetry E. Symmetries of the combined ground electronic-vibrational and the rotational states are then A for $K = 0$ or a multiple of 3, and E for K not a multiple of 3. If the nuclear spin of the three identical atoms is I, there are in all $(2I + 1)^3$ spin functions †: $\frac{1}{3}(2I + 1) \times [(2I + 1)^2 + 2]$ have symmetry A, and $\frac{1}{3}(2I + 1)[(2I + 1)^2 - 1]$ pairs have symmetry E. Corresponding to over-all wave functions of symmetry A, there are $\frac{1}{3}(2I + 1)[(2I + 1)^2 + 2]$ spin functions for K equal

† We neglect the weights of nuclei in non-symmetrical positions. These cancel in the ratio g_I/Q_r and hence have no significance here.

to zero or a multiple of 3 and $\frac{1}{3}(2I + 1)[(2I + 1)^2 - 1]$ spin functions for K not a multiple of 3. Only one-third of all possible combinations of wave functions have the proper symmetry. The reduced statistical weight here is the number of spin functions from which over-all wave functions of symmetry A arise, divided by $(2I + 1)^3$. It is given in Table 4.4.

Table 4.4. Values of g_I for symmetric-top molecules of symmetry C_3 or C_{3v}

$\psi_e\psi_v$ has symmetry A	One Set of Identical Nuclei of Spin I	Two Sets of Identical Nuclei of Spin I_1 and I_2
K divisible by 3 (including zero)	$\dfrac{1}{3}\left[1 + \dfrac{2}{(2I + 1)^2}\right]$	$\dfrac{1}{3}\left[1 + \dfrac{2}{(2I_1 + 1)^2(2I_2 + 1)^2}\right]$
K not divisible by 3	$\dfrac{1}{3}\left[1 - \dfrac{1}{(2I + 1)^2}\right]$	$\dfrac{1}{3}\left[1 - \dfrac{1}{(2I_1 + 1)^2(2I_2 + 1)^2}\right]$
$\psi_e\psi_v$ has symmetry E		
K divisible by 3 including zero)	$\dfrac{1}{3}\left[1 - \dfrac{1}{(2I + 1)^2}\right]$	$\dfrac{1}{3}\left[1 - \dfrac{1}{(2I_1 + 1)^2(2I_2 + 1)^2}\right]$
K not divisible by 3	$\dfrac{1}{3}\left[1 + \dfrac{1}{2(2I + 1)^2}\right]$	$\dfrac{1}{3}\left[1 + \dfrac{1}{2(2I_1 + 1)^2(2I_2 + 1)^2}\right]$

For a molecule which has two sets of three identical nuclei and which belongs to point group C_3 (for example, CH_3SiF_3), the total number of nuclear-spin functions is $(2I_1 + 1)^3(2I_2 + 1)^3$. Of these functions, $\frac{1}{3}(2I_1 + 1)(2I_2 + 1)[(2I_1 + 1)^2(2I_2 + 1)^2 + 2]$ have symmetry A, and $\frac{1}{3}(2I_1 + 1)(2I_2 + 1)[(2I_1 + 1)^2(2I_2 + 1)^2 - 1]$ pairs of functions have symmetry E for rotations of $2\pi/3$ and $4\pi/3$ about the figure axis. As for one set of three identical nuclei, it is easily seen that the over-all wave function must have symmetry A for these rotations. Thus, the total number of spin functions corresponding to over-all wave functions of proper symmetry is the same as for the previous case if $(2I_1 + 1) \times (2I_2 + 1)$ be substituted for $(2I + 1)$. Reduced nuclear statistical weights are given in Table 4.4. These statistical weights are also valid if nuclei of one set are identical with nuclei of the other, provided that the molecule has a permanent electric dipole moment.

Nuclear statistical weights of molecules in vibrational states of symmetry E, such as singly excited degenerate vibrations, are obtained in a manner similar to that for the ground vibrational state. These reduced statistical weights are given in Table 4.4. Symmetries of excited vibrational modes are discussed by Herzberg.[44]

For asymmetric-top molecules with a twofold symmetry axis the same considerations hold as for homonuclear diatomic molecules, except for the fact that the symmetry of the rotational state cannot be described by the J value alone. As an example, in SO_2^{16} the over-all wave function must be symmetric with respect to a rotation about the symmetry axis (b in this case). Since the electronic-vibrational ground state is even, the even rotational states (A and B_b in Art. 2.2d) must be paired with even nuclear states, and the odd rotational states with odd nuclear states. But again there are no odd nuclear states for $I = 0$. Thus only the even A (ee) and B_b (oo) rotational states exist. For NO_2, on the other hand, the ground electronic-vibrational state is odd so that only B_a (eo) and B_c (oe) states exist.

The values of g_I for asymmetric-top molecules with two identical nuclei are given for the different possible symmetry axes in Table 4.5,

Table 4.5. Values of g_I for asymmetric-top molecules of symmetry C_{2v} with two identical nuclei of integral spins for even electronic and vibrational states †

Symmetry Axis	Rotational State (see Art. 2.2d)			
	ee	eo	oe	oo
a	$\dfrac{I+1}{2I+1}$	$\dfrac{I+1}{2I+1}$	$\dfrac{I}{2I+1}$	$\dfrac{I}{2I+1}$
	$\dfrac{I+1}{2I+1}$	$\dfrac{I}{2I+1}$	$\dfrac{I}{2I+1}$	$\dfrac{I+1}{2I+1}$
c	$\dfrac{I+1}{2I+1}$	$\dfrac{I}{2I+1}$	$\dfrac{I+1}{2I+1}$	$\dfrac{I}{2I+1}$

† For odd electronic or odd vibrational states or for nuclear spins which are odd multiples of one-half, replace I by $I + 1$, and $I + 1$ by I.

if even electronic and vibrational states and integral spin are assumed. For odd multiples of half-integral spin, or odd electronic or odd vibrational states, the factors I and $I + 1$ are to be exchanged. In H_2O, with the spin of $H = \frac{1}{2}$, for example, for ee and oo states $g_I = \frac{1}{4}$, while for eo and oe states $g_I = \frac{3}{4}$, as seen in Table 4.5. Cases of asymmetric-top molecules with more than two identical nuclei are less common. They are discussed, among other places, in Herzberg's book.[44]

4.6. INTENSITIES OF MOLECULAR ROTATIONAL LINES

The preceding sections show that several factors influence the intensity of a microwave transition. Many investigations are concerned with gaseous molecules at pressures ranging from about 10^{-2} mm to

10 mm of Hg. If the incident power density for them is somewhat less than the saturation limit, Eq. 4.15 represents adequately the line shape. Substituting Eqs. 4.15 and 4.41 in Eq. 4.10 and summing the dipole-moment matrix element over the Zeeman sub-levels yield

$$\alpha = \frac{8\pi^2 N F_v \nu^2 \sum_M (J, i, M| \, \mathbf{\mu} \, |J', i', M')^2 g_i e^{-E(J, i)/kT}}{ckTQ_r} \left[\frac{\Delta\nu}{(\nu - \nu_0)^2 + \Delta\nu^2} \right].$$

(4.51)

The right-hand bracket of Eq. 4.51 has its maximum value $1/\Delta\nu$ at $\nu = \nu_0$. In the pressure range considered we have from Eq. 4.18

$$\Delta\nu \approx \frac{300 P_{\mathrm{mm}} (\Delta\nu)_1}{T},$$

(4.52)

where it is assumed that $\Delta\nu$ varies inversely as T. Here $(\Delta\nu)_1$ is the line breadth at 300° K and 1 mm of Hg pressure and P_{mm} in millimeters of mercury at which the observation is made. The number of molecules per cubic centimeter can be expressed as

$$N = 9.68 \times 10^{18} (P_{\mathrm{mm}}/T).$$

(4.53)

Equations 4.52 and 4.53 substituted in Eq. 4.51 with the specialized values of $\sum_M (J, i, M| \, \mathbf{\mu} \, |J', i', M')^2$, g_i, and Q_r given in previous sections of this chapter yield the formulas for peak absorption given in Chapter 2. These formulas are for transitions integrated over M Zeeman or Stark components and nuclear hyperfine structure. Relative intensities within Stark and Zeeman multiplets are treated in Chapter 3; the relative intensities within hyperfine structure multiplets are given in Sec. 2.6.

REFERENCES

[1] H. I. Ewen and E. M. Purcell, *Phys. Rev. 83*, 881 (1951).

[2] L. Pauling and E. B. Wilson, Jr., *Introduction to Quantum Mechanics* (McGraw-Hill Book Company, New York, 1935), Chapter XI.

[3] J. H. Van Vleck and V. F. Weisskopf, *Revs. Modern Phys. 17*, 227 (1945). See also H. Fröhlich, *Nature 157*, 478 (1946).

[4] R. Karplus and J. Schwinger, *Phys. Rev. 73*, 1020 (1948).

[5] H. A. Lorentz, *The Theory of Electrons and its Applications to the Phenomena of Light and Radiant Heat*, Second Edition (Teubner, Leipzig, 1916), note 57.

[6] P. Debye, *Polar Molecules* (Chemical Publishing Company, New York, 1929), Chapter 5.

[7] C. H. Townes, *Phys. Rev. 70*, 665 (1946).

[8] B. Bleaney and R. P. Penrose, *Proc. Phys. Soc. (London) 59*, 418 (1947).

[9] R. S. Anderson, W. V. Smith, and W. Gordy, *Phys. Rev. 82*, 264 (1951).

[10] R. Beringer, *Phys. Rev. 70*, 53 (1946); J. H. Van Vleck, *Phys. Rev. 71*, 413 (1947); M. W. P. Strandberg, C. Y. Meng, and J. G. Ingersoll, *Phys. Rev. 75*, 1524 (1949); H. R. L. Lamont, *Phys. Rev. 74*, 353 (1948).

[11] B. Bleaney and J. H. N. Loubser, *Nature 161*, 522 (1948); *Proc. Phys. Soc. (London) A63*, 483 (1950).

[12] I. R. Weingarten, *Columbia Rad. Lab. Report* (Edwards Brothers, Ann Arbor, 1948).

[13] D. F. Smith, *Phys. Rev. 74*, 506 (1948).

[14] H. Margenau, *Phys. Rev. 76*, 1423 (1949).

[15] P. W. Anderson, *Phys. Rev. 75*, 1450 (1949).

[16] G. E. Becker and S. H. Autler, *Phys. Rev. 70*, 300 (1946).

[17] M. Mizushima, *Phys. Rev. 83*, 94 (1951).

[18] E. H. Kennard, *Kinetic Theory of Gases* (McGraw-Hill Book Company, New York, 1938).

[19] C. H. Townes, F. R. Merritt, and B. D. Wright, *Phys. Rev. 73*, 1334 (1948).

[20] C. H. Townes, A. N. Holden and F. R. Merritt, *Phys. Rev. 74*, 1113 (1948).

[21] A. G. Smith, W. Gordy, J. W. Simmons, and W. V. Smith, *Phys. Rev. 75*, 260 (1949).

[22] O. R. Gilliam, H. D. Edwards, and W. Gordy, *Phys. Rev. 75*, 1014 (1949).

[23] C. H. Townes and F. R. Merritt, *Phys. Rev. 70*, 558 (1946).

[24] R. B. Lawrance and M. W. P. Strandberg, *Phys. Rev. 83*, 363 (1951).

[25] W. V. Smith and R. R. Howard, *Phys. Rev. 79*, 132 (1950).

[26] P. W. Anderson, *Phys. Rev. 80*, 511 (1950).

[27] R. S. Anderson, W. V. Smith, and W. Gordy, *Phys. Rev. 87*, 561 (1952).

[28] B. Bleaney and R. P. Penrose, *Proc. Roy. Soc. (London) A189*, 358 (1947).

[29] R. M. Hill and W. V. Smith, *Phys. Rev. 82*, 451 (1951).

[30] P. W. Anderson, *Phys. Rev. 76*, 647 (1949).

[31] N. F. Ramsey, *Phys. Rev. 78*, 221 (1950).

[31a] R. Beringer and J. G. Castle, Jr., *Phys. Rev. 81*, 82 (1951); B. V. Gokhale and M. W. P. Strandberg, *Phys. Rev. 84*, 844 (1951); J. O. Artman and J. P. Gordon, *Phys. Rev. 87*, 227 (1952).

[31b] C. M. Johnson and D. M. Slager, *Phys. Rev. 87*, 677 (1952).

[32] R. Howard and W. V. Smith, *Phys. Rev. 77*, 840 (1950).

[33] H. Margenau, *Phys. Rev. 76*, 121 (1949).

[34a] R. M. Hill and W. Gordy, unpublished data.

[34b] R. H. Johnson and M. W. P. Strandberg, *Phys. Rev. 86*, 811 (1952).

[35] B. Bleaney and R. P. Penrose, *Proc. Phys. Soc. (London) 60*, 83 (1948).

[36] R. L. Carter and W. V. Smith, *Phys. Rev. 73*, 1053 (1948).

[37] T. A. Pond and W. F. Cannon, *Phys. Rev. 72*, 1211 (1947).

[38] R. Karplus, *Phys. Rev. 73*, 1120 (1948).

[39] R. Karplus, *Phys. Rev. 74*, 223 (1948).

[40] D. M. Dennison, *Revs. Modern Phys. 3*, 280 (1931).

[41] P. C. Cross, R. M. Hainer, G. W. King, *J. Chem. Phys. 12*, 210 (1944).

[42] M. W. P. Strandberg, T. Wentink, and A. G. Hill, *Phys. Rev. 75*, 827 (1949).

[43] E. B. Wilson, Jr., *J. Chem. Phys. 3*, 276 (1935).

[44] G. Herzberg, *Infrared and Raman Spectra of Polyatomic Molecules* (D. Van Nostrand Co., New York, 1945).

[45] D. K. Coles, *Advances in Electronics 2*, 299 (1950).

5. SPECTRA OF SOLIDS AND LIQUIDS

5.1. PARAMAGNETIC RESONANCE

Paramagnetic resonance absorption spectra, observed first by Zavoisky [1] in 1945 in Russia and shortly after by Cummerow and Halliday [2] in America and by Bagguley and Griffiths [3] in England, represents an important new method for obtaining information about paramagnetic substances. The new information supplements that obtained from measurements of magnetic susceptibilities [4] and paramagnetic relaxation.[5] Since the initial experiments, many researchers have been active in the field. (See Bibliography.) Some of their results are described below.

Although paramagnetic resonance can be observed in the lower-frequency radio region of the spectrum, it is most easily observed in the microwave region, and it is in this region where most measurements have been made.

5.1a. Spectroscopic Splitting Factor. Paramagnetic resonance arises from transitions between Zeeman levels. An external magnetic field is imposed perpendicular to the magnetic component of the radiation field and is of such strength as to give the Zeeman levels the proper splitting to bring the frequency $(E_1 - E_2)/h$ to that chosen for observation. The coupling is through the magnetic vector, and the selection rule $\Delta M = 1$ gives with the Zeeman term energies the resonant frequency (exclusive of fine structure or hyperfine structure)

$$\nu = g\beta H/h = 1.400 \times 10^6 gH, \qquad (5.1)$$

where β is the Bohr magneton. The last form gives ν in cps when H is in gauss. For a g factor of 2 (free electron spin) the magnetic field required to bring the resonance frequency to X band, 9000 Mc/sec, is only 3330 gauss.

The measurement of a resonant frequency with the corresponding magnetic field yields with Eq. 5.1 an experimentally determined g factor. If the paramagnetic atom or ion were free or isolated, one would expect this g factor to correspond to the Landé formula,

$$g = 1 + \frac{J(J + 1) + S(S + 1) - L(L + 1)}{2J(J + 1)}. \qquad (5.2)$$

213

Because of various internal interactions which perturb the Zeeman levels, the g factors obtained by applying Eq. 5.1 to the observed resonance peaks do not correspond to the ideal values expressed by Eq. 5.2. They more frequently approach the free spin value 2 than the free ion value given by Eq. 5.2. Furthermore, the g factor obtained in measuring transitions between Zeeman levels in paramagnetic and ferromagnetic resonance experiments is not, in general, equivalent to the gyromagnetic ratio obtained in the usual gyromagnetic experiments. Kittel has suggested the appropriate term, "spectroscopic splitting factor," for the g factor of Eq. 5.1 to distinguish it from the g factor obtained in experiments of other types. (See Sec. 5.2.)

5.1b. Introduction to Crystalline Field Effects. When the paramagnetic element is not in an S state, the internal crystalline electric field interacts with the resulting non-spherical electron cloud. If this interaction is stronger than the spin-orbit interaction, $\lambda(\mathbf{L} \cdot \mathbf{S})$, as is usually the case in salts of the iron group elements, it breaks down the spin-orbit coupling and lifts the degeneracy of the $2L + 1$ orbital levels either partly or completely, depending upon the symmetry of the internal electric field. This splitting is essentially a Stark splitting of the orbital levels by the internal electric fields. An electric field cannot interact directly with the electron spin, and if there were no spin-orbit coupling the $2S + 1$ spin degeneracy of each orbital level would remain. The crystalline field can, however, interact with the spin levels indirectly through the spin-orbit coupling. The order of magnitude of this indirect splitting of the spin levels is

$$\Delta_S \approx \lambda^2 / \Delta_L, \qquad (5.3)$$

where λ is the spin-orbit coupling constant and Δ_L is the crystalline-field splitting of the orbital levels. When the spin degeneracy is completely lifted by the latter mechanism and when the resulting splitting is wide as compared with a microwave quantum, one cannot observe paramagnetic resonance in the microwave region. However, Kramers [6] has shown that if the number of unpaired electrons of the ion or atom is odd, the spin degeneracy can never be lifted entirely by the crystalline field via the spin-orbit coupling. For this case there remains a double degeneracy of each orbital level, commonly called Kramers' degeneracy, which can be lifted only by the imposition of an external magnetic field. Thus, unless the line is too broad to be detected, one should always be able to detect paramagnetic resonance for odd-electron ions. This is also true of the ions in which the number of unpaired electrons is even, provided that $\lambda \ll \Delta_L$, for then the splitting will be small as compared with the additional displacements which can be produced by an external magnetic field. As will be explained later, the spin-lattice relaxation time increases, and the line width decreases when Δ_L increases in comparison with λ. Therefore, one should be able to observe paramagnetic resonance in the microwave region when $\lambda \ll \Delta_L$, regardless of whether the number of unpaired electrons is even or odd.[7]

For the rare earths in which $\lambda > \Delta_L$, the crystalline field cannot break down the spin-orbit coupling but might lift the degeneracy of the $2J + 1$ levels. One should not, therefore, expect the g factor for the rare earths to approach that of the free electron spin except when the ion is in an S state. The large spin-orbit coupling with only a partial quenching of the orbital momenta by the crystalline field makes the spin-lattice relaxation time short and the resonant lines in most rare-earth salts so broad that they are difficult to detect except at very low temperatures.

Thus the detectability of paramagnetic resonance as well as the nature of the results observed depends upon the spectroscopic ground state of the ion, the value of the spin-orbit coupling constant λ, and particularly upon the nature of the crystalline field.

Bethe [8] has shown from group theory how various degeneracies are lifted in fields of different symmetries. His theory is frequently useful in interpreting results or in predicting whether paramagnetic resonance should be detected in the microwave region. Table 5.2 (see p. 225) shows how the $2L + 1$ and $2S + 1$ degeneracies of the iron-group ions are lifted in fields of various symmetries.

In addition, certain helpful qualitative deductions can be drawn regarding the crystalline-field splitting. (1) In all the salts of the iron group the crystalline Stark splitting of the orbital levels by the predominant field (usually cubic symmetry) is likely to be large, of the order of several thousand cm^{-1}. Frequently, however, some remaining degeneracies are removed by weak-field components of lower symmetry with a resulting splitting which is much smaller and might be of the order of kT at room temperature (~ 200 cm^{-1}), or even $h\nu$ at microwave frequencies. (2) The indirect splitting of the spin levels, which is of the order of λ^2/Δ_L is likely to be small in the salts of the iron group and is frequently of the order of a microwave quantum. (3) When $L = 0$, the splitting of the spin levels by the crystalline electric field is a higher-order process which will be small, usually less than a microwave $h\nu$. (4) Because the unpaired electrons are in deep sub-valence shells and are partly screened from the crystalline field in the rare-earth salts, the crystalline field interaction is usually too small to break down the strong spin-orbit coupling but might cause a splitting of the $2J + 1$ levels. (5) Strong exchange interaction sometimes wipes out the crystalline-field effects. (6) In some instances the crystalline field might be sufficiently strong to break down the coupling so that no resultant L is formed. This is most likely when covalent bonds are formed. The spectroscopic ground state of the ion might also be changed by the formation of a covalent bond.[9]

Expressions for the various crystalline-field potentials can be obtained from a Taylor's expansion about the paramagnetic ion in question of the potential which arises from distant charges. For the lowest symmetry (rhombic) with the axes chosen so as to eliminate cross terms and with higher-order terms neglected,

$$V = V_0 + Ax^2 + By^2 + Cz^2,$$

where $A = \dfrac{1}{2}\left(\dfrac{\partial^2 V}{\partial x^2}\right)_0$, $B = \dfrac{1}{2}\left(\dfrac{\partial^2 V}{\partial y^2}\right)_0$, $C = \dfrac{1}{2}\left(\dfrac{\partial^2 V}{\partial z^2}\right)_0$. If the constant term is neglected and Laplace's equation $\nabla^2 V = 0$ is applied, the rhombic case becomes

$$V_{\text{rhombic}} = Ax^2 + By^2 - (A + B)z^2.$$

For axial symmetry (trigonal, tetragonal), $A = B$ and

$$V_{\text{tetrag}} = A(x^2 + y^2 - 2z^2).$$

For cubic symmetry, all the derivatives with respect to x, y, and z are equal, and, in view of Laplace's equation, $A = B = C = 0$. The first non-vanishing term in the expansion is then

$$V_{\text{cubic}} = D(x^4 + y^4 + z^4),$$

where $D = \dfrac{1}{24}\left(\dfrac{\partial^4 V}{\partial x^4}\right)_0$. In very many crystals the field can be treated as predominantly cubic with a small axially symmetric component superimposed.

5.1c. Characteristic Energies and Line Frequencies. The various factors which constitute the energy of the paramagnetic ion of a crystal in a magnetic field are expressed in their normally decreasing order of importance for the iron-group elements by the total Hamiltonian of Abragam and Pryce,[10]

$$W = W_F + V + W_{LS} + W_{SS} + \beta \mathbf{H} \cdot (\mathbf{L} + 2\mathbf{S}) + W_I - g_I \beta_I \mathbf{H} \cdot \mathbf{I}, \quad (5.4)$$

in which W_F is the energy for the corresponding free ion, V the electrostatic energy in the field of neighboring ions, W_{LS} the spin-orbit interaction, W_{SS} the electronic spin-spin interaction, $\beta \mathbf{H} \cdot (\mathbf{L} + 2\mathbf{S})$ the energy of interaction of the electrons with the external magnetic field, W_I the interaction of the nucleus with the internal electric and magnetic fields, and $g_I\beta_I\mathbf{H}\cdot\mathbf{I}$ the interaction of the nucleus with the externally imposed magnetic field. (Here g_I is the nuclear gyromagnetic ratio, and β_I is the nuclear magneton.) In salts of the iron group the level separations most frequently caused by the internal interactions are of the order: W_F, 10^5 cm^{-1}; V, 10^4 cm^{-1}; W_{LS}, 10^2 cm^{-1}; W_{SS}, 1 cm^{-1}; W_I, 10^{-2} cm^{-1}. When the external field is such as to cause $\beta\mathbf{H}\cdot(\mathbf{L}+2\mathbf{S})$ to be 1 cm^{-1}, then $g_I\beta_I\mathbf{H}\cdot\mathbf{I}$ is of the order of 10^{-3} cm^{-1}.

The calculation of the combined effects of the different interaction energies included in the total Hamiltonian (Eq. 5.4) is very difficult. Fortunately, because of the wide intervals of W_F and V, in most instances only their lowest levels are significantly populated at room temperature. Hence, one is concerned primarily with the splitting of these lowest levels by second-order crystalline field effects, nuclear interactions, external fields, etc. In most commonly studied crystals the predominant crystalline field has cubic symmetry with a weaker component of lower symmetry. Abragam and Pryce [10] have shown that a considerably simplified Hamiltonian can be used to calculate the observed spectra when, as is often true, the anistropy in the g factor has axial symmetry. This occurs when the crystalline field causing the anistropy has trigonal or tetragonal symmetry. When the lowest orbital level is not single, this is made possible by defining an "effective spin," S, such that $2S + 1$ is the multiplicity of the level under consideration. The Hamiltonian then becomes

$$W = \beta\{g_\|H_zS_z + g_\perp(H_xS_x + H_yS_y)\} + D\{S_z{}^2 - \tfrac{1}{3}S(S+1)\}$$

$$+ AS_zI_z + B(S_xI_x + S_yI_y) + Q'\{I_z{}^2 - \tfrac{1}{3}I(I+1)\} - g_I\beta_I\mathbf{H}\cdot\mathbf{I}, \quad (5.5)$$

where the axis of symmetry is taken along the z axis. Here β and β_I are the Bohr magneton and the nuclear magneton, respectively; $g_\|$ and $g_\perp$ are the components of the spectroscopic splitting factor g parallel and perpendicular to the axis of symmetry. The first term in brackets is the principal one and represents the interaction of the effective spin vector with the external field; the second term (that in D) represents the initial splitting of the spin levels by the second-order crystalline-field interaction and may be regarded as giving rise to a fine structure of the principal term; the remaining terms represent nuclear interactions which give rise to the hyperfine structure, the first two of which (those in A and B) correspond to the interaction of the nuclear magnetic moment with the magnetic moments of the unpaired electrons; the third term (that in Q') † represents the interaction of the nuclear

---

† We use Q' for the Q used by the British workers so as to reserve the symbol Q to designate the nuclear quadrupole moment (Chapters 2 and 6).

quadrupole moment with the gradient of the crystalline electric field $\left[Q' = 3eQ \left(\dfrac{\partial^2 V}{\partial z^2}\right) \middle/ 4I(2I - 1) \right]$; and the last term $(-g_I\beta_I\mathbf{H}\cdot\mathbf{I})$ represents the interaction of the nuclear magnetic moment with the external magnetic field. Small departures from axial symmetry are taken into account by adding a term $E(S_x^2 - S_y^2)$ to the Hamiltonian. The components $g_{\parallel}$ and $g_{\perp}$, and the interaction constants, A, B, D, and Q', are, in general, regarded as empirical constants to be evaluated from the observed spectra. In many instances some of these constants are zero, and the Hamiltonian may be further simplified. For example, when $I = 0$, only the first three terms remain.

Abragam and Pryce have used the Hamiltonian, Eq. 5.5, to calculate the g factors and interaction constants in terms of observable spectral intervals for most ions which have been studied. These formulas, which are very useful in the analysis of paramagnetic resonance spectra, require too much space for reproduction here. Although they apply mainly to the iron-group salts, they are applicable in some instances to the rare earths, in particular to Gd^{+++}, which has an S ground state. Specific formulas for certain cases, not including nuclear effects, are also given by Polder,[11] by Kittel and Luttinger,[12] and by Weiss.[13]

Using the simplified Hamiltonian, Eq. 5.5, for crystals having axial symmetry with the additional restriction that the nuclear quadrupole splitting is small as compared with the nuclear magnetic splitting, Bleaney [14] has calculated general formulas for the frequencies of paramagnetic resonance in strong fields, including both the fine structure caused by the crystalline field and the hyperfine structure caused by nuclear interaction. The formulas are derived by perturbation theory and are carried to second order. The expression for the frequencies corresponding to $M_S \to M_S - 1$ in the absence of nuclear interactions is

$$\nu = \frac{1}{h}\left[g\beta H + D\left(M_S - \frac{1}{2}\right)\left\{3\frac{g_{\parallel}^2}{g^2}\cos^2\theta - 1\right\} - \left(\frac{Dg_{\parallel}g_{\perp}\cos\theta\sin\theta}{g^2}\right)^2 \right.$$

$$\cdot \left(\frac{1}{2g\beta H_0}\right)\left\{4S(S + 1) - 24M_S(M_S - 1) - 9\right\} + \left(\frac{Dg_{\perp}^2\sin^2\theta}{g^2}\right)^2$$

$$\left. \cdot \left(\frac{1}{8g\beta H_0}\right)\left\{2S(S + 1) - 6M_S(M_S - 1) - 3\right\}\right], \quad (5.6)$$

where $g^2 = g_{\parallel}^2\cos^2\theta + g_{\perp}^2\sin^2\theta$, and H_0 is the field at which the unperturbed line would occur. To this expression there must be added the frequency splittings caused by the nuclear effects. For $(M_S, M_I) \to (M_S - 1, M_I)$ these are:

$$\Delta\nu = \frac{1}{h}\left[KM_I + \frac{B^2}{4g\beta H_0}\left(\frac{A^2 + K^2}{K^2}\right)\{I(I+1) - M_I^2\}\right.$$

$$+ \frac{B^2}{2g\beta H_0}\frac{A}{K}M_I(2M_S - 1) + \frac{1}{2g\beta H_0}\left(\frac{A^2 - B^2}{K}\right)^2\left(\frac{g_{\parallel}g_{\perp}}{g^2}\right)^2$$

$$\cdot \sin^2\theta\cos^2\theta M_I^2 + \left(\frac{Q'^2\cos^2\theta\sin^2\theta}{2KM_S(M_S - 1)}\right)$$

$$\cdot\left(\frac{ABg_{\parallel}g_{\perp}}{K^2g^2}\right)^2 M_I\{4I(I+1) - 8M_I^2 - 1\} - \left(\frac{Q'^2\sin^4\theta}{8KM_S(M_S - 1)}\right)$$

$$\cdot\left(\frac{Bg_{\perp}}{Kg}\right)^4 M_I\{2I(I+1) - 2M_I^2 - 1\}\right], \quad (5.7)$$

where $K^2g^2 = A^2g_{\parallel}^2\cos^2\theta + B^2g_{\perp}^2\sin^2\theta$. In these expressions θ is the angle between the applied field H and the axis of symmetry of the crystal. M_S and M_I are the magnetic quantum numbers for the electrons and the nucleus, respectively. The selection rules are $\Delta M_S = \pm 1$ and $\Delta M_I = 0$. See also Art. 5.1l.

Frequently, weak lines corresponding to transitions for which $\Delta M_S = 2$ are observed.[15,16] These have an intensity of the order $(D/H)^2$ and vanish for $\theta = 0$. The frequencies of these "double jumps," if hyperfine structure is neglected and if it is assumed as before that the anistropy in g has axial symmetry, are, according to Bleaney,[14]

$$\nu = \frac{1}{h}\left[2g\beta H + 2D(M_S - 1)\left\{3\frac{g_{\parallel}^2}{g^2}\cos^2\theta - 1\right\} - \left(\frac{Dg_{\parallel}g_{\perp}\cos\theta\sin\theta}{g^2}\right)^2\right.$$

$$\cdot\left(\frac{2}{g\beta H_0}\right)\{4S(S+1) - 24M_S(M_S - 2) - 33\} + \left(\frac{Dg_{\perp}^2\sin^2\theta}{g^2}\right)^2$$

$$\cdot\left(\frac{1}{2g\beta H_0}\right)\{2S(S+1) - 6M_S(M_S - 2) - 9\}\right], \quad (5.8)$$

where the various symbols have the same significance as above.

5.1d. Line Breadths. *Spin-spin interactions.* Acting on a given electron in a paramagnetic substance there is an internal magnetic field resulting from the spin magnetic moments of all the other unpaired electrons of the substance. Since the field contributed by each neighboring electron depends on its position and orientation relative to the one under consideration, there is a spread in the total internal magnetic field acting on a given electron and arising from the spin magnetic moments of the other unpaired electrons. This results in a corresponding spread in the Zeeman frequencies. The dipole field falls off inversely as the cube of the distance. The component along the externally applied field contributed at the position of a given electron by a neighbor at r distance away is $\mu(1 - 3\cos^2\theta)/r^3$, where θ is the angle between r and the direction of the external field and μ is the spin magnetic moment of the electron. The mean-square-moment of the line width arising from interactions [17] of spin moments is

$$\langle \Delta H^2 \rangle_{\text{Av}} = \tfrac{3}{4}g^2\beta^2 S(S + 1) \sum_j (1 - 3\cos^2\theta_{ij})^2 r_{ij}^{-6}, \qquad (5.9)$$

where θ_{ij} is the angle between the externally applied field and the line joining the electrons i and j, and where r_{ij} is the separation of electrons i and j. In applying the equation one need include only close neighbors. If a gaussian shape is assumed, the half-width is

$$\Delta H_{\frac{1}{2}} = 1.18\sqrt{\langle \Delta H^2 \rangle_{\text{Av}}}.$$

Equation 5.9 holds for electrons in like atoms. For unlike atoms the right-hand side should be multiplied by $(\tfrac{2}{3})^2$.

It is seen that the spin-spin interaction falls off rapidly with the separation of the ions. Therefore the spin-spin broadening can usually be reduced to insignificance by diluting the substance with a suitable non-magnetic material. Because of the angular dependence indicated by Eq. 5.9, the spin-spin broadening varies with the orientation of the crystal in the external field. It has been pointed out by the Oxford group [7] that the spin-spin broadening alone is probably never so great as to prevent detection of paramagnetic resonance. Van Vleck [17] has shown that broadening of this type tends to make the line more blunted at the peak than is the gaussian curve.

Spin-lattice interaction. According to the uncertainty principle,

$$\Delta E \cdot \Delta t \geq h/2\pi, \qquad (5.10)$$

the spread in the term energy increases, and, hence, the spectral lines involving this energy must increase in width as the lifetime in the state decreases. This lifetime in paramagnetic resonance is measured by the "relaxation time" or the "reorientation time" of the spin vector when the orbital momentum is quenched or of the total momentum vector **J** when **L** is unquenched. Let us assume that **L** is quenched and that the spin vector is oriented in an external field and ask what factors would tend to cause a reorientation. Any force which does this must couple magnetically to the spin magnetic moment of the electron. The two significant forms of this coupling are the spin-orbit coupling and the spin-spin coupling with neighboring electrons. The spin-spin coupling with the nuclei is too weak to be of much importance.

The orbital magnetic moment which is coupled magnetically to the spin vector of the electron is in turn coupled through electrical forces to the crystalline axes. The thermal motions of the ions can alter the direction of L in space and thereby can indirectly perturb the electron-spin orientation. Likewise, the spin-spin interactions depend on the direction and separation of the interacting dipoles, and hence are influenced by the lattice vibrations. Through each of these couplings, transitions between the Zeeman levels can be induced,[7] either (1) by an exchange of quanta with the lattice vibrations (resonance process) or (2) by a scattering of the "lattice waves" with the exchange of energy taking place through the Raman process.

Detailed calculation of the spin-lattice relaxation time is difficult. For the case of $S = \frac{1}{2}$, Kronig [18] made the following estimates:

$$\tau \approx \frac{10^4 \Delta_L{}^4}{\lambda^2 H^4 T} \qquad \text{(resonance exchange)}, \qquad (5.11)$$

$$\tau \approx \frac{10^4 \Delta_L{}^6}{\lambda^2 H^2 T^7} \qquad \text{(Raman process)}, \qquad (5.12)$$

where τ is the relaxation time in seconds, H is in gauss, λ and Δ_L are in cm^{-1}. Here Δ_L is the separation of the lowest orbital levels. The temperature T is assumed to be small as compared with the "Debye temperature" of the lattice. From these formulas it can be seen that the spin-lattice relaxation increases rapidly with the crystalline-field splitting Δ_L of the orbital levels and decreases with increase of the spin-orbit coupling. Though it is a second-order process, the Raman process is much more effective in broadening the lines at room temperature than is the resonance process because lattice frequencies far removed from the Zeeman frequencies participate in the Raman scattering. From Eq. 5.12, it is seen that broadening of the lines by the Raman process falls off very rapidly with decreasing temperature. However, the British workers [7] estimate that it is probably still more effective than the resonance process even at liquid-oxygen temperatures but probably not at the temperature of liquid helium. When the principal broadening is caused by spin-lattice interactions, one can sharpen the lines very much and can therefore strengthen the resonance peaks greatly by decreasing the temperature.

Exchange interaction. The effects of exchange interaction on line shapes in paramagnetic resonance have been described by Gorter and Van Vleck [19] and developed in detail by Van Vleck.[17] If the interaction is between similar atoms or ions, i.e., ones that have the same energy in the magnetic field, the exchange will decrease the width of the resonance line and give it a sharply peaked shape. Van Vleck [17] shows that the fourth root-mean-moment of the frequency $\langle \Delta \nu^4 \rangle_{Av}^{1/4}$ is increased by such exchange but that the mean-second-moment is unchanged. This means that the line is broadened near the wings but sharpened near the center so that the width measured at the half-power points is decreased. In contrast, exchange interaction between dissimilar atoms contributes to the mean-square-moment of the frequency and increases the line width. Classically, one might explain exchange narrowing on the basis that the rapid exchange of the electrons tends to smooth out the slowly varying internal fields acting on a given electron. If the exchange is between dissimilar atoms—atoms in which the Larmor precession of the electron spin is different—the exchange will tend to average the two precessional frequencies and will thus broaden the lines.

Since the paramagnetic measurements are usually made at a constant frequency with variation of the magnetic field, we express the line width in terms of H. The nth root-mean-moment is then defined as

$$\langle \Delta H^n \rangle_{Av}^{1/n} = \left[\frac{\int_0^\infty A(H)[H - H_{res}]^n \, dH}{\int_0^\infty A(H) \, dH} \right]^{1/n}, \tag{5.13}$$

where $A(H)$ is the amplitude of the absorption for any chosen value of H, and H_{res} is the field strength for maximum $A(H)$. For a purely gaussian distribution,

$$\langle \Delta H^4 \rangle_{Av}^{1/4} / \langle \Delta H^2 \rangle_{Av}^{1/2} = 1.32.$$

Exchange narrowing increases this ratio above 1.32, and dipole-dipole interaction decreases it below 1.32. For a rectangular shape this ratio is 1.16. Thus, by evaluating the above ratio—this can be done satisfactorily by approximate numerical evaluation of the integral, Eq. 5.13, with points read off the experimental absorption curve—one can learn whether there is significant exchange interaction. Table 5.1 gives some line widths calculated by Van Vleck [17] on the assumption of gaussian shape and dipole-dipole broadening as compared to those observed by Zavoisky at 200-cm wavelengths. Van Vleck attributes the considerable narrowing of the observed lines over that calculated primarily to exchange effects.

Cupric salts which have two Cu^{++} ions in unit cell, i.e., two ions with different orientation of crystalline axes, provide an interesting test of the exchange theory. We illustrate with $CuSO_4 \cdot 5H_2O$, which has been studied carefully by Arnold and Kip,[20] and by Bagguley and Griffiths.[21]

Table 5.1. Evidence for exchange narrowing (From Van Vleck.[17])

Line Breadths in Gauss

	Obs.†	Cal.‡
$CuCl_2 \cdot 2H_2O$	125	750
$CuSO_4 \cdot 5H_2O$	175	475
$MnSO_4 \cdot 4H_2O$	400	1500
$MnSO_4$	300	3500

† Observed by Zavoisky, *J. Phys. U.S.S.R. 10*, 170, 197 (1945).
‡ Calculated by Van Vleck, assuming Gaussian shape and dipolar coupling without exchange effects.

The tetragonal axes of the two ions are 82° apart. With the external magnetic field in the plane of these axes two peaks are expected because of the different orientations of the internal fields at the two ions with reference to the external field. The fact that only one peak is observed at wavelengths longer than 1 cm is attributed [21] to the rapid exchange of the electrons between the two ions. This tends to average the g factors for the two orientations and to give a single broad peak. At frequencies so high that the difference in precessional frequencies for the two ions is greater than the exchange frequency, it is possible to resolve the two peaks. This resolution has been achieved by Bagguley and Griffiths [21] at wavelengths of 0.85 cm. From the separation of the two peaks where the lines are barely resolvable, the latter observers estimate the exchange frequency as 0.15 cm^{-1}. With **H** perpendicular to the plane of the two tetragonal axes the precessional frequencies for the two ions are identical, and the exchange interaction narrows markedly the single line which is observed for this orientation of the crystal.

The exchange of electrons between two atoms depends on the overlapping of the wave functions and hence is expected to fall off very rapidly with increase of separation much beyond the sum of the covalent radii of the atoms. For these reasons exchange narrowing is normally expected to occur only when the paramagnetic atoms are closely spaced. However, evidence for exchange narrowing has been found by Lancaster and Gordy [16] in a number of instances where the paramagnetic ions are widely separated by certain atoms or organic radicals. A plausible explanation is that the wave function occupied by the unpaired electron is not a pure atomic wave function but is a composite function with contributions from the orbitals of neighboring atoms. By this process the orbital occupied by the electron is presumably spread out so that exchange with neighboring ions can occur. It appears that the phenomenon of exchange narrowing might be used to investigate the resonance properties of organic radicals.

There is evidence [16] that, other things being equal, exchange narrowing is more pronounced in chlorides than in fluorides even when the paramagnetic ions are closer in the latter salts. Contributions of the $3d$ orbitals of the Cl to the wave function occupied by the unpaired electron seems a plausible explanation. In other words, the $3d$ Cl orbital provides a low-energy path for exchange of the electrons between the paramagnetic ions. This behavior is in harmony with the special tendency of the second-row elements to use the $3d$ orbital to form a coordinate covalent bond. (See Chapter 8.) The pronounced exchange narrowing in sulphates may result partly from a similar use of the $3d$ orbitals of sulphur.

5.1e. Salts of the Iron-Group Elements. *Survey of properties.* From a consideration of the spectroscopic ground states of the ions and the most common field symmetries surrounding them, the Oxford researchers [7] have made qualitative predictions as to results expected with salts of the iron-group elements. They then made observations on a large number of salts in the powder form and in many instances obtained confirming evidence. Following Schlapp and Penney [22] and others, they assumed a predominantly cubic field with a smaller component of lower symmetry.

Brief qualitative descriptions of the expected behavior (if nuclear effects are neglected) of the different ions in the most common crystalline fields are given below. A more quantitative treatment is given in Art. 5.1c.

Ti^{+++}, V^{+++}, Fe^{++}, *and* Co^{++}. Though these ions do not have the same spectroscopic ground state, they are grouped together because it has not proved possible to detect resonance in salts of any of them except at rather low temperatures. They are similar in that all have in a field of cubic symmetry a triplet orbital level which lies lowest. The degeneracy of this triplet level is further broken down by fields of lower symmetry. See Table 5.2. Since the field component of lower symmetry is usually weak, the resulting splitting of this triplet is not expected to be large. With the usual separations of the lowest orbital levels, of the order of hundreds of cm^{-1}, the spin-lattice relaxation time is so short at room temperature that the lines are too broad to detect.

The Oxford workers [7] estimate that a relaxation time of about 10^{-11} seconds is required to make the lines detectable, whereas Δ_L of 100 cm^{-1} gives τ of the order of 10^{-12} even at 10° K.

Table 5.2. Ground states, quantum numbers, and degeneracies † in various fields of ions of the iron group

Ion	Ti^{+++}	V^{+++}	V^{++} Cr^{+++}	Cr^{++} Mn^{+++}	Mn^{++} Fe^{+++}	Fe^{++}	Co^{++}	Ni^{++}	Cu^{++}
S	½	1	3/2	2	5/2	2	3/2	1	½
L	2	3	3	2	0	2	3	3	2
J (free ion)	3/2	2	3/2	0	5/2	4	9/2	4	5/2
λ (cm^{-1})	154	105	55 V^{++} 87 Cr^{+++}	59 Cr^{++}		-100	-180	-355	-852

Orbital degeneracy in fields of various symmetries

Free ion	5	7	7	5	1	5	7	7	5
Cubic	2, 3 ‡	1, 2·3 ‡	1‡, 2·3	2‡, 3	1	2, 3 ‡	1, 2·3 ‡	1‡, 2·3	2‡, 3
Trigonal	1, 2·2	3·1, 2·2	3·1, 2·2	1, 2·2	1	1, 2·2	3·1, 2·2	3·1, 2·2	1, 2·2
Tetragonal	3·1, 2	3·1, 2·2	3·1, 2·2	3·1, 2	1	3·1, 2	3·1, 2·2	3·1, 2·2	3·1, 2
Rhombic	5·1	7·1	7·1	5·1	1	5·1	7·1	7·1	5·1

Spin degeneracy in fields of various symmetries for single orbital level

Free ion	2	3	4	5	6	5	4	3	2
Cubic	2	3	4	2, 3	2, 4	2, 3	4	3	2
Trigonal	2	1, 2	2·2	1, 2·2	3·2	1, 2·2	2·2	1·2	2
Tetragonal	2	1, 2	2·2	3·1, 2	3·2	3·1, 2	2·2	1·2	2
Rhombic	2	3·1	2·2	5·1	3·2	5·1	2·2	1, 2	2

† $a \cdot b$ means that there are a sets of levels of b-fold degeneracy.
‡ Lower level.

Furthermore, when the number of unpaired electrons is even, a small Δ_L, in view of Eq. 5.3, can result in a separation of all the spin levels by an amount which is larger than the microwave $h\nu$. This factor alone could prevent detection of resonance in salts of V^{+++} and Fe^{++}, but, in view of Kramers' degeneracy,[6] cannot do so for Ti^{+++} and Co^{++}. For this reason, one should always be able to detect resonance in salts of the two latter ions, provided that the temperature is sufficiently low; indeed, resonance has been detected in salts of both ions but only at very low temperatures.

Cu^{++} *and* Cr^{++}. Cu^{++} and Cr^{++}, like Ti^{+++} and Fe^{++}, have five orbital levels which, in a cubic field, are split into a triplet and a doublet. However, the levels of Cu^{++} and Cr^{++} are inverted with respect to those of Ti^{+++} and Fe^{++}. In Cu^{++} and Cr^{++} it is the doublet which lies lower. This doublet is non-magnetic and therefore cannot perturb the spin levels. The Δ_L of Eqs. 5.11 and 5.12, which affects the spin-lattice relaxation time, is essentially the separation of the doublet from the triplet rather than the smaller splitting of the doublet by weaker field components of lower symmetry. The spin-lattice relaxation time is therefore long, and resonance in salts of these elements (which have predominantly cubic fields) is easily observed at room temperature. The spin levels cannot be split by the crystalline field in Cu^{++} because $S = \frac{1}{2}$ (Kramers' degeneracy). In Cr^{++} the expected splitting of the spin levels is small (probably less than one cm^{-1}) because it varies inversely as Δ_L, which in most salts is large ($\sim 10^4$ cm^{-1}), and directly as λ^2, which in this ion is small ($\lambda = 57$ cm^{-1}).

V^{++}, Cr^{+++}, and Ni^{++}. In V^{++}, Cr^{+++}, and Ni^{++} a singlet orbital level lies lowest in a cubic field, and hence no weaker field components of lower symmetry can perturb the spin levels. Such perturbation must therefore come from levels of the two triplets, the nearest of which is, for a strong cubic field, several thousand cm^{-1} above. This means that the spin-lattice relaxation time must be rather long for the salts of predominantly cubic field symmetry and that the splitting of the spin levels must be small. This applies particularly to V^{++} and Cr^{+++} in which the spin-orbit couplings are small. (Table 5.2.) With a singlet ground state and a weak spin-orbit coupling, their behavior resembles that of an ion in an S state. The anistropies in their g factors are small. Because of its rather large spin-orbit coupling ($\lambda = -335$ cm^{-1}), the spin-lattice relaxation time in Ni^{++} salts will, in general, be shorter, and the splitting of the spin levels larger, than those of V^{++} and Cr^{+++}. Lines of the Ni^{++} salts have been observed at room temperature in a few instances. The rhombic component of the field in some nickel salts has been found to be nearly as strong as the cubic part.[23]

Mn^{++} and Fe^{+++}. Mn^{++} and Fe^{+++} have $^6S_{5/2}$ ground states, and because $L = 0$ the perturbations of the spin levels are very small and the expected g factor isotropic and nearly 2, the value for spin only. The spin-lattice relaxation time is long, and it should therefore be easy to detect resonance in salts of these elements at room temperature. This agrees with the results of the preliminary survey by the Oxford workers. Because of the large spins, the spin-spin coupling broadens the lines appreciably in salts in which the ions are concentrated. This broadening should never be sufficiently great, however, to prevent detection at room temperatures because in the more concentrated salts the exchange narrowing will tend to offset the spin-spin broadening. The splitting of the spin levels has been found to be of the order of

Table 5.3. Summary for iron-group elements

Ion	$^2D_{3/2}$	$^3F_2$	$^4F_{3/2}$	$^5D_0$	$^6S_{5/2}$	$^5D_4$	$^4F_{9/2}$	$^3F_4$	$^2D_{5/2}$
Free ion state	Ti^{+++}	V^{+++}	V^{++} Cr^{+++}	Cr^{++}	Mn^{++} Fe^{+++}	Fe^{++}	Co^{++}	Ni^{++}	Cu^{++}
Expected spin-lattice relaxation time	Very short	Very short	Long	Long	Long	Very short	Very short	Long	Long
Temperature at which resonance is observed	Only at low temperature	Not yet observed	Room temperature	Room temperature	Room temperature	Only at very low temperature	Only at low temperature	Room temperature	Room temperature
Expected splitting of spin levels in crystalline fields of different symmetry	Degeneracy never lifted	No splitting in cubic. Doublet in trig. or tet. separated ~5 cm⁻¹. Degeneracy completely lifted in rhombic	No splitting in cubic. Two doublets separated ~0.2 cm⁻¹ in trig., tet., and rhombic	Very small	Very small, ~0.1. Degeneracy never completely lifted	Small 1 cm⁻¹	Large 5 to 10 cm⁻¹. Degeneracy never completely lifted	Medium 0.1 to 5 cm⁻¹	Degeneracy never lifted
Lowest orbital level in cubic field	Triplet	Triplet	Singlet	Non-magnetic doublet	Singlet ($L = 0$)	Triplet	Triplet	Singlet	Non-magnetic doublet

0.1 cm^{-1} in certain salts of both ions.[7] Table 5.2 shows how the spin degeneracy is lifted in fields of different symmetry.

Table 5.3 summarizes the behavior expected for the iron-group elements when the crystalline field has a predominantly cubic symmetry.

Results on particular salts. Hundreds of salts have now been investigated. Space does not permit even a complete summary in the present volume. As illustrations of crystalline-field effects (exclusive of hyperfine structure), we mention some of the more definite results. The most complete results so far obtained are on certain cupric salts and chrome alums. These will be discussed in some detail.

(a) *Cupric salts.* Single crystals of $CuSO_4 \cdot 5H_2O$ have been investigated in detail by Bagguley and Griffiths [21] and by Arnold and Kip.[20] X-ray diffraction measurements [24] show that there are two Cu^{++} ions in each unit cell with each ion at the center of an electric field of cubic symmetry with a strong tetragonal component superimposed. Their tetragonal axes are oriented 82° apart. The theory of the crystalline-field splitting has been worked out by Polder [11] and by Abragam and Pryce.[10] By the cubic field the orbital levels are split into a triplet and a doublet with the doublet lying lower. The tetragonal field splits them further into a doublet and three singlets with one of the singlets lying lowest. Since $S = \frac{1}{2}$, the lowest level is a Kramers' doublet, the degeneracy of which is removed by an external magnetic field. The crystalline field is sufficiently large to cause the lowest orbital level to fall several thousand wave numbers below the nearest orbital state above. This, combined with the strong spin-orbit coupling, makes the spin-lattice relaxation time long and the resonance easy to observe at ordinary temperatures. Since there is only one unpaired electron per ion, the paramagnetic absorption arises essentially from a flipping of the electron-spin vector in the external field. However, the large spin-orbit coupling with the crystalline field makes the g factor greater than 2 and anisotropic.

Polder's theory [11] yields the g factors for the tetragonal axes parallel and perpendicular to the external magnetic field, $g_{\parallel}$ and $g_{\perp}$, respectively, as

$$g_{\parallel} = 2\left[1 - \frac{4\lambda}{E_4 - E_3}\right], \qquad (5.14)$$

$$g_{\perp} = 2\left[1 - \frac{\lambda}{E_5 - E_3}\right], \qquad (5.15)$$

where λ is the spin-orbital coupling constant and E_3 is the lowest orbital level, and E_4 and E_5 are higher levels. Since λ is negative, the observed

g factor will be greater than 2. For any arbitrary orientation, θ, of its tetragonal axis from the external field the observed g factor for a particular ion is

$$g = \sqrt{g_\parallel{}^2 \cos^2 \theta + g_\perp{}^2 \sin^2 \theta}. \tag{5.16}$$

By making measurements at known angles θ, the above-mentioned researchers [20, 21] have obtained $g_\parallel$ and $g_\perp$ and have calculated with Polder's formulas the splitting of the lowest orbital levels by the crystalline field. The results of Bagguley and Griffiths,[21] $g_\parallel = 2.47$ and $g_\perp = 2.06$, give with Eqs. 5.14 and 5.15

$$E_4 - E_3 = 14,000 \text{ cm}^{-1} \qquad E_5 - E_3 = 28,000 \text{ cm}^{-1}.$$

The copper Tutton salts, which have the chemical formula $CuM_2(SO_4)_2 \cdot 6H_2O$ or $CuM_2(SeO_4)_2 \cdot 6H_2O$ where M is a monovalent, diamagnetic ion, have been investigated by Bleaney, Penrose, and Plumpton.[25] Although no X-ray determination of their structure had been made, Polder,[11] from a comparison of the known structure of a similar salt of Mg, assumed two ions in the unit cell with tetragonal symmetry of the crystalline field through each and obtained formulas like those of Eqs. 5.14 and 5.15 for the g factor. To a first order of approximation the paramagnetic resonance results of Bleaney, Penrose, and Plumpton confirm the structural feature assumed by Polder. However, some of the salts investigated showed departure from tetragonal symmetry. Particularly, $CuK_2(SO_4)_2 \cdot 6H_2O$ showed evidence of a strong rhombic component of the field. †

An unusual behavior has been found by Lancaster and Gordy [16] in the paramagnetic resonance spectra of copper acetate. A peculiar splitting of a resonance line which collapsed into a single line at very high fields was found. Also, a rather strong line at approximately twice the frequency of the main transition was observed. The latter decreased rapidly with increasing fields and disappeared at the highest fields used. These effects were ascribed to a coupling of electrons of neighboring Cu ions, with the high frequency line being ascribed to a simultaneous flipping of two coupled electron spin vectors. Bleaney and Bowers [26] have investigated this salt with single crystals and at low temperature and have obtained convincing evidence confirming this interpretation. The behavior of the resonance with decrease in temperature is shown to be in agreement with the susceptibility measurement of Guha,[23] who found that the susceptibility of copper acetate decreases

---

† It was pointed out by Bagguley and Griffiths [*Proc. Phys. Soc.* A65, 594 (1952)] that the tetragonal field might have a different sign in the copper Tutton salts from that assumed by Polder. In that case, $g_\parallel \approx 2.0$, $g_\perp = 2(1 - 3\lambda/\Delta E)$.

rapidly with temperature and that at about 50° K it should vanish entirely. This result, with the microwave spectra, shows without doubt that the two Cu ions in unit cell are coupled strongly by exchange interaction and that at very low temperatures all the electrons are aligned in an anti-parallel fashion by exchange interaction. Bleaney and Bowers found that the paramagnetic resonance disappears entirely at 20° K.

(b) Chrome alums. The chrome alums have the general chemical formula $CrM(SO_4)_2 \cdot 12H_2O$, where M is a monovalent, diamagnetic ion such as K^+, Cs^+, or NH_4^+. X-ray diffraction shows that the Cr^{+++} is surrounded by an octahedron of water molecules which produces a large electric field of cubical symmetry with, however, a small superimposed field of trigonal symmetry, the axis of which is directed along a body diagonal of the cube. The unit cell contains four Cr^{+++} ions. The ground state of Cr^{+++} is $^4F_{3/2}$ with a rather weak spin-orbit coupling, $\lambda = 87$ cm^{-1}. The seven orbital levels are split by the cubic field into a singlet and two triplets, with the singlet lying lowest by several thousand wave numbers so that at ordinary temperatures it is the only one which is populated. Through the spin-orbit coupling the trigonal component of the field splits the four spin levels into two doublets (corresponding to $M_s = \pm\frac{1}{2}$ and $\pm\frac{3}{2}$) with separations of a fraction of a wave number. An external magnetic field further displaces these levels and removes the remaining degeneracy (Kramers' degeneracy).

Several chrome alums have now been studied. (See Bibliography.) All were found to have the structural features predicted by Van Vleck,[27] i.e., a strong cubic crystalline field with a superimposed trigonal component which has its axis along a body diagonal of the cube. In all, the initial separation of the spin doublets was found to be of the order of 0.15 cm^{-1} at room temperature. See Table 5.4.

Table 5.4. Splittings (cm^{-1}) in various chromic alums at low temperatures by Bleaney [30]

Temperature, °K	Ammonium	Potassium	Rubidium	Cesium	Methylamine
290	0.135	0.12	0.165	0.145	0.165
193	0.085	0.055	0.126	0.134	
90	0.035	$\begin{cases} 0.26 \\ 0.15 \pm 0.01 \end{cases}$	0.108 ± 0.002	0.133 ± 0.002	0.170 ± 0.003
80	$\begin{cases} 0.314 \pm 0.003 \\ 0.242 \pm 0.003 \end{cases}$				
20	$\begin{cases} 0.317 \pm 0.003 \\ 0.240 \pm 0.003 \end{cases}$	$\begin{aligned} 0.270 &\pm 0.003 \\ 0.15 &\pm 0.01 \end{aligned}$	0.108 ± 0.002	0.133 ± 0.002	0.170 ± 0.003

Figure 5.1 shows the energy levels of potassium chrome alum as a function of the external field H for two different crystal orientations

with the predicted resonant lines at 9375 Mc.   Figure 5.2 shows the observed spectrum for one orientation.

Analytical expressions for the energies for particular orientations of the magnetic field and the trigonal axes have been worked out.[10,12,13]

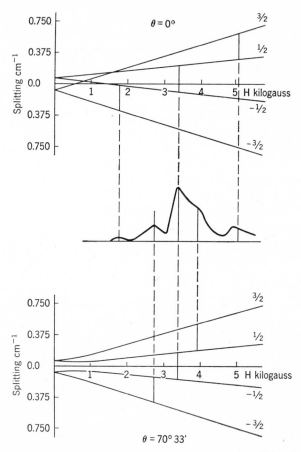

FIG. 5.1.   The spectrum of $CrK(SO_4)_2 \cdot 12H_2O$.   The magnetic field is oriented along one of the body diagonals of the unit cube and so makes an angle $\theta = 0°$ with the cylindrical electric field of one ion and an angle $\theta = 70° 33'$ with that of the other three ions.   Energy levels for these two cases are shown, and the transitions possible at a frequency of 9375 Mc are indicated.   These are compared with the observed spectrum.   The energy levels are labeled with the strong-field quantum number M_s.
[From Kikuchi and Spence, *Am. J. Phys.* 18, 167 (1950).]

These allow a determination of the initial splitting of the spin levels from the resonant peaks.   For example, when the external field is perpendicular to the (110) plane the trigonal axes at two of the Cr^{+++} ions in unit cell are perpendicular to the magnetic field, and their energies [28] are

$$E = \pm\tfrac{1}{2}\xi + (\xi^2 \mp \xi + 1)^{\frac{1}{2}}$$

and   (5.17)

$$\pm\tfrac{1}{2}\xi - (\xi^2 \mp \xi + 1)^{\frac{1}{2}}.$$

The other two ions are oriented 35° 16′ with the external field and have energies determined by

$$E^4 - E^2(2 + \tfrac{5}{2}\xi^2) - 2\xi^2 E + (1 - \tfrac{3}{4}\xi^2)^2 = 0. \qquad (5.18)$$

In these equations E is the energy in units of $\delta/2$, where δ is the splitting of the spin levels in zero field $[E = W(2/\delta)]$ and ξ is the Zeeman energy

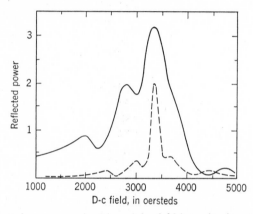

FIG. 5.2. Reflected power as a function of d-c field intensity for potassium chrome alum with the field perpendicular to the (111) face. Undiluted salt given by solid curve; diluted by dashed curve. (From Whitmer, Weidner, Hsiang, and Weiss.[28])

in the same units $[\xi = g\beta H(2/\delta)]$. Selection rules for the strong-field case, $\Delta M_s = \pm 1$, apply for absorption of waves of 3 cm or shorter for which $h\nu$ is large compared with δ.

An interesting variation of δ with temperature was found for potassium and ammonium chrome alums by Bleaney and Penrose.[29] These observers noted that the values for δ for these alums as previously obtained from low-temperature paramagnetic relaxation measurements are about twice the values obtained from the new microwave paramagnetic resonance results at room temperature. Upon making microwave measurements at 20° K, they found that the paramagnetic resonance results were in good agreement with the low-temperature results obtained by other methods. The splitting, δ, was then measured as a function of temperature. This variation for the ammonium alum is shown in Fig. 5.3. The splitting was found to decrease approximately linearly with temperature down to about 9° K, and then to increase suddenly, with further decrease of temperature, to a value more than twice that at room temperature. The results are interpreted qualitatively as a gradual change of symmetry in the crystal until a point of sudden transition to a new stable structure with a different crystalline-field symmetry is reached. Below the transition temperature, δ changes

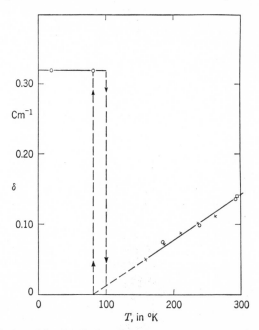

Fig. 5.3. Variation of Stark splitting with temperature in ammonium chrome alum. +, before shattering. o, after shattering. (From Bleaney and Penrose.[29])

but little with temperature. The potassium alum showed a similar behavior except that the transition is gradual rather than of a discontinuous nature. In both these alums two values of δ are found below the transition point. (See Table 5.4.) In ammonium chrome alum they are attributed by Bleaney [30] to two different atoms in the unit cell. No satisfactory explanation for the complete behavior of the potassium alum has been found. For a discussion of its peculiarities, see the paper by Bleaney.[30] None of the other chrome alums investigated by Bleaney showed significant variation of δ with temperature. Table 5.4 summarizes his results.

(c) Titanium alums (Ti^{+++}). The titanium alums have the same general chemical formula as the chromium alums, $TiM(SO_4)_2 \cdot 12H_2O$, where M is a diamagnetic, monovalent ion such as K^+, Rb^+, or Cs^+.

They presumably also have similar crystal structures; i.e., the Ti^{+++} is subjected to a strong crystalline field of cubic symmetry with a small trigonal component.[30] However, unlike Cr^{+++}, the Ti^{+++} has only a single unpaired electron, and its ground state is $^2D_{3/2}$. The cubic field splits the five orbital levels into a doublet and a triplet, of which the triplet lies lower. The trigonal component of the field splits the ground triplet into a doublet and a singlet, of which the singlet is lower. Since $S = 1/2$, the spin degeneracy of the orbital levels cannot be lifted by the crystalline field, and paramagnetic resonance should always be observable in the microwave region, provided that the spin-lattice relaxation time is not so short as to cause the lines to be too broad for detection.

Efforts made by the Oxford group[7] to detect resonance absorption in cesium titanium alum at temperatures as low as 20° K failed. Later Bijl[31] was able to detect in the powder at 8° K a single resonant peak which gave a g factor of 1.34. This was interpreted by Bleaney[30] as $g_\perp$ (g for external field perpendicular to the trigonal axis). He pointed out that for random orientation in the powder the line corresponding to $g_\perp$ should represent the stronger peak because of the greater geometrical probability of the $\perp$ orientation. From this he calculated the separation, Δ_L, of the two lowest orbital levels as 410 cm^{-1}, and, using the latter, calculated $g_\parallel$ as 1.75. Thus, there is considerable anisotropy in the g factor. The small value of Δ_L obtained, accounts for the small spin-lattice relaxation time which prevents detection of the resonance absorption at ordinary temperatures.

5.1f. Rare Earths. The most complete studies of rare-earth salts are on the ethyl sulphates. These have the general formula $M(C_2H_5SO_4)_3 \cdot 9H_2O$, where M represents the rare-earth element. These salts were employed by Bleaney and Scovil[32] in the determination of the spins of Nd^{143}, Nd^{145}, and Er^{167}. A preliminary theoretical treatment of their paramagnetic resonance has been given by Elliott and Stevens.[33] This treatment may be applied to other salts having similar crystalline fields. It illustrates the difference between the approach to the study of the rare earths and to that of the iron-group salts. For this reason, it will be summarized here.

It was assumed by Elliott and Stevens[33] that the crystalline-field symmetry is of the D_{3h} type and that it is not sufficiently strong to break down the spin-orbit coupling, but that it lifts the $2J + 1$ degeneracy partly or completely. The first-order perturbation treatment is employed, and the axis of symmetry is taken as the z axis. The total momentum, **J**, then has quantized components, J_z, along z. With these assumptions, the following predictions were made by Elliott and Stevens.

Ce^{+++}. This ion has an $^2F_{5/2}$ ground state and one unpaired $4f$ electron. A doublet corresponding to $J_z = \pm 5/2$ lies lowest. At temperatures sufficiently low so that only this lowest level is significantly populated, no resonance is expected since a transition between the $+5/2$ and $-5/2$ level is forbidden.

Nd^{+++}. The ground state of this ion is $^4I_{9/2}$. It has three unpaired $4f$ electrons. The doublet $J_z = \pm 7/2$ lies lowest, with that for $J_z = \pm 5/2$ not far above. To account for the observed spectrum, a mixing of these two states to give the lowest states, $a\ (7/2) + b\ (-5/2)$ and $a\ (-7/2) + b\ (5/2)$, is postulated. With $|a| = 0.9$ and $|b| = 0.4$, Elliott and Stevens obtained $g_{\parallel} = 3.54$ and $g_{\perp} = 2.0$, in good agreement with the values of 3.61 and 2.05 observed by Bleaney and Scovil.[32a] The hyperfine structure resolved by the latter observers was found to conform to Bleaney's [14] general theory based on the reduced Hamiltonian of Abragam and Pryce.[10] (See Art. 5.1c.)

Gd^{+++}. Because in its ground state this ion has no orbital momentum (S state), the crystalline field will exert only second-order effects to produce a fine structure, treated in Art. 5.1c. Several different Gd^{+++} salts have been studied,[7, 16] and in each the g factor was found to be nearly 2. The hyperfine structure has not yet been resolved and must be presumed to be extremely small.

Dy^{+++}. The ground state of this ion is $^6H_{15/2}$. Elliott and Stevens predicted the lowest state to be $J_z = \pm 15/2$ with some contribution from $J_z = \pm 3/2$. No transition is allowed by the selection rules, and, so far, no resonant absorption has been reported.

Er^{+++}. The ground state of this ion is $^4I_{15/2}$. Bleaney and Scovil have observed $g_{\parallel} = 1.47$ and $g_{\perp} = 8.85$ in erbium ethyl sulphate. It is shown by Elliott and Stevens that two different combinations of levels could account for the observed g factor. These are admixtures of $J_z = \pm 5/2$ and $\pm 7/2$, which are low-lying levels according to their assumed potential function, or of $J_z = \pm 1/2$, lying lowest, with small contributions from the $\pm 11/2$ and $\pm 13/2$ states. The hyperfine structure was found to conform to the general theory of Bleaney (see Art. 5.1c, Art. 5.1l), which assumes axial symmetry.

Yb^{+++}. The ground state is $^2F_{7/2}$. Elliott and Stevens predicted the lowest levels as $J_z = \pm 3/2$, between which no transitions are allowed. In agreement with this, no resonant absorption has been found.

5.1g. Uraniun Salts. Ghosh, Hill, and Gordy [34] have observed paramagnetic resonance in the powdered uranium salts UF_3 and UF_4. The lines were very weak and broad at room temperature. That of UF_3 became stronger at the temperature of liquid air. The g factor was found to be greater than the free-spin value and 2.2 for UF_4 and 2.4

for UF_3. The UF_3 resonance was found to be asymmetric with the strongest peak corresponding to a g factor of 2.4. This suggests a magnetic axis of symmetry with $g_\perp = 2.4$. Details are yet to be worked out.

5.1h. Organic Free Radicals. Organic free radicals have unpaired electron spins and thus exhibit paramagnetic absorption. Work in this potentially large field is just beginning. Although a paramagnetic resonance line of an organic free radical was detected by Holden, Kittel, Merritt, and Yager [35] in 1949, only a few other free radicals have since been studied. Some of the later results are summarized in Table 5.5.

Table 5.5.   Free radical results of Holden, Kittel, Merritt, and Yager [35]

	g	Line Half-Width (gauss)
Diphenyl trinitrophenyl hydrazyl $(C_6H_5)_2N—NC_6H_2(NO_2)_3$	2.0036 ± 0.0002	1.35
Di-*para*-anisyl nitric oxide $(p—CH_3OC_6H_4)_2NO$	2.0063 ± 0.0005	15.7
β-(Phenyl nitrogen oxide)-β-methyl pentane-δ-one oxime N-phenyl ether $ON(C_6H_5)C(CH_3)_2CH_2C(CH_3)N(C_6H_5)O$	2.0057 ± 0.0002	9.2

A striking feature of the results shown in Table 5.5 is the narrowness of the lines, particularly that in diphenyl trinitrophenyl hydrazyl. Holden, Kittel, Merritt, and Yager [35] pointed out that the line half-width for these compounds should be about 100 gauss from spin-spin broadening alone. They attributed the narrowness to the exchange effects predicted by Gorter and Van Vleck.[19] Townes and Turkevich,[36] who also investigated diphenyl trinitrophenyl hydrazyl, showed that, if the unpaired electron remained on one of the N atoms, the spread in the hyperfine structure would be much greater than the observed line width. They attributed the absence of hyperfine structure to the migration of the unpaired electron in the organic radical. The latter observers obtained additional proof for exchange narrowing by studying the radical in benzene solution. The line width was actually greater by several fold in the solution, even though the dipole-dipole broadening should be less for the more widely separated radicals.

The g factors observed for these radicals are also of interest. In all cases they are very close, but not exactly equal, to that of the free-electron spin. The deviations are evidence for a small amount of spin-orbit coupling. The evidence for spin-orbit coupling is greatest for the last radical listed in Table 5.5. For it, the g factor is anisotropic and varies from 2.0035 to 2.0073 for different orientations.

These few results indicate the potentialities of paramagnetic resonance spectra for investigating the electronic structures in the chemically important organic free radicals. The possibilities of using the sharp lines obtained for electronic applications should not be overlooked. Frequent use is already made of the sharp, accurately measured line of diphenyl trinitrophenyl hydrazyl for the measurement of magnetic field strengths.

5.1i. Irradiated Crystals and Plastics. Color centers in irradiated crystals, such as alkali halides or alkali earth halides, have unpaired

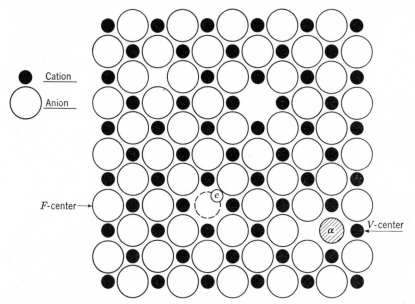

FIG. 5.4.   Illustration of F-centers and V-centers in crystals.   (From Schneider and England.[38])

electrons trapped in regions called F centers or V centers, according to the way the unpaired electrons are held.   In F centers the electrons are essentially unbound, trapped between cations in a hole or vacancy normally filled by an anion.   In the positive V centers they presumably reside on neutral atoms formed by the removal of an electron from the anions.   The neutral atoms are trapped in "positive holes" to form V centers.   Figure 5.4 illustrates the two kinds of centers.

Paramagnetic resonance absorption in irradiated crystals was first observed by Hutchison [37] in LiF and KCl irradiated with neutrons. Figure 5.5 reproduces his original curve.   It is obviously asymmetric and about 160 gauss in width.   Hutchison reports that its intensity after irradiation for 24 hours in a flux of approximately 10^{12} neutrons per cm^2 was about $\frac{1}{10}$ that of an equal amount of $CuSO_4 \cdot 2H_2O$. Within the experimental error, a g factor of that for the free electron was obtained.

Paramagnetic resonance in KCl irradiated with X-rays has been obtained by Schneider and England.[38] In this experiment a g factor

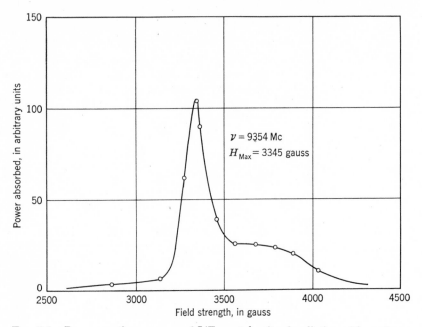

FIG. 5.5.   Paramagnetic resonance of LiF crystals after irradiation with neutrons. (From Hutchison.[37])

of 1.998 ± 0.003, slightly different from that of the free-electron spin, was obtained. These observers suggest as a possible explanation of this discrepancy a resonance between F centers and V centers. The width of the line for KCl is about 40 gauss. Schneider and England report that the line width varied slowly with the concentration of color centers, but more rapidly with temperature change. Similar investigations were made on NaCl and KBr by these researchers.

Paramagnetic resonance in irradiated crystals is a new method of investigation of the interesting phenomena of color centers in crystals. If, as Schneider and England suggested, observable resonance effects occur between F centers and V centers, the line widths and g factors can be used to obtain information about the separations of F centers and V centers. Another possible application is the study of the rates of formation or disappearance of these centers. Also, one might design a neutron or X-ray flux meter based on this principle. The investigation of nuclear hyperfine structure of the atom in the V center having unpaired electrons is an interesting possibility. However, the exchange effects between F centers and V centers suggested by Schneider and England could wipe out the hyperfine structure.

A new field of investigation with paramagnetic resonance has been opened up by Schneider, Day, and Stein,[39] who observed sharp resonance in many plastics after irradiation with X-rays. The unpaired state of the electrons is presumably caused by the breaking of a bond, with the two electrons of the bond then migrating to different radicals in the plastic. Figure 5.6 shows their results on polymethylmethacrylate

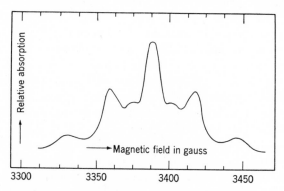

FIG. 5.6.   Magnetic resonance spectrum of irradiated Perspex at $\nu = 9500$ Mc. (From Schneider, Day, and Stein.[39])

(Perspex). The structure of the line is now believed by Schneider [40] to be a hyperfine structure arising from the interaction of the unpaired electrons with hydrogen nuclei in the organic radicals. This interpretation is a revision by Schneider of the original one that the free electrons are concentrated in regions like F centers in crystals. The revised interpretation appears to be the correct explanation although quantitative details are yet to be worked out. The same structure was obtained for colored and uncolored Perspex, but slightly different g factors were observed for the two. It seems likely that the production of paramagnetic spectra in organic substances might be induced by ultraviolet light as well as by X-rays.

5.1j. Alkali Metals in Solution.   The alkali metals dissolved in liquid ammonia and certain other solvents dissociate into positive metal ions and electrons. The metallic ions have the noble gas configuration and cannot exhibit paramagnetic absorption. However, the electron "gas" thus formed in the solution does have a paramagnetic resonance which arises from the electron spin.

Paramagnetic resonance absorption of the electrons of potassium metal solutions in liquid ammonia was detected by Hutchison and Pastor [41] at a frequency of 23,700 Mc. The line was found to be extremely sharp, only 3 Mc (or 0.1 gauss), and was displayed by the ordinary frequency-sweep technique employed in the spectroscopy of gases. The g factor obtained, 2.0012 with a mean deviation of 0.0002, is very nearly, but not exactly, that of an entirely free electron, 2.0023. Measurements have since been made by Garstens and Ryan [42] on Na and K solutions in liquid NH_3 in the microwave region and at low radiofrequencies. The results obtained are similar to those of Hutchison and Pastor. Also, in the low r-f region similar results have been obtained on solutions of the alkali metals in methylamine and in ethylenediamine, as well as in ammonia, by Levinthal, Rogers, and Ogg.[43] The latter observers obtained line widths as low as 0.08 gauss.

The lines in alkali metal solutions appear to be even sharper than those of organic free radicals and are extremely promising for the measurement of magnetic fields and the stabilization of electromagnets. It is not yet evident what information about the nature of solutions can be obtained from studies of this type.

5.1k. Conduction Electrons in Metals. Spin resonance of conduction electrons in metallic sodium has been observed by Griswold, Kip, and Kittel [43a] at room temperature and at 77° K. Fine particles of the sodium (diameters of 10^{-3} to 10^{-4} cm produced by supersonic waves) were suspended in paraffin wax. The resonance, observed at a frequency of 9240 Mc, was found to have a half-width of 78 oersteds. Within the experimental error, the g factor was that of the free electron spin. It is expected that much sharper resonances can be obtained in later work. This experiment provides an interesting new approach to the study of conduction electrons in metals.

5.1l. Hyperfine Structure. A development of considerable consequence is the resolution of hyperfine structure in paramagnetic resonance, which was first accomplished by Penrose [44] (1949). This field has been rapidly explored by other Oxford researchers, particularly by Bleaney, Pryce, Abragam, Ingram, Bowers, and Scovil. (See Bibliography.) The nuclear spins of several rare-earth elements have already been determined. In addition to spins and magnetic moments, information about nuclear quadrupole moments can be obtained in many instances. Indeed, it appears that nuclear moments of practically all stable isotopes of the iron-group and rare-earth elements will eventually yield to this method. Usually the measurements must be made at low temperatures—that of liquid hydrogen or helium—and with specimens diluted with non-magnetic materials to avoid the various broadening effects already discussed (Art. 5.1d) which prevent resolution of the hyperfine structure under ordinary conditions.

The theory for the spacing of the hyperfine frequency components is discussed in Art. 5.1c. Although no completely general formula has

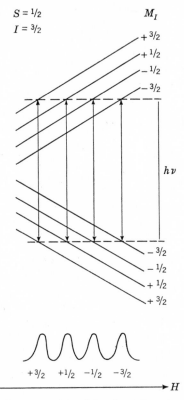

FIG. 5.7. Energy-level diagram and resulting hyperfine structure in paramagnetic resonance for $S = \frac{1}{2}$, $I = \frac{3}{2}$. (From Bleaney.[14])

been developed, Eq. 5.7 by Bleaney has wide application. To a first approximation the hyperfine structure consists of $2I + 1$ equally spaced components of equal intensity with separation

$$\Delta \nu = K M_I / h, \qquad (5.19)$$

where

$$K = \frac{1}{g} (A^2 g_\parallel{}^2 \cos^2 \theta + B^2 g_\perp{}^2 \sin^2 \theta)^{\frac{1}{2}}, \qquad (5.20)$$

as given by the first term in Bleaney's formula, Eq. 5.7. This simple formula holds when the intervals of the hyperfine structure are small as compared with $g\beta H$, and when the nuclear magnetic interaction is large as compared with the quadrupole interaction. The first-order quadrupole interaction displaces equally all levels with the same M_I, and, as

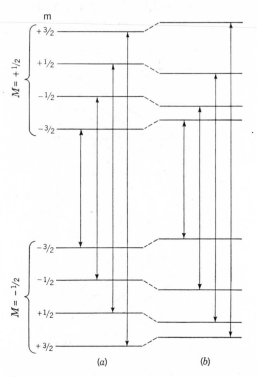

FIG. 5.8. Hyperfine structure and allowed transitions in strong magnetic field for the case, $S = \frac{1}{2}$, and $I = \frac{3}{2}$. (a) Magnetic interaction only; (b) electric quadrupole interaction added. (From Bleaney.[14])

long as the selection rule $\Delta M_I = 0$ holds, has no effect on the separation of the hyperfine frequency components. Thus one can usually determine the nuclear spin by simply counting the components of each main transition and can obtain the interaction constant K by measuring the line spacing.

During observation of the spectrum the radiation frequency is usually held constant and the magnetic field is varied. Figure 5.7 illustrates a simple spectrum of this type. Figure 5.8 illustrates the displacement of the levels by quadrupole interaction.[14] Note that the frequencies of the allowed transitions are not changed by the quadrupole effects. Figure 5.9 reproduces an observed hyperfine spectrum of $MnSO_4$ in aqueous solutions at room temperature. Note the six peaks corresponding to $I = \frac{5}{2}$ for Mn^{55}. Because of the S ground state of Mn^{++} the spin-lattice relaxation time is sufficiently long to make the obser-

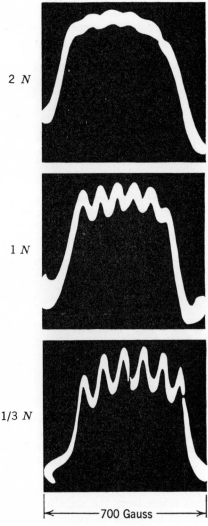

FIG. 5.9.   Hyperfine structure of MnSO$_4$ at different concentration in aqueous solution. The lines are broadened rapidly by exchange interaction as the concentration is increased. (From Schneider and England.[38])

vation possible at room temperature. Figure 5.10 illustrates hyperfine structure in single crystals for nuclear spins of $\frac{3}{2}$ (Cu$^{63, 65}$) and $\frac{7}{2}$ (Co^{59}).

The quantum number F, so conspicuous in the theory of hyperfine structure of isolated atoms and molecules, is notably absent in the theory of hyperfine structure of microwave paramagnetic resonance. In paramagnetic salts F is not well defined because of the crystalline-field effects. The hyperfine structure is somewhat analogous to the Back-Goudsmit effect in the atomic hyperfine structure, except that, while

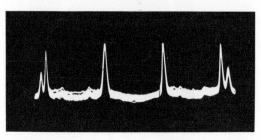

Fig. 5.10a. Hyperfine structure of paramagnetic resonance of copper potassium sulphate. Smaller lines of end doublets are due to Cu^{65}, larger ones to Cu^{63}. Lines barely visible are due to quadrupole effects. (Compare with Fig. 5.11.) [From Bleaney, Bowers, and Ingram, *Proc. Phys. Soc. (London) A64*, 758 (1951).]

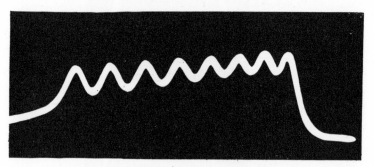

Fig. 5.10b. Hyperfine structure of the paramagnetic resonance of cobalt ammonium sulphate. The spacings are unequal because of second-order effects. Note the $2I + 1$ components corresponding to a spin of $\frac{7}{2}$ for Co^{59}. [From Bleaney and Ingram, *Proc. Roy. Soc. A208*, 143 (1951).]

S precesses about the external field, **I** precesses about the resultant field at the nucleus which arises from the unpaired electrons. The latter field is several hundred kilogauss as compared with the usually few kilogauss of the applied field. The relatively weak coupling between **H** and **I** accounts for the selection rule $\Delta M_I = 0$. As the value of M_S changes, that of M_I remains constant. The resulting change in the field at the nucleus caused by the reorientation of **S** brings about a change in the interaction energy of **S** and **I** which must be made up by the radiation field. This change in interaction energy varies with different values of M_I and is proportional to **S·I**.

It has been mentioned above that first-order nuclear quadrupole effects cause no observable change in the spectrum. However, if the Q' is not small as compared with K, second-order quadrupole interaction produces a change in separation of the hyperfine lines, as is indicated by Eq. 5.7, which varies from group to group. Bleaney [14] has pointed out that this feature allows a determination of the signs of A, B, and D, which cannot be determined from the first-order spectrum, and, in addition, allows an estimate of Q'. The second-order quadrupole effects are distinguishable from other second-order effects because the former cannot be eliminated by strong fields and because the separations of the hyperfine lines do not show a uniform variation but are greatest either at the end or at the middle of the group.[14] Furthermore, the quadrupole effects can be detected through the first-order forbidden transitions. These transitions produce small satellites of the magnetic hyperfine lines which have intensities of the order of $(Q'/K)^2$ as compared with those of the latter. Approximate formulas for the positions and intensities of these satellites have also been worked out by Bleaney [14] and are reproduced here for convenience. For the lines corresponding to $(M_S, k \pm \frac{1}{2}) \rightarrow (M_S - 1, k \mp \frac{1}{2})$,

$$E = Kk \pm \{K(M_S - \tfrac{1}{2}) + Q''k - \gamma'\} \qquad (5.21)$$

$$\text{Int} = 4k^2\{(I + \tfrac{1}{2})^2 - k^2\}X, \qquad (5.22)$$

where k takes values $(I - \frac{1}{2})$, $(I - \frac{3}{2})$, $\cdots$, $-(I - \frac{1}{2})$. For the lines $(M_S, M_I \pm 1) \rightarrow (M_S - 1, M_I \mp 1)$,

$$E = KM_I \pm \{K(2M_S - 1) + 2Q''M_I - 2\gamma'\}, \qquad (5.23)$$

$$\text{Int} = \{(I + 1)^2 - M_I^2\}\{I^2 - M_I^2\}Y, \qquad (5.24)$$

where M_I takes values $(I - 1)$, $(I - 2)$, $\cdots$, $-(I - 1)$. In these equations

$$X = \frac{Z}{2I + 1}\left[\frac{Q'}{2KM_S(M_S - 1)}\right]^2 \left(\frac{ABg_{\parallel}g_{\perp}}{K^2g^2}\right)^2 \cos^2\theta \sin^2\theta,$$

$$Y = \frac{Z}{2I + 1}\left[\frac{Q'}{8KM_S(M_S - 1)}\right]^2 \left(\frac{Bg_{\perp}}{Kg}\right)^4 \sin^4\theta,$$

$$Q'' = Q'\left(\frac{3A^2g_{\parallel}^2}{K^2g^2}\cos^2\theta - 1\right),$$

$$\gamma' = g_I\beta_I H(Ag_{\parallel}\cos^2\theta + Bg_{\perp}\sin^2\theta)/Kg,$$

$$Q' = eQ\,\frac{\partial^2 V}{\partial z^2}\left[\frac{3}{4I(2I - 1)}\cdot\right]$$

Z depends on several factors [14] but is constant for a given hyperfine multiplet. Figure 5.11 shows the appearance of these satellites as a

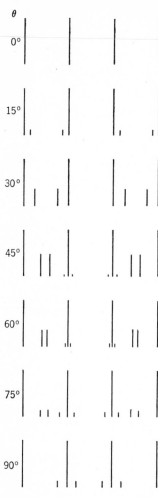

function of θ as predicted by Bleaney [14] for the particular case where $A = B = 5Q'$, $g^{\|} = g_\perp$, $S = \frac{1}{2}$, and $I = \frac{3}{2}$. The four strong, equally spaced lines are the magnetic hyperfine spectrum and do not change with θ since $g_{\|} = g_\perp$. The satellites which first appear at $\theta = 15°$ increase in intensity and move away from the main lines as θ increases up to $\theta = $ arc cos $1/\sqrt{3}$, where the two pairs of lines cross, then separate and get weaker as indicated. The satellites appearing at $\theta = 90°$ correspond to $\Delta M_I = \pm 2$. They become weaker with decreasing θ and coincide with the main lines at $\theta = $ arc cos $1/\sqrt{3}$. The magnitude of Q' can be determined from a measurement of the position of the satellites by application of the above formula. Because of the symmetry of the pattern, the sign of Q' cannot be determined.

The term in $g_I\beta_I H$ which has been neglected becomes of importance for high values of H. This is simply the Larmor precessional energy of the nuclear spin about the external field, the quantity which is measured directly in the well-known nuclear magnetic resonance experiments. For fields of 10 kilogauss, these frequencies are of the order of 15 Mc. This energy acts to increase the separation of the quadrupole satellite doublets on one side of the spectrum and to decrease it on the other side. As a result of the destruction of the symmetry of the pattern, it becomes possible [14] to determine the signs of A, B, and Q'.

FIG. 5.11. Quadrupole effects in spectrum for $S = \frac{1}{2}$, $I = \frac{3}{2}$, with no anisotropy and $A = B = 5Q'$. (From Bleaney.[14])

The hyperfine structure in a large number of iron-group and rare-earth salts has already been investigated, and the constants, A, B, D, $g_{\|}$, $g_\perp$, and, in a few cases, Q' have been determined. These are too extensive for listing here. In Table 5.6 are summarized the nuclear moments which have been checked or originally determined by this method. Salts having axial symmetry have, in general, been employed, and Bleaney's formula, Eq. 5.7, has been found adequate to account for practically all results.

Table 5.6.   Summary of nuclear properties from paramagnetic resonance

	Spin	μ (nucl. magnetons)	Quadrupole Moment Q(in 10^{-24} cm^2)	Ref.
			Iron Group	
Cu^{63}	$\frac{3}{2}$ †		$-0.12_7 \pm 0.01$	‡
Cu^{65}	$\frac{3}{2}$ †		$-0.11_7 \pm 0.01$	‡
Co^{59}	$\frac{7}{2}$ †			‡
Mn^{55}	$\frac{5}{2}$ †			‡
V^{51}	$\frac{7}{2}$ †			‡
V^{50}	6			‡
Cr^{53}	$\frac{3}{2}$			‡
			Rare Earths	
Nd^{143}	$\frac{7}{2}$	1.4	≤ 25	32a, 33
Nd^{145}	$\frac{7}{2}$	0.85	≤ 25	32a, 33
Eb^{167}	$\frac{7}{2}$	0.6	≤ 17	32b, 33
Gd$^{155, 157}$	No hyperfine structure could be observed.			‡

† Previous spin determination confirmed.
‡ For references, see Table A.7.

An interesting feature discovered in paramagnetic hyperfine structure is that the nuclear magnetic interactions in several of the iron-group salts were found to be many times larger than calculated for the expected spectroscopic ground state of the ions. For example, in Mn^{++} salts the spacing of the hyperfine lines is of the order of 100 times greater than that predicted for the $^6S_{5/2}$ ground state [45] and is essentially the same in different salts. These abnormal splittings have been accounted for satisfactorily by assuming small contributions from higher states having unpaired s electrons. It was suggested by Abragam [45] that in these excited states, one of the 3s electrons is promoted to a 4s orbital. No such evidence for excited-state contributions has been obtained for the rare-earth ions.

Zero-field case. In some instances the internal interactions are such as to allow observation of radio-frequency resonance absorption in paramagnetic salts in zero magnetic field. The hyperfine structure of these transitions is treated by Bleaney.[14] The theory is more involved than that for the strong-field case. However, the transitions sometimes allow a direct determination of the nuclear quadrupole coupling. The spectrum is usually complex, but certain cases are relatively simple.

5.2. FERROMAGNETIC RESONANCE

Magnetic resonance absorption in ferromagnetic substances was discovered by Griffiths.[46] Its existence had been predicted earlier by Landau and Lifshitz.[47] It has been further investigated by Yager and Bozorth [48] and by a number of other researchers. (See Bibliography.) It is the ferromagnetic analog of the paramagnetic effects already discussed. Because of the relatively high conductivity of ferromagnetic materials, the methods of observation differ somewhat from those of paramagnetic resonance, and because of the effects of the demagnetization field, the formula for the resonant frequencies must be modified.[49]

In the original work of Griffiths the observed resonant frequencies were found to be several times higher than those predicted for Larmor frequencies of electron-spin vectors. This apparent anomaly was satisfactorily explained with classical macroscopic theory by Kittel,[49] who attributed the effects to the demagnetization field. Van Vleck [50] and Polder [51] have shown that quantum theory leads to the same results as the simpler macroscopic theory employed by Kittel.

The resonant frequencies were shown to depend upon the shape of the sample. For a plane surface with both the applied field H and the magnetic vector of the radiation parallel to the plane of the specimen,

$$\nu = g\beta\sqrt{BH}/h; \tag{5.25}$$

and with H perpendicular to the plane and with the magnetic vector of the radiation in the plane of the specimen,

$$\nu = g\beta(H - 4\pi M)/h. \tag{5.26}$$

For small spherical specimens the usual Larmor theorem applies, and the frequencies are

$$\nu = g\beta H/h. \tag{5.27}$$

For a long, circular cylinder with the constant H along the axis and the magnetic vector of the radiation perpendicular to it,

$$\nu = g\beta(H + 2\pi M)/h. \tag{5.28}$$

In these formulas, g is the spectroscopic splitting factor, β is the Bohr magneton, H is the applied d-c magnetic field, B is the magnetic induction in the sample, and M is the magnetization. Equations 5.26–5.28

apply only when the skin depth for the resonant frequency is large in comparison with the radius of the specimen. Absorption can be observed for small cylindrical specimens even for zero external fields. Resonance in unmagnetized specimens, "natural ferromagnetic resonance," has been observed by Welch, Nicks, Fairweather, and Roberts.[52] The above formulas are special cases of the more general formula

$$\nu = \frac{g\beta}{h} [\{H_z + (N_y - N_z)M_z\}\{H_z + (N_x - N_z)M_z\}]^{\frac{1}{2}} \quad (5.29)$$

derived by Kittel. Here N_x, N_y, and N_z represent the demagnetization factors for fields along x, y, and z; M_z is the magnetization along z in the

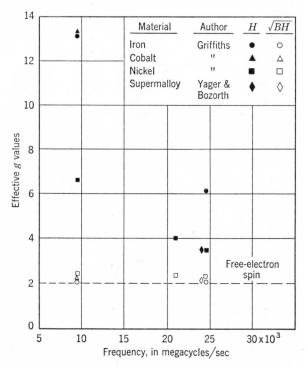

FIG. 5.12. Application of Kittel theory to ferromagnetic resonance experiments. (From Kittel.[49])

direction of the applied fields H_z. The direction of the magnetic component of the r-f field is taken along x. This formula assumes uniform magnetization throughout the specimen. It does not take into account possible anisotropy in the g factor, also treated by Kittel. (See below.)

Kittel's theory was found to be in good agreement with observation. Figure 5.12 demonstrates this agreement for several ferromagnetic metals with plane specimens. The theory has been applied to small, spherically shaped polycrystalline specimens of manganese ferrite by Guillaud, Yager, Merritt, and Kittel.[53] A g factor very close to 2 was obtained with Eq. 5.27. Because the two ions in manganese ferrite, Mn^{++} and Fe^{+++}, are isoelectronic, the predicted g factor is independent of the manner in which the two ions are coupled. It was pointed out by these observers that the fact that the observed g factor is

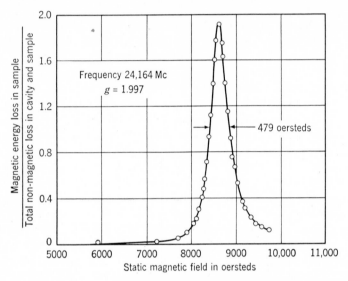

FIG. 5.13. Ferromagnetic resonance in polycrystalline manganese ferrite (sphere of 0.024-in. diameter). (From Guillaud, Yager, Merritt, and Kittel.[53])

in agreement with this theory is confirmation of the simple ionic model of the electronic structure of the ferrites. The resonance curve which they obtained is shown in Fig. 5.13.

Kittel [49] also shows that for single ferromagnetic crystals the resonant frequencies depend upon the angle of the magnetic field with the crystalline axes. For an uniaxial crystal with the axis parallel to H, the value of the effective H is increased by $2K/M$, where K is the anisotropy constant. More generally,

$$\nu = \frac{g\beta}{h} \{[H_z + (N_x - N_z)M_z + f_1(\theta)][H_z + (N_y - N_z)M_z + f_2(\theta)]\}^{1/2},$$

$$(5.30)$$

where θ is the angle between the z axis and an axis in the crystal. For a cubic crystal with θ as the angle between z and the (100) plane

$$f_1(\theta) = \frac{2K_1}{M_z} \cos 4\theta$$

and

$$f_2(\theta) = \frac{K_1}{M_z} \left(\frac{3}{2} + \frac{1}{2} \cos 4\theta \right).$$

Specific values of $f_1(\theta)$ and $f_2(\theta)$ for certain other cases are given in the papers by Kittel,[49] Van Vleck,[50] and by Bickford.[54] The theory has been applied by Kip and Arnold [55] to a single crystal of iron and found to account satisfactorily for the observed frequencies, with only a slight modification to take into account the fact that the direction of magnetization may deviate from the direction of the applied field. It has also been applied by Bickford [54] to single crystals of magnetite.

The g factor in these equations is not equivalent to the magneto-mechanical ratio obtained in the usual gyromagnetic measurements. This has been emphasized by Kittel,[56] who calls the g factor obtained in paramagnetic or ferromagnetic experiments the "spectroscopic splitting factor" and designates it as g. The corresponding gyromagnetic factor he designates as g'. These distinctions and notations are now commonly accepted. The difference here does not arise from the large effects of the magnetization fields accounted for in Kittel's formulas, just discussed, but is caused by the smaller effects of the coupling of the angular-momentum vector of the electron to the crystal lattice. Table 5.7

Table 5.7. Comparison of representative values of spectroscopic splitting factor (g) and magnetomechanical ratio (g') for ferromagnetic substances, from Kittel [56]

	Microwave Resonance, g	Gyromagnetic Experiments, g'
Iron	2.12–2.17	1.93
Cobalt	2.22	1.87
Nickel	2.19–2.42	1.92
Magnetite	2.20	1.93
Heusler alloy	2.01	2.00
Permalloy	2.07–2.14	1.91

illustrates these differences. It should be noted that deviations from 2 are in the opposite direction in the two experiments. This is in agreement with expectation.[50, 56] Kittel shows that the two factors become equivalent, $g = g'$, when the electronic angular momentum is not coupled to the crystal lattice. Note in Table 5.7 that for Heusler's alloy,

$g \cong g' \cong 2$. Some difficulties are yet to be resolved. Theory [50, 56] indicates that the deviations from 2 in g and g' should be equal and opposite $(g - 2 = 2 - g')$. Table 5.7 indicates that the agreement is only qualitative.

The effects of exchange interaction on ferromagnetic resonance has been discussed by Kittel and Herring.[57] Exchange interaction has no

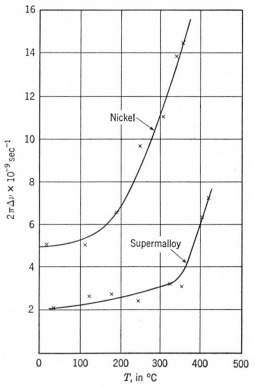

Fig. 5.14. Ferromagnetic resonance line widths as a function of temperature. (From Bloembergen.[53])

effect on the resonant frequency, provided that the specimen is uniformly magnetized. Because of the small skin depths in pure metals at microwave frequencies, the microwave component of magnetization is not uniform under most conditions of observation, and, as a result, exchange interaction will influence both the frequency and the line width. Kittel and Herring show, however, that these effects are significant only at low temperatures, where the skin depth is extremely small. For example, they predict that at 24,000 Mc the field strength required for resonance in iron is changed only about 5 gauss by the exchange interaction, whereas at liquid-hydrogen temperature, because of the decreased skin depth, it will be altered about 500 gauss. The line width will be increased by approximately the same amount. Consequently, the line widths in metals will be appreciably increased by exchange interaction at low temperatures. This allows an investigation of exchange interaction in ferromagnetic substances. These effects are not nearly so pronounced in alloys because of their smaller conductivity.

Bloembergen [58] has studied the effects of temperature variation on ferromagnetic resonance in nickel and supermalloy. Measurements

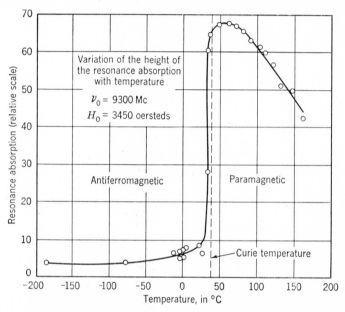

FIG. 5.15. Variation of resonance absorption of powdered Cr_2O_3 with temperature. (From Trounson, Bleil, Wangsness, and Maxwell.[59])

were made both at 9300 Mc and 24,400 Mc with H parallel to a surface of the specimen. Although the decrease in saturation magnetization causes a shift of the maximum to higher fields with increasing temperature, the g factors, 2.20 for nickel and 2.12 for supermalloy, were found to be independent of temperature within the limits of error (2 per cent). The width of the resonance line for nickel increased with temperature from 250 gauss at room temperature to 750 gauss at 358° C. The increase was more rapid as the Curie point was approached. In supermalloy the width of 110 gauss at room temperature remained relatively constant between 20° C and 300° C, and then increased rapidly to 350 gauss at 420° C. This behavior is shown in Fig. 5.14. The increase in width above 300° C varies approximately as T^2 and is attributed to the decrease in the spin-lattice relaxation time. The failure of the width in supermalloy to change significantly with temperature below 300° C and the fact that the nickel curve (Fig. 5.14) appears to become almost independent of temperature below 100° C are not fully understood.[50b, 58]

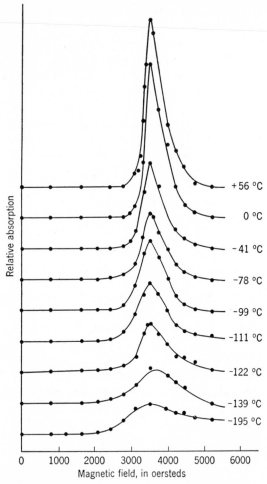

FIG. 5.16. Resonance absorption of MnS at different temperatures. (From Okamura, Torizuka, and Kojima.[60])

Neither substance showed a discontinuity at the Curie point, but the absorption of both dropped rapidly with temperature increase beyond their Curie points.

Antiferromagnetic materials. Magnetic resonance in the antiferromagnetic substance Cr_2O_3, which has a Curie temperature near 40° C, has been observed by Trounson, Bleil, Wangsness, and Maxwell.[59]

The peak absorption was found to drop strikingly as the temperature was lowered through the Curie point (see Fig. 5.15), and the line width spread out accordingly. This is in contrast to the results of Bloembergen [58] on nickel and supermalloy. It is also different from that of the antiferromagnetic materials MnO, MnS, and MnSe, which have Curie points $-151°$ C, $-75°$ C, and $-123°$ C, respectively. Magnetic resonance in the latter materials was recently studied by Okamura, Torizuka, and Kojima. [60] They obtained results similar to those of Bloembergen [58] on the ferromagnetic substances of nickel and supermalloy in that they observed no discontinuity at the Curie point but a continuous broadening as the Curie point was passed over. In the antiferromagnetic substances the Curie point is approached from the high-temperature side, whereas in ferromagnetic materials, it is approached from the low-temperature side. Figure 5.16 shows the results of the Japanese workers on MnS.

The theory of magnetic resonance in antiferromagnetic substances has been treated by Bleil and Wangsness, [61] by Stevens, [62] and by Tsuya and Ichikawa. [63] Variations in the resonance curves with temperature have not yet been completely explained.

5.3. PURE NUCLEAR QUADRUPOLE SPECTRA

An important new field of r-f spectroscopy was opened up by Dehmelt and Krüger [64] when they observed direct transitions between nuclear quadrupole levels in solids. In America, a number of measurements have been made by Livingston, [65] at the Oak Ridge National Laboratory, and, at Harvard, by Pound and his co-workers.

Although these first measurements were at sub-microwave frequencies (30 Mc to 800 Mc) and no such transitions have yet been observed in the microwave region, there are a number of nuclei which may have solid-state quadrupole couplings sufficiently large so that their pure quadrupole spectra reach the microwave region. This applies essentially to nuclei with atomic numbers above 50. For this reason and for the reason that the quadrupole coupling in solids correlates closely with those observed in the microwave spectroscopy of gases, it seems appropriate to include this subject in a book on microwave spectroscopy.

The interaction of a nuclear quadrupole moment with the static crystalline field ε is the scalar product of two tensors, $E = Q \cdot \nabla \varepsilon$. This interaction Hamiltonian can be reduced to the form

$$H = \frac{eQ}{2I(2I+1)} \left[\frac{\partial^2 V}{\partial x^2} I_x{}^2 + \frac{\partial^2 V}{\partial y^2} I_y{}^2 + \frac{\partial^2 V}{\partial z^2} I_z{}^2 \right],$$

where I_x, I_y, and I_z are the components of the nuclear spin momentum

along the space-fixed x, y, and z axes which are so oriented as to eliminate the cross terms. In general, the solution for the eigenvalues is
involved, but, when, as is frequently true, axial symmetry can in the
first approximation be assumed, it is greatly simplified. For axial
symmetry about z, $(\partial^2 V)/(\partial x^2) = (\partial^2 V)/(\partial y^2)$, and with the aid of
Laplace's equation the Hamiltonian reduces immediately to the form

$$H = \frac{eQ}{4I(2I+1)} \left[\frac{\partial^2 V}{\partial z^2} (I_x{}^2 + I_y{}^2 - 2I_z{}^2) \right].$$

Since $I_x{}^2 + I_y{}^2 = I(I+1) - I_z{}^2$ and $I_z{}^2 = M_I{}^2$, the expression for
characteristic energies in the axially symmetric case [64, 66] is

$$E_Q = \left(eQ \frac{\partial^2 V}{\partial z^2} \right) \frac{[3M_I{}^2 - I(I+1)]}{4I(2I-1)}, \tag{5.31}$$

in which the various symbols have their usual significance. Deviations
from axial symmetry are treated by perturbation theory. See the
formulas given below.

Although the orientation energy (for non-paramagnetic solids which
we consider here) is determined by the nuclear quadrupole interactions
with the crystalline electric field, the coupling to the radiation field is
through the magnetic dipole moment of the nucleus. The dipole selection rule, $\Delta M_I = \pm 1$, therefore applies. The coupling of the quadrupole moment with the radiation field is too weak to induce observable
transitions. The quantum number M_I has the same significance here as
in the strong-field Stark and Zeeman effects, except that the reference
axis, z, is taken along the fixed direction of the internal field rather than
along that of an externally applied field. Allowed values of M_I are
therefore

$$M_I = I, I - 1, \cdots, - I.$$

It is obvious from the form of Eq. 5.31 that we need consider only
absolute values of M_I.

Applying the selection rules with Eq. 5.31 gives the spectral fre-
quencies, with $|M_I|$ the larger value involved, as

$$\nu = eQq \left[\frac{3}{4I(2I-1)} \right] (2|M_I| - 1), \tag{5.32}$$

where $q = \dfrac{\partial^2 V}{\partial z^2}$. To be consistent with Eq. 2.31 the coupling factor
should be eQq/h. Following the custom of American workers, we omit
the h and express eQq in frequency units. We see from Eq. 5.32 that

with the assumed axial symmetry of the crystalline field the quadrupole spectrum consists of a series of equally spaced lines, the highest frequency of which is

$$\nu_{max} = eQq\left(\frac{3}{4I}\right). \tag{5.33}$$

If we arbitrarily assume the lowest microwave frequency as 1000 Mc (see page 1), it is seen that there would be lines observable in the microwave region for $eQ\dfrac{\partial^2 V}{\partial z^2} > 2000$ Mc with $I = \frac{3}{2}$ and $eQ\dfrac{\partial^2 V}{\partial z^2} > 3400$ Mc for $I = \frac{5}{2}$. The coupling constant for I^{127} (spin $\frac{5}{2}$) in ICl is 3000 Mc. Many nuclei have Q greater than that of I^{127}, and it therefore seems likely that pure quadrupole transitions will be observed in the microwave region.

When there are deviations from axial symmetry of the field gradient, Eqs. 5.31 and 5.32 no longer hold. The lines of the series ($I > \frac{3}{2}$) are then not equally spaced. Dehmelt and Krüger detected deviations from symmetry in I^{127} compounds. The deviations from symmetry are expressed in terms of the asymmetry parameter

$$\epsilon = \left| \frac{\left| \dfrac{\partial^2 V}{\partial x^2} - \dfrac{\partial^2 V}{\partial y^2} \right|}{\dfrac{\partial^2 V}{\partial z^2}} \right|. \tag{5.34}$$

Table 5.8 gives some observed deviations from symmetry. These are

Table 5.8. Evidence for deviations from axial symmetry in the field gradient of I^{127} coupling in solids, from Dehmelt [64e]

Substance		ν_1 in Mc	$\nu_2 - 2\nu_1$ in Mc	$\epsilon(\%)$
CHI:CHI (trans)		277.1 ± 0.9	-0.38 ± 0.02	2.3
CH$_3$I		263.0 ± 0.8	-0.50 ± 0.02	2.7
ICN		382.4 ± 1.3		
ICl	I_1	455.6 ± 1.5		
	I_2	$\nu_1(I_1) + 2.610$		
SnI$_4$	I_1	204.5 ± 0.7	$+0.010 \pm 0.005$	~ 0
	I_2	$\nu_1(I_1) - 1.030$	-0.044 ± 0.005	0.9
I$_2$		332.4 ± 1.1	-21	15

relatively small except in I$_2$. Note that the two iodines with different surroundings in the crystals of ICl and SnI$_4$ are distinguished by these deviations. One iodine in unit cell of SnI$_4$ has axial symmetry, whereas the other shows deviations from this symmetry.

Formulas for pure quadrupole frequencies in slightly asymmetric fields (ϵ small) are given below for the most common nuclear spin values. They are derived from perturbation theory. For $I = 1$ and $\frac{3}{2}$ they are obtained from the matrix elements given by Pound.[66] For $I = \frac{5}{2}$ and $\frac{7}{2}$ they are taken from Dehmelt and Krüger.[67]

For $I = 1$,

$$\nu = \tfrac{3}{4}[eQq](1 \pm \epsilon). \tag{5.35}$$

For $I = \frac{3}{2}$,

$$\nu = \tfrac{1}{2}[eQq][1 + (\epsilon^2/3)]^{\frac{1}{2}}. \tag{5.36}$$

For $I = \frac{5}{2}$,

$$\nu_1 = (\nu_2/2)(1 + 1.296\epsilon^2 - 0.55\epsilon^4),$$
$$\nu_2 = \tfrac{3}{10}[eQq](1 - 0.2037\epsilon^2 + 0.18\epsilon^4). \tag{5.37}$$

For $I = \frac{7}{2}$,

$$\nu_1 = (\nu_3/3)(1 + 3.733\epsilon^2 - 6.86\epsilon^4),$$
$$\nu_2 = (\tfrac{2}{3}\nu_3)(1 - 0.4667\epsilon^2 + 1.82\epsilon^4),$$
$$\nu_3 = \tfrac{3}{14}[eQq](1 - 0.1000\epsilon^2 - 0.019\epsilon^4). \tag{5.38}$$

When $I = \frac{3}{2}$, only one frequency is observed, and there are two parameters to be evaluated. The asymmetry parameter can, however, be evaluated from the Zeeman pattern for the line. In this way Dean † showed that $\epsilon = 0.08 \pm 0.02$ for the Cl^{35} coupling in solid p-dichlorobenzene.

Livingston [68] has reported that a large number of closely spaced lines are observed for the Cl resonance in certain crystals, whereas, in many others, only a single line is observed. It is obvious that this type of spectroscopy will yield much new information about the solid state.

Table 5.9.   Comparison of nuclear coupling in solid and gaseous state
(For references, see Table $A.6$ in the Appendix.)

Molecule	Nucleus	Solid	Gas
		eQq in Mc	
CH_3I	I^{127}	1753	1931.5
ICN	I^{127}	2549	2420
ICl	I^{127}	3037	2944
CH_3Cl	Cl^{35}	68.40	75.13
CF_3Cl	Cl^{35}	77.58	78.05
CH_3Br	Br^{79}	528.90	577.0

Quadrupole couplings of nuclei in isolated molecules obtained from microwave measurements on gases correspond approximately, but not exactly, to those of the same molecule in the solid state. See Table 5.9. One can use such comparisons to study the changes in the type of

† C. Dean, *Phys. Rev.* **86**, 607 (1952).

bonding in passing from the gaseous to the solid state. Evidence already obtained [65b, 69, 70] indicates that in the homopolar molecules Cl_2, Br_2, and I_2 the couplings eQq in the solid and the gaseous form are approximately the same. This evidence supports the belief generally held that the bonding in these solids is essentially the covalent type, and that the molecules in both states are held together by relatively pure p-type bonds. The asymmetry in the coupling in solid I_2 has been explained in terms of a small amount of switching of the covalent bonds through resonance.[71]

The shapes and widths as well as the positions of pure nuclear quadrupole lines depend upon the nature of the internal fields. Studies of these properties will also yield much information about the structure of the solid state. For instance, Dehmelt and Krüger [64c] have observed a temperature dependence of the Cl quadrupole spectra in *trans*-dichlorethylene of about

$$-\frac{1}{\nu}\left(\frac{d\nu}{dT}\right) \approx -10^{-4}/\text{degree K.} \qquad (5.39)$$

They attribute this temperature dependence to an increase in the amplitude of the torsional oscillations of the molecule, which thereby changes the average field gradient effective at the nucleus. Their quantitative theoretical relation for the temperature dependence is a function of the frequency of the torsional oscillations which they deduce from their measurements to be about 10^{12} cps. This is of the right order of magnitude for such oscillations, as determined from specific heat or Raman spectra data. Pound [72] has observed a more complicated temperature dependence for the quadrupole transitions in I_2. For this crystal the high- and low-frequency transitions show temperature coefficients of opposite sign. The line widths also vary both with temperature and with state of strain of the crystal. A useful theoretical discussion of line widths and intensities is given by Pound [66, 72] and by Bloembergen, Purcell, and Pound.[73] Figure 7.2 shows the temperature dependence of the Cl^{35} coupling observed by Dean and Pound in various chlorobenzene crystals. Note the discontinuities in curves for *ortho*-dichlorobenzene.

Zeeman splitting of the lines in a single crystal of SnI_4 has been observed by Dehmelt.[64] (See Fig. 5.17.) When the crystal was oriented so that all bond axes made equal angles with the field, a simple Zeeman pattern was observed. The Zeeman splitting is given by [64d]

$$E_H = \pm \tfrac{1}{2}g_I\beta_I H\sqrt{(I + \tfrac{1}{2})^2 \sin^2 \theta + \cos^2 \theta}, \qquad (5.40)$$

when $M_I = \pm \tfrac{1}{2}$ and

$$E_H = g_I\beta_I H M_I \cos \theta, \qquad M_I\,| > \tfrac{1}{2}, \qquad (5.41)$$

where H is the applied field, β_I is the nuclear magneton, g_I is the nuclear g factor, and θ is the angle between H and the z axis.

Pure quadrupole resonance in solids has now been observed for a large number of nuclei, including Cl^{35}, Cl^{37}, Br^{79}, Br^{81}, I^{127}, Sb^{121},

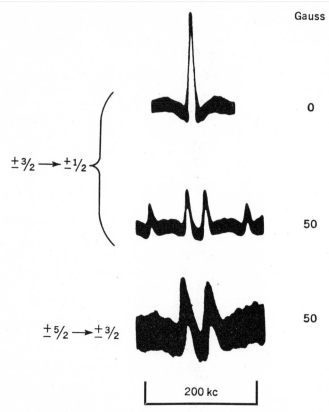

Fig. 5.17.   Pure quadrupole resonance line ($M_I = \pm\frac{3}{2} \rightarrow \pm\frac{1}{2}$) of I^{127} in solid SnI_4 with Zeeman patterns produced by 50 gauss for both the $\pm\frac{3}{2} \rightarrow \pm\frac{1}{2}$ and the $\pm\frac{5}{2} \rightarrow \pm\frac{3}{2}$ transitions.   (From H. G. Dehmelt.[64e])

Sb^{123}, As^{75}, Cu^{63}, Cu^{65}, N^{14}, B^{10}, and B^{11}.   See Table $A.6$ in the Appendix for a survey of results.

5.4. MICROWAVE ABSORPTION OF LIQUIDS

Except for paramagnetic resonance spectra already discussed, no sharp-line spectra of liquids and liquid solutions have been observed in the microwave region.   The large amount of interference from close neighbors of molecules in liquids prevents observation of discrete rotational lines. However, most polar liquids have broad absorption bands in the microwave region which arise from the orientation of the molecules in the radiation field when the E vector is increasing and from their relaxation to thermal equilibrium as the E vector decreases to zero. Their broad regions of absorption have maximum peaks at frequencies of $\nu_0 = 1/2\pi\tau$, where τ is the average relaxation or reorientation time of the molecular dipole. By measurement of the frequency of the maximum absorption, one can evaluate τ.

The relaxation time depends upon a number of properties of the liquid, such as the magnitude of the dipole, the mass and structure of the molecule or the chemical group which is oriented with it, the intermolecular forces, and temperature of the liquid. The absorption is usually expressed in terms of the loss factor, tan δ, where δ is the "loss angle" which is the complement of the phase angle. Usually polar molecules are studied in dilute solution in non-polar solvents. According to the Debye theory, the loss factor is

$$\tan \delta = \frac{(\epsilon + 2)^2}{\epsilon} \frac{4\pi\mu^2 cN\nu}{27kT\nu_0[1 + (\nu/\nu_0)^2]}, \tag{5.42}$$

where δ = loss angle.

ϵ = static dielectric constant of the solution.

μ = dipole moment of the solute molecule.

c = concentration of the solute in number of moles per cubic centimeter.

ν = frequency of the radiation.

$\nu_0 = 1/2\pi\tau$ = frequency of maximum absorption, where τ is the relaxation time of the solute in the solution.

N = Avagadro's number.

k = Boltzmann constant.

T = absolute temperature of the solution.

From measurements of the loss tangent at three or more different frequencies, μ, ϵ, and ν_0 (and hence τ) can be calculated with Eq. 5.42. Or, alternately, one can make the measurement at a fixed frequency and vary the temperature to obtain the data necessary for calculating ϵ, μ, and τ. Although it is not necessary to measure the frequency of the peak absorption to obtain τ, a more accurate evaluation of this constant can probably be obtained in this way.

It is not known how accurately the Debye theory holds. Good agreement with the theory was obtained by Jackson and Powles [74] for solutions of several polar solutes in benzene. Cripwell and Sutherland [75] used Eq. 5.42 with their microwave measurements to calculate the dipole moments of a number of liquids including nitrobenzene, acetone, and methyl cyanide. The agreement with values obtained from other methods was only approximate. Whiffen and Thompson [76] report anomalous behavior for some solutions. The occurrence of a resonant absorption peak in the vicinity of the measurement would cause deviations from the Debye equation.

No attempt will be made to survey what has been written on dielectric absorption and dispersion of liquids and solids at microwave frequencies. Considerable work has been done in the field. A survey of the early work will be found in the report of the general discussion of dielectrics held by the Faraday Society (1946).[77] A more recent review is given by D. H. Whiffen (1950).[78]

REFERENCES

[1] E. Zavoisky, *J. Phys. U.S.S.R. 9*, 211 (1945); *10*, 197 (1946).

[2] R. L. Cummerow and D. Halliday, *Phys. Rev. 70*, 433 (1946).

[3] D. M. S. Bagguley and J. H. E. Griffiths, *Nature 160*, 532 (1947).

[4] J. H. Van Vleck, *The Theory of Electric and Magnetic Susceptibilities* (Clarendon Press, Oxford, England, 1932).

[5] C. J. Gorter, *Paramagnetic Relaxation* (Elsenier Publishing Company, Amsterdam, 1947).

[6] H. A. Kramers, *Proc. Amsterdam Acad. Sci. 33*, 959 (1930).

[7] D. M. S. Bagguley, B. Bleaney, J. H. E. Griffiths, R. P. Penrose, and B. I. Plumpton, *Proc. Phys. Soc. 61*, 542 (1948); *61*, 551 (1948).

[8] H. A. Bethe, *Ann. Physik 3*, 133 (1929).

[9] L. Pauling, *Nature of the Chemical Bond* (Cornell University Press, Ithaca, 1939), Chapter 3.

[10] A. Abragam and M. H. L. Pryce, *Proc. Roy. Soc. (London) A205*, 135 (1951).

[11] D. Polder, *Physica 9*, 709 (1942).

[12] C. Kittel and J. M. Luttinger, *Phys. Rev. 73*, 162 (1948).

[13] P. R. Weiss, *Phys. Rev. 73*, 470 (1948).

[14] B. Bleaney, *Phil. Mag. 42*, 441 (1951); *Physica 17*, 175 (1951).

[15] J. Ubbink, J. A. Poulis, and C. J. Gorter, *Physica 16*, 570 (1950).

[16] F. Lancaster and W. Gordy, *J. Chem. Phys. 19*, 1181 (1951).

[17] J. H. Van Vleck, *Phys. Rev. 74*, 1168 (1948).

[18] R. Kronig, *Physica 6*, 33 (1939).

[19] C. J. Gorter and J. H. Van Vleck, *Phys. Rev. 72*, 1128 (1947).

[20] R. D. Arnold and A. F. Kip, *Phys. Rev. 75*, 1199 (1949).

[21] D. M. S. Bagguley and J. H. E. Griffiths, *Proc. Roy. Soc. (London) A201*, 366 (1950).

[22] R. Schlapp and W. G. Penney, *Phys. Rev. 42*, 666 (1932).

[23] B. C. Guha, *Proc. Roy. Soc. (London) A206*, 353 (1951).

[24] C. A. Beevers and H. Lipson, *Proc. Roy. Soc. (London) A146*, 570 (1934).

[25] B. Bleaney, R. P. Penrose, and B. I. Plumpton, *Proc. Roy. Soc. (London) A198*, 406 (1949).

[26] B. Bleaney and K. D. Bowers, private communication.

[27] J. H. Van Vleck, *J. Chem. Phys. 7*, 61 (1939).

[28] C. A. Whitmer, R. T. Weidner, J. S. Hsiang, and P. R. Weiss, *Phys. Rev. 74*, 1478 (1948).

[29] B. Bleaney and R. P. Penrose, *Proc. Phys. Soc. 60*, 395 (1948).

[30] B. Bleaney, *Phys. Rev. 75*, 1962 (1949).

[31] D. Bijl, *Proc. Phys. Soc. A63*, 405 (1950).

[32] (a) B. Bleaney and H. E. D. Scovil, *Proc. Phys. Soc. A63*, 1369 (1950); (b) *A64*, 204 (1951).

[33] R. J. Elliott and K. W. H. Stevens, *Proc. Phys. Soc. A64*, 205 (1951).

[34] S. N. Ghosh, W. Gordy, and D. G. Hill, *Phys. Rev. 87*, 229 (1952).

[35] A. N. Holden, C. Kittel, F. R. Merritt, and W. A. Yager, *Phys. Rev. 75*, 1614 (1949); *77*, 147 (1950).

[36] C. H. Townes and J. Turkevich, *Phys. Rev. 77*, 148 (1950).

[37] C. A. Hutchison, *Phys. Rev. 75*, 1769 (1949).

[38] E. E. Schneider and T. S. England, *Physica 17*, 221 (1951).

[39] E. E. Schneider, M. J. Day, and G. Stein, *Nature 168*, 644 (1951).

[40] E. E. Schneider, private communication.

[41] C. A. Hutchison and R. C. Pastor, *Phys. Rev. 81*, 282 (1951).

[42] M. A. Garstens and A. H. Ryan, *Phys. Rev. 81*, 888 (1951).

[43] E. C. Levinthal, E. H. Rogers, and R. A. Ogg, *Phys. Rev. 83*, 182 (1951).

[43a] T. W. Griswold, A. F. Kip, and C. Kittel, *Phys. Rev. 88*, 951 (1952).

[44] R. P. Penrose, *Nature 163*, 992 (1949).

[45] (a) A. Abragam and M. H. L. Pryce, *Nature 163*, 993 (1949); (b) *Proc. Phys. Soc. (London) A63*, 409 (1950); (c) A. Abragam, *Phys. Rev. 79*, 534 (1950); (d) B. Bleaney, *Physica 17*, 175 (1951); (e) A. Abragam, *Physica 17*, 209 (1951).

[46] J. H. E. Griffiths, *Nature 158*, 670 (1946).

[47] L. Landau and E. Lifshitz, *Physik. Z. Sowjetunion 8*, 153 (1935).

[48] W. A. Yager and R. M. Bozorth, *Phys. Rev. 72*, 80 (1947).

[49] C. Kittel, *Phys. Rev. 73*, 155 (1948); *76*, 743 (1949); *J. phys. et radium 12*, 291 (1951).

[50] J. H. Van Vleck, (a) *Phys. Rev. 78*, 266 (1950); (b) *Physica 17*, 234 (1951).

[51] D. Polder, *Phil. Mag. 40*, 99 (1949); *Physica 15*, 253 (1949).

[52] A. J. E. Welch, P. F. Nicks, A. Fairweather, and F. F. Roberts, *Phys. Rev. 77*, 403 (1950).

[53] C. Guillaud, W. A. Yager, F. R. Merritt, and C. Kittel, *Phys. Rev. 79*, 181 (1950).

[54] L. R. Bickford, *Phys. Rev. 76*, 137 (1949).

[55] A. Kip and R. Arnold, *Phys. Rev. 75*, 1556 (1949).

[56] C. Kittel, *Phys. Rev. 76*, 743 (1949).

[57] C. Kittel and C. Herring, *Phys. Rev. 77*, 725 (1950).

[58] N. Bloembergen, *Phys. Rev. 78*, 572 (1950).

[59] E. P. Trounson, D. F. Bleil, R. K. Wangsness, and L. R. Maxwell, *Phys. Rev. 79*, 542 (1950).

[60] T. Okamura, Y. Torizuka, and Y. Kojima, *Phys. Rev. 82*, 285 (1951).

[61] D. F. Bleil and R. K. Wangsness, *Phys. Rev. 79*, 227A (1950).

[62] K. W. H. Stevens, *Phys. Rev. 81*, 1058 (1951).

[63] N. Tsuya and Y. Ichikawa, *Phys. Rev. 83*, 1065 (1951).

[64] (a) H. G. Dehmelt and H. Krüger, *Naturwiss. 37*, 111 (1950); (b) *ibid. 37*, 398 (1950); (c) *Z. Physik 129*, 401 (1951); (d) survey by H. Kopfermann, *Physica 17*, 386 (1951); (e) H. G. Dehmelt, *Z. Physik 130*, 356 (1951).

[65] (a) R. Livingston, *Phys. Rev. 82*, 289 (1951); (b) *J. Chem. Phys. 19*, 803 (1951).

[66] R. V. Pound, *Phys. Rev. 79*, 685 (1950).

[67] H. G. Dehmelt and H. Krüger, *Z. Physik 130*, 385 (1951).

[68] R. Livingston, private communication.

[69] W. Gordy, *J. Chem. Phys. 19*, 792 (1951).

[70] H. G. Dehmelt, private communication.

[71] C. H. Townes and B. P. Dailey, *J. Chem. Phys. 20*, 35 (1952).

[72] R. V. Pound, *Phys. Rev. 82*, 343 (1951).

[73] N. Bloembergen, E. M. Purcell, and R. V. Pound, *Phys. Rev. 73*, 679 (1948).

[74] W. Jackson and J. G. Powles, *Trans. Faraday Soc. 42*, Suppl. 101 (1946).

[75] F. J. Cripwell and G. B. B. M. Sutherland, *Trans. Faraday Soc. 42*, Suppl. 149 (1946).

[76] D. H. Whiffen and H. W. Thompson, *Trans. Faraday Soc. 42*, Suppl. 114 (1946).

[77] "A General Discussion on Dielectrics," *Trans. Faraday Soc. 42*, Suppl. (1946).

[78] D. H. Whiffen, *Quarterly Reviews IV*, 131 (1950).

6. NUCLEAR PROPERTIES

Nuclear moments are of great value in establishing selection rules for nuclear reactions and in the formulation of a theory of nuclear structures. The nuclear shell model,[1] which appears at this time to be the opening wedge for the first successful theory of nuclear structure, is based almost entirely on empirical evidences of nuclear moments. The importance of nuclear masses in calculating the energy available in nuclear reactions is well known.

The following well-established facts are useful in the study of nuclear moments. All nuclei having an odd mass number, A ($A = N + Z$, where N is the number of neutrons and Z is the number of protons), have spins which are odd integral multiples of $\frac{1}{2}(h/2\pi)$. All nuclei with an even number of particles have spins which are zero or integral multiples of $h/2\pi$. Except for one case, mentioned by Mack[2] as undocumented, all measured spins for even-even nuclei (N even, Z even) are zero. In two instances, Lu^{176} and V^{50}, spins greater than $\frac{9}{2}$ have been recorded.[2] There is no magnetic moment for a nucleus with zero spin or an electric moment for one with a spin of zero or $\frac{1}{2}$. According to theory,[3] the possible nuclear magnetic moments have 2^l poles where l is an odd integer, and the allowed electric moments have 2^l poles where l is an even integer. This theory follows from the axial symmetry of nuclei and assumes that the centers of mass and of charge coincide. The spins, magnetic moments, and masses of most of the stable nuclei have already been determined. In contrast, only a few moments or masses of the many artifically created nuclei have been experimentally determined. It is for the study of these radioactive nuclei that the microwave method offers most promise. Also, there is much work yet to be done on quadrupole moments of stable nuclei. Many of these have no assigned values, and very few have been measured with accuracy. A table of known nuclear moments and masses is given in the Appendix ($A.2$).

6.1. SPINS

The mechanical moment or spin, I represents in units of $h/2\pi$ the angular momentum of the nucleus. The nuclear hyperfine structure, discussed in Sec. 2.6 and Art. 5.1l, provides an unquestionable identification of the spin of the nucleus involved whenever the hyperfine

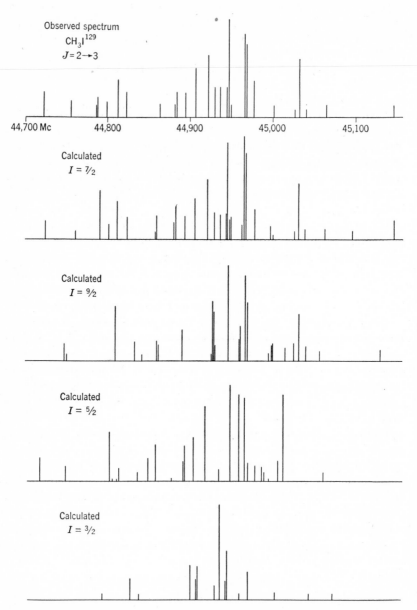

FIG. 6.1. Illustration of the determination of a nuclear spin (I^{129}) from nuclear quadrupole hyperfine structure in molecular rotational spectra. (From Livingston, Gilliam, and Gordy.[16])

structure can be resolved. With the exceptional resolving power obtainable in microwave spectroscopy it is usually possible in rotational spectra, when the nucleus has a quadrupole moment, to obtain the necessary resolution. The principal difficulty in applying the method is in obtaining the nucleus in suitable chemical combination. The molecule employed in rotational spectroscopy must have a dipole moment, must be stable in the vapor state, and must be sufficiently simple so that its spectrum can be analyzed. An additional molecular requirement, which, however, is usually met, is that the electronic cloud about the nucleus must not be spherically symmetric, i.e., $(\partial^2 V/\partial z^2)$ must not be zero. The nucleus in question must, of course, have a quadrupole moment. This limits the method to nuclei having spins greater than $\frac{1}{2}$, although the absence of a hyperfine structure in some instances provides evidence, but not proof, that the spin is zero or $\frac{1}{2}$. Many new determinations have already been made with the method, and, in addition, many values determined by other methods have been substantiated. Examples of spins determined by the microwave method which were found to be incorrectly assigned by earlier optical methods are Cl^{35}, B^{10}, and B^{11}. Figure 6.1 illustrates the determination of a nuclear spin by means of nuclear hyperfine structure of a rotational transition.

In some instances, spins of zero or $\frac{1}{2}$ can be assigned with certainty from a comparison of intensities of rotational lines in the microwave region. This method is made clear by the discussion of the effects of nuclear spin or statistical weights in Chapter 4. An illustration which provides confirmation of the spin of $\frac{1}{2}$ for F^{19} is shown in Fig. 2.7. The spin of zero for O^{18} (see Table $A.7$) was determined from $O^{18} O^{18}$ by the statistical weight method.

In paramagnetic resonance spectra of solids the spin is determined by simply counting the $(2I + 1)$ components of the hyperfine structure (Art. 5.1l). Since it is the nuclear magnetic moment which gives rise to the latter structure, spins of $\frac{1}{2}$ can also be determined. Similarly, spins might be evaluated from nuclear quadrupole spectra in solids (see Sec. 5.3), but so far no new spins have been evaluated by this method.

Table $A.7$ in the Appendix summarizes the spins already assigned with microwave spectroscopy. This list is being rapidly extended.

6.2. NUCLEAR QUADRUPOLE MOMENTS

The electric quadrupole moment, Q, measures the deviation of the nuclear charge from spherical symmetry and, in terms of the nuclear dimensions, is [4]

$$Q = \frac{1}{e} \int \rho r^2 (3 \cos^2 \theta - 1) \, d\tau = Z \langle 3z^2 - r^2 \rangle_{Av}, \qquad (6.1)$$

where ρ is the nuclear charge density; r, the distance from the center of gravity of the charge to the element of volume, $d\tau$; and θ, the angle between r and the spin axis z. In the last expression Z represents the atomic number. The average is taken over the nuclear state with $M_I = I$. A positive value for Q indicates that the nucleus is elongated along the spin axis, i.e., it is a prolate spheroid; and a negative Q indicates that it is flattened along the spin axis, i.e., it is an oblate spheroid.

Assuming the nucleus to be an ellipsoid of revolution with axis of length b taken along the axis of revolution and perpendicular axes of length a, Feld [5] expressed Q in terms of the eccentricity, $\epsilon = (b - a)/(b + a)$, of the ellipsoid. Obviously, ϵ is negative when the nucleus is oblate, and positive when it is prolate. With this assumption,

$$Q = \tfrac{2}{5}Z(b^2 - a^2) = \tfrac{2}{5}Z(b + a)^2\epsilon = \tfrac{8}{5}ZR^2\epsilon, \qquad (6.2)$$

where in the last expression $R = (a + b)/2$ is equal approximately to the nuclear radius when $|\epsilon| \ll 1$. Feld uses the expression $R = 1.5A^{\frac{1}{3}} \times 10^{-13}$ cm to compute from the observed quadrupole moments the eccentricities, ϵ, for a number of nuclei. They range from -0.024 for Cl^{35} to $+0.15$ for Lu^{176} and show in more familiar terminology than do the observed Q's the degree of variation from spherical symmetry.

Quadrupole moments have been found to be loosely related to nuclear shell structure [6] and to nuclear magnetic moments.[6a] When more accurate values of Q become available, more exact forms of these relations can be ascertained, and it seems probable that other important quantities such as scattering cross sections may depend to some extent upon quadrupole moments.

The measurements of the quadrupole hyperfine structure in molecules yield, with the theory described in Sec. 2.6, the quantity eQq, in which e is the charge on the electron, Q is the nuclear quadrupole moment, and $q = \partial^2V/\partial z^2$ where V is the potential at the nucleus which arises from all the extranuclear charges. In a linear or in a symmetric-top molecule, where the atom in question is on the molecular axis, only one component, $(\partial^2V/\partial z^2)$, is required to characterize the coupling of a single atom, where the reference axis, z, is along the molecular axis.† For asymmetric-top molecules or crystals two independent coupling factors are obtained [7] (see Sec. 2.6 and Sec. 7.1). However, one can frequently resolve them along a charge-symmetric "z" axis passing through the particular nucleus. In order to use data on molecular structure for evaluation of Q, the quantity q must be evaluated. A similiar situation applies to

_____

† Subscripts are needed to distinguish the components when more than one is required. Abbreviations frequently used for $(\partial^2V/\partial z^2)$ are q_{zz}, V_{zz}, or ϕ_{zz}, with similar expressions for the second derivatives of V with respect to other axes.

solids since in their quadrupole spectra $eQ(\partial^2 V/\partial z^2)$ is usually obtained from the measurements, where z is a charge-symmetric axis through the nucleus.

The potential, V, at the nucleus caused by a single electron at a distance, r, is e/r and, hence,

$$\frac{\partial^2}{\partial z^2}\left(\frac{e}{r}\right) = \frac{\partial^2}{\partial z^2}\frac{e}{(x^2 + y^2 + z^2)^{1/2}} = \frac{e(3\cos^2\theta - 1)}{r^3}. \tag{6.3}$$

To obtain the contribution of this electron to q, the quantity in Eq. 6.3 must be averaged over the orbital occupied by the electron. Thus for the ith electron,

$$q_i = \frac{e\int\psi_i\left(\dfrac{3\cos^2\theta - 1}{r^3}\right)\psi^*_i\,d\tau}{\displaystyle\int\psi_i\psi^*_i\,d\tau}, \tag{6.4}$$

where ψ_i is the wave function for the orbit of this electron. For molecules it has not proved possible, except for the simple hydrogen molecule,[8] to evaluate this integral theoretically without severe simplifying assumptions and approximations. For atoms it can frequently be evaluated with the help of experimental data, since other measureable quantities depend on $\int\psi(1/r^3)\psi^*\,d\tau$. Approximate solutions for the molecular case can then be obtained by assuming atomic orbitals for the atoms in molecules. This approximation, first used by Townes,[9] and developed by Townes and Dailey,[9] has been applied with fair success in a number of instances.[10] The subject is elaborated below. See also Sec. 7.1.

When the fine structure splitting, $\Delta\nu$, arising from $\mathbf{l}\cdot\mathbf{s}$ coupling is known, then q_i for the case of a maximum projection of l on z ($m = l$) is given by the atomic spectra formula,[11]

$$q_{m=\pm l} = \frac{-4e\,\Delta\nu l}{Z_i R\alpha^2 a_0^3(2l + 1)(2l + 3)}$$

$$= \frac{2.24\times10^{15}\,\Delta\nu l}{Z_i(2l + 1)(2l + 3)}\ \text{esu.} \tag{6.5}$$

For the case of l perpendicular to z, ($m = 0$) this expression is multiplied by $-(l + 1)/(2l - 1)$ and becomes

$$q_{m=0} = \frac{2.24\times10^{15}\,\Delta\nu l(l + 1)}{Z_i(2l + 1)(2l - 1)(2l + 3)}\ \text{esu.} \tag{6.6}$$

In both equations $\Delta\nu$ is in cm^{-1} and $Z_i \approx Z - 4$, except for the lightest atoms. A convenient source of $\Delta\nu$ values is the compilations by Bacher and Goudsmit [12] and by Moore.[13]

One can obtain q_{atom} $(q_{m=l})$ more precisely (since Z_i is not needed) from the relation,[11]

$$q_{atom} = -\frac{aeMj(j+1)}{g_I\beta^2 m(l+1)(2l+3)}, \tag{6.7}$$

when the nuclear magnetic hyperfine structure and nuclear gyromagnetic factor, g_I, are known. In this formula a represents the coupling constant in $a(\mathbf{I}\cdot\mathbf{j})$; e and m represent the charge and mass of the electron, respectively; M, the proton mass; and β, the Bohr magneton. Davis, Feld, Zabel, and Zacharias [14] have used this relation, with the quadrupole coupling observed at the same time on the Cl^{35} atom with the atomic beam method, to obtain an extremely accurate value for the quadrupole moments of the stable Cl isotopes. These are useful for testing the accuracy of the more approximate methods.†

When no experimental measurements are available for determination of q, it can be very roughly approximated from the theoretical formula,[9b]

$$q_{n,l,m=\pm l} \approx -\frac{4eZ^3}{n^3a_0^3(l+1)(2l+1)(2l+3)} \tag{6.8}$$

or

$$q_{n,l,m=0} \approx \frac{4eZ^3}{n^3a_0^3(2l-1)(2l+1)(2l+3)}, \tag{6.9}$$

obtained by theoretical evaluation of the integral, if screening is neglected and hydrogen-like wave functions are assumed for the electron. Although Eqs. 6.8 and 6.9 are by no means accurate, they allow a quick comparison of the coupling constants for different atomic states and are useful in approximating the errors caused by the omission of contributions from excited states. It is apparent from them that q for a particular electron decreases rapidly with increasing n or l (excepting $l = 0$ for which $q = 0$).

There are certain general facts which simplify the calculation of the total or resultant q. (1) Only electrons in the valence shell need be considered, since a closed shell is spherically symmetric and except for small polarization or distortion effects makes no contribution to q. (2) An s electron makes no contribution to q. This may be seen by placing $l = 0$ in Eq. 6.6. (3) When the three p orbitals are equally filled, their combined contribution is zero. (4) When there are "unbalanced" p electrons

† For a discussion of the limitations of this method, see G. F. Koster, *Phys. Rev. 86*, 148 (1952).

in the valence shell, contributions to q from electrons in other states are usually negligible by comparison.[9] This is the condition most frequently encountered.

When only p electrons are considered,

$$q = -[(N_x + N_y)(\tfrac{1}{2}q_{n,1,1} + \tfrac{1}{2}q_{n,1,-1}) + N_z q_{n,1,0}], \qquad (6.10)$$

where N_x, N_y, and N_z are the numbers (or average fractional numbers) of electrons in the p_x, p_y, and p_z orbits, respectively. From Eqs. 6.5 and 6.6 it follows that

$$q_{n,1,-1} = -\tfrac{1}{2}q_{n,1,0}. \qquad (6.11)$$

Therefore,

$$q = \left(\frac{N_x + N_y}{2} - N_z\right) q_{n,1,0} = U_p q_{n,1,0}, \qquad (6.12)$$

where $U_p = (N_x + N_y)/2 - N_z$ is the number of unbalanced p electrons, and where $q_{n,1,0}$ is the contribution per unbalanced p electron given in esu by Eq. 6.6 as $2.98 \times 10^{14} \, \Delta\nu/Z_i$, or obtained in some other manner. The sign of U_p is positive for a deficit of p_z electrons. For example, when p_x and p_y are filled with two unshared electrons each and p_z has, on the average, less than two, U_p is taken as positive. With $q_{n,1,0}$ positive, this gives the correct sign to $\langle \partial^2 V/\partial z^2 \rangle_{\mathrm{Av}}$, which is negative for an excess of electrons along z and positive for a deficit of electrons along this axis. Usually the nuclear quadrupole coupling, eQq, is measured in megacycles, and q is computed in esu. For convenience, the formula,

$$Q \; (\mathrm{cm})^2 = 13.8 \times 10^{-12} \frac{eQq \; (\mathrm{Mc})}{q \; (\mathrm{esu})}, \qquad (6.13)$$

is given.

We assume that the coupling factor q for a free atom can be obtained, and we ask how it will be altered when that atom is combined in a molecule. In the first place, it can be safely assumed that only electrons in the valence shell will be significantly affected by chemical bonding. If small distortion effects are neglected, the combined contributions from all completely filled shells, just as in free atoms, will be zero. Thus, to a first approximation, we need consider only electrons in the valence shells. Furthermore, the non-bonding electrons in the valence shell remain in atomic orbitals, and, when there is no bond-orbital hybridization or formal charge on the atom, their contributions will be the same as in the free atom except for difference in orientation and small distortion effects. Only the bonding electrons appear to present an essentially new problem. It is well known that the orbital of a covalent bond differs appreciably from the free atomic orbitals out of which it is constructed. Nevertheless, the important measurement on the Cl^{35}

coupling in Cl_2 in the solid state by Livingston,[15] together with that in atomic Cl^{35} by Davis, Feld, Zabel, and Zacharias [14a] and by Jaccarino and King [14b], shows that the coupling per bonding electron per atom (after correction for difference in orbital orientation) in the Cl_2 molecule is within about 1 per cent of that in atomic Cl. This indicates that the charge distribution near the nucleus, where the interaction with the nuclear quadrupole moment is large, is not significantly altered by the formation of a pure covalent bond. Even the small deviation observed could be caused by a slight hybridization of the bonding orbital or by interaction between the molecules in the solid state. A better test would be a comparison with the coupling in gaseous Cl_2, which, unfortunately, has not been measured. Nevertheless, it appears that the most probable type of interaction between the Cl_2 molecules in the solid form would tend to reduce the coupling below that for one unbalanced p electron and, hence, to increase rather than decrease the difference between the solid and gaseous values. The close agreement of the solid Cl_2 coupling with that expected for one unbalanced p electron appears, therefore, to indicate nearly pure p single bonding in the elemental Cl_2. Even in the slightly heteropolar molecule BrCl (gas), the Cl coupling deviates only 6 per cent from the atomic value when the latter is multiplied by 2 to correct for difference in orbital orientation. Thus, from the Cl case it appears that to a good approximation, one can divide the shared electronic charge of a pure covalent bond equally between the two atoms and calculate the coupling as though one electron of the shared pair existed in the atomic orbital of each atom. This is a fortunate circumstance which makes it possible to obtain approximate values of nuclear quadrupole moments from their coupling in molecules and to use nuclear quadrupole data to detect hybridization of bonding orbitals and deviations from pure covalent type bonding in molecules. Since the above paragraph was written, similar comparisons for Br have been made possible. The results are in complete agreement with the Cl case. (See Table 7.1.).

If a bond is not entirely covalent but has some "ionic character," the charge cloud of the bonding electron pair can no longer be regarded as divided equally between the two atoms. The deviation of the coupling from that expected for the pure covalent bond then gives a measure of the ionic character. In addition to varying the amount of contributing charge, ionic character produces an indirect effect through an alteration of the nuclear screening. Since electrons in different atomic orbitals have widely different couplings, hybridization of the bonding orbital markedly affects the coupling. The most pronounced hybridization effects are obtained by mixing s orbitals, which have zero coupling, with

p orbitals, which have the largest coupling of any orbital. For illustration, suppose that an atom which normally has a pair of electrons in the s orbital forms a covalent bond with a hybridized orbital of 50 per cent s and 50 per cent p character. Since there is, on the average, only one electron per atom in the bonding orbital, the s electron cloud has been decreased by the hybridization and the p electron cloud increased by the complementary hybridization. Thus, bond-orbital hybridization and unequal possession of the bonding electrons (ionic character) are the principal factors, other than orientation, which cause deviations from the essentially atomic-type coupling.

The problem of determining an approximate Q from microwave molecular spectra usually reduces to that of determining how the p orbitals of the valence shells are filled, i.e., to the evaluation of the number of unbalanced p electrons. This depends upon the nature of the chemical bonds formed by the atom considered, in particular upon the degree and kind of bond-orbital hybridization, upon the ionic character of the bond, and upon resonance between different covalent structures. Information about molecular bond lengths, bond angles, and dipole moments—determined also from microwave data—is therefore useful in the determination of nuclear quadrupole moments. A discussion of these properties, as well as details about the determination of the number of unbalanced p electrons from them, is reserved for Chapters 7 and 8, which deal with molecular properties.

Since a knowledge of q is unnecessary for the determination of the ratios of the quadrupole moments of different isotopes of the same element, these ratios can be precisely evaluated from microwave measurements. Sometimes it is possible to evaluate the Q of the most abundant isotope with atomic spectra, but not that of the element's rare isotopes—either stable or radioactive. The absolute value of Q for these rare isotopes can then be determined by a comparison of their microwave hyperfine structure with that of the abundant isotope in the same molecule. Examples of this are the determination [16] of Q for I^{129} from the known value for I^{127}, and that [17] of Cl^{36} from the value for Cl^{35}.

A list of nuclear quadrupole moments already determined from microwave spectra is given in Table $A.7$ in the Appendix.

6.3. NUCLEAR MAGNETIC MOMENTS

When the nucleus is coupled to the molecular axis through magnetic dipole or electric quadrupole interaction, the nuclear magnetic moment can be determined by means of the Zeeman effect in pure rotational spectra. (See Chapter 3.)

Most stable molecules have $^1\Sigma$ electronic ground states and hence extremely small molecular magnetic moments, of the order of a nuclear magneton or less. For this reason, the coupling of the nuclear magnetic moment to the molecular axis is usually too weak to give a magnetic hyperfine structure sufficiently resolvable to allow determination of nuclear moments. Nevertheless, in some instances the $I \cdot J$ coupling has been detected for molecules in $^1\Sigma$ states. For FCl the magnitude of this coupling indicates a molecular magnetic field of the order of 70 gauss at the Cl nucleus.[18] A few molecules such as NO_2 and ClO_2 are paramagnetic, and the nuclear magnetic hyperfine structure of the pure rotational spectra is easily resolved in the microwave region (Chapter 2). Also, in several instances, nuclear hyperfine structure has been detected in the paramagnetic resonance absorption of salts (Sec. 5.1). The magnetic moments of most nuclei which can be obtained in paramagnetic substances have, however, already been measured to an accuracy higher than can be obtained by this method.

To obtain nuclear magnetic moments from $I \cdot J$ coupling in molecules one must know the value of the molecular magnetic field at the nucleus in question. Because of the complexity of molecular magnetic moments this cannot be easily calculated with accuracy. However, it may sometimes be evaluated experimentally. For example, the molecular moment can be evaluated with an isotope which we shall assume to have a known moment, and the calibrated molecular field can then be used in the calculation of the magnetic moments of other isotopes of the same element from their $I \cdot J$ coupling in the same molecule.

Nuclear magnetic moments of atoms combined in non-paramagnetic molecules can be determined with microwave spectroscopy, provided that the nucleus is coupled to the molecular axes through a quadrupole moment. One can then obtain a Zeeman splitting of the hyperfine structure, from which the nuclear magnetic moment can be calculated as indicated in Sec. 3.2. Three previously unknown nuclear magnetic moments, namely those of I^{129}, S^{33}, and S^{35}, have been determined in this way. The accuracy is limited by the strength of the quadrupole coupling. In favorable cases it is of the order of 1 per cent. This accuracy is not nearly so good as that obtainable with molecular beams and nuclear resonance. The microwave method is therefore of advantage only when for some reason the more accurate methods are inapplicable. Its most important applications will no doubt be to radioactive nuclei where extremely small samples, of the order of a microgram, must be used.

As with molecular beams and nuclear resonance, the quantity directly evaluated from microwave spectroscopy is the nuclear g factor and not the magnetic moment. The g_I factor is the ratio of the magnetic moment to the mechanical moment or spin. The spin, however, if not already known, can be determined from the quadrupole hyperfine structure which must be present when the method of the preceding paragraph is applied.

Here, as with other methods for determination of μ_I, a correction must be made for the diamagnetism of the extranuclear electrons, which set up fields at the nucleus in opposition to the externally applied H. A formula,

$$\bar{H} = 0.319 \times 10^{-4} Z^{\frac{2}{3}} H, \tag{6.14}$$

given by Lamb,[19] allows easy correction for this effect. $\bar{H}$ is the value of the diamagnetic field which must be subtracted from the applied field, H, to give the resultant field at the nucleus. Ramsey [20] has pointed out that this formula, which was derived for free atoms, does not apply exactly to atoms bound in molecules. It is certainly correct, however, beyond the accuracy of the microwave method and is to be recommended for its simplicity. Smaller corrections for various other effects are discussed by Mack.[2] Because the proton-resonance method is now commonly used for calibration of the magnetic fields in all types of magnetic moment studies, attention should be called to the direct and highly accurate measurement of the proton moment with the nuclear-resonance method by Thomas, Driscoll, and Hipple.[21]

6.4. ATOMIC MASSES

Just as in optical spectroscopy, the relative masses of different isotopes can be determined from the effects of mass upon the position of spectral lines. The values are determined most simply and most accurately from diatomic molecules and next in simplicity and accuracy from linear triatomic molecules. As the number of atoms in the molecules increases, it becomes more difficult to obtain equilibrium values of the spectral constants from which to calculate mass ratios, and also more difficult to calculate the probable errors introduced by neglect of the zero-point vibrations.

Assume that the B_e value for a diatomic molecule and that for one of its isotopic species, B'_e, are evaluated from measurements as explained in Chapter 2. The reduced-mass ratios are then determined from the simple formula,

$$\mu'/\mu = B_e/B'_e, \tag{6.15}$$

from which the mass ratios are obtained. Here μ represents the reduced mass, $m_1 m_2/(m_1 + m_2)$ and μ' that of the isotopic species. To evaluate

B_e entirely from microwave data one must measure at least two rotational lines for the ground vibrational state and two for an excited vibrational state. When microwave data on the excited vibrational state cannot be obtained, it is usually possible to calculate the necessary second-order constants from vibrational spectra. However, with the sensitivities now obtainable in microwave spectroscopy, it should usually be possible to obtain the required data for the most abundant isotopic combination. The mass ratios can then be evaluated from the formula,[22]

$$\Delta\nu_r = 2B_e(J + 1)[1 - (\mu/\mu')] - \alpha_e[1 - (\mu/\mu')^{3/2}](J + 1)$$
$$- 4D_J[1 - (\mu/\mu')^2](J + 1)^3, \quad (6.16)$$

where $\Delta\nu_r$ is the isotopic separation of the rotational lines for the ground vibrational state. Thus, data for the excited vibrational state of only one isotopic species are required.

Considerably more data are required to determine precise mass ratios from a linear triatomic molecule, which is next in simplicity to the diatomic molecule. Although there are only two parameters in the linear triatomic molecule, there are three fundamental vibrational frequencies. One must employ two known isotopic species to evaluate the two interatomic distances, and to determine the desired equilibrium values one must obtain data on all three vibrational states as well as on the ground state for each of the isotopic species. When the equilibrium values for the interatomic distances are determined, the mass of a given isotope, m', can be calculated from the formula,

$$\frac{B'_e}{B_e} = \frac{(m'_1 + m_2 + m_3)(m_1 m_2 d_{1,2}^2 + m_2 m_3 d_{2,3}^2 + m_1 m_3 d_{1,3}^2)}{(m_1 + m_2 + m_3)(m'_1 m_2 d_{1,2}^2 + m_2 m_3 d_{2,3}^2 + m'_1 m_3 d_{1,3}^2)}, \quad (6.17)$$

where the notation is made clear by the diagram. The isotope m' can,

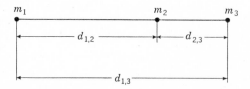

of course, be substituted at any of the three positions if the corresponding change is made in the formula. Here B'_e/B_e represents the ratio of the B_e values for the two isotopic combinations, and $d_{1,3} = d_{1,2} + d_{2,3}$. For an accuracy comparable to that obtainable on the line frequencies, equilibrium values for the d's and B's must be used. In no instance has this so far been done. Fairly accurate results can be obtained by using average ground-vibrational-state values for these constants. Assume that two different isotopic substitutions, m'_1 and m''_1, are made for m_1. If zero-point vibrations are neglected, the mass difference ratios are given by:

$$\frac{m_1 - m'_1}{m_1 - m''_1} = \frac{B''_0}{B'_0}\left(\frac{B'_0 - B_0}{B''_0 - B_0}\right)\left(\frac{m'_1 + m_2 + m_3}{m_1 + m_2 + m_3}\right). \qquad (6.18)$$

It can be shown that the fractional error (caused by neglect of zero-point vibrations) in the mass difference ratios, $(m_1 - m'_1)/(m_1 - m''_1)$, determined in this way, is of the order,[23]

$$\left(\frac{B_e - B_0}{2B_0}\right)\left(\frac{m_1 - m'_1}{m_1}\right), \qquad (6.19)$$

which for the S isotopes in OCS is $\approx 10^{-4}$.

Atomic masses can also be determined from the rotational spectra of symmetric-top or asymmetric-top rotors, but, in general, these determinations are likely to be less accurate than the determinations from the simpler linear molecules. Ratios of the germanium isotopes [24] have been evaluated from the microwave spectrum of GeH_3Cl.

For a summary of the mass ratios already determined from microwave spectra see Table $A.8$ in the Appendix.

REFERENCES

[1] L. W. Nordheim, *Phys. Rev. 75*, 1894 (1949); E. Feenberg and K. C. Hammack, *Phys. Rev. 75*, 1877 (1949); M. G. Mayer, *Phys. Rev. 75*, 1969 (1949).

[2] J. E. Mack, *Revs. Modern Phys. 22*, 64 (1950).

[3] J. Schwinger, unpublished work quoted by B. T. Feld, reference 5.

[4] H. B. G. Casimir, *On the Interaction between Atomic Nuclei and Electrons* (Teyler's Tweede Genootschap, E. F. Bohn, Haarlem, 1936).

[5] B. T. Feld, *Preliminary Report* No. 2 (1948), Nuclear Science Series, National Research Council.

[6] (a) E. Feenberg and K. C. Hammack, *Phys. Rev. 75*, 1877 (1949); (b) W. Gordy, *Phys. Rev. 76*, 139 (1949).

[7] J. K. Bragg, *Phys. Rev. 74*, 533 (1948).

[8] A. Nordsieck, *Phys. Rev. 58*, 310 (1940).

[9] (a) C. H. Townes, *Phys. Rev. 71*, 909 (1947); (b) see also C. H. Townes and B. P. Dailey, *J. Chem. Phys. 17*, 782 (1949).

[10] W. Gordy, H. Ring, and A. B. Burg, *Phys. Rev. 78*, 512 (1950); C. C. Loomis and M. W. P. Strandberg, *Phys. Rev. 81*, 798 (1951).

[11] H. A. Bethe and R. F. Bacher, *Revs. Modern Phys. 8*, 226 (1936).

[12] R. Bacher and S. Goudsmit, *Atomic Energy States* (McGraw-Hill Book Co., New York, 1932).

[13] C. E. Moore, "Atomic Energy Levels," *National Bureau of Standards Circular* 467 (U.S. Govt. Printing Office, Washington, D. C., 1949).

[14] (a) L. Davis, B. T. Feld, C. W. Zabel, and J. R. Zacharias, *Phys. Rev. 73*, 525 (1948); (b) V. Jaccarino and J. G. King, *Phys. Rev. 83*, 471 (1951).

[15] R. Livingston, *J. Chem. Phys. 19*, 1434 (1951).

[16] R. Livingston, O. R. Gilliam, and W. Gordy, *Phys. Rev. 76*, 149 (1949).

[17] C. H. Townes and L. C. Aamodt, *Phys. Rev. 76*, 691 (1949).

[18] D. A. Gilbert, A. Roberts, and P. A. Griswold, *Phys. Rev. 76*, 1723 (1949).

[19] W. E. Lamb, *Phys. Rev. 60*, 817 (1941).

[20] N. F. Ramsey, *Phys. Rev. 77*, 567 (1950).

[21] H. A. Thomas, R. L. Driscoll, and J. A. Hipple, *Phys. Rev. 75*, 902 (1949); *75*, 992 (1949); and *78*, 787 (1950).

[22] G. Herzberg, *Spectra of Diatomic Molecules* (McGraw-Hill Book Co., New York, 1950), p. 145.

[23] C. H. Townes, A. N. Holden, and F. R. Merritt, *Phys. Rev. 74*, 1113 (1948).

[24] S. Geschwind and R. Gunther-Mohr, *Phys. Rev. 81*, 882 (1951).

7. ELECTRICAL PROPERTIES OF MOLECULES

7.1. NUCLEAR QUADRUPOLE COUPLINGS IN MOLECULES

The measurement of nuclear quadrupole couplings in molecules †
provides a new means of investigating the electronic structures of molecules. The coupling factor (see Sec. 6.2) which is obtained from the
measurement of hyperfine structure of linear or symmetric-top rotors
is eQq, where e represents the electronic charge, Q represents the nuclear
quadrupole moment, and $q \equiv (\partial^2 V)/(\partial z^2)$, where V is the potential of the
molecular field at the nucleus for which the coupling is measured, and
z is the coordinate along the symmetry or bond axis. An additional
quantity obtained in asymmetric rotors or in non-symmetric crystalline
fields will be discussed later in this section. As explained in Sec. 6.2, q
depends almost wholly upon the valence electrons, and when there are
unbalanced p electrons it depends to a first order of approximation upon
the way the p orbitals are occupied. If q can be calculated from a
knowledge of the molecular structure, Q can be determined from the
measurements of eQq. But, what is more important for the present considerations, if Q is known from other sources, q can be determined from
the microwave measurements. Since the Q of a given nucleus is constant, relative values of q in different molecules can be obtained even
when Q is unknown.

From Eq. 6.12, the number of unbalanced p electrons is

$$U_p = \frac{N_x + N_y}{2} - N_z, \qquad (7.1)$$

where N_x, N_y, and N_z represent the number of electrons, or the time-
averaged fractional number, in the p_x, p_y, or p_z orbitals, respectively.
In the count of numbers of electrons in the atomic orbitals, a pair
shared equally in a pure covalent bond is counted as one electron per
atom. See Sec. 6.2. Unequal sharing is taken into account by assignment of ionic character to the bond as described below.

We assume that U_p can be evaluated experimentally as described in
Chapter 6 and proceed to explain how it can be expressed in terms of

---

† A tabulation of measured values is given in Table A.5 in the Appendix.

bond properties. When the bonds of a molecule are pure covalent bonds formed from pure s or p atomic orbitals it is a simple problem to count the number of unbalanced p electrons. When, as is usually true, the bonds are not so idealized, it is customary [1] to consider them hybrids formed by resonance between different hypothetical idealized states. To obtain the U_p for the actual molecule, one simply counts the unbalanced p electrons for the different contributing structures and averages them in accordance with the estimated contributions of these structures to the ground state of the molecule. This simplified approach neglects, among other things, the effects of the interactions of the various contributing structures upon the coupling. Nevertheless, the self-consistency of the results obtained indicates that the approach is of useful accuracy.

We illustrate the determination of U_p for some typical cases. Consider first an atom A, such as a halogen which forms a single bond to complete its octet. The reference z axis is chosen along the bond. If the bond is formed with a pure p orbital and has no ionic character, $N_z = 1$, $N_x = 2$, $N_y = 2$, and $U_p = +1$. Usually, however, the bond has some ionic character, and the bond orbital has some s character. If α represents the per cent s character of the bonding orbital, the orbitals are: $\sqrt{\alpha}\, s + \sqrt{1 - \alpha}\, p_z$, $\sqrt{1 - \alpha}\, s - \sqrt{\alpha}\, p_z$, p_x, and p_y. For the covalent state, then, $N_z = (1 - \alpha) + 2\alpha$, $N_x = 2$, $N_y = 2$, and $U_p = (1 - \alpha)$. For the ionic state with the negative charge on A, there is spherical symmetry, and $U_p = 0$. When the charge on A is positive, $N_z = 2\alpha(1 + c)$, $N_x = 2(1 + c)$, $N_y = 2(1 + c)$, and $U_p = 2(1 + c) \times (1 - \alpha)$. The weighted values for atom A in the actual molecule are:

$$U_p = (1 - \beta)(1 - \alpha) \quad \text{for negative charge on A,} \qquad (7.2)$$

$$U_p = \{1 + \beta(1 + 2c)\}(1 - \alpha)$$
$$\approx (1 + 1.50\beta)(1 - \alpha) \qquad \text{for positive charge on A,} \quad (7.3)$$

where α represents the s character of the bonding orbital of A, β represents the ionic character of the bond, and c is a correction for the change in screening caused by the charge. From the fine structure of the halogens, Townes and Dailey [2] estimate c as 0.25. However, from the internal consistency of the quadrupole couplings this value seems to be too large.

Consider now the case of an atom, A, in a symmetric-top molecule AB_3 with sp hybridized orbitals, three of which form covalent bonds and the fourth of which is filled with an unshared pair. Examples of this type are NH_3, NF_3, AsF_3, and SbF_3. If α represents the per cent

s character of the bonding orbitals, the normalized wave functions can be written:

$$\psi_1 = (1 - 3\alpha)^{\frac{1}{2}}s + (3\alpha)^{\frac{1}{2}}p_z,$$

$$\psi_2 = \alpha^{\frac{1}{2}}s - \left(\frac{1 - 3\alpha}{3}\right)^{\frac{1}{2}}p_z + \left(\frac{2}{3}\right)^{\frac{1}{2}}p_x,$$

$$\psi_3 = \alpha^{\frac{1}{2}}s - \left(\frac{1 - 3\alpha}{3}\right)^{\frac{1}{2}}p_z - \left(\frac{1}{6}\right)^{\frac{1}{2}}p_x + \left(\frac{1}{2}\right)^{\frac{1}{2}}p_y,$$

$$\psi_4 = \alpha^{\frac{1}{2}}s - \left(\frac{1 - 3\alpha}{3}\right)^{\frac{1}{2}}p_z - \left(\frac{1}{6}\right)^{\frac{1}{2}}p_x - \left(\frac{1}{2}\right)^{\frac{1}{2}}p_y.$$

The orbital which has the unshared pair is directed along the symmetry or z axis and is chosen as ψ_1. If the bonds also have some ionic character, the number of unbalanced p electrons is:

$$U_p = -3\alpha \left[1 - 3\beta + \frac{2\beta}{1 + c}\right]$$

$$\approx -3\alpha(1 - 1.40\beta) \quad \text{for negative charge on A} \tag{7.4}$$

$$U_p = -3\alpha[1 - 3\beta + 4\beta(1 + c)]$$

$$\approx -3\alpha(1 + 2\beta) \quad \text{for positive charge on A,} \tag{7.5}$$

where β represents the ionic character of each bond, α represents the s character of the bonding orbitals, and c the correction for changes in screening caused by the charge. These formulas are derived from an averaging of the unbalanced p electrons of the contributing structures with the correction for change in screening, as indicated above.

The case of an atom which forms double or triple bonds is of interest. The components of a multiple bond are unlike. One component is axially symmetric and is formed by an orbital which is an sp hybrid. This is the σ bond in molecular orbital terminology. The other components are presumably formed with pure p orbitals. They are the π bonds of molecular orbital theory. For example, a triple bond such as the $C\equiv N$ bond in HCN is made up of a σ bond formed by an sp hybridized orbital and two π bonds formed with pure p orbitals. If α represents the per cent s character of the σ bond, the wave functions for the orbitals can be written as: $\sqrt{\alpha}\,s + \sqrt{1 - \alpha}\,p_z$, $\sqrt{1 - \alpha}\,s - \sqrt{\alpha}\,p_z$, p_x, and p_y. If the orbital $\sqrt{1 - \alpha}\,s - \sqrt{\alpha}\,p_z$ has an unshared pair and there is no ionic character, $U_p = -\alpha$. The determination of the effects of ionic character is complicated by the fact that an atom exhibits a greater electronegativity through an s orbital or an sp hybridized orbital than through a pure p orbital. To a first approximation, however, one may assume that each component of the multiple bond has the same amount of ionic character.

Table 7.1.   Comparison of calculated and observed unbalanced p electrons with pure p bonding orbitals assumed

Molecule	Per cent Ionic Character † $100 \dfrac{\mid x_A - x_B \mid}{2}$	Theoretical U_p from Eq. 7.2 or 7.3	Observed U_p = $\dfrac{\text{molecular } eQq \ddagger}{2 \times \text{atomic } eQq}$
Cl^{35} (2 × atomic eQq = −109.74 Mc) §			
Cl_2 (solid)	0	1.00	0.99
BrCl	10	0.90	0.94
ICl	25	0.75	0.75
TlCl	80	0.20	0.14
NaCl	100	0	0.01
CH_3Cl	25	0.75	0.69
CF_3Cl	25	0.75	0.71
SiH_3Cl	60	0.40	0.36
SiF_3Cl	60	0.40	0.39
GeH_3Cl	65	0.35	0.42
CH_3HgCl	60	0.40	0.38
Br^{79} (2 × atomic eQq = 769.62 Mc) ‖			
Br_2 (solid)	0	1.00	0.99
BrCl	10	1.15	1.14
NaBr	95	0.05	0.01
CH_3Br	15	0.85	0.75
CF_3Br	15	0.85	0.80
SiH_3Br	50	0.50	0.44
SiF_3Br	50	0.50	0.57
GeH_3Br	55	0.45	0.49

† Electronegativities used are those of Pauling, Table 8.4 (p. 309) except 1.4 for Tl (determined from the force constant and bond length of TlCl).
‡ Values of molecular eQq used are from Table A.6 in the Appendix.
§ From Jaccarino and King.[3]
‖ From J. G. King and V. Jaccarino, private communication.

The Cl^{35} and Br^{79} couplings have been measured in many molecules. From the atomic beam measurements of Jaccarino and King the coupling per unbalanced p electron is determined as −109.74 Mc in Cl^{35} and 769.62 Mc in Br^{79}. The number of unbalanced p electrons for Cl or Br in a molecule is the observed coupling divided by twice the atomic eQq. Table 7.1 gives the experimentally determined U_p for

Cl^{35} and Br^{79} in some simple molecules. These may be compared with those calculated from Eq. 7.2 or 7.3 with assumed values for the s character of the bonding orbital and the ionic character of the bond. The observed bond lengths indicate that the double bond character in the molecules can be neglected.

The cases of BrCl and Cl_2 are particularly important because the number of unbalanced p electrons shows that the bonding orbital of Cl is very close to a pure p orbital in these molecules.[4,5] The case of Cl_2 is not complicated by ionic character, but some uncertainty arises from the fact that the measurement was made on molecules in the solid state. (See, however, Sec. 6.2.) The number of unbalanced p electrons in BrCl is only 6 per cent below unity, despite the fact that the ionic character as well as the s character of the bonding orbital would reduce U_p below unity. Thus, if smaller effects such as double bond character, distortion of orbitals, and contribution from higher electronic states are neglected, an upper limit of 6 per cent is set for both the s character of the bonding orbital and the ionic character of the bond. From the electronegativity difference of 0.2, an ionic character of a few per cent would be expected. Therefore, as previously pointed out,[4,5] it appears that the Cl bonding is close to the pure p type. Although some difference in bond-orbital hybridization would be expected in different molecules, it is difficult to justify a larger Cl hybridization in ICl than in BrCl, in view of the smaller energy of the ICl bond. If a pure p bond is assumed for the Cl bonding orbital, the ionic character required to account for the Cl coupling in ICl is 25 per cent. This does not seem unreasonably high considering the difference, 0.5, in the electronegativity of I and Cl.

The Cl couplings in TlCl and NaCl, determined by molecular beam measurements,[6,7] show either that these bonds have a high ionic character or that the Cl bonding orbitals have exceptionally high s character. The latter is improbable, but the former would be expected from the large electronegativity differences of the bonded atoms. We have assumed pure p bonding orbitals, as in BrCl, in calculating the theoretical U_p in Table 7.1, and we have used a similar procedure for the other molecules listed there. Although small amounts of s hybridization and double-bond character may exist in some of these, it is not believed that the constancy or accuracy of the electronegativity values justifies attempts to include their effects. In particular, if one assigns 5 to 10 per cent s bond character to the bonding orbitals of Cl, Br, and I when these elements are combined with elements of the first row of the atomic table, a better over-all agreement of the calculated and observed U_p is obtained.[4]

Figure 7.1 shows a graph of $1 - U_p$ against the electronegativity differences of the bonded atoms. If it is assumed that ionic character is represented by $1 - U_p$, the plot suggests that an electronegativity-ionic character relation of the form,[4]

$$\beta = \text{Ionic character} \approx a \left| x_A - x_B \right| \approx \frac{\left| x_A - x_B \right|}{2}, \qquad (7.6)$$

can be used for predicting ionic character. In this assumption the effects upon the coupling of the interaction between ionic and covalent states are neglected. Regardless of this interaction, Fig. 7.1 shows how

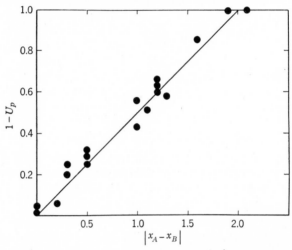

FIG. 7.1.   Plot of observed $(1 - U_p)$ against electronegativity difference $\left| x_A - x_B \right|$ for couplings listed in Table 7.1 for which $U_p < 1$.

the molecular coupling depends upon the electronegativity difference of the bonded atoms. The electronegativity scale of Pauling[8] is to be used with Eq. 7.6. The values from it are tabulated in Table 8.4. The applications to atoms with a large positive charge are less certain because an additional estimated parameter c is involved. Hence, FCl and FBr are not included. However, their quadrupole coupling indicates some double-bond character as well as s hybridization of the bonding orbitals.

The atomic coupling has been measured[9] for As. It shows the coupling per unbalanced p electron to be about 600 Mc. The As coupling in arsine, -164 Mc, measured by Loomis and Strandberg,[10] allows a fairly precise calculation of the bond-orbital hybridization of As. The observed $U_p = -\frac{164}{600} = -0.28$. Here double-bond character is out of the question, and the electronegativity difference of As and H shows that the ionic character would be very small, $\beta = 0.05$, with the positive charge on As. Equation 7.5 shows that the s character of the As bonding orbital is nearly 9 per cent. The large amount of ionic character in AsF_3 (electronegativity difference 2.0) makes the estimate of the hybridization in this molecule from the nuclear coupling highly uncertain. Also, the problem is complicated by possible contributions from structures of Type II. However, if the molecule is assumed to consist principally of the three forms of I

the s character of the As bonding orbital as calculated from the As coupling is about 8 per cent. The larger angle in this molecule over that in AsH_3 could be caused by the larger repulsion of the F atoms over the hydrogens and by contributions from form II. The observed bond lengths indicate some double-bond character.

Deviations from rotational symmetry in the quadrupole coupling of a single nucleus in a linear or symmetric-top molecule cannot be detected from the hyperfine structure of rotational spectra. In them, only one coupling factor is obtained from the analysis of the spectrum. However, in asymmetric rotors or in quadrupole spectra of solids (see Sec. 2.6 and Sec. 5.3), two independent coupling factors are obtained.† These can be expressed as eQq_{zz} and $\epsilon = (q_{xx} - q_{yy})/q_{zz}$, where $q_{zz} \equiv \partial^2 V/\partial z^2$, $q_{xx} \equiv \partial^2 V/\partial x^2$, and $q_{yy} \equiv \partial^2 V/\partial y^2$. (The latter quantities are also frequently abbreviated as ϕ_{zz}, etc., or V_{zz}, etc. When only one such quantity is involved as in symmetric rotors, the simpler abbreviation q, as used in previous sections, is frequently employed.) The quadrupole-coupling information in asymmetric rotors is obtained with reference to the principal axes, a, b, and c (Sec. 2.6). The coupling factors can then be converted with Eq. 2.83 to new orientations,

---

† There are cross terms such as $q_{xy} = \dfrac{\partial^2 V}{\partial x \partial y}$ in the quadrupole term of the expansion of the electrical energy of the nucleus in the molecular field. Nevertheless, the coordinates can always be so oriented that only the three diagonal elements remain. In view of Laplace's equation, $\nabla^2 V = 0$ (which holds since the charge on the nucleus is not considered in the calculation of the molecular field gradient), there are only two independent quantities even in the general asymmetric case, and, when there is axial symmetry, say, about z, $q_{xx} = q_{yy}$, and only one independent quantity q_{zz} remains.

x, y, and z, which may be more convenient for interpretation in terms of bond orbitals. Frequently one of the principal axes lies along a bond axis or an axis of symmetry and can be chosen as x, y, or z without rotation. The z axis is usually chosen so that q_{zz} is the largest of the three components.

In solids or in gaseous symmetric-top molecules where more than one coupling factor can be measured, correspondingly more information can be obtained about the bonding. Goldstein and Bragg,[11] for example, have pointed out that the asymmetry parameter can be used to evaluate double-bond character. From it they have predicted that the CCl bonds in CH_2CHCl and in CH_2CFCl have about 5 per cent double-bond character. Townes and Dailey [12] suggested that the large value, $\epsilon = 0.15$, obtained by Dehmelt [13] in solid I_2 indicates some resonance switching of the bond in the crystalline phase. Dean [13a] has interpreted the asymmetry, $\epsilon = 0.08$, which he observed in the Cl^{35} coupling in solid p-dichlorobenzene to indicate partial double-bond character of the CCl bond.

If it is assumed, as before, that the principal terms in the coupling arise from p electrons, simple rules can be formulated for determining bond characteristics from ϵ. Let us choose the z axis along a bond to the coupling nucleus. The x and y axes then lie in a plane perpendicular to the bond. From comparison with Eq. 6.12 we can write

$$eQq_{xx} = \left(\frac{N_y + N_z}{2} - N_x\right) \times (\text{coupling for } U_p = 1), \qquad (7.7)$$

$$eQq_{yy} = \left(\frac{N_x + N_z}{2} - N_y\right) \times (\text{coupling for } U_p = 1), \qquad (7.8)$$

$$eQq_{zz} = \left(\frac{N_x + N_y}{2} - N_z\right) \times (\text{coupling for } U_p = 1), \qquad (7.9)$$

and

$$\epsilon = \frac{q_{xx} - q_{yy}}{q_{zz}} = \frac{3(N_y - N_x)}{N_x + N_y - 2N_z}. \qquad (7.10)$$

Note that Eq. 7.10 is independent of the quadrupole moment of the nucleus and of the coupling per p electron. To the approximation allowed by the assumptions involved, the measurable quantity ϵ depends only upon the way the p orbitals are filled.

Assume, for example, that the p_z orbital is directed along the z axis. (The orbital could be pure p_z or an sp_z hybrid.) If from structural information the direction of the other p orbitals is known relative to the principal axes of inertia, x can be chosen along one and y along the other of the p orbitals which lie in the xy plane. The quantity ϵ can then be obtained from the measurable quantities, $q_{aa} = \dfrac{\partial^2 V}{\partial a^2}$,

$q_{bb} = \dfrac{\partial^2 V}{\partial b^2}$, $q_{cc} = \dfrac{\partial^2 V}{\partial c^2}$, (by proper rotation of coordinates) and can be compared with the quantity on the right of Eq. 7.10, with assumed values of N_x, N_y, and N_z. Additional information can be obtained from eQq_{zz} in the manner previously described for symmetric coupling.

Figure 7.2 shows the pure quadrupole resonance frequencies observed by Dean and Pound in various solid chlorobenzene compounds. If rotational symmetry about the bond is assumed, the coupling eQq is twice the resonance frequency (see Sec. 5.3). Note the differences in the couplings produced by the various substitutions and by the variations in temperature. Dean and Pound point out that the discontinuities in certain curves probably result from phase changes. It seems likely that many correlations will be found between quadrupole-coupling data and other physical and chemical properties of the molecules.

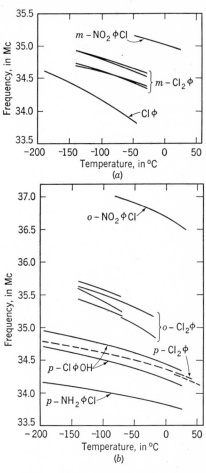

Fig. 7.2. Pure quadrupole resonance frequencies in various solid chlorobenzene (ϕ) compounds as a function of temperature. [From C. Dean and R. V. Pound, *J. Chem. Phys.* **20**, 195 (1952).]

7.2. DIPOLE MOMENTS

Precise electric dipole moments are obtained from microwave spectroscopy by measurements of the Stark effect, discussed in Sec. 3.1. Approximate dipole moments can also be obtained from measurements of the absorption coefficients, and particularly from dielectric absorption in liquids and solutions (Sec. 5.4). Stark-effect data yield dipole moments appropriate to the vibrational level measured. This situation may be contrasted with measurements of the temperature dependence of electric susceptibility, which yield mean values for the dipole moment average over all the molecular states. This specificity of microwave data to particular molecular states is the same for dipole moments as for interatomic distances. Variations of dipole moment with rotational state or with isotopic species appear to be within present experimental error. However, differences in the dipole moment for different vibrational states have been detected.[14, 15, 16]

7.2a. Measured Values. Dipole moments of a number of molecules, as determined from the Stark effect in microwave spectroscopy, are listed in Table $A.5$ in the Appendix. For asymmetric-top molecules, Stark-effect data give dipole moments along the principal axes of inertia. These components may or may not correspond to axes of electrical symmetry. For partially deuterated arsine, phosphine, and stibine, the data have been reduced to give the dipole moment of each molecule along the axis of electrical symmetry. For CH_3OH, with internal rotation, the data give the dipole moment in the direction of the C—O bond. The molecules ethylene oxide and ethylene sulfide are particularly good examples of the care that must be taken in interpreting dipole-moment components. These molecules are obviously structurally similar, yet for one molecule μ_a is listed, while for the other, μ_b. This is because the substitution of S for O changes the ordering of the moments of inertia ($I_a < I_b < I_c$ by definition) with respect to the axis of symmetry of the molecule. As a result, the spectra of the two structurally similar molecules are entirely different (see Sec. 2.2).

The accuracy of microwave dipole-moment determinations is limited by different factors for different molecules. An uncertainty in the knowledge of the location of adjacent rotational levels may limit the theoretical accuracy for asymmetric-top molecules. The spectra of molecules with weak dipole moments may be inadequately split by electric fields low enough to avoid electrical breakdown. In general, however, the present limit to the accuracy of microwave dipole determinations is in the attainment of a uniform, known electric field.

The simplest measuring system utilizes a constant d-c voltage applied to the Stark electrode. For most purposes this system is not sensitive enough, but it illustrates the major sources of error in microwave Stark-effect measurements. A known electrode voltage does not imply a known uniform electric field. There are two sources of non-uniformity of the electric field: accidental variations in the electrode spacing and edge effects inherent in the geometrical structures generally used for Stark cells. The present status of precision Stark-cell design appears to be that an uncertainty in the knowledge of the average electric field for a well-constructed cell contributes a systematic error of about 0.3 per cent. Fluctuations in the average field cause fluctuations in the displacements of the Stark lines. For molecules possessing linear Stark effects these fluctuations would average to zero except for the fact that more molecules are located in the weaker-field regions of the guide. For small fluctuations this effect may be neglected. If the Stark effect is quadratic, the net displacement of a spectrum line is small and calculable.[16] A more serious effect of the field fluctuations is that the Stark line is broadened (and its peak lowered) so that the center of the displaced line cannot be estimated as closely as that for the undisplaced line. In typical cases this contributes a random uncertainty of ± 0.3 per cent, giving an over-all accuracy of about ± 0.5 per cent attained, for instance, by Shulman and Townes.[16]

If the Stark field is applied, for modulation purposes, as a square wave, errors in voltage measurement and in the wave form of the square wave must be taken into account. Shulman and Townes [16] found that the combination of a large d-c bias with a small a-c square wave for modulation could be designed so that the error in voltage measurement was negligible. For molecules with a quadratic Stark effect, the effective voltage applied is $E_0 \left(1 + \dfrac{E^2}{E_0{}^2} \right)$ where E_0 is the d-c voltage and E is one-half of the peak-to-peak modulating voltage. For a linear Stark effect there would be no correction.

In evaluating new dipole moments, the spectrometer is frequently calibrated with simple molecules having accurately known moments. A convenient standard of comparison is $O^{16}C^{12}S^{32}$, the moment of which is 0.7085 ± 0.004 Debye units in the ground vibrational state,[16,17] and 0.700 ± 0.004 in the $v_2 = 1$ excited vibrational state.[14,16]

7.2b. Nature of Molecular Dipoles. When it is possible to understand their origin, dipole moments can throw much light on the nature of molecular bonds. Except in special cases molecular dipole moments are complex quantities contributed to by a number of different factors even in simple diatomic molecules. Some progress has been made, however, in the quantum mechanical interpretation of them, particularly by Mulliken,[18] and by Coulson.[19] The measurement of nuclear quadrupole coupling in molecules, which provides a new method of arriving at the asymmetry of electronic charge distribution around the atoms, is helping to clarify the subject. The accurate measurements of molecular structures are also of value since in polyatomic molecules the observed moment is the resultant of several components directed along different axes or bonds in the molecule. The principal problem in the interpretation of dipole moments is the calculation of the components along the different chemical bonds from known or assumed electronic structures of the molecule. When this is done, it is a rather straightforward geometrical problem—if the molecular dimensions are known—to calculate the resultant to be compared with the observed moment. The agreement thus obtained gives a measure of the correctness of the various assumptions made.

An understanding of the factors which determine the dipole moment of a chemical link can be obtained from the molecular-orbital treatment by Mulliken [18] for a single bond in a diatomic molecule AB. The treatment also applies to a localized σ bond in a polyatomic molecule. The two bonding electrons are assumed to be in a molecular orbital, ψ, which is represented by a linear combination of the atomic orbitals of A and B,

$$\psi = a\psi_A + b\psi_B, \tag{7.11}$$

where coefficients are normalized by

$$a^2 + 2abS_{AB} + b^2 = 1,$$

in which S_{AB} signifies the overlap integral, $\int \psi_A \psi^*_B \, d\tau$. The dipole moment contributed by the two electrons is,

$$P_{AB} = -2e \int \psi z \psi^* \, d\tau. \tag{7.12}$$

The coordinate z is chosen along the bond axes in the direction $A \rightarrow B$ with the origin at a point halfway between the nuclei.

Substituting Eq. 7.11 in Eq. 7.12 yields

$$P_{AB} = -2e \left[a^2 \int \psi_A z \psi^*_A \, d\tau + 2ab \int \psi_A z \psi^*_B \, d\tau + b^2 \int \psi_B z \psi^*_B \, d\tau \right].$$

$$\tag{7.13}$$

Equation 7.13 can be written in the form,

$$P_{AB} = -2e[a^2 \bar{z}_A + 2abS_{AB}\bar{z}_s + b^2 \bar{z}_B], \tag{7.14}$$

where

$$\bar{z}_A = \int \psi_A z \psi^*_A \, d\tau = \text{Average distance from the origin of the} \atop \text{electronic charge in atomic orbital } \psi_A, \tag{7.15}$$

$$\bar{z}_B = \int \psi_B z \psi^*_B \, d\tau = \text{Average distance from the origin of the} \quad (7.16)$$
$$\text{electronic charge in atomic orbital } \psi_B,$$

and

$$\bar{z}_s = \frac{\int \psi_A z \psi^*_B \, d\tau}{\int \psi_A \psi^*_B \, d\tau} = \text{Average distance from the origin of the} \quad (7.17)$$
$$\text{charge in the overlap region.}$$

If ψ_A and ψ_B are unhybridized atomic orbitals, the centers of gravity of their electronic clouds coincide with the respective nuclei, and

$$\bar{z}_B = \tfrac{1}{2} d_{AB} = -\bar{z}_A, \quad (7.18)$$

where d_{AB} is the distance from nucleus A to B. However, when the atomic orbitals are hybridized, the centers of gravity of the electronic cloud in ψ_A and ψ_B are not at the respective nuclei, and corrections must be added. In this case,

$$\bar{z}_A = -\tfrac{1}{2} d_{AB} + \xi_A, \quad (7.19)$$

and

$$\bar{z}_B = \tfrac{1}{2} d_{AB} + \xi_B, \quad (7.20)$$

and Eq. 7.14 can now be expressed as

$$P_{AB} = -e(b^2 - a^2)d_{AB} - 4eab S_{AB}\bar{z}_s - 2e(a^2 \xi_A + b^2 \xi_B). \quad (7.21)$$

Equation 7.21 includes only the contributions of the two bonding electrons. To this must be added a term P_c which results from the polarization of the core A^+B^+ by the primary moment. Also to the hybridization moment there must be added another term, defined below, to correct for any hybridized non-bonding orbitals in the core which contain electrons. Thus the total dipole moment of AB contains four components:

$$P_{AB} = -eQ_{AB}d_{AB} + eQ_s\bar{z}_s + P_h + P_c. \quad (7.22)$$

The significance of the first term on the right, the primary moment, $-eQ_{AB}d_{AB}$, is fairly obvious. The factor, $Q_{AB} = b^2 - a^2$, designated by Mulliken as the bond charge, represents the difference in the fractional parts of the bonding electron cloud in the atomic orbitals ψ_A and ψ_B. If it is assumed that the overlap cloud is divided equally between the atoms A and B, then Q_{AB} corresponds numerically to the ionic character of the bond and can be determined from the electronegativity difference by Eq. 7.6 or in some instances obtained from the nuclear quadrupole couplings.

The second term, designated by Mulliken as the overlap moment, $eQ_s\bar{z}_s$, arises from the fractional parts of the electron cloud which occupies the overlap region, i.e., the charge held jointly by A and B. In units of e this charge is

$$Q_s = -4abS_{AB} \approx \frac{-2S_{AB}}{1 + S_{AB}}. \tag{7.23}$$

A table of numerical values for S_{AB} for many different bond types has been given by Mulliken.[20] Because of symmetry ($\bar{z}_s = 0$) the overlap moment vanishes for atoms of equal size but can be a Debye unit or more when A and B differ greatly in size, since the magnitude of $\bar{z}_s$ is of the order $\left| r - \frac{1}{2}d_{AB} \right|$, where r is the radius of the smaller atom. Measured from the midpoint of AB, the center of gravity of the overlap cloud is always toward the smaller atom. Hence the negative pole of the overlap moment is always directed toward the smaller atom. The overlap moment thus adds to the primary moment when the smaller atom is the more electronegative and opposes it when the larger atom is the more electronegative.

Suppose that the atomic orbital ψ_A employed is an sp hybrid represented by

$$\psi_A = c\psi_s + \sqrt{1 - c^2}\,\psi_{p_z}. \tag{7.24}$$

Equation 7.15 can then be written as

$$\bar{z}_A = c^2 \int \psi_s z \psi^*_s \, d\tau + 2c\sqrt{1 - c^2} \int \psi_s z \psi^*_{p_z} \, d\tau + (1 - c^2) \int \psi_{p_z} z \psi^*_{p_z} \, d\tau$$

$$= -\frac{d_{AB}}{2} + 2c\sqrt{1 - c^2}\, S_{sp_z} \bar{z}_{sp_z}. \tag{7.25}$$

Thus the increment, ξ_A, which has been added above to take care of the hybridization moment has the value,

$$\xi_A = 2c\sqrt{1 - c^2}\, S_{sp_z} \bar{z}_{sp_z}, \tag{7.26}$$

where

$$S_{sp_z} = \int \psi_s \psi^*_{p_z} \, d\tau \quad \text{and} \quad \bar{z}_{sp_z} = \frac{\int \psi_s z \psi^*_{p_z} \, d\tau}{\int \psi_s \psi^*_{p_z} \, d\tau},$$

and where c^2 represents the s character of the hybrid atomic orbital. Each of these quantities can be calculated from the atomic wave functions, provided that the degree of hybridization is known. The evaluation of the hybridization moment of B is made in the same manner, but the corresponding hybridization moment of B will be in the opposite direction and will tend to cancel that of A.

The above treatment has included only the moment produced by the two bonding electrons. The remaining core, A^+B^+, can have a moment which is produced either by a complementary hybridization or by polarization of the atomic core by the primary dipole. (Of course, if AB is a pair of bonded atoms in a polyatomic molecule, A^+B^+ will have moments produced by the other bonds, which, however, might be dealt with in a manner similar to that already described.) If the atomic orbital complementary to that in Eq. 7.24,

$$\psi'_A = \sqrt{1 - c^2}\, \psi_s - c\psi_{p_z}, \tag{7.27}$$

has an unshared pair, it will contribute a moment, $4ec\sqrt{1 - c^2}\, S_{sp}\bar{z}_{sp_z}$, which is opposite in sign and $1/a^2$ times as large as that contributed by the hybridization of the bonding atomic orbital ψ_A.

The atomic moment depends not only upon the hybridization but also upon the way the hybridized orbitals are filled. The hybridization moment of a given orbital is frequently counterbalanced by complementary hybridization in other orbitals. For example, the atomic moment of C in methyl iodide is small because the four hybridized orbitals are almost equally filled, and, of course, this is exactly true in a symmetrical molecule such as CH_4. However, in such molecules as methyl chloride or methyl fluoride the resultant atomic moment of C is not negligible even if the bond orbitals are equivalent sp^3 tetrahedral ones, because the orbitals are not equally filled with electrons. The ionic character of the form $H_3C^+(Hal)^-$, as well as that of $H_3^+C^-Hal$, causes the electron density in the C orbitals directed toward the hydrogens to be greater than that of the one directed toward the halogen. As a result, there will be in CH_3F a rather large C atomic moment with its positive pole directed toward the F. This moment then opposes the primary moments, and it will decrease with the ionic character and hence with the primary moments. The C atomic moment thus tends to equalize the over-all moments of the methyl halides. If there is hybridization also in the halogen, the complementary hybridization in the non-bonding orbitals which are occupied by electron pairs would cause a halogen atomic moment in the same direction as the primary moment. This would decrease with the ionic character of the C—Hal bond and would likewise tend to equalize the over-all moments of the methyl halides.

The atomic hybridization moments are particularly important in N and O because of complementary hybridization in non-bonding orbitals. The very small moment of NF_3 (see Table $A.5$ in the Appendix) probably results from a partial cancellation of the primary moments of the

$N^+F_3^-$ structures by the hybridization moment of the unshared electron pair. The large dipole moment associated with the unshared electron pairs occupying hybridized orbitals appears to be largely responsible for the strong hydrogen-bond-forming properties of these atoms. The "mechanism" for the hydrogen-bond formation is probably the interaction of the XH dipole with the moment of an atomic orbital having an unshared electron pair.

Although the above treatment helps in an understanding of the nature of dipole moments, it is seldom possible to obtain more than qualitative agreement of calculated and observed values. None of the four factors mentioned can at present be calculated with accuracy. The rather large probable errors which must be attached to each factor make possible a considerable error in the final resultant. In addition, the possible contributions from bonding structures other than the ones considered can cause large errors.

7.3. MOLECULAR QUADRUPOLE MOMENTS

In previous sections the electrostatic quadrupole moments of atomic nuclei have been discussed. In dealing with forces between molecules—forces which, during collision, may interrupt microwave radiations—the electric fields arising from the nuclear quadrupole moments are completely insignificant. The nuclear charges, however, combined with the charges of the circulating electrons, give rise to molecular moments—dipole, quadrupole, etc.—and these molecular moments are important during collisions. If the molecules have no dipole moments, the molecular quadrupole moment Q_{Mol} is often the most important term. Of course, such non-polar molecules in general have no microwave spectra, but their collision cross sections for the interruption of radiation of another gas, such as NH_3 (which is a strong absorber of microwave energy) can be measured.[21-25] Let us assume that the only important forces between an NH_3 molecule and a molecule X arise from the interaction of the NH_3 dipole moment with the X quadrupole moment. The ratio of the X quadrupole moment to the NH_3 dipole moment can then be related to the ratio of the $NH_3 - X$ collision diameter to the $NH_3 - NH_3$ collision diameter.[22] Details of the calculations, which employ time-dependent perturbation theory with a dipole-quadrupole interaction Hamiltonian, will not be given, but some results are listed in Table A.3 in the Appendix. Because of necessary approximations in the analysis, the absolute quadrupole moments listed in Table A.3 may be in error by as much as 50 per cent, although the relative values are much more accurate. Improvements in the theoretical analysis, now in progress at many places, should ultimately yield more accurate moments from the microwave data. Nonetheless, the qualitative results already obtained have proved interesting in estimating sp hybridization of N_2 and O_2.[26] The relative magnitudes of the quadrupole moments of C_2H_2, C_2H_4, and C_2H_6 are also interesting, as they demonstrate an increase in quadrupole moment with bond order for this group of molecules. Such a sequence seems consistent with the accepted structures of the molecules, although exact calculations have not yet been made.

In Table $A.3$ in the Appendix, it will be noted that for O_2 and C_2H_6 only an upper limit for the quadrupole moment is given. For them the microwave collision diameters are not significantly larger than kinetic theory diameters, so that shorter-range forces may contribute to the observed cross section. Some values for linear polar molecules are also given. The assumption here is that the average period of rotation of these molecules is small as compared with the collision duration, so that the dipole interaction averages to zero. This assumption is only fair.

The definition of Q_{Mol} † is

$$Q_{\mathrm{Mol}} = \int q_i \rho_i^2 (3 \cos^2 \theta_i - 1) \, d\tau, \qquad (7.28)$$

where q_i is an element of charge (electron or nucleus).

ρ_i is the distance of the charge from the mass center of the molecule.

θ_i is the angle between the symmetry axis and ρ_i.

For symmetrical non-polar molecules the origin for calculating Q_{Mol} is immaterial. For unsymmetrical molecules the origin must be chosen as the mass center.

Equation 7.28 may be expanded to

$$Q_{\mathrm{Mol}} = Q^n{}_{\mathrm{Mol}} + Q^e{}_{\mathrm{Mol}}$$

$$Q^n{}_{\mathrm{Mol}} = +e \sum_n Z_n \rho^2{}_n (3 \cos^2 \theta_n - 1) = \text{Nuclear contribution}$$

$$\qquad (7.29)$$

$$Q^e{}_{\mathrm{Mol}} = -e \int \psi \sum_e \rho^2{}_e (3 \cos^2 \theta_e - 1) \psi^* \, d\tau = \text{Electronic contri-}$$

bution,

where e is the magnitude of the electronic charge. The term in Eq. 7.29 of interest in interpreting molecular properties is the electronic contribution to the quadrupole moment. If an orthogonal combina-

† This definition differs from the nuclear Q definition (Sec. 6.2) by a factor of e. It corresponds, however, to prevalent molecular usage.

tion of molecular orbitals ψ_{mo} is chosen as a basis for calculation, $Q^e{}_{\text{Mol}}$ is given by

$$Q^e{}_{\text{Mol}} = -e \sum_{mo} \int \psi_{mo}{}^2{}_e \rho{}^2{}_e (3 \cos^2 \theta_e - 1)\psi^*{}_{mo} \, d\tau, \qquad (7.30)$$

a sum of contributions from each molecular orbital. Evidently Eqs. 7.29 and 7.30 form a basis for evaluating choices of orbitals for molecular ground states from measured molecular quadrupole moments. These measurements are so recent that only a few quadrupole moments have been calculated to date. It is interesting that the sp hybridization estimated for N_2 and O_2 from the observed moments [26] (20 per cent and 5–10 per cent, respectively) agree with Mulliken's values [27] of 22 per cent and 9 per cent. These latter values were obtained by choosing orbitals so as to minimize the ground-state energy.

7.4. MOLECULAR ROTATIONAL MAGNETIC MOMENTS

The origin and nature of the rotational magnetic moment in molecules is of interest because of its relation to the electronic structures. Classically, one expects rotating charges to give rise to magnetic fields. In a neutral molecule, however, the effects of the rotating positive charges tend to counterbalance the magnetic fields set up by the revolving clouds of electrons which surround the nuclei. The early theory of Condon [28] combined with measurements of rotational magnetic moment μ_J for the hydrogen molecules made with molecular-beam techniques [29] showed that the concept of fixed charges rigidly attached to, and rotating with, the molecular frame could not account for the rotational magnetic moment. The theory that the electrons and nuclei rotate together in a rigid model not only gave an incorrect magnitude but the wrong sign for the μ_J of H_2. Using quantum mechanical perturbation methods, Wick [30] showed that the experimental moment of H_2 could be accounted for if the electrons did not rotate rigidly with the nuclei around the center of gravity of the molecule but lagged, or slipped behind the nuclei. In H_2 this electron slip is so great that the two protons may be regarded as revolving in a fixed electron cloud.

Wick's theory of the electron slip has been extended to polyatomic molecules by Jen [31] and by Eshbach and Strandberg [32] to account for rotational magnetic moments obtained from microwave spectroscopy. Only the outer valence-shell electrons of non-hydrogen atoms need be considered, since to a good approximation the inner closed shells can be regarded as rotating rigidly with their respective nuclei. So far, Jen's theory has been applied in a qualitative manner only, because of inadequate knowledge of the electronic wave functions in the polyatomic molecules studied. The theory is in qualitative agreement with the data of Table 3.1, where the larger moments are seen to be those for the relatively light molecules containing hydrogens. The rapid revolution of the nuclei in these molecules, combined with the large amount of slipping behind of the electrons of the hydrogens could account for their large rotational moments.

It is apparent that, when more data are obtained and a more detailed theoretical understanding of the rotational g_J factors is achieved, the Zeeman effect in microwave spectroscopy may become a valuable new method for investigation of the properties of molecular bonds.

REFERENCES

[1] L. Pauling, *Nature of the Chemical Bond* (Cornell University Press, Ithaca, 1939), Chapter IV.

[2] C. H. Townes and B. P. Dailey, *J. Chem. Phys.* *17*, 782 (1949).

[3] V. Jaccarino and J. G. King, *Phys. Rev.* *83*, 471 (1951).

[4] W. Gordy, *J. Chem. Phys.* *19*, 792 (1951).

[5] R. Livingston, *J. Chem. Phys.* *19*, 803 (1951).

[6] C. A. Lee, R. O. Carlson, B. P. Fabricand, and I. I. Rabi, *Phys. Rev.* *78*, 340 (1950).

[7] W. A. Nierenberg and N. F. Ramsey, *Phys. Rev.* *72*, 1075 (1947).

[8] L. Pauling, reference 1, p. 59.

[9] H. Schüler and M. Marketu, *Z. Physik* *102*, 703 (1936).

[10] C. C. Loomis and M. W. P. Strandberg, *Phys. Rev.* *81*, 798 (1951).

[11] J. H. Goldstein and J. K. Bragg, *Phys. Rev.* *78*, 347 (1950).

[12] C. H. Townes and B. P. Dailey, *J. Chem. Phys.* *20*, 35 (1952).

[13] H. G. Dehmelt, *Z. Physik* *130*, 356 (1951).

[13a] C. Dean, *Phys. Rev.* *86*, 607 (1952).

[14] M. W. P. Strandberg, T. Wentink, and R. L. Kyhl, *Phys. Rev.* *75*, 270 (1949).

[15] M. W. P. Strandberg, T. Wentink, and A. G. Hill, *Phys. Rev.* *75*, 827 (1949).

[16] R. G. Shulman and C. H. Townes, *Phys. Rev.* *77*, 500 (1950).

[17] J. N. Shoolery and A. H. Sharbaugh, *Phys. Rev.* *82*, 95 (1951).

[18] R. S. Mulliken, *J. chim. phys.* *46*, 497 (1949).

[19] C. A. Coulson, *Trans. Faraday Soc.* *38*, 433 (1942).

[20] R. S. Mulliken, *J. Am. Chem. Soc.* *72*, 4493 (1950).

[21] B. Bleaney and R. P. Penrose, *Proc. Phys. Soc.* *(London)* *60*, 540 (1948).

[22] W. V. Smith and R. Howard, *Phys. Rev.* *79*, 132 (1950).

[23] R. M. Hill and W. V. Smith, *Phys. Rev.* *82*, 451 (1951).

[24] J. Weber, *Phys. Rev.* *83*, 1058 (1951).

[25] C. A. Potter, A. V. Bushkovitch, and A. G. Rouse, *Phys. Rev.* *83*, 987 (1951).

[26] C. Greenhow and W. V. Smith, *J. Chem. Phys.* *19*, 1298 (1951).

[27] R. S. Mulliken, *J. Chem. Phys.* *19*, 900 (1951).

[28] E. U. Condon, *Phys. Rev.* *30*, 781 (1927).

[29] I. Estermann and O. Stern, *Z. Physik* *85*, 17 (1933); N. F. Ramsey, *Phys. Rev.* *58*, 226 (1940).

[30] G. C. Wick, *Z. Physik* *85*, 25 (1933).

[31] C. K. Jen, *Phys. Rev.* *81*, 197 (1951); *Physica*, *17*, 378 (1951).

[32] J. R. Eshbach and M. W. P. Strandberg, *Phys. Rev.* *85*, 24 (1952).

8. MOLECULAR STRUCTURES

8.1. DETERMINATION OF MOLECULAR DIMENSIONS FROM ROTATIONAL CONSTANTS

Information about the positions of atoms in a molecule is obtained from the spectroscopic constants A, B, and C discussed in Chapter 2. These spectroscopic constants are simply related to the principal moments of inertia of the molecule by

$$A = \frac{h}{8\pi^2 I_a} \qquad B = \frac{h}{8\pi^2 I_b} \qquad C = \frac{h}{8\pi^2 I_c}. \tag{8.1}$$

In more convenient form the moment of inertia

$$I_a \ (10^{-40} \ \text{gm cm}^2) = \frac{8.38911 \times 10^5}{A \ (\text{Mc})}, \tag{8.2}$$

or for I_a expressed in physical atomic mass units (amu) and in Angstrom units (A)

$$I_a \ (\text{amu A}^2) = \frac{5.05480 \times 10^5}{A \ (\text{Mc})}, \tag{8.3}$$

with similar expressions for I_b and I_c. The value of h is $6.623773 \pm 0.000180 \times 10^{-27}$ erg sec.

In diatomic molecules the one observable moment of inertia, along with the physical atomic masses, is sufficient to obtain the interatomic distance. For symmetric tops only one of the moments of inertia can be obtained from rotational spectra; however, it is possible to derive all three moments of inertia from the microwave spectra of asymmetric tops. The structure of a triatomic asymmetric top which forms an isosceles triangle (symmetry group C_{2v}, example H_2S) may be uniquely determined from the spectrum from any two of the moments of inertia. Because of the well-known theorem for a rigid planar body,

$$I_c = I_a + I_b, \tag{8.4}$$

a maximum of two independent equations linking the molecular dimensions with the rotational constants can be obtained for a triatomic molecule. Hence, if there are three independent structural parameters, as in a non-linear XYZ molecule, the structure cannot be completely determined from the rotational spectrum without the aid of isotopic substitution.

Since to a high order of approximation the internuclear distances depend upon the electrical properties of the atoms and not upon their masses, one can employ isotopic substitution to obtain additional equations involving the interatomic distances and measurable quantities. In general, however, only one substitution at a given atomic position gives additional independent equations. Further substitutions are useful in the estimation of the errors inherent in this method.

In most polyatomic molecules the factor limiting the accuracy of the determination of the interatomic distances is the difference in zero-point vibrations of the various isotopic species which are employed in the evaluation. For many molecules already investigated more isotopic combinations have been measured than are required for a complete evaluation of the structure. The additional data allow an estimate of the zero-point errors through the internal consistency of the results. The inconsistency is usually not greater than 0.2 per cent except for substitution in the light hydrogen atom.

When it is not possible to obtain sufficient isotopic combinations to determine the structure unambiguously from microwave data alone, it is frequently possible to obtain a complete determination of the structure from a combination of the microwave data with data from other sources. For example, the electron diffraction method frequently gives certain distances in a molecule quite accurately, though yielding little or no information about other distances in the same molecule. This partial information can be used to advantage to supplement the microwave results in the complete structural determination. This is illustrated, for example, by the work of Shoolery, Schomaker, et al.[1] on CF_3CCH. When no data are available to supplement the microwave results it is usually possible to estimate certain distances from the various rules given in this chapter. It is more desirable to determine the structure from microwave data alone because more accurate results are obtained, despite the limitations usually imposed by zero-point vibrations.

Sometimes even in relatively simple molecules the order of arrangement of atoms is not known. This order can be established readily from the microwave spectra. For example, Beard and Dailey [2] showed from microwave data that isothiocyanic acid (HNCS) rather than its isomer, thiocyanic acid (HSCN), exists in the gas phase. Previously it was thought that thiocyanic acid was the more probable form. Wilcox and Goldstein [3] have shown from the nature of its microwave spectrum that pyrrole has a planar structure.

8.1a. Diatomic Molecules. The interatomic distance r in a diatomic molecule is simply

$$r = \left[I \left(\frac{1}{m_1} + \frac{1}{m_2} \right) \right]^{1/2}, \tag{8.5}$$

where m_1 and m_2 are the masses of the two atoms. A distinction between the hypothetical equilibrium distance r_e and the average distance in the ground vibrational state r_0 must be made. From B_e the spectroscopic constant, r_e is obtained. This distance corresponds to a hypothetical state of the molecule where no vibration takes place, and the molecule rotates very slowly. However, in the ground vibrational state the molecule has a half-quantum of vibrational energy, and r_0, obtained from B_0 through Eqs. 8.2 or 8.3 and 8.5, is an average value of the interatomic distance over the vibration. As pointed out by Teller,[4] r_0 is not a simple average, but instead

$$\frac{1}{r_0} = \left\langle \frac{1}{r^2} \right\rangle_{\text{Av}}^{1/2}. \tag{8.6}$$

Even if the vibration of the diatomic molecule were harmonic, r_0 and r_e would be different with $r_0 < r_e$. This would require α (Chapter 2), which depends upon r_0 and r_e, to be negative. However, since α is positive for all diatomic molecules thus far studied in the microwave region, the anharmonic contribution to α is positive and more than compensates for the harmonic effects. Herzberg has discussed the dependence of α on the form of the potential function.[5] A comparison of r_0 and r_e for CO and FCl is given in Table 8.1. Values of r_0 for the

Table 8.1. Illustration of variations of interatomic distances in diatomic molecules (from data in Table $A.4$)

Isotopic Species	r_e (A)	r_0 (A)
$C^{12}O^{16}$	1.1282_7	1.13078_9
$C^{13}O^{16}$	1.1282_7	1.13072_5
$F^{19}Cl^{35}$	1.62822	1.63167
$F^{19}Cl^{37}$	1.62821	1.63163

diatomic molecules listed in Table $A.7$ in the Appendix range from about 0.1 per cent to 0.4 per cent higher than the corresponding values of r_e. Since the shape of the potential function depends primarily on the electron configuration and not on the masses of atoms involved, the equilibrium distances r_e would be expected to be the same for all isotopic combinations. However, r_0 should not be the same, since α is dependent upon the vibrational frequency, which in turn depends upon the reduced mass of the molecule. This effect is not very noticeable for diatomic molecules but becomes a significant limitation upon the accuracy of the structures of polyatomic molecules as evaluated with microwave spectroscopy.

8.1b. Linear Polyatomic Molecules. A linear polyatomic molecule of n atoms has in general $n - 1$ independent structural parameters. The moment of inertia I is a function of all $n - 1$ distances and is conveniently written in terms of the coordinate r_i of atom n_i from the center of gravity along the molecular axis,

$$I = \sum_{i=1}^{n} m_i r_i^2. \tag{8.7}$$

In addition,

$$\sum_{i=1}^{n} m_i r_i = 0. \tag{8.8}$$

In these equations m_i is the mass of the ith atom. The distance d_{ij} between successive atoms i and j in the molecule is

$$d_{ij} = |r_i - r_j|. \tag{8.9}$$

Determination of all the interatomic distances in the molecule requires $n - 2$ additional independent data which frequently may be obtained through the effect on I of isotopic substitutions in the molecule.

If for a rigid linear molecule $\cdots$ X—Y—Z $\cdots$ an isotopic form exists in which isotope X' replaces atom X, then the moment of inertia $I^{X'}$ of the isotopic modification is related to the moment of inertia I of the original molecule, X—Y—Z $\cdots$, by the relation

$$I^{X'} = I + \frac{m \, \Delta m_X}{m + \Delta m_X} r_X^2, \tag{8.10}$$

where r_X is the distance of nucleus X from the center of gravity in the original molecule, m is the total mass of the original molecule, and $m + \Delta m_X$ is the mass of the modification $\cdots$ X'—Y—Z $\cdots$. Equation 8.10 follows simply from Steiner's theorem.[6] Rearranging Eq. 8.10 into a more convenient form gives

$$|r_X| = \left[\frac{(I^{X'} - I^X)(m + \Delta m_X)}{m \, \Delta m_X} \right]^{\frac{1}{2}}. \tag{8.11}$$

In like manner r_Y or r_Z can be found if the moments of inertia for isotopic forms of the molecule containing a different isotope of atom Y or atom Z are known. By application of Eq. 8.9, the distances between X and Y or Y and Z can then be determined. Occasionally it is possible to obtain the moment of inertia of an isotopic form of the molecule containing two isotopic substitutions, say X' and Z'. The moment of inertia is then

$$I^{X', Z'} = I + \Delta m_X r_X^2 + \Delta m_Z r_Z^2 - \frac{(\Delta m_X r_X + \Delta m_Z r_Z)^2}{m + \Delta m_X + \Delta m_Z}. \quad (8.12)$$

This expression is not so convenient to use since it is a quadratic in two unknowns. However, if either r_X or r_Z is known, the other distance is easily found. If the molecular structure is known approximately, spectral absorption lines of the various isotopic species may be identified by comparison of their positions (computed with Eq. 8.10) relative to the absorption lines of the most abundant isotopic combination. A comparison of the relative intensities of the lines with the relative concentrations of the isotopic forms present in the sample is also very helpful in the identification.

From an examination of Eq. 8.11 it is apparent that r_X is quite sensitive to the mass difference between the isotopes of element X and also to the difference in moments of inertia of the two isotopic species under consideration. The larger Δm_X is, the greater will be the spacing between the spectral lines of the two isotopic modifications and the more accurately can the change in I be determined. Thus for structural determinations it is pertinent to know the frequency differences between lines resulting from isotopic modifications more accurately than the absolute line frequencies. It can also be readily seen from Eq. 8.11 that, to the rigid-body approximation, the substitution of isotopes more than once in the same position in the molecule does not furnish additional independent data concerning the structure of the molecule. However, when more than two isotopes of the same element are available, and the moments of inertia of the species are known, the extent of the validity of the rigid-body approximation may be estimated from the consistency of r.

A serious limitation on structural determinations by isotopic substitution is the effect of zero-point vibrations. Since the average value of B_0 over the zero-point vibrations is obtained from the spectrum of a molecule, $\langle 1/I \rangle_{Av}$ is derived from it, and consequently the interatomic distances obtained are a rather complicated average. Since all the α's (see Eq. 2.26) have not yet been measured for any polyatomic molecule from the microwave spectra, no equilibrium interatomic distances have been obtained. However, the effects of zero-point vibrations on the structure of linear triatomic molecules have been estimated by several researchers.[7, 8] Approximate equilibrium values can be obtained from the formula,[8]

$$(d_{ij})_e = (d_{ij})_0 \left(1 - \sum_n \alpha_n d_n / 2B_0 \right)^{\frac{1}{2}}, \qquad (8.13)$$

where the sum on the right side is taken over all modes of vibration and where $(d_{ij})_e$ is the equilibrium distance and $(d_{ij})_0$ is the distance for the lowest vibrational state between two atoms in the molecule. It is assumed that $\sum_n \alpha_n d_n / 2B_0$ is the same for the two isotopic species from which the structure was calculated. The value of $\sum_n \alpha_n d_n / 2B_0$ for OCS has been estimated as 0.00428. Thus for OCS the equilibrium interatomic distances are lower than the distances in the ground state by about 0.2 per cent. Interatomic distances from various combinations of isotopic species of OCS and HCN are shown in Table 8.2. Inaccurate mass differences may account for the poor agreement in some instances.

In the previous discussion it was assumed that $\sum_n \alpha_n d_n / 2B_0$ is a constant for all isotopic species. This does not hold where the change in mass of an isotope is not small in comparison with the mass of the isotope itself,

Table 8.2. **Comparison of interatomic distances for the ground state from various combinations of isotopic species**

OCS [7a]

Combination	d_{CO} (A)	d_{CS} (A)
$O^{16}C^{12}S^{32}-O^{16}C^{12}S^{34}$	1.1647	1.5576
$O^{16}C^{12}S^{32}-O^{16}C^{13}S^{32}$	1.1629	1.5591
$O^{16}C^{12}S^{34}-O^{16}C^{13}S^{34}$	1.1625	1.5594
$O^{16}C^{12}S^{32}-O^{18}C^{12}S^{32}$	1.1552	1.5653

HCN [7b]

	d_{CH} (A)	d_{CN} (A)
$HC^{12}N^{14}-HC^{13}N^{14}$	1.0674	1.1557
$DC^{12}N^{14}-DC^{13}N^{14}$	1.0658	1.1555
$HC^{12}N^{14}-DC^{12}N^{14}$	1.0623	1.1567
$HC^{13}N^{14}-DC^{13}N^{14}$	1.0624	1.1563
$HC^{12}N^{14}-DC^{13}N^{14}$	1.0619	1.1568
$HC^{13}N^{14}-DC^{12}N^{14}$	1.0625	1.1566

since the α's and B_0 vary with different powers of the mass ratio. Consequently, the r_0's for the various isotopic species are not the same. In N_2O for example, I for $N^{15}N^{14}O^{16}$ is slightly larger than that for the heavier molecule $N^{15}N^{15}O^{16}$.[9] Substitution of these moments of inertia in Eq. 8.11 leads to a very small imaginary value of r for the distance from the center of gravity of the nitrogen adjacent to the oxygen. This behavior is undoubtedly the result of differences in zero-point vibration in the two isotopic species.

8.1c. Symmetric-Top Molecules. Among the symmetric tops of interest, the more common ones contain one set of three or more identical atoms symmetrically placed about the figure axis. For a rigid molecule of this type, say $X_pYZ \cdots$ (belonging to point group C_{pv} where $p > 2$), the moment of inertia I_b is

$$I_b = \frac{I_a}{2} + pm_X r_X^2 + \sum_i m_i r_i^2. \tag{8.14}$$

Also

$$pm_X r_X + \sum_i m_i r_i = 0. \tag{8.15}$$

Here $I_a = pm_X s_X^2$, r_i is the coordinate of the ith atom from the center of gravity measured along the symmetry axis, r_X is the coordinate along the symmetry axis from the center of gravity to the X_p plane, s_X is the distance of the X atoms from the figure axis, and the summations in Eqs. 8.14 and 8.15 are taken over only the atoms situated on the figure axis. For n atoms on the figure axis there are $n + 1$ distances and one angle to be evaluated. Since Eqs. 8.9–8.12 are applicable to the linear portion of the molecule, the distances between atoms on the figure axis may be evaluated by the methods described for linear molecules. The XY distance is given by

$$d_{XY} = [s_X^2 + (r_X - r_Y)^2]^{1/2}. \tag{8.16}$$

Either α, the angle that the X—Y bond makes with the figure axis, or β, the angle XYX is usually reported in the literature. Angle α is simply

$$\alpha = \text{arc tan} \frac{s_X}{\mid r_X - r_Y \mid}, \tag{8.17}$$

and in terms of α, β is given by

$$\beta = 2 \text{ arc sin} \left(\sin \frac{\pi}{p} \sin \alpha \right). \tag{8.18}$$

Symmetrical substitution of isotopes for the atoms which are not on the figure axis with a total increase in mass $p \, \Delta m_X$ leads to the following result:

$$I_b^{pX'} = I_b + \frac{1}{2} (I_a^{pX'} - I_a) + \frac{mp \, \Delta m_X}{m + p \, \Delta m_X} r_X^2 \tag{8.19}$$

$$= I_b + \frac{p}{2} \Delta m_X s_X^2 + \frac{mp \, \Delta m_X}{m + p \, \Delta m_X} r_X^2,$$

where $I_a^{pX'}$ and $I_b^{pX'}$ are the moments of inertia about principal axes a and b for the isotopic modification. $I_b^{pX'}$ is usually much less sensitive to r_X than to s_X, so that s_X can be determined from Eq. 8.19 with much greater accuracy than is possible for r_X. An additional substitution of isotopes in the identical positions allows s_X and r_X to be found directly in principle. However, in practice this procedure is not very satisfactory because of the insensitivity of $(I_b^{pX'} - I_b)$ to changes in r_X. Substitution of isotopes for some, but not all, of the identical nuclei destroys the molecular symmetry, and the molecule must be treated as an asymmetric top.

When there is more than one set of identical nuclei which are not on the figure axis (point group C_p where $p \geq 3$), the extension of the foregoing treatment is evident. In Eq. 8.14 the term $pm_X r_X^2$ will be replaced by similar terms, one for each set of identical nuclei, and I_a will be the sum of terms of the form $pm_X s_X^2$. Equation 8.19 is valid for a symmetrical substitution of isotopes in one set of identical nuclei.

It is sometimes possible to obtain I_a for symmetric tops from infrared data. When rotation-vibration bands have been resolved for all fundamentals of symmetry E, the sum rule of Johnson and Dennison [10] (see also Herzberg [11]),

$$\Sigma \, \Delta\nu_i = \frac{h}{8\pi^2 c}\left[2f\left(\frac{1}{I_a} - \frac{1}{I_b}\right) - \frac{2}{I_a} \Sigma \zeta_i \right], \qquad (8.20)$$

is a useful relationship. In this equation $\Delta\nu_i$ is the spacing between the P and R branches of the rotational fine-structure in a degenerate vibration band, and $\zeta_i h/2\pi$ is the rotational angular momentum resulting from the excited degenerate vibration, the sums being taken over all the degenerate modes of vibration. For XY_3 molecules, $f = 2$ and $\zeta_3 + \zeta_4 = (I_a/2I_b) - 1$, so that Eq. 8.20 becomes

$$\Delta\nu_3 + \Delta\nu_4 = \frac{h}{8\pi^2 c}\left(\frac{6}{I_a} - \frac{5}{I_b}\right); \qquad (8.21)$$

and, for XYZ_3 molecules, $f = 3$ and $\zeta_4 + \zeta_5 + \zeta_6 = I_a/2I_b$ reduce Eq. 8.20 to

$$\Delta\nu_4 + \Delta\nu_5 + \Delta\nu_6 = \frac{h}{8\pi^2 c}\left(\frac{6}{I_a} - \frac{7}{I_b}\right). \qquad (8.22)$$

When I_b is known from microwave data, I_a can be found from these relations. However, it must be pointed out that moments of inertia in Eqs. 8.20–8.22 are for excited vibrational states, so that the values of I_a thus obtained are to be regarded only as approximations. This method is useful when insufficient isotopic substitutions are available for complete determination of structure.

At present, little is known about the effects of zero-point vibrations in symmetric tops since for them there are usually more modes of vibration of a more complex nature than there are for simpler linear molecules. Isotopic modifications of the methyl halides, in particular methyl chloride, have been studied extensively. (See Bibliography.) Simmons [12] showed that moments of inertia calculated for completely deuterated methyl halides are 0.3 to 0.5 per cent higher than those observed if the structures of the corresponding molecules containing ordinary hydrogen are used in the calculations. Matlack, Glockler, Bianco, and Roberts [13] studied four partially deuterated modifications of methyl chloride and found that these data, together with the symmetric-top modifications, could not be fitted by one set of structural parameters. This behavior they attributed to the change in zero-point energy upon substitution of deuterium for hydrogen, and evaluation of the structure of CH_3Cl in this manner gave an error of 0.6 per cent in the C—H distance and 0.5 per cent in the H—C—H angle. Substitution of deuterium for hydrogen in a methyl group is an extreme case, since the percentage of change in isotopic mass is greater for hydrogen than for any other element, and one would expect smaller effects in groups containing heavier atoms.

8.1d. Asymmetric-Top Molecules. Because of the varied structural symmetries of asymmetric-top molecules, simple generalized expressions cannot be given for the moments of inertia or for changes in the moment of inertia upon substitution of isotopes. For the general approach, the reader is referred to Coles' treatment.[14] However, a few simple rules can be given for certain types of symmetrical molecules.

If an atom lies on a principal axis, the substitution of an isotope for that atom will not change the moment of inertia about that axis, but will change the moments of inertia about the other two principal axes equally. This change, ΔI, is given by

$$\Delta I = \frac{m \, \Delta m}{m + \Delta m} \, r^2, \tag{8.23}$$

where r is the distance of the atom from the center of gravity in the original molecule, m is the mass of the original molecule, and Δm is the increase in mass resulting from the isotopic substitution. An example of this would be substitution of C^{13} for one of the C^{12}'s in CH_2CF_2, where the C—C axis is the a axis. This isotope substitution does not change the moment of inertia I_a, but does change both I_b and I_c by an amount given by Eq. 8.23.

Planar molecules have only two independent moments of inertia (Eq. 8.4). When there is a plane of symmetry perpendicular to the molecular plane, the intersection of these two planes is both an axis of symmetry and a principal axis (either axis a or axis b). For convenience we shall use the two smallest moments of inertia and designate them as I_s for the moment about the symmetry axis and I_p for the moment about the axis perpendicular to the symmetry axis and lying in the plane of the molecule. (I_s may be either I_a or I_b, depending upon the molecular dimensions.) The structure of a triatomic asymmetric top X_2Y having an axis of symmetry is completely determined by I_s and I_p. If d is the X—Y distance and θ the XYX angle, then

$$d = \left[\frac{1}{2m_X}\left(\frac{m}{m_Y}I_p + I_s\right)\right]^{1/2} \tag{8.24}$$

and

$$\theta = 2 \arctan\left(\frac{m_Y I_s}{m I_p}\right)^{1/2}. \tag{8.25}$$

For an $X_2YZ \cdots$ planar molecule with Y, Z $\cdots$ on the axis of symmetry, substitutions of isotopes in the Y, Z $\cdots$ positions give rise to distances r_Y, r_Z, $\cdots$ from the center of gravity in the original molecule, according to the formula

$$|r_Y| = \left[\frac{(I_p^{Y'} - I_p)(m + \Delta m_Y)}{m \, \Delta m_Y}\right]^{1/2}, \tag{8.26}$$

with similar formulas for r_Z, $\cdots$. From I_p and these distances, r_X, the distance from the center of gravity to the perpendicular projection of the X atoms on the symmetry axis can be determined. The perpendicular distance, s_X, of the X atoms from the symmetry axis is given by

$$s_X = \left(\frac{I_s}{2m_X}\right)^{1/2}, \tag{8.27}$$

and the X—Y bond distance is

$$d_{XY} = [s_X^2 + (r_X - r_Y)^2]^{1/2}, \tag{8.28}$$

and

$$\angle XYX = 2 \arctan\frac{s_X}{|r_X - r_Y|}. \tag{8.29}$$

Non-planar X_2YZ_2 molecules having two perpendicular symmetry planes, which are the X_2Y plane and the YZ_2 plane, have an axis of symmetry containing Y. (An example of this type of molecule is SiH_2F_2.) Let us designate the principal moments of inertia as follows: I_x is the moment about the principal axis in XYX plane and perpendicular to the symmetry axis, and I_z is the moment about the principal axis in the ZYZ plane and perpendicular to the symmetry axis. From Eq. 8.23, $(I_x^{Y'} - I_x)$ is equal to $(I_z^{Y'} - I_z)$ and

$$|r_Y| = \left[\frac{(I_x^{Y'} - I_x)(m + \Delta m_Y)}{m\, \Delta m_Y}\right]^{1/2}, \qquad (8.30)$$

where $I_x^{Y'}$ and $I_z^{Y'}$ are the new moments of inertia when isotope Y' is substituted for Y. Equations 8.27, 8.28, and 8.29 are applicable to this type of molecule for finding the interatomic distances and angles. Extension of this treatment to molecules of the same symmetry which have more than one atom on the symmetry axis is obvious.

Evidence of zero-point vibrations can be obtained from the spectrum of one isotopic species of a planar molecule if all three moments of inertia can be obtained. Because the molecule is not rigid in the ground vibrational state, I_c does not exactly equal the sum $I_a + I_b$. Darling and Dennison [15] have termed $\Delta = I_c - I_a - I_b$ the quantum defect which can be calculated if all the normal frequencies are known. The quantum defect is an extremely small constant in comparison with the moments of inertia. Values of Δ together with the moments of inertia of SO_2 and CH_2O are shown in Table 8.3. The accuracy with which the structural

Table 8.3. Moments of inertia and quantum defects for SO_2 and CH_2O

Molecule	I_a^0	I_b^0	I_c^0	Δ	Ref.
	($\times 10^{-40}$ gm cm^2)				
SO_2	13.803	81.307	95.336	0.226	16, 17
CH_2O	2.974	21.600	24.669	0.095	18

parameters for the ground vibrational state of planar molecules can be found is thus limited by the order of magnitude of Δ and is of the same order of magnitude as for other types of polyatomic molecules.

Table A.9 in the Appendix lists the molecular dimensions ascertained with microwave spectroscopy.

8.2. FACTORS AFFECTING BOND LENGTHS AND BOND ANGLES

Bond lengths and bond angles, when properly interpreted, can give important information about the nature of chemical bonds. Pauling's approach [19] is to set up a table of idealized covalent radii for the most common and well-behaved chemical elements, assigning different values for single, double, and triple bonds. If the bond lengths in a molecule are found to differ significantly from the sum of the idealized radii of the bonded atoms, he treats the molecule as a resonant hybrid of idealized

Table 8.4. Covalent radii † and electronegativities ‡

Radius in Angstroms

Element	Single Bond	Double Bond	Triple Bond	Electro-negativity
H	0.32^t			2.1
Li	1.34^s			1.0
Be	0.98^t	0.86^g		1.5
B	0.88	0.76	0.68	2.0
C	0.79^g	$0.67_5{}^g$	0.60	2.5
N	0.74^s	0.62	0.55	3.0
O	0.73^g	0.60^g	0.53	3.5
F	0.71^t	0.60^p		3.0
Na	1.54^s			0.9
Si	1.17	1.07	1.00	1.8
P	1.10	1.00	0.92	2.1
S	1.04	0.95	0.88	2.5
Cl	0.99	0.90		3.0
K	1.96			0.8
Zn	1.16^t			1.5^h
Ge	1.22	1.12		1.7
As	1.21	1.11		2.0
Se	1.17	1.08		2.4
Br	1.14	1.05		2.8
Rb	2.11^s			0.8
Cd^t	1.34^t			1.5^h
Sn	1.40	1.30		1.7
Sb	1.41	1.31		1.8
Te	1.37	1.28		2.1
I	1.33			2.5
Cs	2.25^s			0.7
Hg	1.34^t			1.8^h

† The values which have no identifying symbol are from Pauling's *Nature of the Chemical Bond* (Cornell University Press, Ithaca, N. Y., 1939), p. 154. The values marked *s* are revised values by Schomaker and Stevenson [*J. Am. Chem. Soc. 63*, 37 (1941)]. The values marked *g* are revised values by Gordy [*J. Chem. Phys. 15*, 81 (1947)], and those marked *t* are assignments of the present work. The Schomaker-Stevenson correction for ionic character, $-\beta| x_A - x_B |$, must be used with the revised values.

‡ Values with no identifying symbol are from Pauling's *Nature of the Chemical Bond* (Cornell University Press, Ithaca, N. Y., 1939), p. 64. Values marked *h* are from Haissinsky, *J. phys. et radium 7*, 7 (1946).

structures having pure electron-pair bonds. Pauling also showed that the effective covalent radius as well as the angles between bonds depends upon the hybridization of the atomic orbitals employed in the bonding. It was pointed out by Schomaker and Stevenson [20] that ionic character frequently shortens significantly the lengths of bonds. Most microwave spectroscopists use the qualitative methods outlined by Pauling for preliminary evaluation of structures in order to predict the correct region in which to search for rotational lines. Little progress has yet been made in the prediction of bond lengths from molecular-orbital theory, although a start in this direction has been made [21] by Mulliken, Coulson, Lennard-Jones, and others. It is to be hoped that the accurate dimensions now available from microwave spectroscopy will lead to further progress in the understanding of interatomic distances in terms of electronic structures.

For convenience in the prediction of unknown structures as well as in interpretation of results of microwave spectroscopy, the covalent radii of Pauling,[19] with later revisions, and the Pauling electronegativity scale [19] are given in Table 8.4.

8.2a. Covalent Resonance or Bond Conjugation. If a bond has properties intermediate between those of an ideal single and an ideal double bond between the same atoms, Pauling described it as a single bond with double-bond character. Likewise, a bond intermediate in length, energy, etc., between a double and triple bond is treated as a double bond with triple-bond character. The classic illustration of bond lengths which are influenced by covalent resonance is the CC bonding in benzene. The principal resonating structures are the two equivalent Kekulé forms, which give each of the bonds 50 per cent double-bond character. Actually, the bond properties such as bond lengths, force constants, and bond energies are nearer to those of a CC double bond than to those of a CC single bond because of the extra strengthening of the bonds by the resonance energy. Nevertheless, it is convenient, though frequently misleading, to think of the bond as the arithmetic mean of a pure single bond and a pure double bond. Pauling [19] gives the empirical equation,

$$x = (R_1 - R)/(R_1 - 3R_2 + 2R), \qquad (8.31)$$

for estimating the amount of double-bond character, x, from the measured bond lengths, R, and the idealized single- and double-bond lengths R_1 and R_2, respectively. This equation was derived from the CC bonds in hydrocarbons but is frequently used for bonds between other atoms. The similar equation $x = (R_2 - R)/(R_2 - 2R_3 + R)$ is used to estimate triple-bond character of a double bond. Because of the effects of other factors on bond length, particularly those of ionic character and bond hybridization, the formula must be applied with caution. The term, bond character, as used by Pauling should not be confused with the fractional "bond order" commonly used in molecular-orbital theory. Although the two terms describe the same phenomenon, they differ numerically (see below).

When double-bond character can result from a combination of π_y and π_z character, Pauling [19] predicts a greater shortening of the bond for a given amount of total double-bond character than when π_y or π_z alone is possible. Equation 8.31 applies to the latter case. This extra shortening resulting from π_y and π_z resonance is most pronounced in dative bonds of O or F to second-row elements. Pitzer [21b] has questioned the existence of resonance of the latter type and has suggested that the observed bond shortening results from differences in repulsions of the electron shells in the various combinations. Though it seems probable that differences in electron repulsions are not inconsequential, strong evidence exists (see Sec. 8.3) for some double-bond resonance when atoms having unshared pairs are joined to first- or second-row elements having empty orbitals in their valence shells.

In the molecular-orbital treatment of multiple bonds, one component, designated as the σ bond, is regarded as localized between the two atoms in question, whereas the remaining components, the π bonds, are made up of migrating or mobile electrons which belong to the molecule as a whole. Usually the wave function of a π electron is expressed as a linear combination of atomic wave functions,

$$\psi = a_1\psi_1 + a_2\psi_2 \cdots a_k\psi_k, \tag{8.32}$$

where the coefficients when properly normalized give a measure of the relative time the particular electron occupying the orbital remains in the vicinity of the different atoms $1, 2, \cdots k$. As pointed out by Coulson,[22] the product $a_r a_s$ gives a measure of the contribution of the electron in question to the order of the bond r—s, and the total bond order N of this bond is then

$$N = 1 + \sum_n a_r^{(n)} a_s^{(n)}, \tag{8.33}$$

where the summation is taken over all the π electrons in the molecule. The unit value is added to take care of the contribution of the localized σ bond. The fractional bond orders given by Eq. 8.33 are more nearly in line with the physical properties than the fractional bond character defined by Pauling. For example, the bond order of the CC bonds in benzene is 1.77 according to this concept, which correctly indicates that the bond properties should be nearer to those of a double CC bond than to those of a single CC bond. In the molecular-orbital treatment, the extra stability of the bond, attributed to resonance in the Pauling method, is accounted for in a direct way by the selection of the molecular orbitals of lowest energy for the π electrons.

Molecular-orbital theory has been applied by Mulliken, Rieke, and Brown [23] to a number of simple hydrocarbons. They obtain the remarkable result that the CC bonds in ordinary unsaturated hydrocarbons have a greater stability than would be expected for ideal single CC bonds and that their bond orders are about 10 per cent greater than unity. The extra stability arises from the fact that the electrons forming the CH bonds are not completely localized but migrate to a certain extent through the molecule. On the basis of this result, it has been suggested [24] that the idealized single-bond covalent radius of C be changed from 0.77 to 0.79 A. With the bond orders obtained by Mulliken, Rieke, and Brown, and from a consideration of other bonds, it has been shown empirically [25] that the bond-order bond-length relation is of the form:

$$N = aR^{-2} + b$$

$$= \frac{R^{-2} - R_2^{-2}}{R_2^{-2} - R_1^{-2}} + 2, \tag{8.34}$$

where N is the bond order, R is the observed bond length, and R_1 and R_2 are the idealized single and double bond lengths, respectively. This relation allows the estimation of the order of a bond from its length.

Lennard-Jones and Coulson [26] have shown that

$$E = (1 - p)E_1 + pE_2, \tag{8.35}$$

where p is the mobile bond order $(N - 1)$, E is the actual bond energy, and E_1 and E_2 are the energies of the corresponding pure single and pure double bonds, respectively. Combining this expression with Eq. 8.34 yields [25]

$$E = lR^{-2} + m$$

$$= \frac{R^{-2} - R_2^{-2}}{R_2^{-2} - R_1^{-2}} (E_2 - E_1) + E_2. \tag{8.36}$$

These relations allow one to estimate the energies of fractional bonds directly from the measured interatomic distances and energies of the bonds of integral order. In polyatomic molecules Eq. 8.36 applies to the mean energy assignable to a given bond from the total energy required to dissociate the entire molecule into atoms. For a discussion of these and other relations connecting bond length with bond order, bond energy, and other properties, see reference 21a.

8.2b. Ionic Character. Schomaker and Stevenson [20] showed that single bonds between atoms of different electronegativity tend to be shorter than the sum of their covalent radii even when double-bond resonance is not present. This effect is most noticeable with bonds to F or O, which has a high electronegativity as compared with other atoms. They gave the approximate empirical rule,

$$R = r_A + r_B - \beta| x_A - x_B |, \tag{8.37}$$

for the calculation of the interatomic distance R from the covalent radii r_A and r_B of the bonded atoms A and B, where x_A and x_B are the electronegativities of the atoms and the empirical constant $\beta = 0.09$. For most molecules considered in the present work we have found $\beta = 0.06$ for single bonds is more satisfactory. It has been shown [24] that the rule also applies approximately to double bonds with $\beta = 0.06$ and to triple bonds with $\beta = 0.03$. In using this rule one must employ the revised radii [20] for H, F, and O rather than Pauling's values, which were determined from bonds having appreciable ionic character. For a further revision of the H radius see Art. 8.3a.

Although in many instances the Schomaker-Stevenson rule gives good agreement with experiment, in other instances the additivity rule without the correction gives better agreement. This is illustrated with a few examples in Table 8.5. It is not surprising that this oversimplified rule

Table 8.5. Comparison of observed bond lengths with those estimated from covalent radii and electronegativities

Molecule	Link AB	Added Radii, $r_A + r_B$, in Angstroms	$r_A + r_B$, $-0.06\| x_A - x_B \|$, in Angstroms	Observed Bond Length, in Angstroms
FCl		1.70	1.64	1.628
FBr		1.85	1.78	1.759
ICl		2.32	2.29	2.323
NaCl		2.53	2.39	2.361
KCl		2.95	2.82	2.667
KI		3.29	3.19	3.23
NF$_3$	NF	1.45	1.39	1.371
PCl$_3$	PCl	2.09	2.04	2.043
AsCl$_3$	AsCl	2.20	2.14	2.161
SbCl$_3$	SbCl	2.40	2.33	2.325
CH$_3$F	CF	1.50	1.41	1.385
CH$_3$Cl	CCl	1.78	1.75	1.782
CH$_3$Br	CBr	1.93	1.91	1.938
CH$_3$I	CI	2.12	2.12	2.140
SiH$_3$Cl	SiCl	2.16	2.09	2.048
SiH$_3$Br	GeCl	2.31	2.25	2.209
GeH$_3$Br	GeBr	2.36	2.29	2.297
SnH$_3$CH$_3$	SnC	2.19	2.11	2.143

should have many exceptions. There are several factors which might cause the length of the bond A—B to differ from the added radii of A and B defined as $\frac{1}{2}$ the length of the bonds A—A and B—B. At least two of them depend on the electronegativity difference $| x_A - x_B |$. They are the shortening of the bond caused by resonance of ionic and covalent forms and the variation caused by the difference in the sum of the effective ionic radii from the sum of the covalent radii. In addition, bond-orbital hybridization affects electronegativity as well as covalent radius, and for this reason bond lengths may vary with effective electronegativity difference.

For cases where $| x_A - x_B |$ is about 2 or greater, as in the alkali halides, the bonds are essentially ionic. The resonance energy is then negligible, and the deviation from the additivity rule is caused almost entirely by the difference in the sum of the effective ionic radii from the sum of the covalent radii. The application of the Schomaker-Stevenson rule to this type of molecule appears to have no very sound basis, and it is not surprising that exceptions occur.

8.2c. Bond-Orbital Hybridization. Bond lengths are affected by changes in the hybridization of the orbitals forming the bonds. The most complete experimental evidence for this variation is with bonds to carbon. The earlier evidence from optical spectra and electron diffraction has been amplified by a large number of structural determinations from microwave spectroscopy. This evidence indicates that the length of a bond to carbon decreases with increasing s character of the bonding orbital employed by the carbon. The decrease is 0.02 A in passing from tetrahedral orbitals (25 per cent s character) to sp^2 orbitals (33 per cent s character), and 0.04 A in passing from tetrahedral to sp orbitals (50 per cent s character). It has been observed in a number of CC as well as CH bonds. Figure 8.1 shows a plot of some CH lengths against s character of the bonding orbital of C.

The smallness of this variation is impressive. It explains why most large deviations from the additivity rule can be accounted for either in terms of fractional bond orders or of ionic character. Indeed, a large part of the decrease in the CH bond length in passing from saturated to acetylenic C may be attributed to increased ionic resonance energy caused by the increased electronegativity of C. There is evidence [27] that this increase in electronegativity is about 0.3. This alone should cause a decrease in the CH bond length by about 0.02 A. When the atom joined to C has a higher electronegativity than has C, the electronegativity difference will be decreased, and the shortening by ionic character will be reduced rather than increased, provided that this change is not offset by changes in the electronegativity of the second atom. As pointed out by

Duchesne,[28] there would be a tendency of the hybridization of the second atom to change in such a way as to increase the overlap integral.

The most pronounced structural effects of bond-orbital hybridization are on bond angles. These effects have a quantum mechanical basis in the directed valence theories of Heitler, London, Slater, and Pauling. As is now well known, s orbitals have no preferred direction; p orbitals are mutually orthogonal; the completely hybridized sp^3 orbitals are tetrahedral, $109° 28'$ apart; complete sp^2 hybridization yields three orbitals which are in a plane $120°$ apart; and complete sp hybridization

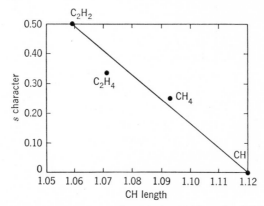

FIG. 8.1.   Effects of s character of C bonding orbital on the CH bond length.

yields two orbitals which are $180°$ apart.† According to the theory of directed valence the bond will be formed in such a direction as to cause maximum overlap of the orbitals employed by the two atoms in forming the bond.

The effects of directed valence are often obscured by interaction of non-bonded atoms. For example, the bond angles in AsH_3 and AsF_3 differ by $8°$, whereas the nuclear coupling indicates that the As bond-orbital hybridization is about the same in the two molecules (see Sec. 7.1). The larger apex angle in AsF_3 must, therefore, be caused mainly by the mutual repulsions of the electronegative fluorine atoms. Because energy considerations show that the bonds would be nearly p bonds, Pauling [29] ascribes the large deviation from $90°$ of the H_2O angle primarily to the repulsion of the hydrogens. In H_2S, PH_3, AsH_3, and SbH_3, where, because of the large separation of the hydrogens and small electronegativity difference of H and M, the repulsion of the H atoms is small, the H—M—H angles are closer to $90°$. See Fig. 8.2. That

† For a discussion of directed valence involving d orbitals, see Pauling, reference 19, p. 90.

some deviations from orthogonality here are caused by hybridization is supported by nuclear quadrupole-coupling data of Loomis and Strandberg [30] which indicate about 8 per cent s character in the bonding orbitals of As in AsH_3. From a comparison of bond angles, the same hybridization, about 8 per cent, is predicted for S in H_2S.

Unfortunately, it is not possible, except in special cases, to make more than qualitative predictions about bond-orbital hybridizations from the

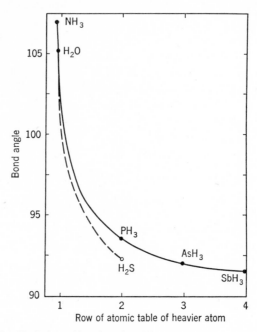

Fig. 8.2. Variation of bond angle with atomic row of central atom.

measured bond angles. In many instances more reliable assignment of the bond orbitals can be made from nuclear quadrupole couplings, but, as we have seen (Sec. 7.1), this requires a detailed knowledge of the ionic character and the covalent resonance in the molecules.

8.3. CONSIDERATION OF PARTICULAR STRUCTURES

8.3a. Bonds to Hydrogen. Microwave spectroscopy has greatly extended the number of accurately measured bond lengths involving hydrogen. (See Table $A.9$.) These new data warrant a re-examination of the effective radius of hydrogen in different conbinations. Pauling [19] has assigned an average radius of 0.30 A to hydrogen; Schomaker and

Stevenson [20] recommend that the value of 0.37 A (one-half of the H_2 bond length) be used with their correction, $-0.09| x_1 - x_2 |$, for ionic character in M—H bonds. Although the ionic character seems to produce some shortening of M—H bonds, it does not account for all the decrease in the H radius on passing from H—H to M—H bonds. The electronegativity differences for PH and AsH are so small as to make insignificant the corrections for ionic character; yet the effective radius of hydrogen in these bonds is 0.05 or 0.06 A shorter than it is in H_2. A possible explanation for this is the differences in the overlapping of the wave functions in M—H and H—H bonds caused by the small size of H as compared with M. The effect of relative size may be of significance in bonds of other types, but it is likely of most significance for H. By choosing the radius of H as 0.32 A in M—H bonds and by making a correction of $-0.06 | x_M - x_H |$ for ionic character, we have been able to obtain a fairly good over-all agreement for bonds of H with different elements. The results are shown in Table 8.6.

Table 8.6. Apparent radius of H with different atoms (in units). Upper figure is observed radius; † lower is calculated with $r = 0.32 - 0.06| x_M - x_H |$

B	C	N	O	F	Si	P	S	Cl
0.32	0.30	0.27	0.23	0.21	0.33	0.32	0.29	0.28
0.31	0.30	0.27	0.24	0.21	0.30	0.32	0.29	0.27

Ge	As	Se	Br	Sn	Sb	Te	I
0.31	0.31		0.27	0.30	0.30		0.27
0.30	0.31	0.30	0.28	0.30	0.30	0.32	0.29

† The apparent radius of H used here for comparison is the observed length of MH less the covalent radius of M from Table 8.4.

The C—H lengths in hydrocarbons are of special interest because of their wide occurrence. Microwave measurements bear out the earlier infrared evidence that the C—H bond length to a carbon in a pure, saturated hydrocarbon is about 1.10 A, to ethylenic or double-bonded carbon about 1.07 A, and to acetylenic or triple-bonded carbon about 1.06 A. This decrease in length is believed to result primarily from a shrinking of the single-bond radius of C, caused by the increasing s character of its bonding orbital. The C—H bond force constant varies in the opposite sequence. The methyl halides have now been investigated with several isotopic combinations. The evidence indicates a small increase in d_{CH} in passing from the iodide to the fluoride. The variations are in the sequence expected from the C—H stretching force constants, but they are on the border line of the errors caused by zero-point vibrations. The important result is that the variation is small

($\sim$0.01 A) in the change from the iodide (electronegativity 2.45) to the combination with the most electronegative of all the elements, fluorine.

An unexpected result obtained in microwave spectroscopy is that C—H distances in chloroform and bromoform are less than the tetrahedral methane value and are, in fact, close to those for ethylenic carbon. See Table A.9 for references.

8.3b. Halogen Bonds to C, Si, and Ge. Figure 8.3 shows the deviations of observed C—Hal, Si—Hal, and Ge—Hal bond lengths from those estimated from the Schomaker-Stevenson rule,[20] with $\beta =$ 0.06. The extra shortening of the Si—Hal bonds over those of C—Hal

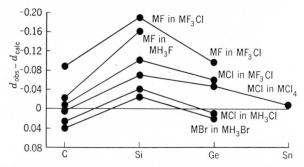

FIG. 8.3.   Deviations of observed bond lengths from those calculated with the relation $d = r_A + r_B - 0.06 \, | \, x_A - x_B \, |$.

and Ge—Hal is evidence for significant contributions from structures of type I. The negative charge on Si is probably more than counter-

$$\text{X—}\overset{\displaystyle X}{\underset{\displaystyle X}{\text{Si}^-}}\text{=(Hal)}^+ \qquad\qquad \text{X—}\overset{\displaystyle X}{\underset{\displaystyle X}{\text{Si}^+}}\ \text{(Hal)}^-$$

I   II

balanced by combined contributions from II so that the effective charge on Si is positive. Structures of type I would not be important in the carbon halides because there is no available orbital in the valence shell of C, and they would not be very important in Ge, and still less in Sn, compounds because of the decreasing tendency to form multiple bonds with increasing size of the atom. The dip in the dipole moments at SiH$_3$Cl (1.87 for CH$_3$Cl, 1.31 for SiH$_3$Cl, 2.13 for GeH$_3$Cl) provides additional evidence for this interpretation. On the basis of electronegativity differences alone, one would expect the dipole moments to increase in the order: CH$_3$Cl, SiH$_3$Cl, GeH$_3$Cl. To estimate the amount of double-bond character in the Si compounds, one must correct for the abnormal length of the pure single bonds, as evidenced by the positive deviations of 0.02 to 0.03 A by the C and Ge bonds to Cl and Br. This indicates that the Si—Cl and Si—Br bonds are about 0.05 or 0.06 A shorter than normal single bonds after the corrections for ionic character are made. With the Pauling rule for π_y and π_z resonating double bonds, this shortening indicates about 10 per cent double-bond character for these bonds. This type of resonance should lengthen the Si—H bonds in $SiH_3(Hal)$, and the experimental evidence bears this out (see Table 8.6).

Another noticeable feature in Fig. 8.3 is the extra shortening of the M—F bonds in MF_3H over those in MH_3F. Similar effects have been detected in electron diffraction measurements and have been attributed by Pauling [19] to resonance contributions from structures of type I,

$$
\begin{array}{cc}
\begin{array}{c}
F^+ \\
\| \\
F^- \quad M\!-\!H \\
| \\
F
\end{array}
&
\begin{array}{c}
F^- \\
\\
F\!-\!M^+\!-\!H \\
| \\
F
\end{array}
\\
\text{I} & \text{II}
\end{array}
$$

Other probable factors are the decrease in the effective radius of M caused by the positive charge in II and the coulomb attraction of the F atoms in I.

The C—Cl distance in CF_3Cl is shorter than that in methyl chloride. This difference may be explained by the participation of the Cl in resonating structures of type I above. The bromides show a similar behavior, and so do the corresponding chlorides and bromides of silicon. The C—I bond in CF_3I is about the same as that in CH_3I.

8.3c. Hydrides and Halides of N, P, As, and Sb. With the exception of SbF_3 and NH_3, complete or partial structural determinations have been made on the hydrides, fluorides, and chlorides of N, P, As, and Sb. (See Table $A.9$.) The structures of PF_3 and AsF_3 have been completed with the help of electron diffraction results, and those of PH_3 with the help of infrared spectra.

Figure 8.4 shows graphically the deviations of the observed lengths in these molecules from these calculated with the equation

$$R = r_A + r_B - 0.06 \left| x_A - x_B \right|. \tag{8.38}$$

The radius used for H is 0.32 (Table 8.5). It is seen that chlorides obey this rule rather precisely. There is no evidence for double-bond character in the chlorides. There is, however, evidence for double-bond character in PF_3 and AsF_3, particularly in PF_3. The fact that there is no comparable evidence for NF_3 suggests that the double-bond character is primarily of form I rather than of form II:

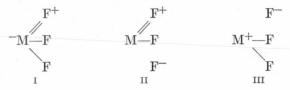

Contributions from III are probably greater than those from I, so that the charge on the more electropositive atom M is positive. This is in agreement with the behavior of the C, Si, and Ge series (see Art. 8.3b).

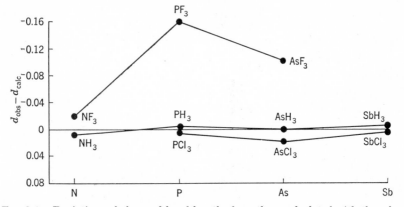

FIG. 8.4. Deviations of observed bond lengths from those calculated with the relation $d = r_A + r_B - 0.06 \, | \, x_A - x_B \, |$.

Like Si in the latter series, P shows exceptional tendency to form double bonds and for the same reason, i.e., the availability of the d orbitals in the valence shell. This tendency falls off rapidly with descending rows in the atomic table and has essentially vanished for the fourth-row elements Sn and Sb. Only the second-row elements show a strong tendency to employ the d orbitals to form double bonds of this type. However, the tendency is still noticeable for the third-row elements, particularly when they are combined with first-row elements.

The bond angles of the hydrides are plotted in Fig. 8.2. The angles decrease with the descent of the heavier element in the atomic table, but this change is not rapid except between the first and second row. This large decrease between N and P is certainly caused partly by the decreasing repulsions of the hydrogens but appears to be caused partly by decreasing bond-orbital hybridization. Since the nuclear coupling indicates about 8 per cent hybridization in AsH_3 (Sec. 7.1), angle 92°, the s character of the bonding orbitals of P in PH_3, angle 93.5°, should be 12 to 15 per cent, and perhaps that of N in NH_3 would be 15 to 18 per cent. Because of the large interaction of the non-bonded atoms in the halides and because of the large double-bond character of form I above in the fluorides, little can be learned about the bond-orbital hybridization from their bond angles.

8.3d. Inter-Halogens. Because of the strong tendency which has been found for the second-row atoms Si and P to use the $3d$ orbitals of the valence shell to form double bonds with F—and to a moderate degree also the third-row elements Ge and As—one would expect Cl and Br to show some tendency to employ the $3d$ orbital in bond formation. There is evidence from nuclear quadrupole couplings for small contributions of $F^+=Cl^-$ and $F^+=Br^-$ to the ground states of FCl and FBr. The interatomic distances support this evidence. Figure 8.5 shows the deviations of the observed lengths in inter-halogen diatomic molecules from

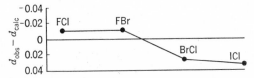

Fig. 8.5. Deviations of observed bond lengths from those calculated with the relation $d = r_A + r_B - 0.06 \mid x_A - x_B \mid$.

those calculated from the additivity rule with the previously used correction for ionic character, $-0.06 \mid x_A - x_B \mid$. The observed lengths are shorter than those calculated only for FCl and FBr. The deviations, however, are not very significant.

Microwave measurements have shown (for references see Table $A.9$) that the inter-halogen molecule ClF_3 has the unusual structure of a "T," with the Cl atom at the intersection of the "T" arms. The two ClF bonds forming the equal arms are 1.70 A in length, and the third ClF bond is only 1.56 A. The FClF bond angles are nearly but not exactly 90°. H. G. Dehmelt has suggested to us that the bonding orbitals of the Cl are probably one pure p and two pd hybrids. These account for the "T" structure and also for the Cl nuclear coupling.

8.3e. Boron Compounds. Borine carbonyl is of special interest not only because of its unorthodox electronic structure but also because it is the simplest of a large group of carbonyls of metals. In agreement with electron diffraction [31] and infrared [32] results, it was found to have the symmetric-top configuration.[33] Its structural dimensions, listed in Table $A.9$, have been interpreted on the basis that it consists of loosely coupled BH_3 and CO molecules with the BC bond order about ½. The

C—O length, 1.131 A, is almost identically that of free carbon monoxide, 1.1308 A. The B—H length is that expected for a normal B to H bond (see Table 8.6). The H—B—H angle is about halfway between the tetrahedral value and that for the planar configuration which is predicted for free BH_3.

Bromodiborane has an interesting structure which has been evaluated by microwave spectroscopy. (See Table A.9 for dimensions and reference.) It was shown to have a hydrogen-bridged structure,

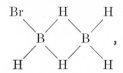

similar to that of diborane. All atoms in the molecule lie in a plane except the two hydrogens forming the bridge, one of which lies above and the other below the plane.

8.3*f*. Interaction of Single and Triple Bonds. In CH_3CCH, CH_3CN, HCCCl, and ClCN a lengthening of the triple bond by about 0.01 A over those in HCN or HCCH has been found. However, in H—C≡C—C≡N there is no detectable increase in either the C≡C or C≡N bonds, though the C—C bond which lies between is reduced from the normal single C—C length to 1.382 A. (Compare structures in Table A.9.) This shortening, 0.16 A, is exactly twice that, 0.08 A, of the C—C bond adjacent to the triple bond in methyl cyanide or methyl acetylene. If we assume a shortening of 0.035 A per adjacent triple bond to be caused by the increased s character of the C (see Sec. 7.2.), a double-bond character of 17 per cent is indicated for the bond situated between the two triple bonds and 8 per cent for a C—C bond adjacent to only one triple bond. (This is in addition to the double-bond character of 11 per cent indicated for all C—C bonds by Mulliken, Rieke and Brown.[23]) Thus it appears that the contribution per triple bond to the stability of the adjacent C—C bond is about the same in HC≡C—C≡N as in CH_3CN and CH_3CCH. The fact that no lengthening of the triple bond occurs in HC≡C—C≡N suggests that each triple bond gains as much through exchange of electrons with the other triple bond as it loses through conjugation with the single bond. The strengthening of the central bond in this type of molecule can therefore be attributed entirely to a greater bonding efficiency of the π electrons caused by their increased freedom of motion. It is expected both from molecular-orbital theory and from the covalent resonance concept that the bond of lower order would gain much more in stability than the energy lost by the bond of higher order with which it couples.

8.3g. Nature of Bonding of Zn, Cd, and Hg. The mercury methyl halides have been found by microwave spectroscopy to have symmetric-top configurations.[34] This is in agreement with electron diffraction studies [35] of $Hg(Hal)_2$ molecules, which show that the two bonds formed by divalent Hg are 180° apart. The bonding orbitals [36] of divalent Hg are therefore most likely $(1/\sqrt{2})s + (1/\sqrt{2})p_z$ and $(1/\sqrt{2})s - (1/\sqrt{2})p_z$. This is also true of the similar elements Zn and Cd which have two electrons in the outer shell.

Table 8.7 lists the covalent radii of divalent Zn, Cd, and Hg, as determined from the methyl mercury halides and other molecules with

Table 8.7. Covalent radii of divalent Zn, Cd, and Hg in various molecules

Molecule		Length, in angstroms	Hg Radius,[†] in angstroms
CH_3HgCl	CHg	2.059	1.31
	HgCl	2.282	1.36
$HgCl_2$		2.28 ‡	1.36
$HgBr_2$		2.43 ‡	1.35
HgI_2		2.61 ‡	1.32
			Cd Radius †
$CdCl_2$		2.23 ‡	1.34
$CdBr_2$		2.39 ‡	1.34
CdI_2		2.60 ‡	1.34
			Zn Radius †
ZnI_2		2.42 ‡	1.16

† Calculated from $d_{AB} = r_A + r_B - 0.06| x_A - x_B |$.
‡ From electron diffraction [Allen and Sutton, *Acta Cryst. 3*, 46 (1950)].

Eq. 8.38. It is seen that the results are reasonably consistent. For the Hg electronegativity we have used the value 1.8 determined from the divalent halides by the electronegativity force-constant relation of Gordy.[27] The value is in good agreement with 1.7 determined by Haissinsky [37] for divalent Hg with the Pauling method. The force-constant relation applied to HgH yields a significantly lower value for the electronegativity of Hg, and for this reason it appears that Hg forms a nearly pure p bond in this molecule. The effective radius of Hg in HgH is accordingly larger than the radius of divalent Hg.

REFERENCES

[1] J. N. Shoolery, R. G. Shulman, W. F. Sheehan, Jr., V. Schomaker, and D. M. Yost, *J. Chem. Phys. 19*, 1364 (1951).
[2] C. I. Beard and B. P. Dailey, *J. Chem. Phys. 18*, 1437 (1950).

[3] W. S. Wilcox and J. H. Goldstein, *J. Chem. Phys. 20*, 1656 (1952).

[4] E. Teller, *Hand und Jahrbuch der chemischen Physik*, Vol. 9 (1934).

[5] G. Herzberg, *Spectra of Diatomic Molecules* (D. Van Nostrand Company, New York, 1950), p. 108.

[6] G. Joos, *Theoretical Physics* (Hafner Publishing Company, New York, 1934), p. 139.

[7] (a) C. H. Townes, A. N. Holden, and F. R. Merritt, *Phys. Rev. 74*, 1113 (1948); (b) J. W. Simmons, W. E. Anderson, and W. Gordy, *Phys. Rev. 77*, 77 (1950); errata, *Phys. Rev. 86*, 1055 (1952).

[8] M. W. P. Strandberg, T. Wentink, and R. L. Kyhl, *Phys. Rev. 75*, 270 (1949).

[9] D. K. Coles and R. H. Hughes, *Phys. Rev. 76*, 178A (1949).

[10] M. Johnson and D. M. Dennison, *Phys. Rev. 48*, 868 (1935).

[11] G. Herzberg, *Infrared and Raman Spectra* (D. Van Nostrand Company, New York, 1945), Chapter 4.

[12] J. W. Simmons, *Phys. Rev. 83*, 485A (1951).

[13] G. Matlack, G. Glockler, D. R. Bianco, and A. Roberts, *J. Chem. Phys. 18*, 332 (1950).

[14] D. K. Coles, *Advances in Electronics, II* (Academic Press, Inc., New York, N. Y., 1950), p. 299.

[15] B. T. Darling and D. M. Dennison, *Phys. Rev. 57*, 128 (1940).

[16] G. F. Crable and W. V. Smith, *J. Chem. Phys. 19*, 502L (1951).

[17] M. H. Sirvetz, *J. Chem. Phys. 19*, 938 (1951).

[18] R. B. Lawrance and M. W. P. Strandberg, *Phys. Rev. 83*, 363 (1951).

[19] (a) L. Pauling, *The Nature of the Chemical Bond* (Cornell University Press, Ithaca, 1939), Chapter V; (b) *Jour. Phys. Chem. 56*, 361 (1952).

[20] V. Schomaker and D. P. Stevenson, *J. Am. Chem. Soc. 63*, 37 (1941).

[21] (a) See, for example, "Discussion of Bond Energies and Bond Lengths," *Proc. Roy. Soc. (London), A207*, 1 (1951); "Symposium on Bond Strengths," *J. Phys. Chem. 56*, March (1952). (b) K. S. Pitzer, *J. Am. Chem. Soc. 70*, 2140 (1948).

[22] C. A. Coulson, *Proc. Roy. Soc. (London) A169*, 413 (1939).

[23] R. S. Mulliken, C. A. Rieke, and W. G. Brown, *J. Am. Chem. Soc. 63*, 41 (1941).

[24] W. Gordy, *J. Chem. Phys. 15*, 81 (1947).

[25] W. Gordy, *J. Chem. Phys. 15*, 305 (1947).

[26] J. E. Lennard-Jones and C. A. Coulson, *Trans. Faraday Soc. 35*, 811 (1939).

[27] W. Gordy, *J. Chem. Phys. 14*, 305 (1946).

[28] J. Duchesne, *J. Chem. Phys. 19*, 246 (1951).

[29] L. Pauling, reference 19, Chapter III.

[30] C. C. Loomis and M. W. P. Strandberg, *Phys. Rev. 81*, 798 (1951).

[31] S. H. Bauer, *J. Am. Chem. Soc. 59*, 1804 (1937).

[32] R. D. Cowan, *J. Chem. Phys. 17*, 218 (1949).

[33] W. Gordy, H. Ring, and A. B. Burg, *Phys. Rev. 78*, 512 (1950).

[34] W. Gordy and J. Sheridan, *Phys. Rev. 79*, 224A (1950).

[35] L. R. Maxwell, *J. Opt. Soc. Am. 30*, 374 (1940).

[36] L. Pauling, reference 19, p. 89.

[37] M. Haissinsky, *J. phys. et radium 7*, 7 (1946).

9. APPLICATIONS IN OTHER FIELDS

9.1. ELECTRONIC APPLICATIONS

9.1a. Spectrum-Line Frequency Stabilization of Oscillators. The existence of sharp spectral lines in the microwave region implies the possibility of using these lines as electronic control elements. The obvious primary application is to control the frequency of an oscillator. If a fraction of the power output of an oscillator is applied to a circuit which is resonant at a frequency ν_0, the frequency-dependent response of the circuit can be used to maintain the average frequency of the oscillator at some definite value, which may be identical to ν_0, may be a multiple or sub-multiple of ν_0, or may differ from these values by a heterodyne frequency f. A microwave absorption cell containing a gas with a spectral frequency ν_0 is a special example of such a resonant circuit and has been used to stabilize an oscillator's frequency.[1, 2, 3, 4] Simple extensions of the stabilization technique allow the oscillator to be frequency modulated about the center frequency, and so to transmit intelligence.

Spectral lines as frequency control elements have to compete with high-Q cavities and piezoelectric crystals. Both cavities and crystals are secondary control elements whose resonant frequencies depend on their physical dimensions and on the ambient temperature. The resonant frequencies of microwave absorption lines in gases are relatively independent of such factors and are easily reproduced in a wide variety of detection systems. If both transmitter and receiver of a communications system are frequency stabilized with reference to the same absorption line, they are sure to remain in tune. An absorption cell can be designed to provide a single reference frequency, or many different reference frequencies, according to the choice of absorbing gas. The spectral line widths can be easily made narrower than the response curves of resonant cavities, and comparable with those of good crystals.

Nuclear quadrupole lines in solids have not been observed above 1000 Mc, but some transitions are expected to fall in the microwave region. If these transitions are as narrow as the lines at lower frequencies, they may compete favorably with gas absorption lines as frequency control elements. They have one advantage over the sharp lines of gases: the lines of the solid are not saturated at moderate power levels.[5]

Although it is altogether possible that quadrupole spectra in solids will ultimately furnish excellent frequency standards in the microwave region, the field is too new to permit a proper evaluation. An undesirable feature is an observed temperature-dependence of the resonant frequency (Sec. 5.3). Because the field of quadrupole spectra in solids is relatively undeveloped, the remainder of this section is devoted to an analysis of frequency stabilization by spectral lines in gases. The subject is of interest from its importance both as a laboratory and a potential industrial technique, and as an introduction to the discussion of spectrum lines as primary frequency or time standards.

The discussion in Chapter 4 of line intensities and line shapes shows that the apparent ultimate limitation on a spectrum line width is the Doppler breadth. In Art. 9.1b, means of avoiding this limitation will be discussed. For ordinary laboratory applications, however, the practical limitations are pressure broadening, saturation effect, and physical size of equipment. An accurate knowledge of the stabilized frequency implies a sharp or high-Q line ($Q = \nu_0/2\,\Delta\nu$, where $2\,\Delta\nu$ is the line width at half-power). A strong control signal implies a high power level incident on the gas, and a strong fractional absorption of the incident power by the gas. Consideration of the saturation effect shows that these design criteria are to some extent conflicting. The line will be broadened and the fractional absorption decreased unless the power density is maintained less than the saturation limit (Sec. 4.3). Power densities of a few milliwatts per square centimeter are sufficient to saturate most electrically polar molecules if the line widths are 1 Mc or less. Furthermore, the saturation plateau is proportional to the square of the line width, and hence power saturation presents a problem when sharp lines are used. However, this limitation can be overcome by proper cell design.

Discriminator and stabilization circuit design. Stabilization circuits have been proposed by Smith and co-workers,[1] Hershberger,[2] and Fletcher and Cooke.[3] Fletcher and Cooke's circuit will be described in some detail. In its simplest form, stabilization is attainable either at the line frequency or at a frequency differing from the line frequency by a fixed i-f frequency, typically 30 Mc. Simple modifications in the design allow stabilization at any frequency, however.

The basic stabilization circuit is shown in Fig. 9.1. A 30-Mc i-f oscillator is used to modulate the klystron-reflector voltage, thus frequency-modulating the klystron, and to provide a phasing voltage for a 30-Mc lock-in amplifier. The klystron output is fed into the absorption cell by means of a directional coupler or tee and is detected by a crystal mixer. The 30-Mc component of this mixer is fed into an amplifier chain culminating in a 30-Mc lock-in amplifier whose output reproduces the anomalous dispersion line shape, and hence gives a typical discriminator output

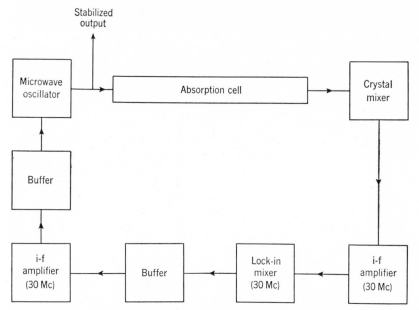

FIG. 9.1.   Block diagram for frequency stabilization of a microwave oscillator on a spectrum line.   (From Fletcher and Cooke.[3])

of opposite polarity for frequency deviation above and below the line frequency (Fig. 9.2).   This discriminator voltage is then fed to the reflector of the klystron in such phase as to correct for any drifts of the

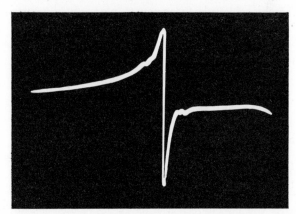

FIG. 9.2.   Output from a spectral line discriminator ($N^{14}H_3$ 3,3 line showing effects of satellite structure).   (From Smith, de Quevedo, Carter, and Bennett.[1])

oscillator frequency. The klystron output contains 30-Mc side bands, which are generally not objectionable in laboratory uses. An analysis indicates that the circuit of Fig. 9.1 used with an absorption cell containing ammonia at low pressures is theoretically capable of a frequency stability of a few cycles per second.

9.1b. Spectrum Lines as Primary Frequency Standards: the Atomic or Molecular Clock. A spectrum line Q of 100,000 makes possible a stabilized frequency of a few parts in 10^7. The short-time stability obtainable with this Q is much higher, perhaps 1 in 10^8. This accuracy, with a Q of 100,000, is not sufficiently great to compete with the accuracy of the mean solar day, the present quasi-primary time standard.† The mean solar day occasionally fluctuates by a few parts in 10^8 but has a much smaller long-time drift. The design of a time standard based on the constant frequency of a spectrum line that can compete with the earth's rotation as a standard is therefore not an easy problem. It seems more logical, nevertheless, to define the frequency of molecular vibrations as permanently invariant than to so define any astronomical motions.

There are essentially three features of importance in the design of a molecular clock: the attainment of a very high-Q (10^6 to 10^7) spectral line; frequency stabilization of an oscillator by such a line; and frequency division to actuate clock mechanism for comparison with solar time. Of these problems, the third is a rather specialized technique that has been well engineered by the Lyons group at the National Bureau of Standards and will not be described here. The first two features are also under investigation at the Bureau and elsewhere, and indeed Lyons and his co-workers have actuated a clock mechanism by the ammonia 3,3 line, and have thereby achieved a frequency stable to about 5 parts in 10^8 over periods of several days.[4] Also under investigation at the Bureau are "clocks" based on molecular beam techniques with Cs vapor, and on the magnetic dipole absorption of O_2 at 5-mm wavelength.[6]

In decreasing spectrum line widths by lowering the pressure, one soon arrives at a limit set by the Doppler width (Eq. 4.12). Low molecular velocities, achieved with heavy molecules and low temperatures, minimize this width.

An obvious method of circumventing the Doppler limit is the use of molecular beams with the beams directed across the direction of power propagation. A molecular beam with a collimation ratio of 10 would increase the Q to 10^7. Methods of obtaining lines sharper than the

---

† The sidereal year (average period of the earth's rotation around the sun) and "Newtonian time" determined from the motions of a large number of astronomical bodies provide more accurate standards.

Doppler limit are described by Newell and Dicke [7a] and by Johnson and Strandberg.[7b]

Once spectrum line Q's of 10^7 are actually attained, it appears that ultimately a spectrum-line frequency standard may be made stable to a few parts in 10^9. When this is accomplished it is probable that such a standard will become a primary, rather than a secondary, frequency standard.

9.1c. Absorption Lines as Secondary Frequency Standards. In the development of microwave spectroscopy, the frequencies of new spectral lines are being determined to an increasing extent by inter-comparison with known lines. This technique is particularly useful in laboratories where reception of standard WWV frequency broadcasts is poor. Furthermore, the apparatus used is relatively inexpensive (see Sec. 1.6). The list of lines measured to accuracies of 100 kc or better already covers the frequency range between 19,000 Mc and 130,000 Mc with few gaps greater than 1000 Mc. In many regions known lines are clustered at intervals of less than 100 Mc. Some of the known frequencies are accurate to better than 20 kc.

Any table of known microwave frequencies is likely to become obsolete as soon as it is published. Certain molecules, however, have already become useful as secondary frequency standards. The most convenient coverage of the 20,000- to 30,000-Mc region is afforded by the rich and strong $N^{14}H_3$ inversion spectrum. The series of $O^{16}C^{12}S^{32}$ lines, harmonic except for a known centrifugal distortion effect, gives convenient frequency standards at the highest obtainable frequencies. The absence of quadrupole splittings and the small value of the line-breadth parameter, $\Delta\nu = 6$ Mc/mm, render this series of lines particularly important. Other linear and symmetric-top molecules yield similar, almost harmonic, series of lines. The constants required for calculation of the rotational frequencies in these molecules are listed in the Appendix, Table $A.4$. Asymmetric-top molecules will probably become the most convenient standards in known regions, however, since they have the richest spectra. Unfortunately, as yet relatively few such spectra have been measured accurately over wide-frequency regions. Tables of microwave spectra are published by the Bureau of Standards.[8] The Landolt-Börnstein [9] tables contain a complete list of spectra published through 1950.

9.1d. The Stabilization of Magnetic Fields. Whereas most microwave spectral lines are relatively insensitive to magnetic fields, the frequencies of transitions in paramagnetic substances are primarily determined by the magnetic field. Some of the paramagnetic absorptions in solids and liquids are only a few megacycles (or less than 0.1 gauss) in width (Chapter 5). If a sample of such a paramagnetic substance is placed in the field of an electromagnet or a permanent magnet with a small auxiliary electromagnet winding, and a portion of the output of a microwave oscillator is passed through the sample, the detected output from the sample will vary with changes in either magnetic field or frequency. If the oscillator frequency is stabilized, the variations in detector response arising from fluctuations in the magnetic field can be used to regulate the current in the magnet in such a fashion as to stabilize the magnetic field. The application is similar to the stabilization of magnetic fields by nuclear magnetic resonance spectra.[10]

9.2. APPLICATIONS TO ASTRONOMY

In contrast to laboratory experiments where only absorption spectra have been observed in the microwave region, only emission spectra have so far been observed from astronomical sources. Both continuous and line spectra have been observed. The sole example of line spectra found to date is the 1420-Mc hydrogen emission line reported by Ewen and Purcell,[11a] and by Muller and Oort.[11b] This line originates from an extended source in the vicinity of the galactic center, as evidenced by a variation of Doppler shift during the time of observation. It has a temperature difference of $40° \pm 5°$ C with respect to the continuous background, and it has a width of 80 kc.

The continuous emission spectrum may be treated as black-body radiation corresponding to a temperature T. If a microwave antenna is focused on a source whose angular aperture is large as compared with the beam width of the antenna, the antenna is effectively within an inclosure whose walls are at the source temperature. Under these conditions, the power available at the input terminals of a receiver, and in the frequency interval $\Delta\nu$, is $kT\,\Delta\nu$. This noise may be compared with that arising from a standard noise source, as is done in Dicke's microwave radiometer;[12] or it may be compared with a line emission in the same frequency region, as done by Ewen and Purcell.[11a] If the antenna beam width is larger than the angular aperture of the noise source, the receiver power will be less than $kT\,\Delta\nu$ of the noise source by a calculable ratio.[13]

If the source were an ideal black body, the observed temperature would be independent of the frequency at which the observations are made. Such is not the case for microwave and radio-frequency observations, however, and it is precisely this variation of "effective temperature" with frequency that is one of the most interesting features of astronomical observations at microwave and radio frequencies.

The most extensive microwave astronomical measurements are on the temperature of the sun. They bridge the gap of earlier optical measurements which yielded an apparent solar temperature of 6000° K, and radio-frequency measurements giving apparent solar temperatures ranging from 125,000° at 25 cm to about 1,000,000° at 200 cm.[14,15] These radio-frequency measurements give the temperature of the "quiet" sun—even larger bursts of noise are associated with sun-spot activity. The earliest microwave measurements were those of Southworth [16] whose value of 16,000° at 3.2 cm compares favorably with later measurements, although his measurements at 1.25 cm and 10 cm appear to be too low. Other values are 6740° at 0.85 cm (Hagen [13]), 11,000° at 1.25 cm (Dicke and Beringer [17]), and 25,000° to 58,000° at 10 cm (McCready, Pawsey, and Payne-Scott,[4] and Covington [18]). Hagen [13] has interpreted these results on the basis of a variation in electron temperature and density with height in the sun's photosphere. The sun's emission radiation in the optical and millimeter-wave regions originates at or near the visible surface of the sun, whereas the longer wavelength radiation apparently originates in the photosphere. Dicke and Beringer's observation [17] (during an eclipse), that the apparent diameter of the sun at 1.25 cm is the same as in the optical region, is a confirmation of the similarity of many optical and millimeter-wave observations of solar properties. On the other hand, Hagen [13] reports excess noise bursts at 0.85 cm, accompanying sun-spot activity which, in the visible region, appears as centers of decreased light emission. Hagen's resolution of 0.2° at 8.5 mm was achieved by using a 10-foot diameter paraboloidal cast-aluminum reflector built by the U.S. Naval Research Laboratory. With this parabola, he was able to map the regions of the sun giving rise to excess millimeter-wave noise, and to show that these regions corresponded to visible sun spots.

Except for Ewen and Purcell's sharp-line observation, microwave data on galactic radiation are negative in nature, i.e., the radiometer is not sufficiently sensitive to detect the continuous radiation. These negative observations yield an upper limit of 20° K for the galactic radiation at 1.25 cm.[19] Radio-frequency observations, on the other hand, show apparent milky-way temperature increasing with increasing wavelength from about 150° K at 500 Mc to 100,000° at 10 Mc. The frequency behavior of the galactic noise temperature is thus qualitatively similar to that for the sun, only displaced to longer wavelengths. Herbstreit [20] has summarized these data and the present indecisive state of the theory on the origin of cosmic noise.

9.3. ANALYSES

The remarkably high resolution attainable in the microwave spectra of molecules immediately suggests the use of microwave spectroscopes in chemical and isotopic analyses. As examples of special fields of application, microwave analysis has already been used to follow the exchange reactions between NH_3 and D_2 on an iron catalyst [21] and in the determination of the half-life [22] of Cl^{36}. Analyses of N^{15} in normal and isotopically enriched ammonia have been performed [23] but not applied to a particular problem. Undoubtedly such stable isotope tracer analyses will become standard techniques of biochemical investigations in the future. Although the present discussion will be restricted to the gaseous phase, the possibilities of analysis of condensed samples should not be overlooked. (See Chapter 5.)

One immediately obvious limitation for analysis in the gaseous phase is that the compounds must have a vapor pressure (about 10^{-3} mm of Hg) at the operating temperature of the spectrometer. Progress in high-temperature cell design is currently proceeding at such a rapid pace [24] that it is pointless to set a specific limit; nonetheless, it is obvious that volatile compounds will always be the easiest with which to work. A second limitation is that the molecule must have a dipole moment, or, more strictly, a transition moment. (R. M. Talley and A. H. Nielsen suggest the possibility of observing vibration-rotation transitions in C_2D_2 in the microwave region.[25] Bending vibrations of some long-chain molecules can also be expected to fall in the microwave region.)

9.3a. Isotopic Analysis. In the microwave branch of spectroscopy, there is virtually no difference between the problems of chemical analysis and isotopic analysis. The spectrum of $Cl^{35}CN$, for instance, is as easily distinguished from $Cl^{37}CN$ as it is from CH_3OH or any other molecule. This is because the frequencies of the rotational spectra found in the microwave region are inversely proportional to the moments of inertia of the molecules, and hence these frequencies vary in a very direct fashion with changes of isotopic mass. There are, of course, exceptional cases where the isotopic substitution occurs very near the mass center of the molecule, but these cases are rare. Furthermore, it is always possible to find some other molecule in which the mass differences of the nucleus in question do give adequate separation of the spectra.

To utilize microwave spectroscopy for isotopic analysis, it is necessary to synthesize suitable molecules containing the isotopes. For instance, analysis of N^{15} in N^{14}-N^{15} mixtures is most conveniently performed with NH_3. (In chemical analysis it is common practice to convert the nitrogen in most nitrogen compounds to NH_3 by the Kjeldahl method.)

The limitation is more severe than with conventional mass spectroscopes where a variety of volatile compounds can be used to provide ionized elements or radicals for analysis. Background and impurity effects for microwave spectrometers are quite different from those for conventional mass spectroscopes. In the microwave type there is no background caused by other nuclei or radicals of the same mass, such as OH and O^{17}, for instance. Impurities in a microwave spectrograph can only lower the sensitivity somewhat, but they will not change the measured-mass ratio. All the common elemental constituents of biochemical compounds can be converted into molecules suitable for microwave analysis. Since the main application for isotopic analysis is that of stable isotope tracers for organic chemistry or biology, the relative inexpensiveness of a microwave spectroscope may be expected to make it an important research tool in these fields.

The design of a spectrograph for mass analysis is not fundamentally different from the design of any other spectrograph. It is necessary that all the components be well engineered since breakdown of various parts will often change the calibration of the instrument. A special problem is the necessity of engineering a convenient means of degassing the cell between different sample runs. These problems have all been investigated at the Oak Ridge National Laboratory, where N^{15} and C^{13} analyses were performed with NH_3 and ClCN, respectively.[23] With the spectrograph used, it was possible to measure isotope ratios in the range of 1 in 200 to 1 in 10 parts, to an accuracy of 1 per cent, using an experimentally determined calibration curve. No doubt industrial engineering of microwave spectrometers will further improve the accuracy while simultaneously achieving more compact instruments.

In addition to its potential use in stable isotope analysis, the small number of molecules needed for a microwave analysis make it ideally suited to investigations of radioactive isotopes. A good example is the determination of the concentration of Cl^{36} in a given sample, a measurement which was used in the determination of the half-life of this isotope.[22]

9.3b. Chemical Analysis. Although the possible applications of microwave spectroscopy in chemical analysis are numerous, they are not unlimited. Many chemicals are unsuited to its use because they are non-polar or unsatisfactory in some other way. However, the many chemicals whose spectra have been identified already, and the many others potentially identifiable, are obvious candidates for chemical analyses. For these chemicals, microwave spectroscopy offers a simple identification by specific absorption frequencies. Usually a listing of only three frequencies serves to identify a particular chemical uniquely; it is particularly well adapted to qualitative analysis. A conservative estimate of the spectral space available for chemical identification in the range of 20,000 Mc to 220,000 Mc is to allow $\frac{1}{3}$ Mc for resolution of each line. With this criterion, 600,000 spaces are available.

One limitation on the use of microwave spectroscopy for analysis is the sensitivity obtainable. The usual Stark-spectrometer sensitivity, 10^{-8} cm^{-1}, for instance, allows detection of a gas of peak absorption 10^{-6} cm^{-1} in a dilution of at most 100 to 1. On the other hand, a possibly obtainable sensitivity of 10^{-10} cm^{-1} allows detection of $N^{14}H_3$ ($\alpha_0 = 8 \times 10^{-4}$ cm^{-1}) in a dilution of approximately 1 part in 10 million. Since microwave spectrometers operate at very low pressures, they are ideal for measuring very small samples. Less than 1 micromole (of a pure sample) is necessary for a qualitative analysis. The sample is not altered by the process of analysis (except for the possibility of incidental decomposition) and may often be recovered.

The problems of quantitative analysis of chemical compounds are somewhat more difficult than those of isotopic analysis. A preferential adsorption on the surfaces of the absorption cell may be expected from components of gas mixtures. D. F. Smith [26] has used a technique of plotting observed spectral intensities as a function of time, after letting the sample into a well-degassed cell. Logarithmic extrapolation to zero time gives the initial intensities. A by-product of the experiment is data on relative adsorption in gas mixtures.

A second difficult problem in quantitative analysis is the variation in line-breadth parameter with composition of the gas mixtures (Sec. 4.2). If integrated intensities of absorption rather than peak intensities are compared, the absorption is independent of the line-breadth parameter. (This precaution is less important in isotopic analysis, although Weber [27] has reported a difference of about 10 per cent in the NH_3 line widths for NH_3—NH_3 collisions as compared to NH_3—NH_2D collisions.) For further discussions of chemical analysis see papers by Dailey,[28] Coles,[29] and Hughes.[30]

REFERENCES

[1] W. V. Smith, J. L. G. de Quevedo, R. L. Carter, and W. S. Bennett, *J. Appl. Phys. 18*, 1112 (1947).

[2] W. D. Hershberger and L. E. Norton, *RCA Review, 9*, 38 (1948).

[3] E. W. Fletcher and S. P. Cooke, *Cruft Lab. ONR Report* 64 (May, 1950).

[4] *National Bureau of Standards Technical Report* 1320 (January, 1949).

[5] H. G. Dehmelt and H. Krüger, *Z. Phys. 129*, 401 (1951).

[6] H. Lyons, *Proc. N. Y. Acad. Sci. 55*, 831 (1952).

[7] (a) G. Newell and R. H. Dicke, *Phys. Rev. 83*, 1064 (1951); (b) H. R. Johnson and M. W. P. Strandberg, *Phys. Rev. 85*, 503 (1952).

[8] P. Kisliuk and C. H. Townes, *National Bureau of Standards Journal of Research 44*, 611 (1950).

[9] Landolt-Börnstein, *Physical-Chemical Tables*, Sixth Edition, Vol. 1, Part 2 (Julius Springer, Berlin, 1951).

[10] H. W. Knoebel and E. L. Hahn, *Rev. Sci. Instr.* **22**, 904 (1951).

[11] (a) H. I. Ewen and E. M. Purcell, *Phys. Rev.* **83**, 881 (1951); *Nature* (London) *168*, 356 (1951); (b) C. A. Muller and J. H. Oort, *Nature* (London) *168*, 357 (1951).

[12] R. H. Dicke, *Rev. Sci. Instr.* *17*, 268 (1946).

[13] J. P. Hagen, *Astrophys. J.* *113*, 547 (1951).

[14] L. L. McCready, J. L. Pawsey, and R. Payne-Scott, *Proc. Roy. Soc. (London)* A, *190*, 357 (1947); F. J. Lehaney and D. E. Yabsley, *Nature 161*, 645 (1948).

[15] M. Ryle and D. D. Vonberg, *Proc. Roy. Soc. (London)* A, *193*, 98 (1948).

[16] G. C. Southworth, *J. Franklin Inst.* *239*, 285 (1945) and *Erratum 241*, No. 3 (1946).

[17] R. H. Dicke and R. Beringer, *Astrophys. J.* *103*, 375 (1946).

[18] A. E. Covington, *Proc. I.R.E.* *36*, 454 (1948).

[19] R. H. Dicke, R. Beringer, R. L. Kyhl, and A. B. Vane, *Phys. Rev.* *70*, 340 (1946).

[20] J. W. Herbstreit, *Advances in Electronics I* (Academic Press, Inc., 1948), p. 347.

[21] J. Weber and K. J. Laidler, *J. Chem. Phys.* *19*, 381 (1951).

[22] C. S. Wu, C. H. Townes, and L. Feldman, *Phys. Rev.* *76*, 692 (1949).

[23] A. L. Southern, H. W. Morgan, G. W. Keilholtz, and W. V. Smith, *Analytical Chemistry 23*, 1000 (1951).

[24] See, for instance, L. J. Rueger, H. Lyons, and R. G. Nuckolls, *Rev. Sci. Instr.* *22*, 428 (1951), also M. L. Stitch, A. Honig, and C. H. Townes, *Phys. Rev. 86*, 607 (1952).

[25] R. M. Talley and A. H. Nielsen, *J. Chem. Phys. 19*, 805 (1951).

[26] D. F. Smith (ORNL), private communication.

[27] J. Weber, *Phys. Rev. 83*, 1058 (1951).

[28] B. P. Dailey, *Analytical Chemistry 21*, 540 (1949).

[29] D. K. Coles, *Advances in Electronics II* (Academic Press, Inc., 1950), p. 299.

[30] R. H. Hughes, *Westinghouse Labs. Sci. Paper 1536* (1950).

APPENDIX

Table $A.1$. Fundamental physical constants and conversion factors †

$h = 6.623773 \pm 0.000180 \times 10^{-27}$ erg sec
$N = 6.025438 \pm 0.000107 \times 10^{23}$ molecules per mole
$c = 299790.22 \pm 0.86$ km sec^{-1}
$k = 1.3802565 \pm 0.0000615 \times 10^{-16}$ erg deg^{-1}
β (Bohr magneton) $= 0.92712031 \pm 0.0000219 \times 10^{-20}$ erg gauss^{-1}
β_I (nuclear magneton) $= 0.505038 \pm 0.000036 \times 10^{-23}$ erg gauss^{-1}.
1 a.m.u. $= 1.65963 \pm 0.00003 \times 10^{-24}$ gm

† Taken from "A Least-Squares Adjustment of the Atomic Constants as of December, 1950," a report to the National Research Council Committee on Constants and Conversion Factors of Physics, by Jesse W. M. DuMond and E. Richard Cohen (California Institute of Technology).

Table $A.2$. Isotopic abundances, masses, and moments

Isotopes are listed with the atomic number Z in the first column and the mass number A in the third column. A few radioactive elements which do not occur naturally are included. These are indicated by dots in the abundance column. Masses and abundances are taken from the isotope chart compiled by E. Segrè [taken from *The Science and Engineering of Nuclear Power*, Vol. II (Addison-Wesley Press, Inc., Cambridge, Mass., 1949)], and are brought up to date from current literature as indicated by references. Those masses not listed may be estimated from the Bohr-Wheeler formula,

$$M = A - 0.00081Z - 0.00611A + 0.014A^{2/3} + 0.083 \left(\frac{A}{2} - Z \right)^2 A^{-1} + 0.000627Z^2A^{-1/3} + \delta$$

where $\delta = 0$ for A odd, $\delta = -0.036A^{-3/4}$ for both A and Z even, and $\delta = 0.036A^{-3/4}$ for A even and Z odd [as quoted by M. G. Mayer and E. Teller, *Phys. Rev. 76*, 1226 (1949)].

Nuclear spins, magnetic moments, and quadrupole moments were obtained from a table compiled by J. E. Mack [*Revs. Modern Phys. 22*, 64 (1950)], and revised by P. F. A. Klinkenberg [*Revs. Modern Phys. 24*, 63 (1952)] with more recently determined values substituted or added. Where newer values are used the sources are indicated by references, except those for microwave spectroscopy, for which references are given in Table $A.7$.

For brevity, limits of error have been omitted. The last figure given is always uncertain, and where there are several digits, as in masses and magnetic moments, the uncertainty usually enters the next to the last figure.

Z	Element	A	Abundance (%)	Mass (a.m.u.)	Spin	Magnetic Moment (nuclear magnetons)	Quadrupole Moment (10^{-24} cm^2)
1	H	1	99.98	1.008123	½	2.79255	
		2	0.02	2.014708	1	0.857354	0.00273
		3 †	....		½	2.978643	
2	He	3	$\sim10^{-5}$	3.01700	½	$(-)2.127414$	
		4	100	4.00390	0		
3	Li	6	7.5	6.01697	1	0.82189	$< 9 \times 10^{-4}$
		7	92.5	7.01822	3½	3.25586	0.02
4	Be	9	100	9.01503	3½	-1.1774	(0.02)

Table *A.2.* Isotopic abundances, masses, and moments—*Continued*

Z	Element	A	Abundance (%)	Mass (a.m.u.)	Spin	Magnetic Moment (nuclear magnetons)	Quadrupole Moment (10^{-24} cm^2)
5	B	10	18.83	10.01618	3	1.8004	0.06
		11	81.17	11.01284	$\frac{3}{2}$	2.68858	0.03
6	C	12	98.88	12.00382	0		
		13	1.12	13.00751	$\frac{1}{2}$	0.70225	
7	N	14	99.62	14.00751	1	0.40365	0.02
		15	0.38	15.00489	$\frac{1}{2}$	−0.28299	
8	O	16	99.757	16.000000	0		
		17	0.039	17.00450	$\frac{5}{2}$	−1.8935	−0.005
		18	0.204	18.00490	0		
9	F	19	100	19.00450	$\frac{1}{2}$	2.6285	
10	Ne	20	90.51	19.99877	(0)		
		21	0.28	20.9996	$\geq \frac{3}{2}$	<0	
		22	9.21	21.99844	(0)		
11	Na	22 †	....	22.0014 [n]	3	1.74582	
		23	100	22.99618	$\frac{3}{2}$	2.21711	
		24 †	....	23.9986 [n]	4		
12	Mg	24	78.41	23.9924	(0)		
		25	10.18	24.9938	$\frac{5}{2}$	−0.8552	
		26	11.41	25.9898	(0)		
13	Al	27	100	26.9899	($\frac{5}{2}$)	3.6408	0.156
14	Si	28	92.27	27.9866	(0)		
		29	4.68	28.9866	($\frac{1}{2}$)	(−0.55538)	
		30	3.05	29.9832	(0)		
15	P	31	100	30.9843	$\frac{1}{2}$	1.13165	
16	S	32	95.1	31.98199 [a]	0		
		33	0.74	32.98187 [a]	$\frac{3}{2}$	0.6436	−0.08
		34	4.2	33.97890 [a]	(0)		
		35 †	....	34.98046 [a]	$\frac{3}{2}$		0.06
		36	0.016	35.97954 [a]	(0)		
17	Cl	35	75.4	34.97867	$\frac{3}{2}$	0.82191	−0.07894
		36 †	....		2		−0.0168
		37	24.6	36.97750	$\frac{3}{2}$	0.68414	−0.06213
18	A	36	0.35	35.9780	(0)		
		38	0.081	37.974			
		40	99.57	39.9756	(0)		
19	K	39	93.38	38.9747	$\frac{3}{2}$	0.391	
		40 †	0.012	39.9760	4	−1.291	
		41	6.61	40.97466	$\frac{3}{2}$	0.215	
20	Ca	40	96.92	39.9753	(0)		
		42	0.64	41.9711			
		43	0.132	42.9723			
		44	2.13	43.9692 [o]			
		46	0.0032				
		48	0.179				

Table $A.2$. Isotopic abundances, masses, and moments—*Continued*

Z	Element	A	Abundance (%)	Mass (a.m.u.)	Spin	Magnetic Moment (nuclear magnetons)	Quadrupole Moment (10^{-24} cm²)
21	Sc	45	100	44.9669	$\frac{7}{2}$	4.757	
22	Ti	46	7.95	45.96697 [b]			
		47	7.75	46.96668 [b]			
		48	73.45	47.96317 [b]			
		49	5.51	48.96358 [b]			
		50	5.34	49.96077 [b]			
23	V	50	0.24	49.96330 [c]	6		
		51	99.76	50.96052 [b]	$\frac{7}{2}$	(+)5.1478	
24	Cr	50	4.31	49.96210 [b]			
		52	83.75	51.95707 [b]			
		53	9.55	52.95772 [b]	$\frac{3}{2}$	(−)0.45	
		54	2.38	53.9563 [b]			
25	Mn	55	100	54.95581 [b]	$\frac{5}{2}$	3.4681	
26	Fe	54	5.81	53.9504 [b]			
		56	91.068	55.95272 [b]			
		57	2.20	56.95359 [b]		~0	
		58	0.33	57.9520 [b]			
27	Co	59	100		$\frac{7}{2}$	4.6484	
28	Ni	58	67.76	57.95345 [b]			
		60	26.16	59.94901 [b]			
		61	1.25	60.94907 [b]		~0	
		62	3.66	61.94681 [b]			
		64	1.16	63.94755 [b]			
29	Cu	63	69.0	62.94926 [b]	$\frac{3}{2}$	2.22617	−0.13
		65	31.0	64.94835 [b]	$\frac{3}{2}$	2.3845	−0.12
30	Zn	64	48.9	63.94955 [b]	(0)		
		66	27.8	65.94722 [b]	(0)		
		67	4.1	66.94815 [b]	$\frac{5}{2}$	0.87378 [d]	
		68	18.6	67.94686 [b]	(0)		
		70	0.6	69.94779 [b]			
31	Ga	69	61.2	68.955	$\frac{3}{2}$	2.0167	0.2318
		71	38.8	70.953	$\frac{3}{2}$	2.5614	0.1461
32	Ge	70	21.2	69.9447 [e]	(0)		
		72	27.3	71.9430 [e]	(0)		
		73	7.9		$\frac{9}{2}$		−0.2
		74	37.1	73.9426 [e]	(0)		
		76	6.5	75.9433 [e]	(0)		
33	As	75	100	74.9432 [e]	$\frac{3}{2}$	1.4387	0.3
34	Se	74	0.87	73.9439 [e]	(0)		
		76	9.02	75.9423 [p]	(0)		
		77	7.58	76.9440 [p]	$\frac{1}{2}$	0.5333 [f]	
		78	23.52	77.9423 [p]	(0)		
		79 †	....		$\frac{7}{2}$		1.2
		80	49.82	79.9436 [p]	0		
		82	9.19	81.9458 [p]	(0)		

Table A.2.   Isotopic abundances, masses, and moments—*Continued*

Z	Element	A	Abundance (%)	Mass (a.m.u.)	Spin	Magnetic Moment (nuclear magnetons)	Quadrupole Moment (10^{-24} cm^2)
35	Br	79	50.56	78.94438 ^{g}	$\frac{3}{2}$	2.10576	0.335 ^{q}
		81	49.47	80.94228 ^{g}	$\frac{3}{2}$	2.2696	0.280 ^{q}
36	Kr	78	0.34	77.945			
		80	2.23				
		82	11.50	81.939	(0)		
		83	11.48		$\frac{9}{2}$	−0.9704	0.15
		84	57.02	83.938	(0)		
		86	17.43	85.939	(0)		
37	Rb	85	72.8	84.931 ^{r}	$\frac{5}{2}$	1.3532	
		86 †	....		2	(−1.68)	
		87	27.2	86.930 ^{r}	$\frac{3}{2}$	2.7501	
38	Sr	84	0.55				
		86	9.75				
		87	6.96		$\frac{9}{2}$	−1.1	
		88	82.74		(0)		
39	Y	89	100		$\frac{1}{2}$	−0.14	
40	Zr	90	48.0	89.9318 ^{s}			
		91	11.5		$\frac{5}{2}$	$\sim$−1.1 ^{h}	
		92	22.0				
		94	17.0				
		96	1.5				
41	Cb (Nb)	93	100		$\frac{9}{2}$	6.1659	$\sim$0
42	Mo	92	15.85		(0)		
		94	9.12	93.9343 ^{e}	(0)		
		95	15.7	94.946	$\frac{5}{2}$	−0.9140	
		96	16.5	95.944	(0)		
		97	9.45	96.945	$\frac{5}{2}$	−0.9332	
		98	23.75	97.943	(0)		
		100	9.65	99.9386 ^{s}	(0)		
43	Tc	99 †	....		$\frac{9}{2}$ ^{i}	5.6805 ^{i}	
44	Ru	96	5.68	95.945			
		98	2.22	97.943			
		99	12.81	98.944	$\frac{5}{2}$ ^{t}	$\mu^{101}\mu^{99} = 1.09$ ^{t}	
		100	12.70	99.942			
		101	16.98	100.946	$\frac{5}{2}$ ^{t}		
		102	31.34	101.941			
		104	18.27				
45	Rh	103	100	102.941	$\frac{1}{2}$	(−)0.11	
46	Pd	102	0.8	101.941			
		104	9.3	103.941			
		105	22.6	104.942	$(\frac{5}{2})$	(−0.6)	
		106	27.2	105.941			
		108	26.8	107.941			
		110	13.5	109.941			

Table A.2. Isotopic abundances, masses, and moments—*Continued*

Z	Element	A	Abundance (%)	Mass (a.m.u.)	Spin	Magnetic Moment (nuclear magnetons)	Quadrupole Moment $(10^{-24}\ cm^2)$
47	Ag	107	51.9	106.945	½	−0.111	
		109	48.1	108.944	½	−0.129	
48	Cd	106	1.2	105.9398 ^{u}			
		108	0.9	107.9386 ^{u}			
		110	12.4	109.9386 ^{u}	0		
		111	12.7	110.9398 ^{u}	½	−0.59492	
		112	24.1	111.9388 ^{u}	(0)		
		113	12.3	112.9406 ^{u}	½	−0.62238	
		114	28.9	113.9400 ^{u}	(0)		
		116	7.6	115.9420 ^{u}	(0)		
49	In	113	4.23	112.9404 ^{u}	9½	5.486	1.144
		115	95.77	114.9404 ^{u}	9½	5.500	1.161
50	Sn	112	0.9	111.9407 ^{u}			
		114	0.61	113.9394 ^{u}			
		115	0.35	114.940	½	−0.91779	
		116	14.07	115.939	0		
		117	7.54	116.937	½	−0.99982	
		118	23.98	117.937	(0)		
		119	8.62	118.938	½	−1.04600	
		120	33.03	119.937	(0)		
		122	4.78	121.945			
		124	6.11	123.944			
51	Sb	121	57.2		5½	3.360	∼−0.5
		123	42.7		7½	2.547	∼−0.6
52	Te	120	0.09	119.9429 ^{u}			
		122	2.43	121.9419 ^{u}			
		123	0.85	122.9437 ^{u}	½	−0.73579	
		124	4.59	123.9428 ^{u}			
		125	6.97	124.9446 ^{u}	½	−0.88705	
		126	18.71	125.9427 ^{e}	(0)		
		128	31.85	127.9471 ^{e}	(0)		
		130	34.51	129.9467 ^{e}	(0)		
53	I	127	100	126.9453 ^{u}	5½	2.8090	−0.7
		129 †	....		7½	2.6181	−0.5
54	Xe	124	0.094				
		126	0.088				
		128	1.90				
		129	26.23		½	−0.777	
		130	4.07				
		131	21.17		3½	0.700	∼−0.15
		132	26.96		(0)		
		134	10.54		(0)		
		136	8.95		(0)		
55	Cs	133	100		7½	2.5771	│ ≤0.3
		134 †	....		4 ^{k}	2.96 ^{k}	
		135 †	....		7½	2.7271	
		137 †	....		7½	2.8397	

Table $A.2$. Isotopic abundances, masses, and moments—*Continued*

Z	Element	A	Abundance (%)	Mass (a.m.u.)	Spin	Magnetic Moment (nuclear magnetons)	Quadrupole Moment (10^{-24} cm^2)
56	Ba	130	0.101				
		132	0.097				
		134	2.42		(0)		
		135	6.59		3/2	0.8346	
		136	7.81	135.9488 ^{e}	(0)		
		137	11.32	136.9502 ^{e}	3/2	0.9351	
		138	71.66	137.9498 ^{e}	(0)		
57	La	138 †	0.089				
		139	99.9	138.953	7/2	2.7760	
58	Ce	136	0.19				
		138	0.25				
		140	88.48	139.9489 ^{e}			
		142	11.1	141.9537 ^{e}			
59	Pr	141	100		5/2	4.5938	
60	Nd	142	27.1				
		143	12.2		7/2	−1.0	<25
		144	23.9	143.9560 ^{e}			
		145	8.3	144.962	7/2	−0.65	<25
		146	17.2	145.962			
		148	5.7	147.962			
		150	5.6	149.9687 ^{e}			
62	Sm	144	3.0				
		147	16.1		7/2	(−0.32)	
		148 †	14.2				
		149	14.1		(7/2)	(−0.26)	
		150	11.6				
		152	20.7				
		154	18.9				
63	Eu	151	47.77		5/2	3.6	1.2
		153	52.23		5/2	1.6	2.5
64	Gd	152	0.21				
		154	2.14	153.971			
		155	14.86	154.971	≥3/2 ^{h}	$\mid\sim0.3\mid$ ^{h}	
		156	20.61	155.972			
		157	15.66	156.973	≥3/2 ^{h}	$\mid\sim0.25\mid$ ^{h}	
		158	24.75	157.973			
		160	21.77	159.974			
65	Tb	159	100		3/2		
66	Dy	158	0.1				
		160	0.1				
		161	21.1				
		162	26.6				
		163	24.8				
		164	27.3				
67	Ho	165	100		3/2		

Table *A.2.* Isotopic abundances, masses, and moments—*Continued*

Z	Element	A	Abundance (%)	Mass (a.m.u.)	Spin	Magnetic Moment (nuclear magnetons)	Quadrupole Moment (10^{-24} cm^2)
68	Er	162	0.1				
		164	1.5				
		166	32.9				
		167	24.4		$\frac{7}{2}$	0.6	$\lvert 10.2 \rvert$
		168	26.9				
		170	14.2				
69	Tm	169	100		$\frac{1}{2}$		
70	Yb	168	0.06				
		170	4.21				
		171	14.26		$\frac{1}{2}$	0.45	
		172	21.49				
		173	17.02		$\frac{5}{2}$	−0.65	3.9
		174	29.58				
		176	13.38				
71	Lu	175	97.5		$\frac{7}{2}$	2.9	5.9
		176 †	2.5		≥ 7	4.2	7
72	Hf	174	0.18				
		176	5.30	175.9923 ^{e}			
		177	18.47		$(\frac{1}{2}, \frac{3}{2})$		
		178	27.10	177.9936 ^{e}	(0)		
		179	13.85		$(\frac{1}{2}, \frac{3}{2})$		
		180	35.11	180.0029 ^{e}	(0)		
73	Ta	181	100	181.0031 ^{e}	$\frac{7}{2}$	2.1	6
74	W	180	0.135				
		182	26.41	182.0033 ^{e}	(0)		
		183	14.40	183.0059 ^{e}	$\frac{1}{2}$		
		184	30.64	184.0052 ^{e}	(0)		
		186	28.41		(0)		
75	Re	185	37.07		$\frac{5}{2}$	3.1714	(2.8)
		187	62.93		$\frac{5}{2}$	3.2039	2.6
76	Os	184	0.018				
		186	1.59				
		187	1.64				
		188	13.3				
		189	16.1	189.04	$\frac{1}{2}$	0.7	
		190	26.4	190.03			
		192	41.0	192.04			
77	Ir	191	38.5	191.04	$\frac{3}{2}$	>0	
		193	61.5	193.04	$\frac{3}{2}$	>0	
78	Pt	192	0.8				
		194	30.2	194.039	(0)		
		195	35.3	195.039	$\frac{1}{2}$	0.60592	
		196	26.6	196.039	(0)		
		198	7.2	198.05			
79	Au	197	100	197.04	$\frac{3}{2}$	0.23	

Table $A.2$. Isotopic abundances, masses, and moments—*Continued*

Z	Element	A	Abundance (%)	Mass (a.m.u.)	Spin	Magnetic Moment (nuclear magnetons)	Quadrupole Moment (10^{-24} cm^2)
80	Hg	196	0.15				
		198	10.1		0		
		199	17.0		½	0.50413	
		200	23.3		(0)		
		201	13.2		3½	−0.5590	0.5
		202	29.6		(0)		
		204	6.7		(0)		
81	Tl	203	29.46	203.05	½	1.61166	
		205	70.54	205.05	½	1.62750	
82	Pb	204	1.3	204.05	(0)		
		206	25.15	206.05	(0)		
		207	21.11	207.05	½	0.58950	
		208	52.38	208.0416 *l*	(0)		
83	Bi	209	100	209.0466 *l*	9½	4.082	−0.4
89	Ac	227 †	....		3½		
90	Th	232 †	100	232.1093 *m*			
91	Pa	231 †	....		3½		
92	U	234 †	0.00518	234.1129 *m*			
		235 †	0.719		(5½, 7½)		
		238 †	99.274	238.1241 *m*			
93	Np	237 †	....		5½		

† Radioactive.
a S. Geshwind and R. Gunther-Mohr, *Phys. Rev. 81*, 882 (1951).
b T. L. Collins, A. O. Nier, and W. H. Johnson, Jr., *Phys. Rev. 86*, 408 (1952).
c W. H. Johnson, Jr., *Phys. Rev. 87*, 166 (1952).
d S. S. Dharmatti and H. E. Weaver, *Phys. Rev. 85*, 927 (1952).
e H. E. Duckworth, C. K. Kegley, J. M. Olson, and G. S. Stanford, *Phys. Rev. 83*, 1114 (1951).
f S. S. Dharmatti and H. E. Weaver, Jr., *Phys. Rev. 86*, 259 (1952).
g K. Ogata, *Phys. Rev. 75*, 200 (1949).
h S. Suwa, *Phys. Rev. 86*, 247 (1952).
i K. G. Kessler and W. F. Meggers, *Phys. Rev. 80*, 905 (1950).
j H. Walchli, R. Livingston, and W. J. Martin, *Phys. Rev. 85*, 479 (1952).
k V. Jaccarino, B. Bederson, and H. H. Stroke, *Phys. Rev. 87*, 676 (1952).
l P. I. Richards, E. E. Hays, and S. A. Goudsmit, *Phys. Rev. 85*, 630 (1952).
m G. S. Stanford, H. E. Duckworth, B. G. Hogg, and J. S. Geiger, *Phys. Rev. 85*, 1039 (1952).
n C. W. Li, *Phys. Rev. 88*, 1038 (1952).
o T. L. Collins, A. O. Nier, and W. H. Johnson, Jr., *Phys. Rev. 84*, 717 (1951).
p Determined from the relative masses given by S. Geschwind, H. Minden, and C. H. Townes [(*Phys. Rev. 78*, 174 (1950)] and the absolute mass of Se^{74}.
q J. G. King and V. Jaccarino, private communication.
r E. E. Hays, P. I. Richards, and S. A. Goudsmit, *Phys. Rev. 84*, 824 (1951).
s H. E. Duckworth, R. S. Preston, and K. S. Woodcock, *Phys. Rev. 79*, 188 (1950).
t J. H. E. Griffiths and J. Owen, *Proc. Phys. Soc. (London) 65*, 951 (1952).
u R. E. Halsted, *Phys. Rev. 88*, 666 (1952).

Table $A.3$. Molecular quadrupole moments obtained from microwave collision diameters

Mole-cule	$b \times 10^8$ (cm) Kinetic Theory	$b \times 10^8$ (cm) from NH_3 3,3 Line Broadening				Q_{Mol} $(10^{-26}$ esu)†
	Bib. Ref.:	405	639, 726	771	750	
N_2	4.09	6.4	5.54			1.5 ‡
O_2	4.02	4.85	3.86	4.18	$\begin{cases} 4.02 \\ 4.31 \end{cases}$	<0.55 §
NO	3.90		5.64			1.4
CO	3.96		5.97			1.6
CO_2	4.46		7.59			3.1
COS			7.56			2.9
CS_2			7.72			3.1
N_2O	4.35		7.32		$\begin{cases} 11.2 \\ 10.7 \end{cases}$	4.4 ‡
HCN			10.0			7.7
ClCN			11.9			11.5
C_2H_2			8.79			5.3
C_2H_4	4.79		6.67			2.3
C_2H_6	4.86		5.64			<1.3

† Values of Q_{Mol} for the rotating molecules.
‡ Average of experimental values is used here to calculate Q_{Mol}.
§ The value $b = 4.18 \times 10^{-8}$ cm, which is considered to be most reliable, is used to obtain the upper limit for Q_{Mol}.

Table A.4. Molecular rotational constants from microwave spectroscopy

Diatomic Molecules

Molecule	B_e (Mc)	α_e (Mc)	Bibliography Reference
$C^{12}O^{16}$	57,897.75 ± 0.13	524.16 †	628
$C^{13}O^{16}$	55,345.1 ± 0.2	488.48 †	628
$F^{19}Cl^{35}$	15,483.688 ± 0.026	130.666 ± 0.029	519, 627
$F^{19}Cl^{37}$	15,189.221 ± 0.029	126.957 ± 0.029	519, 627
$F^{19}Br^{79}$	10,706.95	156.3	681
$F^{19}Br^{81}$	10,655.7	155.8	681
$Br^{79}Cl^{35}$	4,570.92 ± 0.04	23.22 ± 0.03	682
$Br^{81}Cl^{35}$	4,536.14 ± 0.04	22.95 ± 0.03	682
$Br^{79}Cl^{37}$	4,399.84 ± 0.04	21.94 ± 0.03	682; a
$Br^{81}Cl^{37}$	4,365.01 ± 0.04	21.67 ± 0.03	682
$I^{129}Cl^{35}$	3,422.30 ± 0.02	16.06 ± 0.02	459, 462, 350
$Na^{23}Cl^{35}$	6,536.9 ± 0.3	48.1 ± 0.1	844
$Na^{23}Cl^{37}$	6,396.9 ‡	46.7	844
$K^{39}Cl^{35}$	3,856.4	23.7	843
$Cs^{133}Cl^{35}$	2,163.8 ± 0.2	10.06 ± 0.06	844
$Cs^{133}Cl^{37}$	2,071.4 ‡	9.59	844

Linear Polyatomic Molecules

Molecule	B_0 (Mc)	D (kc)	α_1 (Mc)	α_2 (Mc)	$q\S$ (Mc)	Bibliography Reference
$HC^{12}N^{14}$	44,315.97 ± 0.10				223.5	679, 676, 833
$HC^{13}N^{14}$	43,169.83 ± 0.15					679, 833

Molecule						
DC¹²N¹⁴	36,207.40 ± 0.15				185.9	679, 770, 833
DC¹³N¹⁴	35,587.57 ± 0.15					679
Cl³⁵C¹²N¹⁴	5,970.82 ± 0.02			−16.39 ± 0.02	7.500 ± 0.015	449, 458
Cl³⁶C¹²N¹⁴	5,908 ‡					555
Cl³⁷C¹²N¹⁴	5,847.26 ± 0.02					449, 458
Cl³⁵C¹³N¹⁴	5,939.78 ± 0.03					449, 458
Cl³⁷C¹³N¹⁴	5,814.71 ± 0.03					449, 458
Br⁷⁹C¹²N¹⁴	4,120.198 ± 0.009	0.91 ± 0.09	15.54	−11.56	3.91	449, 458, 678, 845
Br⁷⁹C¹²N¹⁵	3,944.846 ± 0.009					845
Br⁷⁹C¹³N¹⁴	4,073.373 ± 0.007					449, 845
Br⁸¹C¹²N¹⁴	4,096.788 ± 0.007	0.81 ± 0.09	15.48	−11.49	3.85	449, 458, 678, 845
Br⁸¹C¹²N¹⁵	3,921.787 ± 0.010					845
Br⁸¹C¹³N¹⁴	4,049.608 ± 0.007					449, 845
I¹²⁷C¹²N¹⁴	3,225.578 ± 0.018	0.88 ± 0.09	9.33	−9.50	2.69	449, 458, 678
I¹²⁷C¹³N¹⁴	3,177.03 ‡	5.75 ± 0.05				449
N¹⁴N¹⁴O¹⁶	12,561.66 ± 0.03	1.27 ± 0.05	18.12	−10.59	6.39	511, 304, 729
N¹⁴N¹⁵O¹⁶	12,560.78 ‡					511, 304
N¹⁵N¹⁴O¹⁶	12,137.30 ‡					511
N¹⁵N¹⁵O¹⁶	12,137.39 ‡					511
O¹⁶C¹²S³²	6,081.494 ± 0.010			−10.59	6.39	309, 554, 729
O¹⁶C¹²S³³	6,004.92					456, 458
O¹⁶C¹²S³⁴	5,932.84 ± 0.01	1.4 ± 0.1		−10.37	6.07	309, 554, 458
O¹⁶C¹²S³⁵	5,864.351 ‡					773
O¹⁶C¹²S³⁶	5,799.67 ‡					534
O¹⁶C¹³S³²	6,061.92 ± 0.01			−9.98	6.43	554, 458
O¹⁶C¹³S³⁴	5,911.73 ± 0.03 ‡					458
O¹⁶C¹⁴S³²	6,043.25 ± 0.25			−9.4 ± 0.3	6.7 ± 0.1	443

Table A.4. Molecular rotational constants from microwave spectroscopy—Continued

Linear Polyatomic Molecules—Continued

Molecule	B_0 (Mc)	D (kc)	α_1 (Mc)	α_2 (Mc)	$q\S$ (Mc)	Bibliography Reference
$O^{17}C^{12}S^{32}$	5,883.67 ‡					534
$O^{18}C^{12}S^{32}$	5,704.83 ± 0.02 ‡		16.18	−10.17	5.65 ± 0.05	458, 507
$O^{18}C^{12}S^{34}$	5,559.90 ± 0.05 ‡					507
$O^{18}C^{13}S^{32}$	5,690.95 ± 0.05 ‡					507
$O^{16}C^{12}Se^{74}$	4,095.793 ± 0.005					553
$O^{16}C^{12}Se^{76}$	4,068.465 ± 0.005			−7.00	3.24	553
$O^{16}C^{12}Se^{77}$	4,055.300 ± 0.005		13.48	−6.98	3.21	553
$O^{16}C^{12}Se^{78}$	4,042.460 ± 0.005	0.830 ± 0.05	13.40	−6.96	3.19	553
$O^{16}C^{12}Se^{79}$	4,029.855 ‡					813
$O^{16}C^{12}Se^{80}$	4,017.677 ± 0.005	0.755 ± 0.02	13.27	−6.92	3.15	553
$O^{16}C^{12}Se^{82}$	3,994.009 ± 0.005	0.875 ± 0.05	13.12	−6.86	3.13	553
$O^{16}C^{13}Se^{78}$	4,005.112 ± 0.005					553
$O^{16}C^{13}Se^{80}$	3,980.045 ± 0.005					553
$S^{32}C^{12}Se^{76}$	2,050.2 ± 0.3 ‡			−1.5	1.1	606
$S^{32}C^{12}Se^{77}$	2,042.3 ± 0.3 ‡			−1.3	0.5	606
$S^{32}C^{12}Se^{78}$	2,031.3 ± 0.3 ‡			−1.7	1.7	606
$S^{32}C^{12}Se^{80}$	2,016.9 ± 0.3 ‡			−1.6	1.3	606
$S^{32}C^{12}Se^{82}$	2,001.8 ± 0.3 ‡			−3.3	2.3	606
$Te^{122}C^{12}S^{32}$	1,584.1216					836
$Te^{123}C^{12}S^{32}$	1,580.9199					836
$Te^{124}C^{12}S^{32}$	1,577.7904					836
$Te^{125}C^{12}S^{32}$	1,574.6908					836
$Te^{126}C^{12}S^{32}$	1,571.6519					836
$Te^{128}C^{12}S^{32}$	1,565.7021					836

	B_0 (Mc)		D_{JK} (kc)	D_J (kc)	Bibliography Reference
$Te^{130}C^{12}S^{32}$	1,559.9306				836
$HC^{12}C^{12}Cl^{35}$	5,684.24				559
$HC^{12}C^{12}Cl^{37}$	5,572.38				559
$DC^{12}C^{12}Cl^{35}$	5,187.01				559
$DC^{12}C^{12}Cl^{37}$	5,084.24				559
$HC^{12}C^{12}C^{12}N^{14}$	4,549.07				691
$HC^{13}C^{12}C^{12}N^{14}$	4,408.45				691
$HC^{12}C^{13}C^{12}N^{14}$	4,529.84				691
$HC^{12}C^{12}C^{13}N^{14}$	4,530.23				691
$HC^{12}C^{12}C^{12}N^{15}$	4,416.91				691
$DC^{12}C^{12}C^{12}N^{14}$	4,221.60				691
$DC^{13}C^{12}C^{12}N^{14}$	4,107.21				691
$DC^{12}C^{13}C^{12}N$	4,207.59				691
$DC^{12}C^{12}C^{13}N$	4,202.54				691
$DC^{12}C^{12}C^{12}N^{15}$	4,100.41				691

Symmetric-Top Molecules

Molecule	B_0 (Mc)	D_{JK} (kc)	D_J (kc)	Bibliography Reference
$B^{10}H_3C^{12}O^{16}$	8,979.94	390		631, 552
$B^{10}D_3C^{12}O^{16}$	7,530.34	290		631
$B^{11}H_3C^{12}O^{16}$	8,657.22	360		631
$B^{11}D_3C^{12}O^{16}$	7,336.56	240		631
$B_5{}^{11}H_9$	7,002.85 ‡			815
$B^{10}B_4{}^{11}H_9$	7,090 ‡			815
$N^{14}F_3{}^{19}$	10,681.07 ± 0.05	−25.7	177	673, 729
$N^{15}F_3{}^{19}$	10,629.35	−25	14.2	673
$P^{31}F_3{}^{19}$	7,820.01	−11.7 ± 0.1	7.5 ± 0.1	520, 729
$P^{31}Cl_3{}^{35}$	2,617.1 ± 0.1			646

Table A.4. Molecular rotational constants from microwave spectroscopy—*Continued*

Symmetric-Top Molecules—Continued

Molecule	B_0 (Mc)	D_{JK} (kc)	D_J (kc)	Bibliography Reference
$P^{31}Cl_3^{37}$	$2,487.5 \pm 0.2$			646
$P^{31}O^{16}F_3^{19}$	$4,594.282 \pm 0.009$	1.25 ± 0.05	1.10 ± 0.05	848, 729, 664
$P^{31}O^{18}F_3^{19}$	$4,395.27 \pm 0.20$			848
$P^{31}O^{16}Cl_3^{35}$	$2,015.20 \pm 0.04$			848
$P^{31}O^{16}Cl_3^{37}$	$1,932.38 \pm 0.08$			848
$P^{31}S^{32}F_3^{19}$	$2,657.663 \pm 0.009$	1.8	0.30 ± 0.05	848, 729
$P^{31}S^{33}F_3^{19}$	$2,614.73 \pm 0.04$			848
$P^{31}S^{34}F_3^{19}$	$2,579.77 \pm 0.04$	1.8		848
$P^{31}S^{32}Cl_3^{35}$	$1,402.64 \pm 0.05$			848
$P^{31}S^{32}Cl_3^{37}$	$1,355.72 \pm 0.05$			848
$P^{31}S^{34}Cl_3^{35}$	$1,370.13 \pm 0.05$			848
$As^{75}F_3^{19}$	$5,879.3\ \ddagger$			411
$As^{75}Cl_3^{35}$	$2,147.2 \pm 0.2$			646
$As^{75}Cl_3^{37}$	$2,044.7 \pm 0.3$			646
$Sb^{121}Cl_3^{35}$	$1,753.9\ \ddagger$			731
$Sb^{123}Cl_3^{35}$	$1,750.7\ \ddagger$			731
$C^{12}H_3F^{19}$	$25,535.91 \pm 0.05$	443 ± 20	32.5	520, 729
$C^{12}D_3F^{19}$	$20,449.83 \pm 0.05$	228 ± 8	32.5	729
$C^{13}H_3F^{19}$	$24,862.37$			520
$C^{12}H_3Cl^{35}$	$13,292.95 \pm 0.01$	189 ± 1	26.4 ± 0.3	422, 678
$C^{12}H_3Cl^{36}$	$13,187.66$		26.5	729a
$C^{12}H_3Cl^{37}$	$13,088.24 \pm 0.02$	184 ± 2	27.0 ± 0.4	422, 678
$C^{12}D_3Cl^{35}$	$10,841.88$			763, 837
$C^{12}D_3Cl^{37}$	$10,658.43$			763, 837
$C^{13}H_3Cl^{35}$	$12,796.2$			515

$C^{13}H_3Cl^{37}$	12,590.0			515
$C^{12}H_3Br^{79}$	9,568.188 ± 0.025	129.4 ± 0.3	11.1 ± 0.8	422, 545, 678
$C^{12}H_3Br^{81}$	9,531.845 ± 0.015	129.0 ± 0.2	10.7 ± 0.7	422, 545, 678
$C^{12}D_3Br^{79}$	7,714.57			763, 837
$C^{12}D_3Br^{81}$	7,681.23			763, 837
$C^{13}H_3Br^{79}$	9,119.507	129	11.1	680
$C^{13}H_3Br^{81}$	9,082.860	129	10.7	680
$C^{12}H_3I^{127}$	7,501.310 ± 0.007	99.4 ± 0.5	7.95 ± 0.09	422, 678
$C^{12}D_3I^{127}$	6,040.28			763, 837
$C^{13}H_3I^{127}$	7,119.04 ‡			422
$C^{12}H_3C^{12}N^{14}$	9,198.83	178		644, 620
$C^{12}H_3C^{12}N^{15}$	8,921.81			620
$C^{12}H_3C^{13}N^{14}$	9,194.28			644, 620
$C^{12}D_3C^{12}N^{14}$	7,857.93	113		644
$C^{12}D_3C^{13}N^{14}$	7,848.51	110		644
$C^{13}H_3C^{12}N^{14}$	8,933.15			620
$C^{12}H_3N^{14}C^{12}$	10,052.90	223		644
$C^{13}H_3N^{14}C^{13}$	9,695.91	141		644
$C^{12}D_3N^{14}C^{12}$	8,582.06	130		644
$C^{12}D_3N^{14}C^{13}$	8,278.79			644
$C^{12}H_3C^{12}C^{12}H$	8,545.87 ± 0.03	164 ± 2	3.12	688, 712
$C^{12}H_3C^{12}C^{12}D$	7,788.14 ± 0.03	140		688
$C^{12}H_3C^{12}C^{13}H$	8,290.24 ± 0.03	130		688
$C^{12}H_3C^{13}C^{12}H$	8,542.28 ± 0.03	160		688
$C^{13}H_3C^{12}C^{12}H$	8,313.23 ± 0.03	160		688
$C^{12}D_3C^{12}C^{12}D$	6,734.31 ± 0.03	90		688
$C^{12}H_3C^{12}C^{12}Br^{79}$	1,561.11	11.4		672, 839
$C^{12}H_3C^{12}C^{12}Br^{81}$	1,550.42	11.1		672, 839

Table A.4. Molecular rotational constants from microwave spectroscopy—Continued

Symmetric-Top Molecules—Continued

Molecule	B_0 (Mc)	D_{JK} (kc)	D_J (kc)	Bibliography Reference
$C^{12}H_3C^{12}C^{12}I^{127}$	1,259.02	7.2		839
$C^{12}H_3C^{12}F_3^{19}$	5,185.3 ± 0.5 ‡			412
$C^{12}H_3C^{12}Cl_3^{35}$	2,372.6			811
$C^{12}H_3Si^{28}H_3$	10,968.96			650
$C^{12}H_3Si^{28}D_3$	9,622.78			650
$C^{12}H_3Si^{29}H_3$	10,885.54			650
$C^{12}H_3Si^{29}D_3$	9,572			650
$C^{12}H_3Si^{30}H_3$	10,806.53			650
$C^{12}H_3Si^{30}D_3$	9,525			650
$C^{12}H_3Si^{28}F_3^{19}$	3,715.63			759
$C^{12}H_3Si^{28}Cl_3^{35}$	1,769.83			c
$C^{12}H_3Si^{28}Cl_3^{37}$	1,699.79			c
$C^{12}H_3Sn^{116}H_3$	6,910.50 ± 0.03 ‡			735
$C^{12}H_3Sn^{117}H_3$	6,905.30 ± 0.03 ‡			735
$C^{12}H_3Sn^{118}H_3$	6,900.20 ± 0.03 ‡			735
$C^{12}H_3Sn^{119}H_3$	6,895.13 ± 0.03 ‡			735
$C^{12}H_3Sn^{120}H_3$	6,890.17 ± 0.03 ‡			735
$C^{12}H_3Hg^{198}Cl]^{35}$	2,077.44	21.0		632; b
$C^{12}H_3Hg^{198}Cl]^{37}$	2,006.14	19.5		632; b
$C^{12}H_3Hg^{199}Cl]^{35}$	2,077.13	21.0		632; b
$C^{12}H_3Hg^{199}Cl]^{37}$	2,005.79	19.5		632; b
$C^{12}H_3Hg^{200}Cl]^{35}$	2,076.82	21.0		632; b
$C^{12}H_3Hg^{200}Cl]^{37}$	2,005.45	19.5		632; b
$C^{12}H_3Hg^{202}Cl]^{35}$	2,076.20	21.0		632; b
$C^{12}H_3Hg^{202}Cl]^{37}$	2,004.76	19.5		632; b

$C^{12}H_3Hg^{204}Cl^{35}$	2,075.59	21.0		632; b
$C^{12}H_3Hg^{204}Cl^{37}$	2,004.09	19.5		632; b
$C^{12}H_3Hg^{198}Br^{81}$	1,125.5 ± 0.2			632; b
$C^{12}H_3Hg^{202}Br^{79}$	1,140.0 ± 0.2			632; b
$C^{12}H_3Hg^{202}Br^{81}$	1,122.2 ± 0.2			632; b
$C^{12}HF_3^{19}$	10,348.74			520
$C^{12}DF_3^{19}$	9,921.35			811
$C^{13}HF_3^{19}$	10,422.00			811
$C^{12}HCl_3^{35}$	3,301.94 ± 0.01 ‡			689
$C^{12}HCl_3^{37}$	3,129.51 ± 0.01			811
$C^{12}DCl_3^{35}$	3,250.17 ± 0.01 ‡			689
$C^{12}HBr_3^{79}$	1,247.61 ± 0.025			694; d
$C^{12}HBr_3^{81}$	1,217.30 ± 0.025			694; d
$C^{12}DBr_3^{79}$	1,239.45 ± 0.025			d
$C^{12}DBr_3^{81}$	1,209.51 ± 0.025			d
$C^{12}F_3^{19}Cl^{35}$	3,335.56			512
$C^{12}F_3^{19}Cl^{37}$	3,251.51			512
$C^{12}F_3^{19}Br^{79}$	2,098.06	1.26		666, 838
$C^{12}F_3^{19}Br^{81}$	2,078.50	1.22		666, 838
$C^{12}F_3^{19}I^{129}$	1,523.23	0.6		838
$C^{12}F_3^{19}C^{12}N^{14}$	2,945.535	5.8	0.4	838
$C^{12}F_3^{19}C^{12}N^{15}$	2,855.859	5.6	0.4	838
$C^{12}F_3^{19}C^{12}C^{12}H$	2,877.948	6.3	0.24	706, 760a
$C^{12}F_3^{19}C^{12}C^{12}D$	2,696.073	6.2	0.26	706, 760a
$C^{12}F_3^{19}C^{13}C^{12}H$	2,854.99 ± 0.04			760a
$C^{12}F_3^{19}C^{12}C^{13}H$	2,787.63 ± 0.04			760a

Table A.4. Molecular rotational constants from microwave spectroscopy—Continued

Symmetric-Top Molecules—Continued

Molecule	B_0 (Mc)	D_{JK} (kc)	D_J (kc)	Bibliography Reference
$C^{12}F_3{}^{19}S^{32}F_5{}^{19}$	$1,097.6 \pm 0.4$			825
$(C^{12}H_3)_3C^{12}Cl^{35}$	$3,016$			693
$(C^{12}H_3)_3C^{12}Cl^{37}$	$2,954$			693
$(C^{12}H_3)_3C^{12}Br^{79}$	$2,044$			693
$(C^{12}H_3)_3C^{12}Br^{81}$	$2,028$			693
$(C^{12}H_3)_3C^{12}I^{127}$	$1,562$			693
$C^{12}H_2O^{16}C^{12}H_2O^{16}C^{12}H_2O^{16}$	$5,273.6 \ddagger$			701
1-bromo, bicyclo 2,2,2 octane				
$C_8{}^{12}H_{13}Br^{79}$	726.20 ± 0.07			832
$C_8{}^{12}H_{13}Br^{81}$	718.85 ± 0.07			832
$Si^{28}H_3F^{19}$	$14,327.9$			668
$Si^{29}H_3F^{19}$	$14,196.7$			668
$Si^{30}H_3F^{19}$	$14,072.6$			668
$Si^{28}H_3Cl^{35}$	$6,673.8$			444, 515
$Si^{28}H_3Cl^{37}$	$6,512.4$			444, 515
$Si^{30}H_3Cl^{35}$	$6,485.8$			515
$Si^{28}H_3Br^{79}$	$4,321.77$			543
$Si^{28}H_3Br^{81}$	$4,292.63$			543
$Si^{29}H_3Br^{79}$	$4,232.96$			543
$Si^{29}H_3Br^{81}$	$4,203.70$			543

Si^{30}H$_3$Br^{79}	4,149.39			543
Si^{30}H$_3$Br^{81}	4,120.09			543
Si^{28}H$_3$I^{127}	3,215.6			h
Si^{28}HCl$_3{}^{35}$	2,472.45			c
Si^{28}HCl$_3{}^{37}$	2,346.07			c
Si^{28}F$_3{}^{19}$H	7,207.98			759
Si^{29}F$_3{}^{19}$H	7,195.66			759
Si^{30}F$_3{}^{19}$H	7,183.70			759
Si^{28}F$_3{}^{19}$Cl^{35}	2,477.79	1.8		759
Si^{28}F$_3{}^{19}$Cl^{37}	2,413.06			759
Si^{28}F$_3{}^{19}$Br^{79}	1,549.98	0.8		759
Si^{28}F$_3{}^{19}$Br^{81}	1,534.14	0.8		759
Mn^{55}O$_3{}^{16}$F^{19}	4,129.11			817
Ge^{70}H$_3$Cl^{35}	4,401.71			515
Ge^{74}H$_3$Cl^{35}	4,333.91			515
Ge^{74}H$_3$Cl^{37}	4,177.90			515
Ge^{76}H$_3$Cl^{37}	4,146.5			515
Ge^{70}H$_3$Br^{79}	2,438.57			667
Ge^{70}H$_3$Br^{81}	2,410.17			667
Ge^{72}H$_3$Br^{79}	2,406.42			667
Ge^{72}H$_3$Br^{81}	2,378.01			667
Ge^{74}H$_3$Br^{79}	2,375.88			667
Ge^{74}H$_3$Br^{81}	2,347.46			667
Ge^{76}H$_3$Br^{79}	2,346.84			667
Ge^{76}H$_3$Br^{81}	2,318.37			667
Ge^{70}F$_3{}^{19}$Cl^{35}	2,168.52	$<|1|$	0.6	705
Ge^{70}F$_3{}^{19}$Cl^{37}	2,108.13	$<|1|$	0.6	705
Ge^{72}F$_3{}^{19}$Cl^{35}	2,167.53	$<|1|$	0.6	705

Table A.4. Molecular rotational constants from microwave spectroscopy—*Continued*

Symmetric-Top Molecules—Continued

Molecule	B_0 (Mc)	D_{JK} (kc)	D_J (kc)	Bibliography Reference
$Ge^{72}F_3^{19}Cl^{37}$	2,107.04	$<\lvert 1\rvert$	0.6	705
$Ge^{74}F_3^{19}Cl^{35}$	2,166.60	$<\lvert 1\rvert$	0.6	705
$Ge^{74}F_3^{19}Cl^{37}$	2,105.98	$<\lvert 1\rvert$	0.6	705
$Re^{185}O_3^{16}Cl^{35}$	$2,094.23 \pm 0.02$			801
$Re^{185}O_3^{16}Cl^{37}$	$2,025.02 \pm 0.02$			801
$Re^{187}O_3^{16}Cl^{35}$	$2,093.59 \pm 0.02$			801, 702
$Re^{187}O_3^{16}Cl^{37}$	$2,024.36 \pm 0.02$			801, 702

Asymmetric-Top Molecules

Molecule	$\frac{1}{2}(B + C)$ (Mc)	Bibliography Reference
	Almost Linear Asymmetric-Top Molecules	
$HN^{14}N^{14}N^{14}$	$11,907.78 \pm 0.03$	601, 752, 834
$HN^{14}N^{14}N^{15}$	11,524.1	601
$HN^{14}N^{15}N^{14}$	11,907	601
$HN^{15}N^{14}N^{14}$	11,548.4	601
$DN^{14}N^{14}N^{14}$	11,158.1	601
$HN^{14}C^{12}O^{16}$	10,990.9	643
$HN^{15}C^{12}O^{16}$	10,661.8	643
$DN^{14}C^{12}O^{16}$	10,197.4	643
$HN^{14}C^{12}S^{32}$	$B = 5,884.3$ $C = 5,846.8$	607
$HN^{14}C^{12}S^{34}$	5,729	607
$HN^{14}C^{13}S^{32}$	5,847	607

DN^{14}C^{12}S^{32}	5,474	607
DN^{14}C^{13}S^{32}	5,460	607

Almost Axially Symmetric-Top Molecules

C^{12}H$_3$S^{32}C^{12}N^{14}	2,837	505
C^{12}H$_3$N^{14}C^{12}S^{32}	2,526	505
C^{12}H$_3$N^{14}C^{12}S^{34}	2,461	505
C^{12}H$_2$DCl^{35}	12,329	654
C^{12}H$_2$DCl^{37}	12,133	654
C^{12}HD$_2$Cl^{35}	11,527 $2(B - C) = 617.90$	654, 744; e
C^{12}HD$_2$Cl^{37}	11,337	654
C^{12}HD$_2$Br^{79}	$2(B - C) = 317.70$	e
C^{12}HD$_2$Br^{81}	$2(B - C) = 314.44$	e
C^{12}HD$_2$I^{127}	$2(B - C) = 195.44$	e
C^{12}H$_3$S^{32}H	12,645.5 ± 0.1	758
C^{12}H$_3$S^{34}H	12,440 ± 5	758
B^{10}B$_4{}^{11}$H$_9$	$3A + B = 28,513$	815
(B^{10} in ring)	$A + 3B = 28,187$	815
B$_2{}^{10}$B$_3{}^{11}$H$_9$	$3A + B = 28,872$	815
(B^{10} in ring and apex)	$A + 3B = 28,538$	815
B$_2{}^{10}$B$_3{}^{11}$H$_9$	$3A + B = 29,024$	815
(two B^{10} in ring opposite)		
B$_2{}^{10}$B$_3{}^{11}$H$_9$	$3A + B = 28,695$	815
(two B^{10} in ring adjacent)	$A + 3B = 28,685$	815
B$_3{}^{10}$B$_2{}^{11}$H$_9$	$A + 3B = 28,870$	815
(B^{11} in ring and apex)		
B$_3{}^{10}$B$_2{}^{11}$H$_9$	$3A + B = 29,057$	815
(two B^{11} in ring adjacent)	$A + 3B = 29,045$	815

Table A.4. Molecular rotational constants from microwave spectroscopy—Continued

Asymmetric-Top Molecules

Molecule	A (Mc)	B (Mc)	C (Mc)	κ	Bibliography Reference
HDO^{16}	700,700		191,400	−0.696	550
HDS^{32}	290,300	145,200	94,130	−0.47767	727
O_3^{16}	106,530.0 ± 1.1	13,349.06 ± 0.06	11,834.3 ± 1.1		816, *i*
$S^{32}O_2S^{32}O_2^{16}$	60,776.7	10,317.7	8,799.5		710, 764
$N^{14}O^{16}F^{19}$	95,191.73	11,843.91	10,508.45	−0.968460	738
$N^{14}O^{16}Cl^{35}$	85,286	5,738	5,376		751
$N^{14}O^{16}Cl^{37}$	85,556	5,600	5,256		751
$C^{12}H_2O^{16}$	282,106	38,834	34,004	−0.961067	734, 509
$C^{12}H_2C^{12}O^{16}$		10,293.29	9,915.87	−0.997245	605, 730, 821
$C^{12}HDC^{12}O^{16}$		9,647.05	9,174.63	−0.994916	605, 730, 821
$C^{12}D_2C^{12}O^{16}$		9,120.80	8,552.66	−0.991460	605, 730, 821
$C^{12}F_2^{19}O^{16}$		$\dfrac{A-C}{2} = 2,966.2$		0.9796	765
$C^{12}H_2F_2^{19}$	49,138	10,604	9,249		829
$C^{12}H_2Cl_2^{35}$	32,001.8	3,320.4	3,065.2		*f*
$C^{12}H_2Cl^{35}Cl^{37}$	31,878.25	3,231.5	2,988.25		*f*
$C^{12}H_2Cl_2^{37}$	31,754	3,143	2,912		*f*
$C^{12}HDCl_2^{35}$	27,198	3,305	3,027		*f*
$C^{12}HDCl^{35}Cl^{37}$	27,090.5	3,217.5	2,951.5		*f*
$C^{12}D_2Cl_2^{35}$	23,676.5	3,284	2,993.5		*f*
$C^{12}D_2Cl^{35}Cl^{37}$	23,582	3,197.5	2,920		*f*

$C^{12}H_2C^{12}F_2^{19}$	11,001.8		5,345.6	0.7973	542
$C^{12}H_2C^{12}HCl^{35}$		6,030.5	5,445.2	−0.9769	522
$C^{12}H_2C^{12}HCl^{35}$		5,903.7	5,341.3	−0.9779	522
$C^{12}H_2C^{12}HBr^{79}$		4,162.5 ± 0.2	3,862.6 ± 0.2		621, 708a
$C^{12}H_2C^{12}HBr^{81}$		4,138.2 ± 0.2	3,841.6 ± 0.2		621, 708a
$C^{12}H_2C^{12}HI^{127}$		3,258.7 ± 0.5	3,066.9 ± 0.5		750a
$C^{12}H_2C^{12}F^{19}Cl^{35}$			3,448.38	−0.542724	613
$C^{12}H_2C^{12}F^{19}Cl^{37}$			3,380.49	−0.568678	613
$HC^{12}O^{16}O^{16}H$		11,989.0	10,483.0		754
$C^{12}H_2O^{16}C^{12}H_2$	25,483.7 ± 0.6	22,120.9 ± 0.6	14,098.0 ± 0.6	0.40930 ± 0.00005	711
$C^{12}D_2O^{16}C^{12}D_2$	20,399 ± 0.7	15,457 ± 0.7	11,544 ± 0.7	−0.11615 ± 0.0001	711
$C^{12}H_2O^{16}C^{13}H_2$	25,291.2 ± 0.5	21,597.4 ± 0.5	13,825.2 ± 0.5	0.3557 ± 0.0001	711
$C^{12}H_2S^{32}C^{12}H_2$	21,974 ± 4	10,824.9 ± 0.2	8,026.3 ± 0.2	−0.5988 ± 0.0001	711
$C^{12}D_2S^{32}C^{12}D_2$	15,471 ± 3	9,197.6 ± 0.2	6,819.0 ± 0.2	−0.45015	711
$C^{12}H_2S^{34}C^{12}H_2$	21,974 ± 4	10,551.0 ± 0.2	7,874.7 ± 0.2	−0.62045	711
$B^{11}H_3B^{11}H_2Br^{79}$		3,369.65	3,141.48		621
$B^{11}H_3B^{11}H_2Br^{81}$		3,350.75	3,124.95		621
$B^{10}H_3B^{11}H_2Br^{79}$		3,523.72	3,278.42		621
$B^{10}H_3B^{11}H_2Br^{81}$			$\frac{1}{2}(B + C) = 3,383.2$		621

Table A.4. Molecular rotational constants from microwave spectroscopy—*Continued*

Asymmetric-Top Molecules—Continued

Molecule	A (Mc)	B (Mc)	C (Mc)	κ	Bibliography Reference
$B^{11}H_3B^{10}H_2Br^{79}$		3,398.6	3,176.0		621
$B^{11}H_3B^{10}H_2Br^{81}$		3,380.0	3,159.9		621
$C^{12}H_2C^{12}HC^{12}N^{14}$	49,076.2	4,971.33	4,514.05		g
Furan $C_4^{12}H_4O^{16}$	9,447.04		4,670.84	0.916142	764a
$S^{32}O_2^{16}F_2^{19}$	5,139.77	5,077.81	5,057.22		809
$S^{34}O_2^{16}F_2^{19}$	5,139.77	5,073.00	5,052.51		809

† These values derived from infrared measurements of G. Herzberg and K. N. Rao, *J. Chem. Phys. 17*, 1099 (1949).

‡ Values of B calculated from line frequencies reported in the literature if distortion constants are assumed to be zero.

§ *l*-type doubling constant.

(a) D. F. Smith (private communication).
(b) W. Gordy and J. Sheridan (to be published).
(c) R. C. Mockler, J. H. Bailey, and W. Gordy, *Phys. Rev. 87*, 172A (1952).
(d) J. Q. Williams, J. T. Cox, and W. Gordy, *J. Chem. Phys. 20*, 1524 (1952).
(e) S. L. Miller, L. C. Aamodt, G. Dousmanis, C. H. Townes, and J. Kraitchman, *J. Chem. Phys. 20*, 1112 (1952).
(f) R. J. Myers and W. D. Gwinn, *J. Chem. Phys. 20*, 1420 (1952).
(g) W. S. Wilcox, J. H. Goldstein, and J. W. Simmons (private communication).
(h) A. H. Sharbaugh, G. A. Heath, L. F. Thomas, and J. Sheridan, *Nature 171*, 87 (1953).
(i) R. Trambarulo, S. N. Ghosh, C. A. Burrus, Jr., and W. Gordy (to be published).

Table *A*.5. **Molecular dipole moments from the Stark effect in microwave spectroscopy**

Linear Molecules

Mole-cule	Vibrational State	Dipole Moment (Debye units)	Bibliography Reference
FCl	Ground	0.88 ± 0.02	519, 627
FBr	Ground	1.29	681
BrCl	Ground	0.57 ± 0.02	682
ICl	Ground	(0.65 ± 0.06) †	459
OCS	Ground	0.710 ± 0.004	675, 760
	$v_2 = 1$	0.700 ± 0.004	675
OCSe	Ground	0.754	553
	$v_1 = 1$	0.728	553
	$v_2 = 1$	0.730	553
HCN	Ground	3.00 ± 0.02	b
	$v_2 = 1$	2.957 ± 0.025	674
ClCN	Ground	2.802 ± 0.020	677
N_2O	Ground	0.166 ± 0.002	677
HCCCl	Ground	0.44 ± 0.01	559
HCCCN	Ground	3.6 ± 0.2	691

Symmetric-Top Molecules

Molecule	Dipole Moment (Debye units)	Bibliography Reference	Molecule	Dipole Moment (Debye units)	Bibliography Reference
NH_3	1.468 ± 0.009	708	CH_3Br	1.797 ± 0.015	677
PH_3	0.55 ± 0.01	736	CH_3I	1.647 ± 0.014	677
AsH_3	0.22 ± 0.02	736	CH_3CN	3.95 ± 0.06	620, b
SbH_3	0.116 ± 0.003	736	CH_3NC	3.83 ± 0.06	b
NF_3	0.234 ± 0.004	b	CH_3CF_3	2.321 ± 0.034	677
PF_3	1.025 ± 0.009	677, b	CH_3CCH	0.75 ± 0.01	b
AsF_3	2.815 ± 0.025	677	CH_3SnH_3	0.68 ± 0.03	735
POF_3	1.77 ± 0.02	664, b	CF_3CCH	2.36 ± 0.04	760a
SiH_3F	1.268 ± 0.013	668	SiH_3Cl	1.31	515, 516
SiH_3Br	1.31 ± 0.03	667	SiF_3H	1.26 ± 0.01	b
GeH_3Cl	2.13	515	BH_3CO	1.795 ± 0.010	552
Trioxane	2.08 ± 0.01	701		1.770 ± 0.010	552
CHF_3	1.645 ± 0.009	760		(excited vib.	
CH_3F	1.790 ± 0.015	b		state)	
CH_3Cl	1.869 ± 0.010	677	B_5H_9	2.13 ± 0.04	815

Table A.5.   Molecular dipole moments from the Stark effect in microwave spectroscopy—*Continued*

Asymmetric-Top Molecules

Molecule	μ_a ‡	μ_b ‡ (Debye units)	μ_c ‡	Bibliography Reference
H_2O	0	1.94 ± 0.06	0	418
D_2O	0	$1.87 \pm 1\%$	0	c
HDO	$0.64 \pm 1\%$	$1.70 \pm 1\%$	0	550, 453
HDS	1.02 ± 0.02	—	0	727
O_3	0	0.53 ± 0.02	0	a
SO_2	0	$1.59 \pm 1\%$	0	710
CH_2F_2	0	1.93	0	829
CH_2Cl_2	0	1.62	0	d
CH_2O	2.339 ± 0.013	0	0	760
CH_2CO	1.42 ± 0.01	0	0	821
CH_2F_2	0	1.93	0	829
CH_2Cl_2	0	1.62 ± 0.02	0	d
CH_2OCH_2 ⎿__⏌	0	1.88 ± 0.01	0	711
CH_2SCH_2 ⎿__⏌	1.84 ± 0.02	0	0	711
CH_2CF_2	1.366 ± 0.02	0	0	542
Furan	0.661 ± 0.006	0	0	764a
SO_2F_2	0.228 ± 0.004	0	0	809
NOF	1.70	0.62	0	738
NOCl	1.28 ± 0.04	—	0	751
HNCO	1.592 ± 0.010	—	0	762, 760
	1.620 ± 0.015 §	—		762
	1.760 ± 0.015 ‖	—	0	762
DNCO	1.619 ± 0.015	—	0	762
HNCS	1.72 ± 0.05	—	0	607
HN_3	0.847 ± 0.05	—	0	601
CH_3SH	1.26 ± 0.05	—	0	758
CH_3OH	0.895 (along C—O bond)			409
CH_2CHCN	3.68	1.25	0	e

† Estimated from intensities.

‡ Components of dipole moments along the principal axes *a, b, c.*

§ Dipole moment for a low-frequency bending vibration.

‖ Dipole moment for a high-frequency vibration.

(*a*) R. Trambarulo, S. N. Ghosh, C. A. Burrus, and W. Gordy (to be published).

(*b*) S. N. Ghosh, R. Trambarulo, and W. Gordy (to be published).

(*c*) C. I. Beard and D. R. Bianco, *J. Chem. Phys.* **20**, 1488 (1952).

(*d*) R. J. Myers and W. D. Gwinn, *J. Chem. Phys.* **20**, 1420 (1952).

(*e*) W. S. Wilcox, J. H. Goldstein, and J. W. Simmons (private communication).

Table $A.6$. Nuclear quadrupole couplings

From Microwave Spectra of Gases

Linear Molecules and Symmetric Tops

Nucleus	Molecule	$eQ \dfrac{\partial^2 V}{\partial z^2}$ † (Mc)	Bibliography Reference
B^{10}	BH_3CO	3.4 ± 0.1	631, 690
B^{11}	BH_3CO	1.55 ± 0.08	631, 524
N^{14}	NO	-1.7 ± 0.5	608
	N_2O	-1.03 ± 0.10 (end)	448
	N_2O	-0.27 (central)	304
	ClCN	-3.63 ± 0.1	458, 341
	BrCN	-3.83 ± 0.08	458
	ICN	-3.80	448
	HCN	-4.58 ± 0.05	679
	HCCCN	-4.2	691
	NH_3	-4.10 ± 0.02	428, 446, 772
	NF_3	-7.07 ± 0.10	673
	CH_3CN	-4.35 ± 0.20	644
	CF_3CN	-4.70	838
	CH_3NC	$< \lvert 0.51 \rvert$	644
	CH_3NH_2 ‡	$< \lvert 1 \rvert$	420
	HNCO ‡	2.00 ± 0.05	762
	HNCS ‡	1.2 ± 0.2	762
	HN_3 ‡	-4.67 ± 0.04 (end)	834
O^{17}	OCS	-1.32 ± 0.07	718, 810
S^{33}	OCS	-29.07 ± 0.01	456, 807
S^{35}	OCS	20.5 ± 0.2	773, 510
Cl^{35}	FCl	-146.0 ± 0.1	627, 519
	BrCl	-103.6 ± 0.15	682
	ICl	-82.5 ± 1	459
	ClCN	-83.2 ± 0.5	458, 449
	HCCCl	-79.67	559
	CH_3Cl	-75.3	422, 528
	CD_3Cl	-74.41	837
	CF_3Cl	-78.0 ± 0.2	512
	SiH_3Cl	-40.0	444
	SiF_3Cl	-43	759
	GeH_3Cl	-46 ± 1	557
	GeF_3Cl	<50	705
	CH_3HgCl	-42	a
Cl^{36}	ClCN	-18	555
	CH_3Cl	-15.87 ± 0.09	729a, 718a
Cl^{37}	FCl	-114.89 ± 0.13	627, 519
	BrCl	-81.14 ± 0.15	682

Table $A.6$.   Nuclear quadrupole couplings—*Continued*

Nucleus	Molecule	$eQ\dfrac{\partial^2 V}{\partial z^2}$ † (Mc)	Bibliography Reference
Cl³⁷	ClCN	-65.7 ± 0.5	458, 449
	HCCCl	-62.75	559
	DCCCl	-63.12	559
	CH₃Cl	-59.03	422, 528
	CD₃Cl	-58.58	837
	CF₃Cl	-61.4 ± 0.4	512
	SiH₃Cl	-30.8	444
	SiF₃Cl	-34	759
	GeH₃Cl	-36 ± 1	557
	CH₃HgCl	33	a
Mn⁵⁵	MnO₃F	16.8	817
Ge⁷³	GeH₃Cl	-95 ± 3	557
As⁷⁵	AsH₃(AsH₂D)	-164	736
	AsF₃	-235	411
	AsCl₃	-173 ± 20	731
Se⁷⁹	OCSe	754 ± 3	813
Br⁷⁹	FBr	1089.0	681
	BrCl	876.8 ± 0.9	682
	BrCN	686.06 ± 0.45	458, 449, 845
	CH₃Br	577.3	545, 422
	CD₃Br	574.6	837
	CF₃Br	619	838
	SiH₃Br	336	543
	SiF₃Br	440	759
	GeH₃Br	380	667
	CH₃CCBr	647	839
	CH₃HgBr	325	a
Br⁸¹	FBr	909.2	681
	BrCl	732.9 ± 0.5	682
	BrCN	572.27 ± 0.09	458, 449, 845
	CH₃Br	482.4	545, 422
	CD₃Br	479.8	837
	CF₃Br	517	838
	SiH₃Br	278	543
	SiF₃Br	370	759
	GeH₃Br	321	667
	CH₃CCBr	539	839
	CH₃HgBr	270	a
Sb¹²¹	SbH₃	455	736
Sb¹²³	SbH₃	575	736

Table A.6. Nuclear quadrupole couplings—*Continued*

Nucleus	Molecule	$eQ \dfrac{\partial^2 V}{\partial z^2}$ [†] (Mc)	Bibliography Reference
I[127]	ICl	-2930 ± 4	459
	ICN	-2420 ± 1	401, 449
	CH_3I	-1934	422
	CD_3I	-1929	837
	CF_3I	-2150	838
	CH_3CCI	-2230	839
	SiH_3I	-1240 ± 30	s
I[129]	CH_3I	-1422	531
Re[185]	ReO_3Cl	~ 775	801
Re[187]	ReO_3Cl	~ 775	801

Asymmetric Tops

Nucleus	Molecule	$eQ \dfrac{\partial^2 V}{\partial a^2}$ [§] (Mc)	$eQ \dfrac{\partial^2 V}{\partial b^2}$ [§] (Mc)	$eQ \dfrac{\partial^2 V}{\partial c^2}$ [§] (Mc)	Bibliography Reference
N[14]	NO_2F	0.7	1.5	-2.2	841
	CH_2CHCN	-3.0	—	—	b
Cl[35]	ClF_3	-81	-65	146	840
	CH_2Cl_2	-41.8 ± 1	2.6 ± 1	39.2 ± 1	c
	CH_2CHCl	-57.4	26.2		522
	CH_2CFCl	-73.3 ± 0.3	39.8 ± 0.2		613
	NOCl	29.9 ± 1.0	19.6 ± 2.0	-49.5 ± 1.0	751
Cl[37]	NOCl	23 ± 5	14 ± 9	-37 ± 6	751
Br[79]	C_2H_3Br	469 ± 5	-219 ± 3		708a, 621
	B_2H_5Br	293			621
Br[81]	C_2H_3Br	393 ± 5	-181 ± 3		708a, 621
	B_2H_5Br	244			621
I[127]	C_2H_3I	-1650 ± 50	800 ± 80		750a

From Pure Quadrupole Spectra in Solids

Nucleus	Molecule	$\left\lvert eQ \dfrac{\partial^2 V}{\partial z^2} \right\rvert$ [¶] (Mc)	T (° K)	Reference
B[10]	$B(CH_3)_3$	10.15		d ‖
	$B(C_2H_5)_3$	10.42		d ‖
B[11]	$B(CH_3)_3$	4.87		d ‖
	$B(C_2H_5)_3$	5.00		d ‖
N[14]	$(CH_2)_6N_4$	4.40	300	e ‖
	BrCN	3.28	297	e ‖
	ICN	3.39	300	e ‖

Table $A.6$. Nuclear quadrupole couplings—*Continued*

From Pure Quadrupole Spectra in Solids

Nucleus	Molecule	$\left\| eQ \dfrac{\partial^2 V}{\partial z^2} \right\|$ ¶ (Mc)	T (° K)	Reference
Cl^{35}	Cl_2	108.95	20	f
	ClF_3	149.9	20	840
	CH_3Cl	68.40	20	f
	CH_2Cl_2	72.47	20	f, g
	$CHCl_3$	76.98	20	f, g
	CCl_4	81.85	20	f
	CHF_2Cl	70.50	20	f
	CF_3Cl	77.58	20	f
	CF_2BrCl	77.35	20	f
	$CHFCl_2$	73.53	20	f
	CF_2Cl_2	78.16	20	f
	$CFCl_3$	79.63	20	f
	trans-$CHClCHCl$	70.960 ± 0.006	83	h, i
	cis-$HCClCHCl$	70.0	20	l
	C_6H_5Cl	69.24	80	g
	$SOCl_2$	63.99	80	g
	$POCl_3$	57.92	80	g
	CH_3CCl_3	76.3	20	l
	CH_3CHCl_2	71.2	20	l
	CH_3CH_2Cl	66.0	20	l
	$(CH_3)_2CHCl$	64.1	20	l
	$(CH_3)_3CCl$	62.3	20	l
	CCl_3CCl_3	81.6	20	l
	CCl_3CHCl_2	79.9 (—CCl_3)	20	l
		77.7 (—$CHCl_2$)	20	l
	CH_2ClCH_2Cl	68.9	20	l
	$CH_3CH_2CH_2Cl$	66.4	20	l
	$C_2H_5(CH_3)_2CCl$	61.9	20	l
	$CH_2ClCHClCH_2Cl$	69.7	20	l
	CH_2FCl	67.6	20	l
	$C_6H_5CH_2Cl$	67.3	77	l
	$SnCl_4$	48.2	77	l
	$SiCl_4$	40.8	77	l
	$GeCl_4$	51.3	77	l
	PCl_3	52.3	77	l
	$AsCl_3$	50.5	20	l
	BCl_3	43.2	77	l
	$SbCl_3$	40.2	77	l
	HCl	53.4	20	l
	$COCl_2$	71.3	77	l
	FCl	141.4	20	m
	CH_2CHCl	67 ± 2		n
	$CH_2ClCOOH$	73.15	Ext. to 0	o

Table A.6. Nuclear quadrupole couplings—*Continued*

Nucleus	Molecule	$\left\| eQ\dfrac{\partial^2 V}{\partial z^2} \right\|$ ¶ (Mc)	T (° K)	Reference
Cl³⁵	$CH_2ClCOOC_2H_5$	72.50	Ext. to 0	*o*
	$CH_2ClCOCH_2Cl$	72.46	Ext. to 0	*o*
	$(CH_2ClCHO)_3$	71.55	Ext. to 0	*o*
	$CH_2ClCOCH_3$	70.98	Ext. to 0	*o*
	$CH_2ClCONH_2$	70.06	Ext. to 0	*o*
	$CH_2ClCOONa$	70.00	Ext. to 0	*o*
	$CCl_3CH(OH)_2$	$\begin{Bmatrix}76.68\\79.25\end{Bmatrix}$	Ext. to 0	*o*
	CCl_3CONH_2	79.11	77	*o*
	CCl_3COOH	80.25	77	*o*
	CCl_3COCl	$\begin{Bmatrix}67.44\\80.81\end{Bmatrix}$	77	*o*
	$CHCl_2COOH$	76.79	77	*o*
Cl³⁷	CH_2Cl_2	56.73	77	*g*
	$CHCl_3$	60.34	77	*g*
	trans-$CHClCHCl$	55.926 ± 0.006	83	*h, i*
	C_6H_5Cl	54.57	77	*g*
	$SOCl_2$	50.43	77	*g*
	$POCl_3$	45.65	77	*g*
	$SbCl_3$	30.23	83	*r*
Cu⁶³	Cu_2O	52.04	289	*p*
	$K[Cu(CN)_2]$	66.96	289	*p*
Cu⁶⁵	Cu_2O	48.16	289	*p*
	$K[Cu(CN)_2]$	61.96	289	*p*
As⁷⁵	As_4O_6	232.52	292.5	*q*
Sb¹²¹	$SbCl_3$	383.66	83	*r*
Sb¹²³	$SbCl_3$	489.21	83	*r*
Br⁷⁹	Br_2	765	83	*j*
	CH_3Br	528.90 ± 0.06	83	*i*
Br⁸¹	Br_2	639	83	*j*
	CH_3Br	441.82 ± 0.06	83	*i*
I¹²⁷	I_2	2153	300	*k*
	ICl	3037	90	*k*
	ICN	2549	300	*k*
	CH_3I	1753	90	*k*
	trans-$CHICHI$	1847	90	*k*
	SnI_4	1363	300	*k*
Bi²⁰⁹	$Bi(C_6H_5)_3$	669	300	*t*

Notes to Table $A.6$.

† In the coupling $eQ(\partial^2 V/\partial z^2)$, the axis z is the symmetry axis (except for molecules marked ‡) and is sometimes designated in the literature by V_{zz}, φ_{zz}, or simply q.

‡ These molecules are nearly symmetrical, and the couplings along the near axis of symmetry are given.

§ In the coupling constants, a, b, c, are the principal axes of the molecule's momental ellipsoid such that $I_a < I_b < I_c$. The quantities $\partial^2 V/\partial a^2$, etc., are frequently written in the literature as V_{aa}, etc.

‖ Calculated from the frequencies when cylindrical symmetries are assumed.

¶ Only the magnitudes of the nuclear quadrupole couplings are obtained from the quadrupole spectra. Quantities listed in the third column represent the average couplings. The z axis is taken as the symmetry axis (or the bond axis for asymmetrical molecules). In papers by Dehmelt and Krüger $\partial^2 V/\partial z^2$ is denoted by φ_{zz}. For atoms with a spin of $\frac{3}{2}$ axial symmetry is assumed.

(a) W. Gordy and J. Sheridan (to be published).

(b) W. S. Wilcox, J. H. Goldstein, and J. W. Simmons (private communication).

(c) R. J. Myers and W. D. Gwinn, *J. Chem. Phys.* **20**, 1420 (1952).

(d) H. G. Dehmelt (private communication).

(e) G. D. Watkins and R. V. Pound, *Phys. Rev.* **85**, 1062 (1952).

(f) R. Livingston, *J. Chem. Phys.* **19**, 1434 (1951).

(g) R. Livingston, *Phys. Rev.* **82**, 289L (1951).

(h) H. G. Dehmelt and H. Krüger, *Naturwiss* **37**, 111 (1950).

(i) H. G. Dehmelt and H. Krüger, *Z. Physik* **129**, 401 (1951).

(j) H. G. Dehmelt, *Z. Physik* **130**, 480 (1951).

(k) H. G. Dehmelt, *Naturwiss* **37**, 398 (1950).

(l) R. Livingston (private communication).

(m) R. Livingston and D. F. Smith (private communication).

(n) J. H. Goldstein and R. Livingston, *J. Chem. Phys.* **19**, 1613 (1951).

(o) H. C. Allen, Jr. (private communication).

(p) H. Krüger and U. Meyer-Berkhout, *Z. Physik* **132**, 171 (1952).

(q) H. Krüger and U. Meyer-Berkhout, *Z. Physik* **132**, 221 (1952).

(r) H. G. Dehmelt and H. Krüger, *Z. Physik* **130**, 385 (1951).

(s) A. H. Sharbaugh, G. A. Heath, L. F. Thomas, J. Sheridan, *Nature* **171**, 87 (1953).

(t) H. G. Robinson, H. G. Dehmelt, and W. Gordy, Phys. Rev. (in press).

Table A.7. Nuclear moments from microwave spectra

Atom	Spin, I in $h/2\pi$	Bibliography Reference	Quadrupole Moment, Q in 10^{-24} cm^2	Bibliography Reference	Magnetic Moment, μ in n.m.	Bibliography Reference
B^{10}	3	421, 690	$+0.06$	631		
B^{11}	$\frac{3}{2}$	421	$+0.03$	631		
N^{14}	(1) †		$+0.02$	556		
			$+0.01$	673		
O^{17}	($\frac{5}{2}$) †	718	-0.005 ± 0.002	718		
O^{18}	0	743				
S^{33}	$\frac{3}{2}$	456	-0.08	556	0.63 ± 0.01	623
S^{35}	$\frac{3}{2}$	510	$+0.06$	510		
Cl^{35}	$\frac{3}{2}$	341, 317	(-0.066) ‡	458		
Cl^{36}	2	555	-0.0172 ± 0.0004	555		
		729a	-0.0168 ± 0.0001	729a		
Cl^{37}	$\frac{3}{2}$	341, 317	(-0.052) ‡	458		
Cu^{63}	($\frac{3}{2}$) †		$-0.12_7 \pm 0.01$	709P, 703P		
Cu^{65}	($\frac{3}{2}$) †		$-0.11_7 \pm 0.01$	709P, 703P		
Ge^{73}	$\frac{9}{2}$	557	-0.2 ± 0.1	557		
Se^{79}	$\frac{7}{2}$	813	$+1.2$	813		
Br^{79}	($\frac{3}{2}$) †		$+0.28$	458		
			$+0.31$	722		
Br^{81}	($\frac{3}{2}$) †		$+0.23$	458		
			$+0.26$	722		
Sb^{121}	($\frac{5}{2}$) †		-0.35 to -0.50	736		
Sb^{123}	($\frac{7}{2}$) †		-0.45 to -0.62	736		
I^{127}	($\frac{5}{2}$) †		-0.75	458		
			-0.65	722		
I^{129}	$\frac{7}{2}$	531	-0.47	531, 722	(2.72) ‡	523
Nd^{143}	$\frac{7}{2}$	609P	≤ 25	609P, 720P	1.4	609P, 720P
Nd^{145}	$\frac{7}{2}$	609P	≤ 25	609P, 720P	0.85	609P, 720P
Sm^{147}	$\frac{7}{2}$	802P	$|<0.72|$	802P, 805P	0.68 ± 0.1	802P, 805P
Sm^{149}	$\frac{7}{2}$	802P	$|<0.72|$	802P, 805P	0.55 ± 0.1	802P, 805P
Er^{167}	$\frac{7}{2}$	715P	$|10.2|$ [a]	715P, 720P	0.6	715P, 720P
V^{50}	6	809aP,[b]				
Cr^{53}	$\frac{3}{2}$	708aP			0.5 ± 0 1	802aP

Spins Indicated by Absence of Hyperfine Structure

	Spin Indicated	Bibliography Reference
Si^{29}	$\frac{1}{2}$	557, 668
Si^{30}	0	557, 668
S$^{34, 36}$	0	458, 534
Ge$^{70, 72, 74, 76}$	0	557
Se$^{74, 76, 78, 80, 82}$	0	553
Se^{77}	$\frac{1}{2}$	553

† Spin previously known.
‡ More accurate values than these are now known from measurements of other types.
[a] Bogle, Duffus, and Scovil, *Proc. Phys. Soc.* (*London*) *A65*, 761 (1952).
[b] J. M. Baker and B. Bleaney, *Proc. Phys. Soc.* (*London*) *65*, 952 (1952).

Table A.8.   Mass ratios from microwave spectroscopy

Molecules	Mass Ratio	Bibliography Reference
FC	$\dfrac{Cl^{35}}{Cl^{37}} = 0.945977 \pm 0.000004$	519
ICl	$\dfrac{Cl^{35}}{Cl^{37}} = 0.945980 \pm 0.000005$	459
ClCN	$\dfrac{Cl^{37} - Cl^{35}}{Cl^{36} - Cl^{35}} = 1.9968$	768
OCS	$\dfrac{O^{17} - O^{16}}{O^{18} - O^{17}} = 1.00420$	534
SiH$_3$Cl	$\dfrac{Si^{30} - Si^{29}}{Si^{30} - Si^{28}} = 0.49941 \pm 0.00005$	716
OCS	$\dfrac{S^{33} - S^{32}}{S^{34} - S^{32}} = 0.500714 \pm 0.00003$	716
OCS	$\dfrac{S^{35} - S^{32}}{S^{34} - S^{32}} = 1.50155 \pm 0.00015$	773
OCS	$\dfrac{S^{35} - S^{32}}{S^{33} - S^{32}} = 2.99881 \pm 0.00030$	773
OCS	$\dfrac{S^{36} - S^{34}}{S^{34} - S^{32}} = 1.00183 \pm 0.00015$	534
OCSe	$\dfrac{Se^{76} - Se^{74}}{Se^{80} - Se^{74}} = 0.33308$	a
OCSe	$\dfrac{Se^{77} - Se^{76}}{Se^{80} - Se^{77}} = 0.33394$	a
OCSe	$\dfrac{Se^{78} - Se^{76}}{Se^{80} - Se^{78}} = 0.99935$	a
OCSe	$\dfrac{Se^{82} - Se^{76}}{Se^{82} - Se^{80}} = 2.9985$	a
GeH$_3$Cl	$\dfrac{Ge^{72} - Ge^{70}}{Ge^{74} - Ge^{72}} = 0.99911$	716
GeH$_3$Cl	$\dfrac{Ge^{76} - Ge^{70}}{G^{76} - Ge^{72}} = 2.9976$	716

(a) Values compiled by Townes [768] from data of Strandberg, Wentink, and Hill [553] and from Geschwind, Minden, and Townes.[626]

Table A.9. Molecular structures from microwave spectra

Diatomic Molecules

Molecule	r_e (A)	Bibliography Reference
CO	1.128227	628
FCl	1.62811	519, 627
FBr	1.759	681
BrCl	2.138	682
ICl	2.323	459
NaCl	2.3606 ± 0.0003	844
CsCl	2.9041 ± 0.0003	844

Linear Polyatomic Molecules

Molecule	Bond Distance (A)		Bond Distance (A)		Bibliography Reference
HCN	CH	1.064	CN	1.156	679, 833
ClCN	CCl	1.629	CN	1.163	449, 458
BrCN	CBr	1.790	CN	1.159	449, 458
ICN	CI	1.995	CN	1.159	449
NNO	NN	1.126	NO	1.191	304, 511
OCS	CO	1.1637	CS	1.5584	554, 558, 773
OCSe	CO	1.1588	CSe	1.7090	553
TeCS	TeC	1.904	CS	1.557	836
HCCCl	CH	1.052	CC	1.211	559
	CCl	1.632			
HC≡C—CN	CH	1.057	C≡C	1.203	691
	C—C	1.382	CN	1.157	

Symmetric Tops

Molecule	Bond Angle		Bond Distance (A)		Bond Distance (A)		Bibliography Reference
BH₃CO	HBH	113° 52′	BH	1.194	BC	1.540	631
			CO	1.131			
B₅H₉ (C₄ᵥ symmetry)			BB (ring)	1.80 ± 0.01	BB (ring-apex)	1.69 ± 0.02	815
CH₃F	HCH	110° 0′	CH	1.109 ± 0.010	CF	1.385	520
CH₃Cl	HCH	$110° 20′ \pm 1°$	CH	1.103 ± 0.010	CCl	1.782 ± 0.003	422, 547, 744
CH₃Br	HCH	$110° 48′ \pm 1°$	CH	1.101 ± 0.010	CBr	1.938 ± 0.003	422, 680
CH₃I	HCH	$110° 58′ \pm 1°$	CH	1.100 ± 0.010	CI	2.140 ± 0.005	422, 547
CH₃CN	HCH	109° 8′	CH	1.092	CC	1.460	644
			CN	1.158			
CH₃N≅C	HCH	109° 46′	CH	1.094	CN	1.427	644
			N≅C	1.167			
CH₃C≡CH	HCH	108° 14′	CH	1.097 (methyl)	CC	1.460	688
			C≡C	1.207	≡CH	1.056	
CH₃C≡CBr	HCH	(109° 49′)	CH	(1.092 ± 0.01)	CC	1.46 ± 0.02	672, 839
			C≡C	(1.207 ± 0.004)	CBr	1.793 ± 0.005	
CH₃C≡CI	HCH	(109° 49′)	CH	(1.092)	CC	(1.459)	672, 839
			C≡C	(1.207 ± 0.004)	CI	1.991	
CH₃CF₃	HCH	(109° 28′)	CH	(1.093)	CC	(1.54)	412
	FCF	(109°)	CF	(1.33)			
CH₃CCl₃	HCH	(109° 28′)	CH	(1.093)	CC	1.55	811
	ClCCl	(110° 24′)	CCl	(1.767)			
CHF₃	FCF	108° 48′	CH	1.098	CF	1.332	811, 520
CHCl₃	ClCCl	110° 24′	CH	1.073	CCl	1.767	689, 811
CHBr₃	BrCBr	$110° 48′ \pm 16′$	CH	1.068 ± 0.010	CBr	1.930 ± 0.003	694; a

Table $A.9$.   Molecular structures from microwave spectra—*Continued*

Symmetric Tops—Continued

Molecule	Bond Angle		Bond Distance (A)		Bond Distance (A)		Bibliography Reference
CF₃Cl	FCF	(108°)	CF	1.328	CCl	1.740	512, 838
CF₃Br	FCF	(108°)	CF	1.33	CBr	1.908	666, 838
CF₃I	FCF	(108°)	CF	(1.33)	CI	2.134	838
CF₃CN	FCF	(108°)	CF	1.335	CC	1.464	838
			CN	(1.158)			
CF₃C≡CH	FCF	107.5° ± 1.0°	CF	1.335 ± 0.01	CC	1.464 ± 0.02	760a,
			CH	1.056 ± 0.005	C≡C	1.201 ± 0.002	702
CF₃SF₅	FCF	(107° 30′)	CF	(1.35)	CS	1.86	825
	FSF	(90°)	SF	(1.57)			
CH₃SnH₃	HSnH	(109° 28′)	SnH	1.700 ± 0.015	SnC	2.143 ± 0.002	735
	HCH	(109° 28′)	CH	(1.090)			
CH₃HgCl	HCH	109° 7′	CH	(1.092)	CHg	2.059	632; c
			HgCl	2.282			
CH₃HgBr	HCH	(109° 7′)	CH	(1.092)	CHg	2.07	632; c
			HgBr	2.406			
(CH₃)₃CCl	HCH	(109° 28′)	CH	(1.093)	CCl	1.78	693
	CCC	(109° 28′)	CC	(1.54)			
(CH₃)₃CBr	HCH	(109° 28′)	CH	(1.093)	CBr	1.94	693
	CCC	(109° 28′)	CC	(1.54)			
(CH₃)₃CI	HCH	(109° 28′)	CH	(1.093)	CI	2.14	693
	CCC	(109° 28′)	CC	(1.54)			
CH₂OCH₂OCH₂O ⌊_____⌋	COC	(109°)	CO	1.41			701
	OCO	(109°)					
1-bromo,bicyclo-[2,2,2]octane C₈H₁₃Br	(All angles tetrahedral) or if BrC(CH₂)₂ twisted 11.3° with respect to CH(CH₂)		C—Br C—H	(1.939) (1.10)	C—C C—C	1.555 ± 0.003 1.573	832 832
SiH₃F	HSiH	(111° ± 1°)	SiH	1.503 ± 0.036	SiF	1.593 ± 0.003	668
SiH₃Cl	HSiH	110° 57′	SiH	1.50	SiCl	2.048	444, 515
SiH₃Br	HSiH	111° 20′	SiH	1.57 ± 0.03	SiBr	2.209 ± 0.001	543
SiHCl₃	ClSiCl	109° 26′	SiH	(1.50)	SiCl	2.02	b
SiF₃H	FSiF	108° 6′ ± 30′	SiF	1.561 ± 0.005	SiH	(1.55 ± 0.05)	759
SiF₃Cl	FSiF	(108° 30′ ± 1°)	SiF	1.560 ± 0.005	SiCl	(1.989 ± 0.018)	759
SiF₃Br	FSiF	(108° 30′ ± 1°)	SiF	1.560 ± 0.005	SiBr	(2.153 ± 0.018)	759
SiF₃CH₃	FSiF	(109° 28′)	SiF	(1.555)	SiC	1.88	759
	HCH	(109° 28′)	CH	(1.10)			
SiCl₃CH₃	ClSiCl	(109° 46′)	SiCl	2.017	SiC	1.891	b
	HCH	(109° 28′)	CH	(1.093)			
GeH₃Cl	HGeH	111° 4′	GeH	1.52	GeCl	2.147	515
GeH₃Br	HGeH	112° 0′ ± 1′	GeH	1.55 ± 0.05	GeBr	2.297 ± 0.001	667
GeF₃Cl	FGeF	107.7° ± 1.5°	GeF	1.688 ± 0.017	GeCl	2.067 ± 0.005	705
NH₃	HNH	107° ± 2°	NH	1.016 ± 0.008			772
NF₃	FNF	102° 9′	NF	1.371			673
PH₃	HPH	93.5°	PH	1.419			736
PF₃	FPF	(100°)	PF	1.535			520, 848
PCl₃	ClPCl	100° 6′ ± 20	PCl	2.043 ± 0.003			646
POF₃	FPF	102.5° ± 2°	PF	1.52 ± 0.02	PO	1.45 ± 0.03	848
POCl₃	ClPCl	103.6° ± 2°	PCl	1.99 ± 0.02	PO	1.45 ± 0.03	848
PSF₃	FPF	100.3° ± 2°	PF	1.53 ± 0.02	PS	1.87 ± 0.03	848
PSCl₃	ClPCl	100.5° ± 1°	PCl	2.02 ± 0.01	PS	1.85 ± 0.02	848
AsH₃	HAsH	92.0°	AsH	1.523			736
AsF₃	FAsF	(100° ± 5°)	AsF	1.712 ± 0.006			411
AsCl₃	ClAsCl	98° 25′ ± 30′	AsCl	2.161 ± 0.004			646
SbH₃	HSbH	91.5°	SbH	1.712			736
SbCl₃	ClSbCl	99.5° ± 1.5°	SbCl	2.325 ± 0.005			731
ReO₃Cl	OReO	108° 20′ ± 1°	ReO	1.761 ± 0.003	ReCl	2.230 ± 0.004	801, 702

Table A.9. Molecular structures from microwave spectra—*Continued*

Asymmetric Tops

Molecule	Bond Angle		Bond Distance (A)		Bond Distance (A)		Bibliography Reference
ClF$_3$	FClF	174° 58′	ClF	1.70	ClF′	1.60	840; d
(ClF$_2$F′)	F′ClF	87° 29′					
HN$_3$	HN′N″	112° 39′ ± 30′	HN′	1.021 ± 0.01	N′N″	1.240 ± 0.003	601
(HN′N″N‴)	N′N″N‴	(180°)	N″N‴	1.134 ± 0.003			
HNCO	HNC	128° 5′ ± 30′	HN	0.987 ± 0.01	NC	1.207 ± 0.01	643
	NCO	(180°)	CO	1.171 ± 0.01			
HNCS	HNC	136°	HN	(1.01)	NC	1.218	607
	NCS	(180°)	CS	1.557			
CH$_3$OH	HCH	(109° 28′)	CH	(1.10)	CO	1.421	707a
	COH	110° 15′	OH	(0.958			
CH$_3$SH	HCH	(109° 28′)	CH	(1.10)	SH	1.34	758
	HSC	(100°)	CS	1.815			
CH$_3$N=C=S	HCH	(109°)	CH	(1.09)	CN	(1.47)	505
	CNC	142°	C=S	(1.56)	N=C	(1.22)	
CH$_3$SCN	HCH	(109°)	CH	(1.09)	CS	1.81	505
(CH$_3$SC′N)	CSC	142°	C′N	(1.21)	SC′	1.61	
HDO	HOD	104° ± 30′					550
HDS	HSD	92° 20′	HS	1.34	DS	1.34	727
SO$_2$	OSO	119.33°	SO	1.433			764, 710
O$_3$	OO′O	116° 49′ ± 30′	OO′	1.278 ± 0.003			816; h
NOF	ONF	110°	NO	1.13	NF	1.52	738
NO$_2$F	ONO	(125°)	NO	1.23	NF	(1.35)	841
	ONF	(117° 30′)					
CH$_2$O	HCH	118° ± 2°	CH	1.12 ± 0.01	CO	1.21 ± 0.01	734
CH$_2$CO	HCH	122.0° ± 2.5°	CH	1.075 ± 0.010	C′O	(1.16 ± 0.10)	821
(CH$_2$C′O)			CO	2.475 ± 0.003			
CH$_2$F$_2$	HCH	112°	CH	1.09	CF	1.36	829
	FCF	108°					
CH$_2$Cl$_2$	HCH	112° 0′ ± 20′	CH	1.068 ± 0.005	CCl	1.7724 ± 0.0005	e
	ClCCl	111° 47′ ± 1′					
CH$_2$CF$_2$	HCH	110°	CH	1.07	CC	1.31	542
	FCF	110°	CF	1.32			
CH$_2$OCH$_2$	HCH	116° 41′	CH	1.082	CO	1.436	711
⌞__⌟	COC	61° 24′	CC	1.472			
	H$_2$CC	159° 25′					
CH$_2$SCH$_2$	HCH	116° 00′	CH	1.078	CS	1.819	711
⌞__⌟	CSC	65° 48′	CC	1.492			
	H$_2$CC	151° 43′					
CH$_2$CHCN			planar				f
C$_4$H$_4$O (Furan)			planar				764a
C$_4$H$_5$N (Pyrrole)			planar				g
SO$_2$F$_2$	OSO	129° 38′ ± 30′	SO	1.370 ± 0.01	SF	1.570 ± 0.01	809
	FSF	92° 47′ ± 30′					

Values in parentheses are assumed.

(a) J. Q. Williams, J. T. Cox, and W. Gordy, *J. Chem. Phys.* **20**, 1524 (1952).

(b) R. C. Mockler, J. H. Bailey, and W. Gordy (to be published).

(c) W. Gordy and J. Sheridan (to be published).

(d) D. F. Smith (private communication).

(e) R. J. Myers and W. D. Gwinn, *J. Chem. Phys.* **20**, 1420 (1952).

(f) W. S. Wilcox, J. H. Goldstein, and J. W. Simmons (private communication).

(g) W. S. Wilcox and J. H. Goldstein, *J. Chem. Phys.* **20**, 1656 (1952).

(h) R. Trambarulo, S. N. Ghosh, C. A. Burrus, and W. Gordy (to be published)

Table A.10a. **Energies and relative intensities of nuclear quadrupole hyperfine structure**

The column marked $Y(F)$, column 3, in Table $A.10a$ gives values for the common factor $\dfrac{\frac{3}{4}C(C+1) - I(I+1)J(J+1)}{2(2J+3)(2J-1)I(2I-1)}$ in the nuclear quadrupole energy formulas (Eqs. 2.78–2.82), where

$$C = F(F+1) - I(I+1) - J(J+1) \quad \text{and} \quad F = J+I, \ \ J+I-1 \cdots | J-I |.$$

To obtain E_Q/eQq of a symmetric-top molecule for various K values, multiply the $Y(F)$ values given here by the values for $\left(\dfrac{3K^2}{J(J+1)} - 1\right)$ given in Table $A.10b$.

Relative intensities for the case $J \to J+1$ are given. This also represents the intensities for $J+1 \to J$, with $F \to F+1$ corresponding to $F+1 \to F$ and $F \to F-1$ corresponding to $F-1 \to F$. These intensities do not take into account the dependence upon K of a symmetric-top molecule. For K values other than zero the intensities relative to those for $K = 0$ are given by

$$\frac{g_I(K)}{g_I(K=0)} \left[1 - \frac{K^2}{(J+1)^2} \right] e^{-[(A-B)K^2]/kT}$$

where $g_I(K)$ and $g_I(K=0)$ are the nuclear statistical weights of the levels K and $K = 0$, respectively.

For an explanation of the various symbols used, see text.

J	F	$Y(F)$	Relative Intensity $J \to J+1$		
			$F \to F+1$	$F \to F$	$F \to F-1$
		$I = 1$			
0	1	0.000000	100	60.0	20.0
1	2	.050000	100	17.9	1.2
	1	$-.250000$	53.6	17.9	
	0	.500000	23.8		
2	3	.071429	100	8.8	0.2
	2	$-.250000$	69.1	8.8	
	1	.250000	46.7		
3	4	.083333	100	5.1	0.1
	3	$-.250000$	76.7	5.1	
	2	.200000	58.4		
4	5	.090909	100	3.4	0.03
	4	$-.250000$	81.2	3.4	
	3	.178571	65.8		

Table A.10a.   Energies and relative intensities of nuclear quadrupole hyperfine structure—*Continued*

			Relative Intensity $J \to J + 1$		
J	F	$Y(F)$	$F \to F + 1$	$F \to F$	$F \to F - 1$
		$I = 1$—*Continued*			
5	6	0.096154	100	2.4	0.02
	5	−.250000	84.3	2.4	
	4	.166667	70.9		
6	7	.100000	100	1.8	.01
	6	−.250000	86.4	1.8	
	5	.159091	74.7		
7	8	.102941	100	1.4	.01
	7	−.250000	88.1	1.4	
	6	.153846	77.5		
8	9	.105263	100	1.1	.00
	8	−.250000	89.4	1.1	
	7	.150000	79.8		
9	10	.107143	100	0.91	.00
	9	−.250000	90.4	0.91	
	8	.147059	81.7		
10	11	.108696	100	0.76	.00
	10	−.250000	91.2	0.76	
	9	.144737	83.2		
11	12	.110000	100	0.64	.00
	11	−.250000	91.9	0.64	
	10	.142857	84.5		
12	13	.111111	100	0.55	.00
	12	−.250000	92.6	0.55	
	11	.141304	85.7		
13	14	.112069	100	0.48	.00
	13	−.250000	93.1	0.48	
	12	.140000	86.6		
14	15	.112903	100	0.42	.00
	14	−.250000	93.5	0.42	
	13	.138889	87.5		
15	16	.113636	100	0.37	.00
	15	−.250000	93.9	0.37	
	14	.137931	88.2		

Table A.10a. Energies and relative intensities of nuclear quadrupole hyperfine structure—*Continued*

J	F	$Y(F)$	Relative Intensity $J \to J+1$		
			$F \to F+1$	$F \to F$	$F \to F-1$
		$I = 1$—*Continued*			
16	17	0.114286	100	0.33	0.00
	16	$-.250000$	94.3	.33	
	15	.137097	88.9		
17	18	.114865	100	.29	.00
	17	$-.250000$	94.6	.29	
	16	.136364	89.5		
18	19	.115385	100	.26	.00
	18	$-.250000$	94.9	.26	
	17	.135714	90.0		
19	20	.115854	100	.24	.00
	19	$-.250000$	95.1	.24	
	18	.135135	90.4		
20	21	.116279	100	.22	.00
	20	$-.250000$	95.3	.22	
	19	.134615	90.9		
		$I = \frac{3}{2}$			
0	$\frac{3}{2}$	.000000	100	66.7	33.3
1	$\frac{5}{2}$	.050000	100	22.5	2.5
	$\frac{3}{2}$	$-.200000$	52.5	26.7	4.2
	$\frac{1}{2}$	.250000	20.8	20.8	
2	$\frac{7}{2}$	.071429	100	11.4	0.6
	$\frac{5}{2}$	$-.178571$	68.6	14.6	0.8
	$\frac{3}{2}$	.000000	44.8	11.2	
	$\frac{1}{2}$	.250000	28.0		
3	$\frac{9}{2}$	.083333	100	6.9	0.2
	$\frac{7}{2}$	$-.166667$	76.4	9.1	0.3
	$\frac{5}{2}$	$-.050000$	57.4	6.9	
	$\frac{3}{2}$	.200000	42.9		
4	$\frac{11}{2}$	.090909	100	4.7	0.1
	$\frac{9}{2}$	$-.159091$	81.0	6.2	0.1
	$\frac{7}{2}$	$-.071429$	65.2	4.7	
	$\frac{5}{2}$	.178571	52.4		

Table $A.10a$. Energies and relative intensities of nuclear quadrupole hyperfine structure—*Continued*

J	F	$Y(F)$	Relative Intensity $J \rightarrow J+1$		
			$F \rightarrow F+1$	$F \rightarrow F$	$F \rightarrow F-1$
		$I = 3/2$—*Continued*			
5	$13\frac{1}{2}$	0.096154	100	3.4	0.04
	$11\frac{1}{2}$	$-.153846$	84.1	4.5	.05
	$9\frac{1}{2}$	$-.083333$	70.5	3.4	
	$7\frac{1}{2}$	.166667	59.1		
6	$15\frac{1}{2}$	.100000	100	2.5	.02
	$13\frac{1}{2}$	$-.150000$	86.4	4.1	.03
	$11\frac{1}{2}$	$-.090909$	74.4	2.5	
	$9\frac{1}{2}$	.159091	64.1		
7	$17\frac{1}{2}$	.102941	100	2.0	.01
	$15\frac{1}{2}$	$-.147059$	88.0	2.5	.02
	$13\frac{1}{2}$	$-.096154$	77.4	1.9	
	$11\frac{1}{2}$	.153846	68.0		
8	$19\frac{1}{2}$	.105263	100	1.6	.01
	$17\frac{1}{2}$	$-.144737$	89.3	2.0	.01
	$15\frac{1}{2}$	$-.100000$	79.7	1.6	
	$13\frac{1}{2}$	.150000	71.1		
9	$21\frac{1}{2}$	.107143	100	1.3	.01
	$19\frac{1}{2}$	$-.142857$	90.4	1.7	.01
	$17\frac{1}{2}$	$-.102941$	81.6	1.3	
	$15\frac{1}{2}$	.147059	73.7		
10	$23\frac{1}{2}$	.108696	100	1.1	.00
	$21\frac{1}{2}$	$-.141304$	91.2	1.5	.01
	$19\frac{1}{2}$	$-.105263$	83.2	1.1	
	$17\frac{1}{2}$	.144737	75.8		
11	$25\frac{1}{2}$	.110000	100	0.9	.00
	$23\frac{1}{2}$	$-.140000$	91.9	1.3	.00
	$21\frac{1}{2}$	$-.107143$	84.5	0.9	
	$19\frac{1}{2}$	.142857	77.6		
12	$27\frac{1}{2}$	.111111	100	0.8	.00
	$25\frac{1}{2}$	$-.138889$	92.5	1.1	.00
	$23\frac{1}{2}$	$-.108696$	85.6	0.8	
	$21\frac{1}{2}$	.141304	79.2		

Table A.10a.   Energies and relative intensities of nuclear quadrupole hyperfine structure—*Continued*

			Relative Intensity $J \to J+1$		
J	F	$Y(F)$	$F \to F+1$	$F \to F$	$F \to F-1$

$$I = \tfrac{3}{2}\text{—}Continued$$

J	F	$Y(F)$	$F \to F+1$	$F \to F$	$F \to F-1$
13	$2\frac{9}{2}$	0.112069	100	0.7	0.00
	$2\frac{7}{2}$	$-.137931$	93.1	.9	.00
	$2\frac{5}{2}$	$-.110000$	86.6	.7	
	$2\frac{3}{2}$	$.140000$	80.7		
14	$3\frac{1}{2}$	$.112903$	100	.6	.00
	$2\frac{9}{2}$	$-.137097$	93.5	.8	.00
	$2\frac{7}{2}$	$-.111111$	87.4	.6	
	$2\frac{5}{2}$	$.138889$	81.7		
15	$3\frac{3}{2}$	$.113636$	100	.5	.00
	$3\frac{1}{2}$	$-.136364$	93.9	.7	.00
	$2\frac{9}{2}$	$-.112069$	88.2	.5	
	$2\frac{7}{2}$	$.137931$	82.8		
16	$3\frac{5}{2}$	$.114286$	100	.5	.00
	$3\frac{3}{2}$	$-.135714$	94.3	.6	.00
	$3\frac{1}{2}$	$-.112903$	88.8	.5	
	$2\frac{9}{2}$	$.137097$	83.7		
17	$3\frac{7}{2}$	$.114865$	100	.4	.00
	$3\frac{5}{2}$	$-.135135$	94.6	.6	.00
	$3\frac{3}{2}$	$-.113636$	89.4	.4	
	$3\frac{1}{2}$	$.136364$	84.6		
18	$3\frac{9}{2}$	$.115385$	100	.4	.00
	$3\frac{7}{2}$	$-.134615$	94.8	.5	.00
	$3\frac{5}{2}$	$-.114286$	90.0	.4	
	$3\frac{3}{2}$	$.135714$	85.3		
19	$4\frac{1}{2}$	$.115854$	100	.3	.00
	$3\frac{9}{2}$	$-.134146$	95.1	.5	.00
	$3\frac{7}{2}$	$-.114865$	90.4	.3	
	$3\frac{5}{2}$	$.135135$	86.0		
20	$4\frac{3}{2}$	$.116279$	100	.3	.00
	$4\frac{1}{2}$	$-.133721$	95.3	.4	.00
	$3\frac{9}{2}$	$-.115385$	90.9	.3	
	$3\frac{7}{2}$	$.134615$	86.6		

Table *A.10a.* Energies and relative intensities of nuclear quadrupole hyperfine structure—*Continued*

J	F	$Y(F)$	Relative Intensity $J \to J+1$		
			$F \to F+1$	$F \to F$	$F \to F-1$
		$I = 2$			
0	2	0.000000	100	71.4	42.9
1	3	.050000	100	25.9	3.7
	2	−.175000	51.9	32.4	8.3
	1	.175000	19.4	25.0	11.1
2	4	.071429	100	13.6	0.9
	3	−.142857	68.2	19.1	1.8
	2	−.053571	43.6	18.2	1.8
	1	.125000	25.5	12.7	
	0	.250000	12.7		
3	5	.083333	100	8.5	0.3
	4	−.125000	76.2	12.2	0.6
	3	−.091667	56.7	12.0	0.5
	2	.050000	41.2	8.2	
	1	.200000	29.7		
4	6	.090909	100	5.8	0.15
	5	−.113636	80.9	8.5	0.27
	4	−.105519	64.7	8.4	0.22
	3	.017857	51.3	5.7	
	2	.178571	40.7		
5	7	.096154	100	4.2	0.08
	6	−.105769	84.0	6.2	0.13
	5	−.112179	70.2	6.2	0.11
	4	.000000	58.4	4.2	
	3	.166667	48.7		
6	8	.100000	100	3.2	0.04
	7	−.100000	86.3	4.7	0.07
	6	−.115909	74.2	4.7	0.06
	5	−.011364	63.6	3.2	
	4	.159091	54.7		
7	9	.102941	100	2.5	0.03
	8	−.095588	88.0	3.7	0.04
	7	−.118212	77.2	3.7	0.03
	6	−.019231	67.7	2.5	
	5	.153846	59.4		

Table A.10a. **Energies and relative intensities of nuclear quadrupole hyperfine structure—*Continued***

J	F	Y(F)	Relative Intensity $J \to J+1$		
			$F \to F+1$	$F \to F$	$F \to F-1$
		$I = 2$—*Continued*			
8	10	0.105263	100	2.0	0.02
	9	−.092105	89.3	3.0	.03
	8	−.119737	79.6	3.0	.02
	7	−.025000	70.9	2.0	
	6	.150000	63.2		
9	11	.107143	100	1.7	.01
	10	−.089286	90.3	2.5	.02
	9	−.120798	81.5	2.5	.01
	8	−.029412	73.5	1.7	
	7	.147059	66.3		
10	12	.108696	100	1.4	.01
	11	−.086957	91.2	2.1	.01
	10	−.121568	83.1	2.1	.01
	9	−.032895	75.7	1.4	
	8	.144737	69.0		
11	13	.110000	100	1.2	.01
	12	−.085000	91.9	1.8	.01
	11	−.122143	84.4	1.8	.01
	10	−.035714	77.5	1.2	
	9	.142857	71.2		
12	14	.111111	100	1.0	.00
	13	−.083333	92.5	1.5	.01
	12	−.122585	85.6	1.5	.01
	11	−.038043	79.1	1.0	
	10	.141304	73.2		
13	15	.112069	100	0.9	.00
	14	−.081897	93.0	1.3	.01
	13	−.122931	86.5	1.3	.00
	12	−.040000	80.5	0.9	
	11	.140000	74.9		
14	16	.112903	100	0.8	.00
	15	−.080645	93.5	1.2	.00
	14	−.123208	87.4	1.2	.00
	13	−.041667	81.7	0.8	
	12	.138889	76.4		

Table *A.*10*a*. **Energies and relative intensities of nuclear quadrupole hyperfine structure—*Continued***

J	F	$Y(F)$	Relative Intensity $J \to J + 1$		
			$F \to F + 1$	$F \to F$	$F \to F - 1$
		$I = 2$—*Continued*			
15	17	0.113636	100	0.7	0.00
	16	−.079545	93.9	1.0	.00
	15	−.123433	88.1	1.0	.00
	14	−.043103	82.7	0.7	
	13	.137931	77.7		
16	18	.114286	100	0.6	.00
	17	−.078571	94.3	0.9	.00
	16	−.123618	88.8	0.9	.00
	15	−.044355	83.7	0.6	
	14	.137097	78.9		
17	19	.114865	100	0.6	.00
	18	−.077703	94.6	0.8	.00
	17	−.123771	89.4	0.8	.00
	16	−.045455	84.5	0.6	
	15	.136364	79.9		
18	20	.115385	100	0.5	.00
	19	−.076923	94.8	0.8	.00
	18	−.123901	89.9	0.8	.00
	17	−.046429	85.3	0.5	
	16	.135714	80.9		
19	21	.115854	100	0.5	.00
	20	−.076220	95.1	0.7	.00
	19	−.124011	90.4	0.7	.00
	18	−.047297	86.0	0.5	
	17	.135135	81.8		
20	22	.116279	100	0.4	.00
	21	−.075581	95.3	0.6	.00
	20	−.124106	90.9	0.6	.00
	19	−.048077	86.6	0.4	
	18	.134615	82.6		
		$I = \tfrac{5}{2}$			
0	$\tfrac{5}{2}$	0.000000	100	75.0	50.0
1	$\tfrac{7}{2}$	.050000	100	28.6	4.7
	$\tfrac{5}{2}$	−.160000	51.4	36.6	12.0
	$\tfrac{3}{2}$	.140000	18.7	28.0	20.0

Table A.10a. **Energies and relative intensities of nuclear quadrupole hyperfine structure—*Continued***

J	F	$Y(F)$	Relative Intensity $J \to J + 1$		
			$F \to F + 1$	$F \to F$	$F \to F - 1$
		$I = \tfrac{5}{2}$—*Continued*			
2	$\tfrac{9}{2}$	0.071429	100	15.4	1.2
	$\tfrac{7}{2}$	$-.121428$	67.9	22.6	2.9
	$\tfrac{5}{2}$	$-.071429$	42.9	23.1	4.0
	$\tfrac{3}{2}$	.071429	24.0	19.0	3.7
	$\tfrac{1}{2}$	.200000	10.4	13.0	
3	$\tfrac{11}{2}$	.083333	100	9.7	0.5
	$\tfrac{9}{2}$	$-.100000$	76.0	14.8	1.0
	$\tfrac{7}{2}$	$-.100000$	56.1	16.0	1.3
	$\tfrac{5}{2}$	$-.006667$	40.1	14.0	1.0
	$\tfrac{3}{2}$	.110000	27.6	9.2	
	$\tfrac{1}{2}$	.200000	18.4		
4	$\tfrac{13}{2}$	.090909	100	6.7	0.2
	$\tfrac{11}{2}$	$-.086364$	80.8	10.4	0.5
	$\tfrac{9}{2}$	$-.107792$	64.3	11.5	0.6
	$\tfrac{7}{2}$	$-.037662$	50.6	10.2	0.4
	$\tfrac{5}{2}$	.071429	39.3	6.5	
	$\tfrac{3}{2}$	.178571	30.6		
5	$\tfrac{15}{2}$	.096154	100	4.9	0.1
	$\tfrac{13}{2}$	$-.076923$	83.9	7.7	0.2
	$\tfrac{11}{2}$	$-.110256$	69.9	8.6	0.3
	$\tfrac{9}{2}$	$-.053846$	57.9	7.6	0.2
	$\tfrac{7}{2}$	.050000	47.7	4.9	
	$\tfrac{5}{2}$	.166667	39.4		
6	$\tfrac{17}{2}$	.100000	100	3.8	0.1
	$\tfrac{15}{2}$	$-.070000$	86.2	5.9	0.1
	$\tfrac{13}{2}$	$-.110909$	74.0	6.6	0.2
	$\tfrac{11}{2}$	$-.063636$	63.2	5.9	0.1
	$\tfrac{9}{2}$	.036364	53.9	3.8	
	$\tfrac{7}{2}$	.159091	46.2		
7	$\tfrac{19}{2}$	.102941	100	3.0	0.04
	$\tfrac{17}{2}$	$-.064706$	87.9	4.7	0.08
	$\tfrac{15}{2}$	$-.110859$	77.1	5.3	0.09
	$\tfrac{13}{2}$	$-.070136$	67.4	4.7	0.06
	$\tfrac{11}{2}$	.026923	58.8	3.0	
	$\tfrac{9}{2}$	.153846	51.5		

Table *A.10a*.   Energies and relative intensities of nuclear quadrupole hyperfine structure—*Continued*

| J | F | $Y(F)$ | Relative Intensity $J \to J+1$ | | |
			$F \to F+1$	$F \to F$	$F \to F-1$
		$I = \frac{5}{2}$—*Continued*			
8	$21\frac{1}{2}$	0.105263	100	2.4	0.03
	$19\frac{1}{2}$	$-.060526$	89.2	3.8	.05
	$17\frac{1}{2}$	$-.110526$	79.5	4.3	.06
	$15\frac{1}{2}$	$-.074737$	70.6	3.8	.04
	$13\frac{1}{2}$	.020000	62.8	2.4	
	$11\frac{1}{2}$	.150000	55.9		
9	$23\frac{1}{2}$	.107143	100	2.0	.02
	$21\frac{1}{2}$	$-.057143$	90.3	3.2	.03
	$19\frac{1}{2}$	$-.110084$	81.4	3.6	.04
	$17\frac{1}{2}$	$-.078151$	73.3	3.2	.02
	$15\frac{1}{2}$	.014706	66.0	2.0	
	$13\frac{1}{2}$	.147059	59.5		
10	$25\frac{1}{2}$	.108696	100	1.7	.01
	$23\frac{1}{2}$	$-.054348$	91.2	2.7	.02
	$21\frac{1}{2}$	$-.109610$	83.0	3.0	.03
	$19\frac{1}{2}$	$-.080778$	75.5	2.7	.02
	$17\frac{1}{2}$	.010526	68.7	1.7	
	$15\frac{1}{2}$	.144737	62.6		
11	$27\frac{1}{2}$	.110000	100	1.4	.01
	$25\frac{1}{2}$	$-.052000$	91.9	2.3	.02
	$23\frac{1}{2}$	$-.109143$	84.4	2.6	.02
	$21\frac{1}{2}$	$-.082857$	77.4	2.3	.01
	$19\frac{1}{2}$	.007143	71.0	1.4	
	$17\frac{1}{2}$	.142857	65.2		
12	$29\frac{1}{2}$	.111111	100	1.2	.01
	$27\frac{1}{2}$	$-.050000$	92.5	2.0	.01
	$25\frac{1}{2}$	$-.108696$	85.5	2.2	.01
	$23\frac{1}{2}$	$-.084541$	79.0	2.0	.01
	$21\frac{1}{2}$	.004348	73.0	1.2	
	$19\frac{1}{2}$	.141304	67.5		
13	$31\frac{1}{2}$	.112069	100	1.1	.01
	$29\frac{1}{2}$	$-.048276$	93.0	1.7	.01
	$27\frac{1}{2}$	$-.108276$	86.5	1.9	.01
	$25\frac{1}{2}$	$-.085931$	80.4	1.7	.01
	$23\frac{1}{2}$	.002000	74.7	1.1	
	$21\frac{1}{2}$	.140000	69.5		

Table $A.10a$. Energies and relative intensities of nuclear quadrupole hyperfine structure—*Continued*

J	F	$Y(F)$	$F \to F+1$	$F \to F$	$F \to F-1$
			— Relative Intensity $J \to J+1$		

J	F	$Y(F)$	$F \to F+1$	$F \to F$	$F \to F-1$
		$I = \tfrac{5}{2}$—*Continued*			
14	$\frac{33}{2}$	0.112903	100	0.9	0.00
	$\frac{31}{2}$	$-.046774$	93.5	1.5	.01
	$\frac{29}{2}$	$-.107885$	87.4	1.7	.01
	$\frac{27}{2}$	$-.087097$	81.6	1.5	.01
	$\frac{25}{2}$	$.000000$	76.3	0.9	
	$\frac{23}{2}$	$.138889$	71.3		
15	$\frac{35}{2}$	$.113636$	100	0.8	.00
	$\frac{33}{2}$	$-.045455$	93.9	1.3	.01
	$\frac{31}{2}$	$-.107524$	88.1	1.5	.01
	$\frac{29}{2}$	$-.088088$	82.7	1.3	.00
	$\frac{27}{2}$	$-.001724$	77.6	0.8	
	$\frac{25}{2}$	$.137931$	72.8		
16	$\frac{37}{2}$	$.114286$	100	0.8	.00
	$\frac{35}{2}$	$-.044286$	94.2	1.2	.01
	$\frac{33}{2}$	$-.107189$	88.8	1.4	.01
	$\frac{31}{2}$	$-.088940$	83.6	1.2	.00
	$\frac{29}{2}$	$-.003226$	78.8	0.8	
	$\frac{27}{2}$	$.137097$	74.2		
17	$\frac{39}{2}$	$.114865$	100	0.7	.00
	$\frac{37}{2}$	$-.043243$	94.6	1.1	.00
	$\frac{35}{2}$	$-.106880$	89.4	1.2	.00
	$\frac{33}{2}$	$-.089681$	84.5	1.1	.00
	$\frac{31}{2}$	$-.004545$	79.9	0.7	
	$\frac{29}{2}$	$.136364$	75.5		
18	$\frac{41}{2}$	$.115385$	100	0.6	.00
	$\frac{39}{2}$	$-.042308$	94.8	1.0	.00
	$\frac{37}{2}$	$-.106593$	89.9	1.1	.00
	$\frac{35}{2}$	$-.090330$	85.3	1.0	.00
	$\frac{33}{2}$	$-.005714$	80.8	0.6	
	$\frac{31}{2}$	$.135714$	76.7		
19	$\frac{43}{2}$	$.115854$	100	0.6	.00
	$\frac{41}{2}$	$-.041463$	95.1	0.9	.00
	$\frac{39}{2}$	$-.106328$	90.4	1.0	.00
	$\frac{37}{2}$	$-.090903$	86.0	0.9	.00
	$\frac{35}{2}$	$-.006757$	81.7	0.6	
	$\frac{33}{2}$	$.135135$	77.7		

Table *A.10a.* **Energies and relative intensities of nuclear quadrupole hyperfine structure—*Continued***

J	F	$Y(F)$	Relative Intensity $J \rightarrow J+1$		
			$F \rightarrow F+1$	$F \rightarrow F$	$F \rightarrow F-1$

J	F	$Y(F)$	$F \rightarrow F+1$	$F \rightarrow F$	$F \rightarrow F-1$
\multicolumn{6}{c}{$I = 5/2$—Continued}					
20	$45\frac{1}{2}$	0.116279	100	0.5	0.00
	$43\frac{1}{2}$	$-.040700$	95.3	.8	.00
	$41\frac{1}{2}$	$-.106082$	90.9	.9	.00
	$39\frac{1}{2}$	$-.091413$	86.6	.8	.00
	$37\frac{1}{2}$	$-.007692$	82.5	.5	
	$35\frac{1}{2}$	.134615	78.7		
\multicolumn{6}{c}{$I = 3$}					
0	3	0.000000	100	77.8	55.6
1	4	.050000	100	30.7	5.7
	3	$-.150000$	51.1	39.8	15.2
	2	.120000	18.2	30.3	27.3
2	5	.071429	100	16.9	1.5
	4	$-.107142$	67.7	25.4	3.8
	3	$-.078571$	42.3	26.9	6.2
	2	.042857	23.1	23.1	7.7
	1	.171429	9.2	15.4	7.7
3	6	.083333	100	10.8	0.6
	5	$-.083333$	75.8	17.0	1.4
	4	$-.100000$	55.7	19.3	2.1
	3	$-.033333$	39.3	18.3	2.4
	2	.063333	26.2	14.9	1.8
	1	.150000	16.1	9.6	
	0	.200000	8.6		
4	7	.090909	100	7.6	0.3
	6	$-.068182$	80.7	12.1	0.7
	5	$-.103246$	64.1	14.1	0.9
	4	$-.061039$	50.0	13.8	1.0
	3	.019481	38.2	11.4	0.7
	2	.107143	28.8	7.2	
	1	.178571	21.6		
5	8	.096154	100	5.6	0.2
	7	$-.057692$	83.9	9.1	0.3
	6	$-.102564$	69.7	10.7	0.5
	5	$-.074571$	57.4	10.0	0.5
	4	$-.003846$	46.9	8.8	0.3

Table $A.10a$. **Energies and relative intensities of nuclear quadrupole hyperfine structure—*Continued***

| J | F | $Y(F)$ | Relative Intensity $J \to J+1$ | | |
			$F \to F+1$	$F \to F$	$F \to F-1$
			$I = 3$—*Continued*		
5 *Cont.*	3	0.083333	38.1	5.4	
	2	.166667	31.1		
6	9	.100000	100	4.3	0.1
	8	−.050000	86.2	7.0	.2
	7	−.100909	73.8	8.3	.3
	6	−.081818	62.9	8.3	.3
	5	−.018182	53.4	6.9	.2
	4	.068182	45.2	4.2	
	3	.159091	38.5		
7	10	.102941	100	3.4	.1
	9	−.044118	87.9	5.6	.1
	8	−.099095	76.9	6.7	.2
	7	−.086425	67.1	6.6	.2
	6	−.027828	58.4	5.6	.1
	5	.057692	50.8	3.4	
	4	.153846	44.3		
8	11	.105263	100	2.8	.04
	10	−.039474	89.2	4.6	.08
	9	−.097368	79.4	5.5	.10
	8	−.089474	70.5	5.4	.10
	7	−.034737	62.5	4.6	.06
	6	.050000	55.4	2.8	
	5	.150000	49.2		
9	12	.107143	100	2.3	.02
	11	−.035714	90.3	3.8	.05
	10	−.095798	81.3	4.6	.07
	9	−.091597	73.2	4.5	.06
	8	−.039916	65.8	3.8	.04
	7	.044118	59.1	2.3	
	6	.147059	53.2		
10	13	.108696	100	2.0	.02
	12	−.032609	91.2	3.2	.04
	11	−.094394	83.0	3.9	.05
	10	−.093135	75.4	3.9	.05
	9	−.043936	68.5	3.2	.03
	8	.039474	62.3	2.0	
	7	.144737	56.7		

Table A.10a. **Energies and relative intensities of nuclear quadrupole hyperfine structure—*Continued***

J	F	$Y(F)$	$F \to F+1$	$F \to F$	$F \to F-1$
			Relative Intensity $J \to J+1$		

J	F	$Y(F)$	$F \to F+1$	$F \to F$	$F \to F-1$
		$I = 3$—*Continued*			
11	14	0.110000	100	1.7	0.01
	13	$-.030000$	91.9	2.8	.03
	12	$-.093143$	84.3	3.3	.04
	11	$-.094286$	77.3	3.3	.03
	10	$-.047143$	70.9	2.8	.02
	9	.035714	65.0	1.7	
	8	.142857	59.6		
12	15	.111111	100	1.5	.01
	14	$-.027778$	92.5	2.4	.02
	13	$-.092029$	85.5	2.9	.03
	12	$-.095169$	78.9	2.9	.02
	11	$-.049759$	72.9	2.4	.01
	10	.032609	67.3	1.4	
	9	.141304	62.2		
13	16	.112069	100	1.3	.01
	15	$-.025862$	93.0	2.1	.02
	14	$-.091034$	86.5	2.5	.02
	13	$-.095862$	80.3	2.5	.02
	12	$-.051931$	74.6	2.1	.01
	11	.030000	69.3	1.3	
	10	.140000	64.4		
14	17	.112903	100	1.1	.01
	16	$-.024194$	93.5	1.9	.01
	15	$-.090143$	87.3	2.2	.02
	14	$-.096416$	81.6	2.2	.01
	13	$-.053763$	76.2	1.8	.01
	12	.027778	71.1	1.1	
	11	.138889	66.4		
15	18	.113636	100	1.0	.00
	17	$-.022727$	93.9	1.6	.01
	16	$-.089342$	88.1	2.0	.01
	15	$-.096865$	82.6	2.0	.01
	14	$-.055329$	77.6	1.6	.01
	13	.025862	72.7	1.0	
	12	.137931	68.2		

Table A.10a. **Energies and relative intensities of nuclear quadrupole hyperfine structure—*Continued***

J	F	$Y(F)$	Relative Intensity $J \rightarrow J + 1$		
			$F \rightarrow F + 1$	$F \rightarrow F$	$F \rightarrow F - 1$

$I = 3$—*Continued*

J	F	$Y(F)$	$F \rightarrow F + 1$	$F \rightarrow F$	$F \rightarrow F - 1$
16	19	0.114286	100	1.0	0.00
	18	−.021429	94.2	1.5	.01
	17	−.088618	88.8	1.8	.01
	16	−.097235	83.6	1.8	.01
	15	−.056682	78.7	1.5	.01
	14	.024194	74.1	1.0	
	13	.137097	69.8		
17	20	.114865	100	1.0	.00
	19	−.020270	94.6	1.3	.01
	18	−.087961	89.4	1.6	.01
	17	−.097543	84.5	1.6	.01
	16	−.057862	79.8	1.3	.00
	15	.022727	75.4	1.0	
	14	.136364	71.3		
18	21	.115385	100	1.0	.00
	20	−.019231	94.8	1.2	.01
	19	−.087363	89.9	1.4	.01
	18	−.097802	85.2	1.4	.01
	17	−.058901	80.8	1.2	.00
	16	.021429	76.6	1.0	
	15	.135714	72.6		
19	22	.115854	100	1.0	.00
	21	−.018293	95.1	1.1	.00
	20	−.086816	90.4	1.3	.01
	19	−.098022	85.9	1.3	.00
	18	−.059822	81.7	1.1	.00
	17	.020270	77.6	1.0	
	16	.135135	73.8		
20	23	.116279	100	1.0	.00
	22	−.017442	95.3	1.0	.00
	21	−.086315	90.8	1.2	.00
	20	−.098211	86.6	1.2	.00
	19	−.060644	82.5	1.0	.00
	18	.019231	78.6	1.0	
	17	.134615	74.9		

Table $A.10a$. **Energies and relative intensities of nuclear quadrupole hyperfine structure—*Continued***

J	F	$Y(F)$	Relative Intensity $J \to J+1$		
			$F \to F+1$	$F \to F$	$F \to F-1$
		$I = \frac{1}{2}$			
0	$\frac{7}{2}$	0.000000	100	80.0	60.0
1	$\frac{9}{2}$	.050000	100	32.4	6.5
	$\frac{7}{2}$	−.142857	51.0	42.4	17.8
	$\frac{5}{2}$	.107143	17.8	32.2	33.3
2	$11\frac{1}{2}$	.071429	100	18.2	1.8
	$\frac{9}{2}$	−.096939	67.5	27.7	4.8
	$\frac{7}{2}$	−.081633	41.9	30.2	8.2
	$\frac{5}{2}$	.025510	22.5	26.1	11.4
	$\frac{3}{2}$	.153061	8.6	17.1	14.3
3	$13\frac{1}{2}$	.083333	100	11.8	0.7
	$11\frac{1}{2}$	−.071429	75.7	18.9	1.8
	$\frac{9}{2}$	−.097619	55.4	22.0	3.0
	$\frac{7}{2}$	−.047619	38.7	21.8	3.8
	$\frac{5}{2}$	.035714	25.3	18.9	4.0
	$\frac{3}{2}$	.119048	14.7	14.3	3.1
	$\frac{1}{2}$	.178571	6.7	9.4	
4	$15\frac{1}{2}$	.090909	100	8.3	0.3
	$13\frac{1}{2}$	−.055195	80.6	13.6	0.9
	$11\frac{1}{2}$	−.097403	63.3	16.3	1.4
	$\frac{9}{2}$	−.071892	49.5	16.8	1.6
	$\frac{7}{2}$	−.009276	37.4	15.3	1.6
	$\frac{5}{2}$	.065399	27.5	12.2	1.0
	$\frac{3}{2}$	.132653	19.6	7.6	
	$\frac{1}{2}$	.178571	13.6		
5	$17\frac{1}{2}$	.096154	100	6.2	0.2
	$15\frac{1}{2}$	−.043956	83.8	10.3	0.5
	$13\frac{1}{2}$	−.094322	69.5	12.5	0.7
	$11\frac{1}{2}$	−.082418	57.0	13.0	0.8
	$\frac{9}{2}$	−.032051	46.3	12.0	0.8
	$\frac{7}{2}$	.036630	37.1	9.7	0.5
	$\frac{5}{2}$	.107143	29.5	5.9	
	$\frac{3}{2}$	.166667	23.6		
6	$19\frac{1}{2}$	.100000	100	4.8	0.1
	$17\frac{1}{2}$	−.035714	86.2	8.0	0.1
	$15\frac{1}{2}$	−.090909	73.7	9.8	0.2

Table A.10a. Energies and relative intensities of nuclear quadrupole hyperfine structure—*Continued*

J	F	$Y(F)$	Relative Intensity $J \to J+1$		
			$F \to F+1$	$F \to F$	$F \to F-1$

$I = 7/2$—*Continued*

J	F	$Y(F)$	$F \to F+1$	$F \to F$	$F \to F-1$
6 *Cont.*	13/2	−0.087662	62.6	10.3	0.2
	11/2	−.045455	52.9	9.6	.2
	9/2	.018831	44.5	7.8	.1
	7/2	.090909	37.3	4.7	
	5/2	.159091	31.5		
7	21/2	.109241	100	3.8	.03
	19/2	−.029412	87.8	6.4	.08
	17/2	−.087750	76.8	7.9	.12
	15/2	−.090498	66.9	8.4	.14
	13/2	−.054137	58.1	7.8	.12
	11/2	.006787	50.2	6.3	.06
	9/2	.079670	43.5	3.8	
	7/2	.153846	37.8		
8	23/2	.105263	100	3.1	.02
	21/2	−.024436	89.2	5.3	.05
	19/2	−.084962	79.3	6.5	.08
	17/2	−.092105	70.3	6.9	.09
	15/2	−.060150	62.2	6.5	.08
	13/2	.001880	54.9	5.2	.04
	11/2	.071429	48.5	3.1	
	9/2	.150000	43.0		
9	25/2	.107143	100	2.6	.02
	23/2	−.020408	90.3	4.4	.04
	21/2	−.082533	81.3	5.5	.05
	19/2	−.093037	73.0	5.8	.06
	17/2	−.064526	65.5	5.4	.05
	15/2	−.008403	58.7	4.4	.03
	13/2	.065126	52.7	2.6	
	11/2	.147059	47.4		
10	27/2	.108696	100	2.2	.01
	25/2	−.017081	91.1	3.7	.03
	23/2	−.080418	82.9	4.6	.04
	21/2	−.093576	75.3	4.9	.04
	19/2	−.067833	68.3	4.6	.03
	17/2	−.013485	62.0	3.7	.02
	15/2	.060150	56.2	2.2	
	13/2	.144737	51.1		

Table *A.10a*. Energies and relative intensities of nuclear quadrupole hyperfine structure—*Continued*

J	F	$Y(F)$	Relative Intensity $J \to J+1$		
			$F \to F+1$	$F \to F$	$F \to F-1$
		$I = \frac{7}{2}$—*Continued*			
11	$29\frac{1}{2}$	0.110000	100	1.9	0.01
	$27\frac{1}{2}$	$-.014286$	91.9	3.2	.02
	$25\frac{1}{2}$	$-.078571$	84.3	4.0	.03
	$23\frac{1}{2}$	$-.093878$	77.2	4.2	.03
	$21\frac{1}{2}$	$-.070408$	70.7	4.0	.02
	$19\frac{1}{2}$	$-.017551$	64.7	3.2	.01
	$17\frac{1}{2}$	.056122	59.3	1.9	
	$15\frac{1}{2}$	.142857	54.3		
12	$31\frac{1}{2}$	.111111	100	1.6	.01
	$29\frac{1}{2}$	$-.011905$	92.5	2.8	.01
	$27\frac{1}{2}$	$-.076950$	85.4	3.5	.02
	$25\frac{1}{2}$	$-.094030$	78.9	3.7	.02
	$23\frac{1}{2}$	$-.072464$	72.7	3.5	.02
	$21\frac{1}{2}$	$-.020876$	67.1	2.8	.01
	$19\frac{1}{2}$	.052795	61.9	1.6	
	$17\frac{1}{2}$	.141304	57.2		
13	$33\frac{1}{2}$	.112069	100	1.4	.01
	$31\frac{1}{2}$	$-.009852$	93.0	2.4	.01
	$29\frac{1}{2}$	$-.075517$	86.4	3.0	.02
	$27\frac{1}{2}$	$-.094089$	80.3	3.2	.02
	$25\frac{1}{2}$	$-.074138$	74.5	3.0	.01
	$23\frac{1}{2}$	$-.023645$	69.2	2.4	.01
	$21\frac{1}{2}$	.050000	64.2	1.4	
	$19\frac{1}{2}$	.140000	59.7		
14	$35\frac{1}{2}$	.112903	100	1.3	.00
	$33\frac{1}{2}$	$-.008064$	93.5	2.2	.01
	$31\frac{1}{2}$	$-.074245$	87.3	2.7	.02
	$29\frac{1}{2}$	.000000	81.5	2.9	.01
	$27\frac{1}{2}$	$-.075525$	76.1	2.7	.01
	$25\frac{1}{2}$	$-.025986$	71.0	2.2	.01
	$23\frac{1}{2}$	.047619	66.3	1.3	
	$21\frac{1}{2}$	.138889	61.9		
15	$37\frac{1}{2}$	.113636	100	1.1	.00
	$35\frac{1}{2}$	$-.006494$	93.9	1.9	.01
	$33\frac{1}{2}$	$-.073108$	88.1	2.4	.01
	$31\frac{1}{2}$	.000000	82.6	2.5	.01
	$29\frac{1}{2}$	$-.076691$	77.4	2.4	.01

Table A.10a.   Energies and relative intensities of nuclear quadrupole hyperfine structure—*Continued*

J	F	$Y(F)$	$F \to F+1$	$F \to F$	$F \to F-1$
			Relative Intensity $J \to J+1$		

$I = \frac{7}{2}$—*Continued*

J	F	$Y(F)$	$F \to F+1$	$F \to F$	$F \to F-1$
15 *Cont.*	$^2 7\frac{1}{2}$	-0.027989	72.6	1.9	0.00
	$^2 5\frac{1}{2}$	.045567	68.1	1.1	
	$^2 3\frac{1}{2}$	.137931	63.9		
16	$^3 9\frac{1}{2}$	.114286	100	1.0	.00
	$^3 7\frac{1}{2}$	$-.005102$	94.2	1.7	.01
	$^3 5\frac{1}{2}$	$-.072087$	88.8	2.1	.01
	$^3 3\frac{1}{2}$	$-.093976$	83.6	2.3	.01
	$^3 1\frac{1}{2}$	$-.077683$	78.7	2.1	.01
	$^2 9\frac{1}{2}$	$-.029724$	74.0	1.7	.00
	$^2 7\frac{1}{2}$	.043779	69.7	1.1	
	$^2 5\frac{1}{2}$	.137097	65.7		
17	$^4 1\frac{1}{2}$	.114865	100	0.9	.00
	$^3 9\frac{1}{2}$	$-.003861$	94.5	1.5	.00
	$^3 7\frac{1}{2}$	$-.071165$	89.4	1.9	.01
	$^3 5\frac{1}{2}$	$-.093893$	84.4	2.1	.01
	$^3 3\frac{1}{2}$	$-.078536$	79.8	1.9	.01
	$^3 1\frac{1}{2}$	$-.031239$	75.3	1.5	.00
	$^2 9\frac{1}{2}$	.042339	71.2	0.9	
	$^2 7\frac{1}{2}$	.136364	67.3		
18	$^4 3\frac{1}{2}$	.115385	100	0.8	.00
	$^4 1\frac{1}{2}$	$-.002747$	94.8	1.4	.00
	$^3 9\frac{1}{2}$	$-.070330$	89.9	1.7	.01
	$^3 7\frac{1}{2}$	$-.093799$	85.2	1.9	.01
	$^3 5\frac{1}{2}$	$-.079278$	80.7	1.7	.00
	$^3 3\frac{1}{2}$	$-.032575$	76.5	1.4	.00
	$^3 1\frac{1}{2}$	.040816	72.5	0.8	
	$^2 9\frac{1}{2}$	.135714	68.7		
19	$^4 5\frac{1}{2}$	.115854	100	0.7	.00
	$^4 3\frac{1}{2}$	$-.001742$	95.1	1.3	.00
	$^4 1\frac{1}{2}$	$-.069569$	90.4	1.6	.00
	$^3 9\frac{1}{2}$	$-.093700$	85.9	1.7	.00
	$^3 7\frac{1}{2}$	$-.079927$	81.6	1.6	.00
	$^3 5\frac{1}{2}$	$-.033760$	77.6	1.3	.00
	$^3 3\frac{1}{2}$	.039579	73.7	0.7	
	$^3 1\frac{1}{2}$	.135135	70.1		

Table A.10a.   Energies and relative intensities of nuclear quadrupole
hyperfine structure—*Continued*

J	F	Y(F)	Relative Intensity $J \to J+1$		
			$F \to F+1$	$F \to F$	$F \to F-1$

| $I = \frac{7}{2}$—*Continued* | | | | | |

20	$\frac{47}{2}$	0.116279	100	0.7	0.00
	$\frac{45}{2}$	−.000831	95.3	1.2	.00
	$\frac{43}{2}$	−.068873	90.8	1.5	.00
	$\frac{41}{2}$	−.093598	86.5	1.5	.00
	$\frac{39}{2}$	−.080501	82.4	1.4	.00
	$\frac{37}{2}$	−.034820	78.5	1.2	.00
	$\frac{35}{2}$	.038461	74.8	0.7	
	$\frac{33}{2}$	.134615	71.3		

| $I = 4$ | | | | | |

0	4	0.000000	100	81.8	63.6
1	5	.050000	100	33.8	7.2
	4	−.137500	50.8	44.4	20.1
	3	.098214	17.6	33.7	38.0
2	6	.071429	100	19.0	2.1
	5	−.089286	67.4	29.7	5.6
	4	−.082908	41.6	32.4	10.0
	3	.014031	22.0	28.5	14.8
	2	.140306	8.1	18.5	20.0
3	7	.083333	100	12.6	0.8
	6	−.062500	75.6	20.5	2.2
	5	−.094643	55.1	24.3	3.8
	4	−.055952	38.2	24.6	5.3
	3	.017857	24.6	22.0	6.3
	2	.098214	13.9	17.3	6.6
	1	.163690	5.8	11.0	5.9
4	8	.090909	100	8.9	0.4
	7	−.045455	80.5	14.9	1.1
	6	−.091721	63.6	18.2	1.8
	5	−.077110	49.1	19.3	2.3
	4	−.026670	36.8	18.4	2.6
	3	.038729	26.6	16.0	2.5
	2	.102389	18.2	12.3	1.6
	1	.151786	11.6	7.7	
	0	.178571	6.4		

Table $A.10a$. **Energies and relative intensities of nuclear quadrupole hyperfine structure—*Continued***

J	F	$Y(F)$	Relative Intensity $J \to J+1$		
			$F \to F+1$	$F \to F$	$F \to F-1$

$I = 4$—*Continued*

J	F	$Y(F)$	$F \to F+1$	$F \to F$	$F \to F-1$
5	9	0.096154	100	6.7	0.2
	8	−.033654	83.8	11.3	0.6
	7	−.086767	69.4	14.1	0.9
	6	−.085165	56.8	15.2	1.2
	5	−.048077	45.8	14.8	1.3
	4	.008013	36.4	13.1	1.1
	3	.069368	28.4	10.3	0.7
	2	.125000	21.9	6.3	
	1	.166667	16.9		
6	10	.100000	100	5.2	0.1
	9	−.025000	86.1	8.9	0.3
	8	−.081981	73.6	11.2	0.5
	7	−.088474	62.4	12.2	0.7
	6	−.060065	52.5	12.0	0.7
	5	−.010390	43.9	10.7	0.6
	4	.048864	36.4	8.4	0.3
	3	.107955	30.1	5.0	
	2	.159091	25.1		
7	11	.102941	100	4.2	0.1
	10	−.018382	87.8	7.2	0.2
	9	−.077771	76.7	9.1	0.3
	8	−.090417	66.7	9.9	0.4
	7	−.067469	57.8	9.8	0.4
	6	−.022503	49.8	8.8	0.4
	5	.034947	42.8	5.3	0.2
	4	.096154	36.7	4.1	
	3	.153846	31.7		
8	12	.105263	100	3.4	0.1
	11	−.013158	89.2	5.9	0.1
	10	−.074154	79.2	7.5	0.2
	9	−.090132	70.2	8.2	0.3
	8	−.072368	61.9	8.2	0.3
	7	−.031015	54.5	7.4	0.2
	6	.024906	47.9	5.8	0.1
	5	.087500	42.2	3.4	
	4	.150000	37.3		

Table $A.10a$.   Energies and relative intensities of nuclear quadrupole hyperfine structure—*Continued*

J	F	$Y(F)$	$F \to F+1$	$F \to F$	$F \to F-1$
			Relative Intensity $J \to J+1$		

J	F	$Y(F)$	$F \to F+1$	$F \to F$	$F \to F-1$
		$I = 4$—*Continued*			
9	13	0.107143	100	2.9	0.04
	12	−.008929	90.2	4.9	.10
	11	−.071053	81.2	6.3	.15
	10	−.090036	72.9	6.9	.18
	9	−.075780	65.3	6.9	.18
	8	−.037290	58.4	6.2	.14
	7	.017332	52.2	4.9	.07
	6	.080882	46.7	2.8	
	5	.147059	41.9		
10	14	.108696	100	2.4	.03
	13	−.005435	91.1	4.2	.07
	12	−.068384	82.9	5.4	.11
	11	−.089715	75.2	5.9	.13
	10	−.078253	68.2	5.9	.13
	9	−.042089	61.7	5.3	.10
	8	.011421	55.9	4.2	.04
	7	.075658	50.6	2.4	
	6	.144737	45.9		
11	15	.110000	100	2.1	.02
	14	−.002500	91.1	3.6	.05
	13	−.066071	84.2	4.6	.08
	12	−.089286	77.2	5.1	.09
	11	−.080102	70.6	5.1	.09
	10	−.045867	64.5	4.6	.07
	9	.006684	59.0	3.6	.03
	8	.071429	53.9	2.1	
	7	.142857	49.4		
12	16	.111111	100	1.8	.02
	15	.000000	92.5	3.1	.04
	14	−.064053	85.4	4.0	.06
	13	−.088811	78.8	4.4	.07
	12	−.081522	72.6	4.4	.07
	11	−.048913	66.9	4.0	.05
	10	.002804	61.7	3.1	.03
	9	.067935	56.8	1.8	
	8	.141304	52.4		

Table A.10a. Energies and relative intensities of nuclear quadrupole hyperfine structure—Continued

J	F	$Y(F)$	Relative Intensity $J \to J+1$		
			$F \to F+1$	$F \to F$	$F \to F-1$
		$I = 4$—Continued			
13	17	0.112069	100	1.6	0.01
	16	.002155	93.0	2.8	.03
	15	−.062278	86.4	3.5	.04
	14	−.088325	80.2	3.9	.05
	13	−.082635	74.4	3.9	.05
	12	−.051416	69.0	3.5	.04
	11	−.000431	64.0	2.7	.02
	10	.064523	59.4	1.6	
	9	.140000	55.2		
14	18	.112903	100	1.4	.01
	17	.004032	93.5	2.4	.02
	16	−.060708	87.3	3.2	.03
	15	−.087846	81.5	3.5	.04
	14	−.083525	76.0	3.5	.04
	13	−.053507	70.9	3.1	.03
	12	−.003168	66.1	2.4	.01
	11	.062500	61.6	1.4	
	10	.138889	57.6		
15	19	.113636	100	1.3	.01
	18	.005682	93.9	2.2	.02
	17	−.059309	88.1	2.8	.03
	16	−.087382	82.6	3.1	.03
	15	−.084248	77.4	3.1	.03
	14	−.055279	72.5	2.8	.02
	13	−.005514	67.9	2.2	.01
	12	.060345	63.7	1.2	
	11	.137931	59.7		
16	20	.114286	100	1.1	.01
	19	.007143	94.2	2.0	.01
	18	−.058056	88.7	2.5	.02
	17	−.086940	83.5	2.8	.02
	16	−.084842	78.6	2.8	.02
	15	−.056797	73.9	2.5	.02
	14	−.007546	69.6	1.9	.01
	13	.058468	65.5	1.1	
	12	.137097	61.7		

Table _A.10a_. Energies and relative intensities of nuclear quadrupole hyperfine structure—_Continued_

J	F	Y(F)	Relative Intensity $J \to J+1$		
			$F \to F+1$	$F \to F$	$F \to F-1$

$I = 4$—_Continued_

J	F	Y(F)	$F \to F+1$	$F \to F$	$F \to F-1$
17	21	0.114865	100	1.0	0.01
	20	.008446	94.5	1.8	.01
	19	−.056928	89.4	2.3	.02
	18	−.086522	84.4	2.5	.02
	17	−.085337	79.7	2.5	.02
	16	−.058112	75.3	2.3	.01
	15	−.009323	71.1	1.8	.01
	14	.056818	67.1	1.0	
	13	.136364	63.4		
18	22	.115385	100	1.0	.00
	21	.009615	94.8	1.6	.01
	20	−.055907	89.9	2.1	.01
	19	−.086126	85.2	2.3	.02
	18	−.085754	80.7	2.3	.02
	17	−.059262	76.4	2.0	.01
	16	−.010891	72.4	1.6	.01
	15	.055357	68.6	1.0	
	14	.135714	65.0		
19	23	.115854	100	1.0	.00
	22	.010671	95.1	1.5	.01
	21	−.054978	90.4	1.9	.01
	20	−.085754	85.9	2.1	.01
	19	−.086107	81.6	2.1	.01
	18	−.060275	77.5	1.9	.01
	17	−.012283	73.6	1.5	.00
	16	.054054	70.0	1.0	
	15	.135135	66.5		
20	24	.116279	100	1.0	.00
	23	.011628	95.3	1.3	.01
	22	−.054130	90.8	1.7	.01
	21	−.085404	86.5	1.9	.01
	20	−.086411	82.4	1.9	.01
	19	−.061174	78.5	1.7	.01
	18	−.013529	74.8	1.3	.00
	17	.052885	71.2	1.0	
	16	.134615	67.9		

Table A.10a.   Energies and relative intensities of nuclear quadrupole hyperfine structure—*Continued*

J	F	$Y(F)$	Relative Intensity $J \to J+1$		
			$F \to F+1$	$F \to F$	$F \to F-1$

$$I = \tfrac{9}{2}$$

J	F	$Y(F)$	$F \to F+1$	$F \to F$	$F \to F-1$
0	$\tfrac{9}{2}$	0.000000	100	83.3	66.7
1	$\tfrac{11}{2}$	.050000	100	35.1	7.8
	$\tfrac{9}{2}$	$-.133333$	50.6	46.1	22.2
	$\tfrac{7}{2}$	.091667	17.5	34.8	42.9
2	$\tfrac{13}{2}$	.071429	100	20.2	2.3
	$\tfrac{11}{2}$	$-.083333$	67.3	31.3	6.4
	$\tfrac{9}{2}$	$-.083333$	41.3	34.5	11.7
	$\tfrac{7}{2}$	.005952	21.7	30.5	17.8
	$\tfrac{5}{2}$	.130952	5.0	19.7	25.0
3	$\tfrac{15}{2}$	.083333	100	13.3	1.0
	$\tfrac{13}{2}$	$-.055556$	75.5	21.9	2.6
	$\tfrac{11}{2}$	$-.091667$	55.0	26.2	4.6
	$\tfrac{9}{2}$	$-.061111$	37.9	26.9	6.6
	$\tfrac{7}{2}$	.005556	24.1	24.6	8.5
	$\tfrac{5}{2}$	.083333	13.3	19.6	6.7
	$\tfrac{3}{2}$	.152777	5.2	17.5	4.8
4	$\tfrac{17}{2}$	.090909	100	9.5	0.5
	$\tfrac{15}{2}$	$-.037879$	80.5	16.1	1.2
	$\tfrac{13}{2}$	$-.086580$	63.5	20.0	2.2
	$\tfrac{11}{2}$	$-.079545$	48.8	21.5	3.0
	$\tfrac{9}{2}$	$-.037879$	36.4	21.0	3.7
	$\tfrac{7}{2}$	.020563	25.9	19.0	4.0
	$\tfrac{5}{2}$	.081169	17.3	15.6	3.7
	$\tfrac{3}{2}$	.132576	10.4	11.4	2.7
	$\tfrac{1}{2}$	.166667	4.9	3.7	
5	$\tfrac{19}{2}$	.096154	100	7.2	0.3
	$\tfrac{17}{2}$	$-.025641$	83.7	12.3	0.7
	$\tfrac{15}{2}$	$-.080128$	69.3	15.5	1.2
	$\tfrac{13}{2}$	$-.085470$	56.5	17.1	1.6
	$\tfrac{11}{2}$	$-.057692$	45.4	17.2	1.9
	$\tfrac{9}{2}$	$-.010684$	35.8	16.0	1.9
	$\tfrac{7}{2}$	.043803	27.5	13.8	1.7
	$\tfrac{5}{2}$	.096154	20.7	10.6	1.0
	$\tfrac{3}{2}$	.138889	15.0	6.4	
	$\tfrac{1}{2}$	.166667	10.7		

Table $A.10a$. Energies and relative intensities of nuclear quadrupole hyperfine structure—*Continued*

J	F	$Y(F)$	$F \to F+1$	$F \to F$	$F \to F-1$
			Relative Intensity $J \to J+1$		
			$I = \frac{9}{2}$—*Continued*		
6	$21\frac{1}{2}$	0.100000	100	5.6	0.2
	$19\frac{1}{2}$	−.016667	86.1	9.7	0.4
	$17\frac{1}{2}$	−.074242	73.5	12.4	0.7
	$15\frac{1}{2}$	−.087121	62.2	13.8	0.9
	$13\frac{1}{2}$	−.068182	52.2	14.1	1.1
	$11\frac{1}{2}$	−.028788	43.4	13.3	1.1
	$\frac{9}{2}$	.021212	35.7	11.6	0.9
	$\frac{7}{2}$	.073485	29.1	8.9	0.5
	$\frac{5}{2}$	.121212	23.5	5.3	
	$\frac{3}{2}$	.159091	19.2		
7	$23\frac{1}{2}$	.102941	100	4.5	0.1
	$21\frac{1}{2}$	−.009804	87.8	7.8	0.3
	$19\frac{1}{2}$	−.069193	76.7	10.1	0.4
	$17\frac{1}{2}$	−.087104	66.6	11.3	0.6
	$15\frac{1}{2}$	−.074284	57.5	11.6	0.6
	$13\frac{1}{2}$	−.040347	49.4	11.0	0.6
	$11\frac{1}{2}$	.006222	42.2	9.7	0.5
	$\frac{9}{2}$	.058069	35.9	7.5	0.3
	$\frac{7}{2}$	.108974	30.5	4.4	
	$\frac{5}{2}$	.153846	26.2		
8	$25\frac{1}{2}$	.105263	100	3.7	0.1
	$23\frac{1}{2}$	−.004386	89.1	6.5	0.2
	$21\frac{1}{2}$	−.064912	79.2	8.4	0.3
	$19\frac{1}{2}$	−.086404	70.0	9.4	0.4
	$17\frac{1}{2}$	−.078070	61.7	9.7	0.4
	$15\frac{1}{2}$	−.048246	54.2	9.3	0.4
	$13\frac{1}{2}$	−.004386	47.5	8.1	0.3
	$11\frac{1}{2}$	.046930	41.5	6.3	0.2
	$\frac{9}{2}$	.100000	36.3	3.6	
	$\frac{7}{2}$	.150000	31.9		
9	$27\frac{1}{2}$	.107143	100	3.1	0.1
	$25\frac{1}{2}$	.000000	90.2	5.5	0.1
	$23\frac{1}{2}$	−.061275	81.2	7.1	0.2
	$21\frac{1}{2}$	−.085434	72.8	8.0	0.3
	$19\frac{1}{2}$	−.080532	65.2	8.2	0.3
	$17\frac{1}{2}$	−.053922	58.2	7.9	0.3
	$15\frac{1}{2}$	−.012255	51.8	6.9	0.2

Table A.10a. Energies and relative intensities of nuclear quadrupole hyperfine structure—*Continued*

J	F	Y(F)	Relative Intensity J → J + 1		
			$F \to F+1$	$F \to F$	$F \to F-1$
$I = \frac{9}{2}$—*Continued*					
9 *Cont.*	$13\frac{1}{2}$	0.038515	46.2	5.3	0.1
	$11\frac{1}{2}$	.093137	41.2	3.1	
	$9\frac{1}{2}$	.147059	36.8		
10	$29\frac{1}{2}$	.108696	100	2.6	.03
	$27\frac{1}{2}$	−.003623	91.1	4.6	.08
	$25\frac{1}{2}$	−.058162	82.8	6.0	.14
	$23\frac{1}{2}$	−.084382	75.1	6.8	.18
	$21\frac{1}{2}$	−.082189	68.0	7.1	.19
	$19\frac{1}{2}$	−.058162	61.5	6.8	.18
	$17\frac{1}{2}$	−.018307	55.5	5.9	.13
	$15\frac{1}{2}$	.031941	50.1	4.6	.07
	$13\frac{1}{2}$	.087719	45.3	2.6	
	$11\frac{1}{2}$	.144737	41.1		
11	$31\frac{1}{2}$	.110000	100	2.3	.03
	$29\frac{1}{2}$	.006667	91.8	4.0	.06
	$27\frac{1}{2}$	−.055476	84.2	5.2	.10
	$25\frac{1}{2}$	−.083333	77.1	5.9	.13
	$23\frac{1}{2}$	−.083333	70.5	6.1	.14
	$21\frac{1}{2}$	−.061429	64.3	5.9	.13
	$19\frac{1}{2}$	−.023095	58.7	5.2	.09
	$17\frac{1}{2}$	.026667	53.5	4.0	.05
	$15\frac{1}{2}$	.083333	48.9	2.3	
	$13\frac{1}{2}$	.142857	44.8		
12	$33\frac{1}{2}$	.111111	100	2.0	.02
	$31\frac{1}{2}$	.009259	92.5	3.5	.05
	$29\frac{1}{2}$	−.053140	85.4	4.6	.07
	$27\frac{1}{2}$	−.082327	78.7	5.2	.10
	$25\frac{1}{2}$	−.084138	72.5	5.4	.10
	$23\frac{1}{2}$	−.064010	66.8	5.1	.09
	$21\frac{1}{2}$	−.026973	61.4	4.5	.07
	$19\frac{1}{2}$	.022343	56.5	3.5	.03
	$17\frac{1}{2}$	.079710	52.0	2.0	
	$15\frac{1}{2}$	.141304	48.0		
13	$35\frac{1}{2}$	.112069	100	1.7	.01
	$33\frac{1}{2}$	.011494	93.0	3.1	.04
	$31\frac{1}{2}$	−.051092	86.4	4.0	.06

Table *A.*10*a*. **Energies and relative intensities of nuclear quadrupole hyperfine structure—*Continued***

J	F	$Y(F)$	Relative Intensity $J \rightarrow J+1$		
			$F \rightarrow F+1$	$F \rightarrow F$	$F \rightarrow F-1$

$I = \frac{9}{2}$—*Continued*

J	F	$Y(F)$	$F \rightarrow F+1$	$F \rightarrow F$	$F \rightarrow F-1$
13 *Cont.*	$\frac{29}{2}$	-0.081379	80.2	4.5	0.07
	$\frac{27}{2}$	$-.084713$	74.3	4.7	.08
	$\frac{25}{2}$	$-.066092$	68.9	4.5	.07
	$\frac{23}{2}$	$-.030172$	63.8	4.0	.05
	$\frac{21}{2}$	$.018736$	59.1	3.0	.02
	$\frac{19}{2}$	$.076667$	54.8	1.7	
	$\frac{17}{2}$	$.140000$	50.9		
14	$\frac{37}{2}$	$.112903$	100	1.5	.01
	$\frac{35}{2}$	$.013441$	93.5	2.7	.03
	$\frac{33}{2}$	$-.049283$	87.3	3.5	.04
	$\frac{31}{2}$	$-.080496$	81.4	4.0	.06
	$\frac{29}{2}$	$-.085125$	75.9	4.2	.06
	$\frac{27}{2}$	$-.067719$	70.7	4.0	.05
	$\frac{25}{2}$	$-.032855$	65.9	3.5	.04
	$\frac{23}{2}$	$.015681$	61.4	2.7	.02
	$\frac{21}{2}$	$.074074$	57.3	1.5	
	$\frac{19}{2}$	$.138889$	53.4		
15	$\frac{39}{2}$	$.113636$	100	1.4	.01
	$\frac{37}{2}$	$.015152$	93.9	2.4	.02
	$\frac{35}{2}$	$-.047675$	88.0	3.2	.04
	$\frac{33}{2}$	$-.079676$	82.5	3.6	.04
	$\frac{31}{2}$	$-.085423$	77.3	3.8	.05
	$\frac{29}{2}$	$-.069227$	72.4	3.6	.04
	$\frac{27}{2}$	$-.035136$	67.8	3.2	.03
	$\frac{25}{2}$	$.013062$	63.5	2.4	.01
	$\frac{23}{2}$	$.071839$	59.5	1.4	
	$\frac{21}{2}$	$.137931$	55.8		
16	$\frac{41}{2}$	$.114286$	100	1.2	.01
	$\frac{39}{2}$	$.016667$	94.2	2.2	.02
	$\frac{37}{2}$	$-.046236$	88.7	2.9	.03
	$\frac{35}{2}$	$-.078917$	83.5	3.2	.04
	$\frac{33}{2}$	$-.085637$	78.5	3.4	.04
	$\frac{31}{2}$	$-.070430$	73.9	3.2	.03
	$\frac{29}{2}$	$-.037097$	69.5	2.8	.02
	$\frac{27}{2}$	$.010791$	65.3	2.2	.01
	$\frac{25}{2}$	$.069892$	61.4	1.2	
	$\frac{23}{2}$	$.137097$	57.9		

Table A.10a. Energies and relative intensities of nuclear quadrupole hyperfine structure—*Continued*

J	F	$Y(F)$	Relative Intensity $J \to J+1$		
			$F \to F+1$	$F \to F$	$F \to F-1$
		$I = 9/2$—*Continued*			
17	$43/2$	0.114865	100	1.1	0.01
	$41/2$	.018018	94.5	2.0	.01
	$39/2$	−.044943	89.3	2.6	.02
	$37/2$	−.078215	84.4	2.9	.03
	$35/2$	−.085790	79.7	3.0	.03
	$33/2$	−.071458	75.2	2.9	.03
	$31/2$	−.038800	71.0	2.6	.02
	$29/2$	.008804	67.0	2.0	.01
	$27/2$	.068182	63.2	1.1	
	$25/2$	.136364	59.8		
18	$45/2$	.115385	100	1.0	.01
	$43/2$	.019231	94.8	1.8	.01
	$41/2$	−.043773	89.9	2.3	.02
	$39/2$	−.077564	85.2	2.7	.02
	$37/2$	−.085897	80.7	2.8	.02
	$35/2$	−.072344	76.4	2.7	.02
	$33/2$	−.040293	72.3	2.3	.02
	$31/2$	.007051	68.5	1.8	.01
	$29/2$	.066667	64.9	1.0	
	$27/2$	.135714	61.5		
19	$47/2$	.115854	100	0.9	.00
	$45/2$	.020325	95.1	1.6	.01
	$43/2$	−.042710	90.4	2.1	.02
	$41/2$	−.076961	85.9	2.4	.02
	$39/2$	−.085970	81.6	2.5	.02
	$37/2$	−.073116	77.5	2.4	.02
	$35/2$	−.041612	73.6	2.1	.01
	$33/2$	.005493	69.9	1.6	.01
	$31/2$	.065315	66.4	0.9	
	$29/2$	.135135	63.1		
20	$49/2$	.116279	100	0.8	.00
	$47/2$	.021318	95.3	1.5	.01
	$45/2$	−.041741	90.8	1.9	.01
	$43/2$	−.076401	86.5	2.2	.02
	$41/2$	−.086017	82.4	2.3	.02
	$39/2$	−.073792	78.4	2.2	.01
	$37/2$	−.042785	74.7	1.9	.01
	$35/2$	.004100	71.1	1.5	.01
	$33/2$	.064103	67.7	0.8	
	$31/2$	.134615	64.5		

Table A.10b. Values of $\left(\dfrac{3K^2}{J(J+1)} - 1\right)$

Columns are $K = 0$ to 21; rows are $J = 1$ to 21.

$J \backslash K$	0	1	2	3	4	5	6	7	8	9	10	11	12	13	14	15	16	17	18	19	20	21
1	−1	0.5																				
2	−1	−.5	1																			
3	−1	−.75	0	1.25																		
4	−1	−.85	−0.40	0.35	1.4																	
5	−1	−.90	−0.60	−0.10	0.60	1.5																
6	−1	−.92857	−0.71429	−0.35714	0.14286	0.78571	1.57143															
7	−1	−.94643	−0.78571	−0.51786	−0.14286	0.33929	0.92857	1.625														
8	−1	−.95833	−0.83333	−0.62500	−0.33333	0.04167	0.50000	1.04167	1.66667													
9	−1	−.96667	−0.86667	−0.70000	−0.46667	−0.16667	0.20000	0.63333	1.13333	1.70000												
10	−1	−.97273	−0.89091	−0.75455	−0.56364	−0.31818	−0.01818	0.33636	0.74545	1.20909	1.72727											
11	−1	−.97727	−0.90909	−0.79545	−0.63636	−0.43182	−0.18182	0.11364	0.45455	0.84091	1.27273	1.75000										
12	−1	−.98077	−0.92308	−0.82692	−0.69231	−0.51923	−0.30769	−0.05769	0.23077	0.55769	0.92308	1.32692	1.76923									
13	−1	−.98352	−0.93407	−0.85165	−0.73626	−0.58791	−0.40659	−0.19231	0.05494	0.33516	0.64835	0.99451	1.37363	1.78571								
14	−1	−.98571	−0.94286	−0.87143	−0.77143	−0.64286	−0.48571	−0.30000	−0.08571	0.15714	0.42857	0.72857	1.05714	1.41429	1.80000							
15	−1	−.98750	−0.95000	−0.88750	−0.80000	−0.68750	−0.55000	−0.38750	−0.20000	0.01250	0.25000	0.51250	0.80000	1.11250	1.45000	1.80833						
16	−1	−.98897	−0.95588	−0.90074	−0.82353	−0.72426	−0.60294	−0.45956	−0.29412	−0.10662	0.10294	0.33456	0.58824	0.86397	1.16176	1.48162	1.82353					
17	−1	−.99020	−0.96078	−0.91176	−0.84314	−0.75490	−0.64706	−0.51961	−0.37255	−0.20588	−0.01908	0.18027	0.41176	0.65686	0.92157	1.20588	1.50980	1.83333				
18	−1	−.99123	−0.96491	−0.92105	−0.85965	−0.78070	−0.68421	−0.57018	−0.43860	−0.28947	−0.12281	0.06140	0.26316	0.48246	0.71930	0.97368	1.24561	1.53509	1.84210			
19	−1	−.99211	−0.96842	−0.92895	−0.87368	−0.80263	−0.71579	−0.61316	−0.49474	−0.36053	−0.21053	−0.04474	0.13084	0.33421	0.54737	0.77632	1.02105	1.28158	1.55789	1.85000		
20	−1	−.99286	−0.97143	−0.93571	−0.88571	−0.82143	−0.74286	−0.65000	−0.54286	−0.42143	−0.28571	−0.13571	0.02857	0.20714	0.40000	0.60714	0.82857	1.06429	1.31429	1.57857	1.85714	
21	−1	−.99351	−0.97403	−0.94156	−0.89610	−0.83766	−0.76623	−0.68182	−0.58442	−0.47403	−0.35065	−0.21429	−0.06494	0.09740	0.27273	0.46103	0.66234	0.87662	1.10390	1.12771	1.59740	1.86364

Table $A.10c$. Second-order effects $E_Q^{(2)}$ of nuclear quadrupole interactions in linear or symmetric-top molecules, evaluated from Eqs. 2.84 and 2.85 in text. Numerical calculations were made by J. W. Simmons and W. E. Anderson

All factors in table to be multiplied by $\left[\dfrac{(eqQ)^2}{B_0} \times 10^{-3} \right]$

$I = \frac{3}{2}$

J	F	$K = 0$	$K = 1$	$K = 2$	$K = 3$	$K = 4$	$K = 5$	$K = 6$
0	$\frac{3}{2}$	−10.4167						
1	$5\frac{1}{2}$	−6.0000	−9.4688					
	$3\frac{1}{2}$	−2.2500	−10.8750					
	$\frac{1}{2}$	0.0000	−11.7188					
2	$7\frac{1}{2}$	−4.0999	−5.6487	−7.2885				
	$5\frac{1}{2}$	−2.1866	2.4561	−3.8875				
	$3\frac{1}{2}$	10.4167	5.2082	−10.4170				
	$\frac{1}{2}$	0.0000	11.7188	0.0000				
3	$9\frac{1}{2}$	−3.0864	−3.8520	−5.3818	−5.3758			
	$7\frac{1}{2}$	−1.9290	0.2170	3.4721	1.7119			
	$5\frac{1}{2}$	6.0000	3.4466	−2.6042	−7.3244			
	$3\frac{1}{2}$	2.2500	5.6668	10.4170	0.0000			
4	$11\frac{1}{2}$	−2.4652	−2.8917	−3.9090	−4.7287	−4.0384		
	$9\frac{1}{2}$	−1.6904	−0.5944	1.8570	3.1549	−0.8835		
	$7\frac{1}{2}$	4.0998	2.8205	−0.4613	−4.0782	−5.2500		
	$5\frac{1}{2}$	2.1866	3.5660	6.4915	7.3240	0.0000		
5	$13\frac{1}{2}$	−2.0482	−2.3084	−2.9800	−3.7373	−4.0366	−3.1171	
	$11\frac{1}{2}$	−1.4935	−0.8679	0.7160	2.3783	2.6536	−0.5096	
	$9\frac{1}{2}$	3.0864	2.3715	0.4443	−2.0424	−4.0004	−3.9066	
	$7\frac{1}{2}$	1.9290	2.6111	4.2779	5.7901	5.2500	0.0000	
6	$15\frac{1}{2}$	−1.7500	−1.9198	−2.3779	−2.9701	−3.4395	−3.4265	−2.4684
	$13\frac{1}{2}$	−1.3333	−0.9447	0.0971	1.4220	2.4120	2.2022	−0.3188
	$11\frac{1}{2}$	2.4652	2.0288	0.8175	−0.8767	−2.5661	−3.5684	−3.0065
	$9\frac{1}{2}$	1.6904	2.0749	3.0805	4.2634	4.8839	3.9066	0.0000

$I = \frac{5}{2}$

J	F	$K = 0$	$K = 1$	$K = 2$	$K = 3$	$K = 4$	$K = 5$	$K = 6$
0	$\frac{5}{2}$	−5.8333						
1	$7\frac{1}{2}$	−2.8930	−6.1475					
	$5\frac{1}{2}$	−2.0829	−3.6386					
	$3\frac{1}{2}$	−0.5400	−8.2350					
2	$9\frac{1}{2}$	−1.8039	−3.1402	−4.8439				
	$7\frac{1}{2}$	1.8039	2.6858	−0.8261				
	$5\frac{1}{2}$	4.9478	0.0657	−3.9850				
	$3\frac{1}{2}$	−0.1968	5.6991	−5.1118				
	$\frac{1}{2}$	0.0000	−0.8333	−2.0832				
3	$11\frac{1}{2}$	−1.2767	−1.9108	−3.2421	−3.5571			
	$9\frac{1}{2}$	−1.4773	0.3006	3.1402	−0.4417			
	$7\frac{1}{2}$	2.0002	0.7866	−1.6667	−1.7969			
	$5\frac{1}{2}$	1.8072	1.7500	0.7640	−3.5926			
	$3\frac{1}{2}$	0.5400	1.7341	3.0208	−2.6368			
	$\frac{1}{2}$	0.0000	0.8333	2.0833	0.0000			
4	$13\frac{1}{2}$	−0.9753	−1.3193	−2.1601	−2.9227	−2.6497		
	$11\frac{1}{2}$	−1.2289	−0.4042	1.4534	2.4952	−0.3603		
	$9\frac{1}{2}$	0.9756	0.6127	−0.2797	−1.1141	−0.9101		
	$7\frac{1}{2}$	1.5081	1.2013	0.3300	−0.9597	−2.4238		
	$5\frac{1}{2}$	0.8856	1.2000	1.7349	1.2654	−2.2500		
	$3\frac{1}{2}$	0.1968	0.7918	2.0910	2.6368	0.0000		
5	$15\frac{1}{2}$	−0.7835	−0.9894	−1.5290	−2.1682	−2.5167	−2.0281	
	$13\frac{1}{2}$	−1.0446	−0.6066	0.5031	1.6706	1.8734	−0.3198	
	$11\frac{1}{2}$	0.5225	0.3992	0.0704	−0.3410	−0.6301	−0.5106	
	$9\frac{1}{2}$	1.1840	0.9640	0.3562	−0.4822	−1.2888	−1.6970	
	$7\frac{1}{2}$	0.8928	0.9656	1.0935	1.0039	0.2435	−1.8228	
	$5\frac{1}{2}$	0.2756	0.6230	1.4861	2.3272	2.2500	0.0000	
6	$17\frac{1}{2}$	−0.6519	−0.7844	−1.1456	−1.6258	−2.0431	−2.1421	−1.5948
	$15\frac{1}{2}$	−0.9052	−0.6482	0.0404	0.9144	1.5623	1.4089	−0.2855
	$13\frac{1}{2}$	0.2900	0.2466	0.1258	0.0453	−0.2204	−0.3361	−0.3097
	$11\frac{1}{2}$	0.9468	0.8020	0.3961	−0.1836	−0.7938	−1.2316	−1.2380
	$9\frac{1}{2}$	0.8283	0.8321	0.8202	0.7229	0.4239	−0.2394	−1.4762
	$7\frac{1}{2}$	0.2958	0.5081	1.0693	1.7527	2.1803	1.8228	0.0000

Table A.11. Zeeman coefficients

Values of $\alpha_J = \dfrac{F(F+1)+J(J+1)-I(I+1)}{2F(F+1)}$ are tabulated for $J = 1$ through 10, and $I = 1, \frac{3}{2}, \frac{5}{2}, \frac{7}{2}$, and $\frac{9}{2}$.

The quantity $\alpha_I = \dfrac{F(F+1)+I(I+1)-J(J+1)}{2F(F+1)}$ can be obtained by subtracting these values from unity.

$\alpha_I = 1 - \alpha_J.$

$I = 1$

F \ J	1	2	3	4	5	6	7	8	9	10
$J-1$		1.5000	1.3333	1.2500	1.2000	1.1667	1.1428	1.1250	1.1111	1.1000
J	0.5000	0.8333	0.9167	0.9500	0.9667	0.9762	0.9821	0.9861	0.9889	0.9909
$J+1$	0.5000	0.6667	0.7500	0.8000	0.8333	0.8572	0.8750	0.8889	0.9000	0.9091

$I = \frac{3}{2}$

F \ J	1	2	3	4	5	6	7	8	9	10
$J-\frac{3}{2}$		2.0000	1.6000	1.4286	1.3333	1.2728	1.2308	1.2000	1.1765	1.1579
$J-\frac{1}{2}$	-0.6667	-0.8000	0.9714	1.0159	1.0303	1.0349	1.0359	1.0353	1.0341	1.0326
$J+\frac{1}{2}$	0.2667	0.6286	0.7619	0.8283	0.8671	0.8923	0.9098	0.9226	0.9324	0.9399
$J+\frac{3}{2}$	0.4000	0.5714	0.6667	0.7273	0.7692	0.8000	0.8235	0.8421	0.8571	0.8695

$I = \frac{5}{2}$

F \ J	1	2	3	4	5	6	7	8	9	10
$J-\frac{5}{2}$			2.6667	2.0000	1.7143	1.5556	1.4546	1.3846	1.3334	1.2941
$J-\frac{3}{2}$		-1.3333	9.9333	1.8571	1.1746	1.1718	1.1608	1.1487	1.1373	1.1269
$J-\frac{1}{2}$		0.1333	0.6857	0.8571	0.9293	0.9650	0.9846	0.9960	1.0030	1.0075
$J+\frac{1}{2}$	-0.4000	0.3429	0.6032	0.7273	0.7972	0.8410	0.8705	0.8916	0.9073	0.9192
$J+\frac{3}{2}$	0.1143	0.4127	0.5657	0.6573	0.7179	0.7607	0.7925	0.8170	0.8364	0.8521
$J+\frac{5}{2}$	0.2857	0.4444	0.5455	0.6154	0.6667	0.7058	0.7368	0.7619	0.7826	0.7999

$I = \frac{7}{2}$

F \ J	1	2	3	4	5	6	7	8	9	10
$J-\frac{7}{2}$				3.3333	2.0667	2.0000	1.7778	1.6364	1.5385	1.4667
$J-\frac{5}{2}$			-2.0000	1.0667	1.3143	1.3333	1.3131	1.2867	1.2616	1.2392
$J-\frac{3}{2}$			0.0000	0.7429	0.9524	1.0303	1.0629	1.0769	1.0824	1.0836
$J-\frac{1}{2}$		-0.8000	0.2857	0.6349	0.7879	0.8671	0.9128	0.9412	0.9598	0.9725
$J+\frac{1}{2}$		-0.0571	0.3810	0.5859	0.6993	0.7692	0.8157	0.8483	0.8722	0.8903
$J+\frac{3}{2}$	-0.2857	0.1905	0.4242	0.5594	0.6462	0.7059	0.7493	0.7820	0.8075	0.8278
$J+\frac{5}{2}$	0.0635	0.3030	0.4476	0.5436	0.6118	0.6626	0.7018	0.7330	0.7583	0.7793
$J+\frac{7}{2}$	0.2222	0.3636	0.4615	0.5333	0.5882	0.6316	0.6667	0.6957	0.7200	0.7408

$I = \frac{9}{2}$

F \ J	1	2	3	4	5	6	7	8	9	10
$J-\frac{9}{2}$					4.0000	2.8000	2.2857	2.0000	1.8182	1.6923
$J-\frac{7}{2}$				-2.6667	1.2000	1.4857	1.4921	1.4546	1.4126	1.3744
$J-\frac{5}{2}$				-0.1333	0.8000	1.0477	1.1313	1.1609	1.1693	1.1687
$J-\frac{3}{2}$			-1.2000	0.2286	0.6667	0.8485	0.9371	0.9846	1.0118	1.0279
$J-\frac{1}{2}$			-0.2286	0.3492	0.6061	0.7413	0.8205	0.8706	0.9040	0.9274
$J+\frac{1}{2}$		-0.5714	0.0952	0.4040	0.5734	0.6769	0.7451	0.7926	0.8271	0.8530
$J+\frac{3}{2}$		-0.0952	0.2424	0.4336	0.5538	0.6353	0.6935	0.7369	0.7702	0.7965
$J+\frac{5}{2}$	-0.2222	0.1212	0.3217	0.4513	0.5412	0.6068	0.6567	0.6957	0.7270	0.7526
$J+\frac{7}{2}$	0.0404	0.2378	0.3692	0.4627	0.5325	0.5865	0.6294	0.6644	0.6933	0.7178
$J+\frac{9}{2}$	0.1818	0.3077	0.4000	0.4706	0.5263	0.5714	0.6087	0.6400	0.6667	0.6897

BIBLIOGRAPHY

Gases

Pre-1946

101 Cleeton, C. E., and Williams, N. H.   *Phys. Rev. 45*, 234 (1934)   NH₃

102 Van Vleck, J. H., and Weisskopf, V. F.   *Revs. Modern Phys. 17*, 227 (1945)   Press. broad. theory

1946

201 Becker, G. E., and Autler, S. H.   *Phys. Rev. 70*, 300   Cavity, H₂O

202 Beringer, R.   *Phys. Rev. 70*, 53   O₂

203 Bleaney, B.   *Physica 12*, 595   Review

204 Bleaney, B., and Penrose, R. P.   *Nature 157*, 339; *Phys. Rev. 70*, 775L   NH₃

205 Coles, D. K., and Good, W. E.   *Phys. Rev. 70*, 979L   NH₃ Stark, Zeeman, quad. coup.

206 Dailey, B. P.; Kyhl, R. L.; Strandberg, M. W. P.; Van Vleck, J. H.; and Wilson, E. B., Jr.   *Phys. Rev. 70*, 984L   NH₃ nuclear quad. mom.

207 Dakin, T. W.; Good, W. E.; and Coles, D. K.   *Phys. Rev. 70*, 560L   OCS Stark effect

208 Dicke, R. H.   *Rev. Sci. Instr. 17*, 268   Radiometer

209 Dicke, R. H.; Beringer, R.; Kyhl, R. L.; and Vane, A. B.   *Phys. Rev. 70*, 340   Radiometer meas. H₂O

210 Foley, H. M.   *Phys. Rev. 69*, 616   Press. broad. phase shift

211 Fröhlich, H.   *Nature 157*, 478   Dielectric relaxation, theory

212 Good, W. E.   *Phys.Rev.69*,539L; *70*, 109A, 213   NH₃

213 Hadley, L. N., and Dennison, D. M.   *Phys. Rev. 70*, 780L   NH₃ theory

214 Hainer, R. M.; King, G. W.; and Cross, P. C.   *Phys. Rev. 70*, 108A   Predicted lines

215 Hershberger, W. D.   *J. Appl. Phys. 17*, 495   Various gases mod. press.

216   Hershberger, W. D.; Bush, E. T.; and Leck, G. W.   *RCA Rev. 7*, 422   Thermal, acoustic effects in gases

217   Lamb, W. E., Jr.   *Phys. Rev. 70*, 308   Cavity spectrometer, theory

218   Pound, R. V.   *Rev. Sci. Instr. 17*, 490   Freq. stabilizer

219   Roberts, A.; Beers, Y.; and Hill, A. G.   *Phys. Rev. 70*, 112A   Cs

220   Townes, C. H.   *Phys. Rev. 70*, 109A, 665 NH_3 line breadth, sat. effect

221   Townes, C. H., and Merritt, F. R.   *Phys. Rev. 70*, 558L H_2O, HDO

222   Walter, J. E., and Hershberger, W. D.   *J. Appl. Phys. 17*, 814   Gases, general

1947

301   Beard, C. I., and Dailey, B. P.   *J. Chem. Phys. 15*, 762L   HNCS, DNCS

302   Bleaney, B., and Penrose, R. P.   *Proc. Roy. Soc. (London) A 189*, 358; *Proc. Phys. Soc. (London) 59*, 418 NH_3, high press.

303   Carter, R. L., and Smith, W. V.   *Phys. Rev. 72*, 1265L   Freq. markers

304   Coles, D. K.; Elyash, E. S.; and Gorman, J. G.   *Phys. Rev. 72*, 973L N_2O

305   Coles, D. K., and Good, W. E.   *Phys. Rev. 72*, 157A   Stark, Zeeman

306   Dailey, B. P.   *Phys. Rev. 72*, 84L CH_3OH

307   Dailey, B. P.; Golden, S.; and Wilson, E. B., Jr.   *Phys. Rev. 72*, 871L SO_2

308   Dailey, B, P., and Wilson, E. B., Jr.   *Phys. Rev. 72*, 522A SO_2, CH_3OH, CH_3NO_2

309   Dakin, T. W.; Good, W. E.; and Coles, D. K.   *Phys. Rev. 71*, 640L   OCS

310   Feld, B. T.   *Phys. Rev. 72*, 1116L   Quad. interactions definitions

311   Foley, H. M.   *Phys. Rev. 72*, 504   Quad. effects

312   George, W. D.; Lyons, H.; Freeman, J. J.; and Shaull, J. M.   *NBS Report* CR-PL-8-1   Freq. standard

313   Good, W. E., and Coles, D. K.   *Phys. Rev. 71*, 383L $N^{14}H_3$; $N^{15}H_3$

314   Good, W. E., and Coles, D. K.   *Phys. Rev. 72*, 157A   Precision freq. meas.

315   Gordy, W., and Kessler, M.   *Phys. Rev. 71*, 640L NH_3, hyperfine

316   Gordy, W., and Kessler, M.   *Phys. Rev. 72*, 644L   Detection systems

317   Gordy, W.; Simmons, J. W.; and Smith, A. G.   *Phys. Rev. 72*, 344L CH_3Cl, CH_3Br

318	Gordy, W.; Smith, A. G.; and Simmons, J. W.	*Phys.Rev.71*,917L; *72*, 249L	CH₃I
319	Gordy, W.; Smith, W. V.; Smith, A. G.; and Ring, H.	*Phys. Rev. 72*, 259L	BrCN, ICN
320	Hershberger, W. D., and Turkevitch, J.	*Phys. Rev. 71*, 554L	CH₃OH, CH₃NH₂
321	Hillger, R. E.; Strandberg, M. W. P.; Wentink, T., Jr.; and Kyhl, R. L.	*Phys. Rev. 72*, 157A	OCS
322	Hughes, R. H., and Wilson, E. B., Jr.	*Phys. Rev. 71*, 562L	Stark spectrometer
323	Hunt, L. E.	*Proc. IRE 35*, 979	Freq. stand.
324	Jauch, J. M.	*Phys. Rev. 72*, 715, 535A	NH₃, theor. Stark
325	Jen, C. K.	*Phys. Rev. 72*, 986L	Zeeman, NH₃ cavity
326	King, G. W.	*J. Chem. Phys. 15*, 820	Asym. rotor correspondence principle
327	King, G. W., and Hainer, R. M.	*Phys. Rev. 71*, 135A	1.3-cm. HDO ident.
328	King, G. W.; Hainer, R. M.; and Cross, P. C.	*Phys. Rev. 71*, 433	Predicted micro. lines
329	Lamb, W. E., Jr., and Retherford, R. C.	*Phys. Rev. 72*, 241	Lamb shift
330	Nielsen, H. H., and Dennison, D. M.	*Phys. Rev. 72*, 86L, 1101	NH₃ anomalies
331	Pond, T. A., and Cannon, W. F.	*Phys. Rev. 72*, 1121L	Saturation
332	Pound, R. V.	*Proc. IRE 35*, 1405	Freq. stab.
333	Ring, H.; Edwards, H.; Kessler, M.; and Gordy, W.	*Phys. Rev. 72*, 1262L	CH₃CN, CH₃NC
334	Roberts, A.	*Nucleonics 1*, 10, October	Review
335	Smith, W. V.	*Phys. Rev. 71*, 126L	Spin from Stark
336	Smith, W. V., and Carter, R. L.	*Phys. Rev. 72*, 638L	Saturation effect
337	Smith, W. V.; de Quevedo, J. L. G.; Carter, R. L.; and Bennett, W. S.	*J. Appl. Phys. 18*, 1112	Freq. stab.
338	Strandberg, M. W. P.; Kyhl, R.; Wentink, T., Jr.; and Hillger, R. E.	*Phys. Rev. 71*,326L, erratum 639L	NH₃
339	Talpey, R. G., and Goldberg, H.	*Proc. IRE 35*, 965	Freq. standard
340	Townes, C. H.	*Phys. Rev. 71*, 909L	Quad. mom., $\partial^2 V/\partial z^2$
341	Townes, C. H.; Holden, A. N.; Bardeen, J.; and Merritt, F. R.	*Phys. Rev. 71*, 644L, erratum 829L	Quad. mom., spin Br, Cl, N
342	Townes, C. H.; Holden, A. N.; and Merritt, F. R.	*Phys. Rev. 71*, 64L, 479A; *72*, 513L, 740A	Mass ratios *l*-doubling linear molecules

343	Townes, C. H., and Merritt, F. R.	*Phys. Rev. 72,* 1266L	Stark eff., high freq.
344	Van Vleck, J. H.	*Phys. Rev. 71,* 413	O_2
345	Van Vleck, J. H.	*Phys. Rev. 71,* 425	H_2O
346	Van Vleck, J. H.	*Phys. Rev. 71,* 468A	Quad. coup., sym. top
347	Watts, R. J., and Williams, D.	*Phys. Rev. 71,* 639L; *72,* 157A, 263	NH_3, quad. coupling
348	Watts, R. J., and Williams, D.	*Phys. Rev. 72,* 1122L	Double modulation
349	Watts, R. J., and Williams, D.	*Phys. Rev. 72,* 980L	Stark spectrometer
350	Weidner, R. T.	*Phys. Rev. 72,* 1268L	ICl
351	Williams, D.	*Phys. Rev. 72,* 974L	NH_3

1948

401	Bardeen, J., and Townes, C. H.	*Phys. Rev. 73,* 97, 627, erratum 1204L	Quad. effects
402	Bleaney, B.	*Reports on Progress in Physics* XI, 178	Review
403	Bleaney, B., and Loubser, J. H. N.	*Nature 161,* 522	NH_3 to 6 atm.
404	Bleaney, B., and Penrose, R. P.	*Proc. Phys. Soc.* (*London*) 60, 83	Sat. effect
405	Bleaney, B., and Penrose, R. P.	*Proc. Phys. Soc.* (*London*) 60, 540	Gas mixtures
406	Bragg, J. K.	*Phys. Rev. 73,* 1250A; *74,* 533	Quad. mom. asym. tops
407	Carter, R. L., and Smith, W. V.	*Phys. Rev. 73,* 1053; *74,* 123A	Sat. effect
408	Coates, R. J.	*Rev. Sci. Instr. 19,* 586	Grating spectrometer
409	Coles, D. K.	*Phys. Rev. 74,* 1194L	CH_3OH
410	Cunningham, G. L.; LeVan, W. I.; and Gwinn, W. D.	*Phys. Rev. 74,* 1537L	Ethylene oxide
411	Dailey, B. P.; Rusinow, K.; Shulman, R. G.; and Townes, C. H.	*Phys. Rev. 74,* 1245A	AsF_3
412	Edgell, W. F., and Roberts, A.	*J. Chem. Phys. 16,* 1002L	CH_3CF_3
413	Fano, U.	*J. Research NBS 40,* 215	Stark, quad. mom. lin. mol.
414	Foley, H. M.	*Phys. Rev. 73,* 259L	Press. broad.
415	Freymann, M.; Freymann, R.; and LeBot, J.	*J. Phys. et Radium* 9, 1D–60D	Review
416	Gilliam, O. R.; Edwards, H. D.; and Gordy, W.	*Phys. Rev. 73,* 635L	CH_3I, ICN anomalies

417	Golden, S.	*J. Chem. Phys. 16,* 78, 250, erratum *17,* 586L (1949)	Asympt. energies, asym. top
418	Golden, S.; Wentink, T., Jr.; Hillger, R. E.; and Strandberg, M. W. P.	*Phys. Rev. 73,* 92L	H_2O Stark
419	Golden, S., and Wilson, E. B., Jr.	*J. Chem. Phys. 16,* 669	Stark effect rigid asym. top
420	Gordy, W.	*Revs. Modern Phys. 20,* 668	Review
421	Gordy, W.; Ring, H.; and Burg, A. B.	*Phys. Rev. 74,* 1191L, erratum *75,* 208L (1949)	BH_3CO
422	Gordy, W.; Simmons, J. W.; and Smith, A. G.	*Phys. Rev. 74,* 243	Methyl halides
423	Henderson, R. S.	*Phys. Rev. 74,* 107L, erratum 626L	NH_3 fine struc. (mag. effects)
424	Henderson, R. S., and Van Vleck, J. H.	*Phys. Rev. 74,* 106L	Electron spins in rot. poly. mol.
425	Hershberger, W. D.	*J. Appl. Phys. 19,* 411; *Phys. Rev. 73,* 1249A	Min. detectable absorption
426	Hershberger, W. D., and Norton, L. E.	*RCA Review 9,* 38	Freq. stab.
427	Jabloński, A.	*Phys. Rev. 73,* 258L	Press. broad.
428	Jauch, J. M.	*Phys. Rev. 74,* 1262A	NH_3, spin-orbit interaction
429	Jen, C. K.	*Phys. Rev. 73,* 1248A; *74,* 1246A, 1396	CH_3Cl Zeeman mag. mom.
430	Karplus, R.	*Phys. Rev. 73,* 1027	Freq. mod.
431	Karplus, R.	*Phys. Rev. 73,* 1120L; *74,* 223L	Sat. effects
432	Karplus, R.	*J. Chem. Phys. 16,* 1170L	Energy of rot. mol.
433	Karplus, R., and Schwinger, J.	*Phys. Rev. 73,* 1020	Sat. effects
434	Kessler, M., and Gordy, W.	*Phys. Rev. 74,* 123A	Microwave spectrometer
435	Knight, G., and Feld, B. T.	*Phys. Rev. 74,* 354A	Quad. mom. asym. top
436	Lamont, H. R. L.	*Phys. Rev. 74,* 353L	O_2, atmos. abs.; line breadth
437	Merritt, F. R., and Townes, C. H.	*Phys. Rev. 73,* 1249A	Stark effect, high freq.
438	Mizushima, M.	*Phys. Rev. 74,* 705L	NH_3
439	Nierenberg, W. A.; Rabi, I. I.; and Slotnick, M.	*Phys. Rev. 73,* 1430	Stark effect diatomic mol.
440	Nierenberg, W. A., and Slotnick, M.	*Phys. Rev. 74,* 1246A	Stark effect
441	de Quevedo, J. L. G., and Smith, W. V.	*J. Appl. Phys. 19,* 831	Spectral line freq. stab.

442	Richards, P. I., and Snyder, H. S.	*Phys. Rev. 73*, 269L	Sat. effects
443	Roberts, A.	*Phys. Rev. 73*, 1405L	$OC^{14}S$, l-doubling C^{14} spin
444	Sharbaugh, A. H.	*Phys. Rev. 74*, 1870L	SiH_3Cl
445	Shulman, R. G.; Dailey, B. P.; and Townes, C. H.	*Phys. Rev. 74*, 846L	Ethylene oxide
446	Simmons, J. W., and Gordy, W.	*Phys. Rev. 73*, 713; 74, 123A	NH_3
447	Simmons, J. W.; Gordy, W.; and Smith, A. G.	*Phys. Rev. 74*, 1246A	Methyl halides
448	Smith, A. G.; Ring, H.; Smith, W. V.; and Gordy, W.	*Phys. Rev. 73*, 633L	N_2O, ICN
449	Smith, A. G.; Ring, H.; Smith, W. V.; and Gordy, W.	*Phys. Rev. 74*, 123A, 370	Cyanogen halides
450	Smith, D. F.	*Phys. Rev. 74*, 506L	NH_3, press. broad.
451	Snyder, H. S., and Richards, P. I.	*Phys. Rev. 73*, 1178	Sat. effects
452	Strandberg, M. W. P.	*Phys. Rev. 74*, 1245A	D_2O
453	Strandberg, M. W. P.; Wentink, T., Jr.; Hillger, R. E.; Wannier, G. H.; and Deutsch, M. L.	*Phys. Rev. 73*, 188L	HDO
454	Strandberg, M. W. P., and Wentink, T., Jr.	*Phys. Rev. 73*, 1249A	OCSe
455	Townes, C. H.	*Phys. Rev. 74*, 1245A	Quad. mom. N^{14}, I^{127}
456	Townes, C. H., and Geschwind, S.	*Phys. Rev. 74*, 626L	S^{33}
457	Townes, C. H., and Geschwind, S.	*J. Appl. Phys. 19*, 795L	Spectrometer sensitivity
458	Townes, C. H.; Holden, A. N.; and Merritt, F. R.	*Phys. Rev. 74*, 1113	Linear XYZ mol.
459	Townes, C. H.; Merritt, F. R.; and Wright, B. D.	*Phys. Rev. 73*, 1249A, 1334	ICl
460	Unterberger, R. R., and Smith, W. V.	*Rev. Sci. Instr. 19*, 580	Freq. standard
461	Watts, R. J.; Pietenpol, W. J.; Rogers, J. D.; and Williams, D.	*Phys. Rev. 74*, 1246A	Sat. effects
462	Weidner, R. T.	*Phys. Rev. 73*, 254L	ICl
463	Weingarten, I. R.	*Columbia Rad. Lab. Report*, May 1	NH_3, high pressures
464	Wentink, T., Jr.; Strandberg, M. W. P.; and Hillger, R. E.	*Phys. Rev. 73*, 1249A	OCSe Stark
465	Wick, G. C.	*Phys. Rev. 73*, 51	Mag. field of rot. mol.
466	Witmer, E.	*Phys. Rev. 74*, 1247A, 1250A	Asym. top

1949

501	Anderson, P. W.	*Phys. Rev. 75,* 1450L	NH_3, high press.
502	Anderson, P. W.	*Phys. Rev. 76,* 471A, 647	Press. broad.
503	Bak, B.; Knudsen, E.; and Madsen, E.	*Phys. Rev. 75,* 1622L	Organic vapors
504	Beard, C. I., and Dailey, B. P.	*Phys. Rev. 75,* 1318A	HNCS, Stark
505	Beard, C. I., and Dailey, B. P.	*J. Am. Chem. Soc.* 71, 929	CH_3NCS, CH_3SCN
506	Beringer, R., and Castle, J. G.	*Phys. Rev. 75,* 1963L	O_2
507	Bianco, D.; Matlack, G.; and Roberts, A.	*Phys. Rev. 76,* 473A	OCS, CH_3Cl
508	Bragg, J. K., and Golden, S.	*Phys. Rev. 75,* 735	Quad. mom. asym. tops
509	Bragg, J. K., and Sharbaugh, A. H.	*Phys. Rev. 75,* 1774L	Formaldehyde
510	Cohen, V. W.; Koski, W. S.; and Wentink, T., Jr.	*Phys. Rev. 76,* 703L	S^{35}
511	Coles, D. K., and Hughes, R. H.	*Phys. Rev. 76,* 178A	N_2O
512	Coles, D. K., and Hughes, R. H.	*Phys. Rev. 76,* 858L	CF_3Cl
513	Cunningham, G. L.; Boyd, A. W.; Gwinn, W. D.; and LeVan, W. I.	*J. Chem. Phys. 17,* 211L	Ethylene oxide
514	Dailey, B. P.	*Analyt. Chem. 21,* 540	Chem. analysis
515	Dailey, B. P.; Mays, J. M.; and Townes, C. H.	*Phys. Rev. 76,* 136L	GeH_3Cl; SiH_3Cl, CH_3Cl
516	Dailey, B. P.; Mays, J. M.; and Townes, C. H.	*Phys. Rev. 76,* 472A	SiH_3Cl
517	Dailey, B. P.; Minden, H.; and Shulman, R. G.	*Phys. Rev. 75,* 1319A	CH_3CF_3, torsion
518	Edwards, H. D.; Gilliam, O. R.; and Gordy, W.	*Phys. Rev. 76,* 196A	CH_3OH, CH_3NH_2
519	Gilbert, D. A.; Roberts, A.; and Griswold, P. A.	*Phys. Rev. 76,* 1723L	FCl
520	Gilliam, O. R.; Edwards, H. D.; and Gordy, W.	*Phys. Rev. 75,* 1014; 76, 195A	CH_3F, CHF_3, PF_3
521	Golden, S., and Bragg, J. K.	*J. Chem. Phys. 17,* 439	Asym. tops, degenerate levels
522	Goldstein, J. H., and Bragg, J. K.	*Phys. Rev. 75,* 1453L	CH_2CHCl
523	Gordy, W.; Gilliam, O. R.; and Livingston, R.	*Phys. Rev. 76,* 443L	I^{127}, I^{129} mag. mom.
524	Gordy, W.; Ring, H.; and Burg, A. B.	*Phys. Rev. 75,* 1325A	BH_3CO
525	Hainer, R. M.; Cross, P. C.; and King, G. W.	*J. Chem. Phys. 17,* 826	High-J asym. tops

526	Jen, C. K.	*Phys. Rev. 75*, 1319A; *76*, 1494	NH_3, N_2O Paschen-Back
527	Jen, C. K.	*Phys. Rev. 76*, 471A	H_2O, HDO mag. mom.
528	Karplus, R., and Sharbaugh, A. H.	*Phys. Rev. 75*, 889L, erratum 1449L	CH_3Cl
529	Lawrance, R. B.; Kyhl, R. L.; and Strandberg, M. W. P.	*Phys. Rev. 76*, 472A	CH_2O
530	Lenard, A.	*Report, Iowa State Phys. Dept.*	Tables, Stark, Zeeman
531	Livingston, R.; Gilliam, O. R.; and Gordy, W.	*Phys. Rev. 76*, 149L	I^{129}, spin, quad. mom.
532	Loubser, J. H. N., and Townes, C. H.	*Phys. Rev. 76*, 178A	Magnetron harmonics, DI, NH_3
533	Low, W., and Townes, C. H.	*Phys. Rev. 75*, 1319A; *76*, 1295	Stark sym. top
534	Low, W., and Townes, C. H.	*Phys. Rev. 75*, 529L, 1318A	O^{17}, S^{36}
535	Margenau, H.	*Phys. Rev. 76*, 121, 585A, 1423	NH_3, press. broad.
536	McAfee, K. B.; Hughes, R. H.; and Wilson, E. B., Jr.	*Rev. Sci. Instr. 20*, 821	Stark spectrometer
537	Millman, G. H., and Raymond, R. C.	*J. Appl. Phys. 20*, 413L	Several gases, moderate pressure
538	Mizushima, M.	*Phys. Rev. 76*, 1268L, erratum *77*, 149L	Press. broad.
539	Mizushima, M.	*J. Phys. Soc. Japan 4*, 11, 191	NH_3
540	Nielsen, H. H.	*Phys. Rev. 75*, 1961L	CH_3CN and CH_3NC, l-doubling
541	Pietenpol, W. J., and Rogers, J. D.	*Phys. Rev. 76*, 690L	CH_2Br_2
542	Roberts, A., and Edgell, W. F.	*J. Chem. Phys. 17*, 742L; *Phys. Rev. 76*, 178A	CH_2CF_2
543	Sharbaugh, A. H.; Bragg, J. K.; Madison, T. C.; and Thomas, V. G.	*Phys. Rev. 76*, 1419L	SiH_3Br
544	Sharbaugh, A. H.; Madison, T. C.; and Bragg, J. K.	*Phys. Rev. 76*, 1529L	New NH_3 lines
545	Sharbaugh, A. H., and Mattern, J.	*Phys. Rev. 75*, 1102L	CH_3Br
546	Shulman, R. G., and Townes, C. H.	*Phys. Rev. 75*, 1318A	OCS, Stark
546a	Shulman, R. G.; Dailey, B. P.; and Townes, C. H.	*Phys. Rev. 76*, 472A	Dipole mom.
547	Simmons, J. W.	*Phys. Rev. 76*, 686L	CD_3Cl, CD_3I

548	Smith, A. G.; Gordy, W.; Simmons, J. W.; and Smith, W. V.	*Phys. Rev. 75*, 260	3–5 mm.
548a	Smith, W. V., and Howard, R.	*Phys. Rev. 76*, 473A	Press. broad.
549	Smith, W. V., and Unterberger, R. R.	*J. Chem. Phys. 17*, 1348L	$CHCl_3$
550	Strandberg, M. W. P.	*J. Chem. Phys. 17*, 901	HDO
551	Strandberg, M. W. P.; Meng, C. Y.; and Ingersoll, J. G.	*Phys. Rev. 75*, 1524	O_2
552	Strandberg, M. W. P.; Pearsall, C. S.; and Weiss, M. T.	*J. Chem. Phys. 17*, 429L	BH_3CO
553	Strandberg, M. W. P.; Wentink, T.; and Hill, A. G.	*Phys. Rev. 75*, 827	OCSe
554	Strandberg, M. W. P.; Wentink, T., Jr.; and Kyhl, R. L.	*Phys. Rev. 75*, 270	OCS
555	Townes, C. H., and Aamodt, L. C.	*Phys. Rev. 76*, 691L	Cl^{36}
556	Townes, C. H., and Dailey, B. P.	*J. Chem. Phys. 17*, 782	Electronic str. and quad. coupling
557	Townes, C. H.; Mays, J. M.; and Dailey, B. P.	*Phys. Rev. 76*, 700L	Ge, Si, nucl. moments
558	Van Vleck, J. H., and Margenau, H.	*Phys. Rev. 76*, 585A, 1211	Press. broad.
559	Westenberg, A. A.; Goldstein, J. H.; and Wilson, E. B., Jr.	*J. Chem. Phys. 17*, 1319; *Phys. Rev. 76*, 472A	CHCCl

1950

601	Amble, E., and Dailey, B. P.	*J. Chem. Phys. 18*, 1422L	HN_3
602	Anderson, P. W.	*Phys. Rev. 80*, 511	NH_3, quadrupole induced dipole interaction
603	Autler, S. H., and Townes, C. H.	*Phys. Rev. 78*, 340A	Resonant modulation
604	Baird, D. H.; Fristrom, R. M.; and Sirvetz, M. H.	*Rev. Sci. Instr. 21*, 881L	Parallel plate, other Stark cells
605	Bak, B.; Knudsen, E. S.; Madsen, E.; and Rastrup-Anderson, J.	*Phys. Rev. 79*, 190L	CH_2CO
606	Bak, B.; Sloan, R.; and Williams, D.	*Phys. Rev. 80*, 101L	SCSe
607	Beard, C. I., and Dailey, B. P.	*J. Chem. Phys. 18*, 1437, erratum *19*, 975L (1951)	HNCS
608	Beringer, R., and Castle, J. G., Jr.	*Phys. Rev. 78*, 340A, 581	NO
609	Bernstein, H. J.	*J. Chem. Phys. 18*, 1514L	NOCl

610	Bersohn, R.	*J. Chem. Phys. 18,* 1124L	Quad. coupling, three nuclei
611	Birnbaum, G.	*Phys. Rev. 77,* 144L	NH_3, dispersion
612	Bleaney, B., and Loubser, J. H. N.	*Proc. Phys. Soc. (London)* A*63,* 483	High pressure, NH_3, CH_3Cl, CH_3Br
613	Bragg, J. K.; Madison, T. C.; and Sharbaugh, A. H.	*Phys. Rev. 77,* 148L, erratum 571L	CH_2CFCl
614	Burkhalter, J. H.; Anderson, R. S.; Smith, W. V.; and Gordy, W.	*Phys. Rev. 77,* 152L; *79,* 224A, 651	O_2
615	Castle, J. G., Jr., and Beringer, R.	*Phys. Rev. 80,* 114L	NO_2
616	Coester, F.	*Phys. Rev. 77,* 454	Stark-Zeeman
617	Cohen, V. W.; Koski, W. S.; and Wentink, T., Jr.	*Phys. Rev. 77,* 742A	S^{35}
618	Coles, D. K.	*Advances in Electronics II,* 299	Review
619	Coles, D. K.; Good, W. E.; and Hughes, R. H.	*Phys. Rev. 77,* 741A	CH_3OH
620	Coles, D. K.; Good, W. E.; and Hughes, R. H.	*Phys. Rev. 79,* 224A	CH_3CN
621	Cornwell, C. D.	*J. Chem. Phys. 18,* 1118L	C_2H_3Br, bromo-diborane
622	Crawford, B. L., Jr., and Mann, D. E.	*Annual Review of Physical Chemistry I,* 151	Review
623	Eshbach, J. R.; Hillger, R. E.; and Jen, C. K.	*Phys. Rev. 80,* 1106L	S^{33} nucl. moment mag.
624	Fletcher, E. W., and Cooke, S. P.	*Cruft Laboratory ONR Report* 64	Freq. stab.
626	Geschwind, S.; Minden, H.; and Townes, C. H.	*Phys. Rev. 78,* 174L; *79,* 226A	Se isotopes
627	Gilbert, D. A., and Roberts, A.	*Phys. Rev. 77,* 742A	FCl
628	Gilliam, O. R.; Johnson, C. M.; and Gordy, W.	*Phys. Rev. 78,* 140	CO; 2–3 mm
629	Goldstein, J. H., and Bragg, J. K.	*Phys. Rev. 78,* 347A	Double-bond character from quad. coupling
630	Good, W. E.	*Westinghouse Labs. Sci. Paper* 1538	Techniques
631	Gordy, W.; Ring, H.; and Burg, A. B.	*Phys. Rev. 78,* 512	BH_3CO
632	Gordy, W., and Sheridan, J.	*Phys. Rev. 79,* 224A	Methyl mercuric halides
633	Griffing, V.	*J. Chem. Phys. 18,* 744	Saturation effects
634	Hartz, T. R., and van der Ziel, A.	*Phys. Rev. 78,* 473L	Square-wave modulation
635	Henry, A. F.	*Phys. Rev. 79,* 213A; *80,* 396	O_2 Zeeman
636	Henry, A. F.	*Phys. Rev. 80,* 549	NO Zeeman

637	Hershberger, W. D., and Norton, L. E.	*J. Franklin Inst.* *249*, 359	Servo theory stabilizer
638	Howard, R. R., and Smith, W. V.	*Phys. Rev. 77*, 840L	Temp. dep. of line widths
639	Howard, R. R., and Smith, W. V.	*Phys. Rev. 79*, 128, 225A	Collision diameters
640	Hughes, R. H.	*Westinghouse Labs. Sci. Paper* 1536	Chem. analysis
641	Jen, C. K.	*Phys. Rev. 78*, 339A	S^{33} nucl. mag. moment
642	Jones, L. C.	*Phys. Rev. 77*, 741A	Calc. of microwave line shifts
643	Jones, L. H.; Shoolery, J. N.; Shulman, R. G.; and Yost, D. M.	*J. Chem. Phys. 18*, 990L	HNCO
644	Kessler, M.; Ring, H.; Trambarulo, R.; and Gordy, W.	*Phys. Rev. 79*, 54	CH_3CN, CH_3NC
645	Kisliuk, P., and Townes, C. H.	*Phys. Rev. 78*, 347A	PCl_3
646	Kisliuk, P., and Townes, C. H.	*J. Chem. Phys. 18*, 1109	$AsCl_3$, PCl_3
647	Kisliuk, P., and Townes, C. H.	*NBS Journal of Research 44*, 611	Spectra tables
647a	Klages, G.	*Experientia 6*, 321	Review
648	Lamb, W. E., Jr., and Skinner, M.	*Phys. Rev. 78*, 539	Ionized He
649	Lawrance, R. B.	*Phys. Rev. 78*, 347A	CH_2O, centr. distortion
650	Lide, D. R., Jr., and Coles, D. K.	*Phys. Rev. 80*, 911L	CH_3SiH_3, int. rot.
651	Loubser, J. H. N., and Klein, J. A.	*Phys. Rev. 78*, 348A	ND_3, mm region
652	Low, W., and Townes, C. H.	*Phys. Rev. 79*, 224A	Fermi resonance OCS, OCSe
653	Margenau, H., and Henry, A.	*Phys. Rev. 78*, 587	NO
654	Matlack, G.; Glockler, G.; Bianco, D. R.; and Roberts, A.	*J. Chem. Phys. 18*, 332	CH_3Cl
655	McAfee, K. B., Jr.	*Phys. Rev. 78*, 340A	NO_2
656	Minden, H. T.; Mays, J. M.; and Dailey, B. P.	*Phys. Rev. 78*, 347A	CH_3SiF_3
657	Morgan, H. W.; Keilholtz, G. W.; Smith, W. V.; and Southern, A. L.	*ORNL Report* Y-621	ClCN isotopic analysis
658	Nielsen, H. H.	*Phys. Rev. 77*, 130	l-doub. CH_3CN, CH_3NC
659	Nielsen, H. H.	*Phys. Rev. 78*, 296L	l-doub. OCS, HCN
660	Nielsen, H. H.	*Phys. Rev. 78*, 415	Sym. tops, centrifugal distortion
661	Pietenpol, W.; Rogers, J. D.; and Williams, D.	*Phys. Rev. 77*, 741A	NOCl
662	Pietenpol, W.; Rogers, J. D.; and Williams, D.	*Phys. Rev. 78*, 480L	Asym. tops
662a	Rogers, J. D.; Cox, H. L.; and Braunschweiger, P. G.	*Rev. Sci. Instr. 21*, 1014	Freq. std.

663 Rouse, A. G.; Bushkovitch, A. V.; Jones, L. C.; Potter, C. A.; and Sullivan, W. F.　*Phys. Rev. 78*, 347A　Pressure shift

664 Senatore, S. J.　*Phys. Rev. 78*, 293L　POF_3

665 Sharbaugh, A. H.　*Rev. Sci. Instr. 21*, 120　Stark spectrometer

666 Sharbaugh, A. H.; Pritchard, B. S.; and Madison, T. C.　*Phys. Rev. 77*, 302L　CF_3Br

667 Sharbaugh, A. H.; Pritchard, B. S.; Thomas, V. G.; Mays, J. M.; and Dailey, B. P.　*Phys. Rev. 79*, 189L　GeH_3Br

668 Sharbaugh, A. H.; Thomas, V. G.; and Pritchard, B. S.　*Phys. Rev. 78*, 64L　SiH_3F

669 Shaull, J. M.　*Proc. IRE 38*, 6　Freq. time standard

670 Sheridan, J., and Gordy, W.　*Phys. Rev. 77*, 719L　Trifluorosilane derivatives

671 Sheridan, J., and Gordy, W.　*Phys. Rev. 77*, 292L　CF_3Br, CF_3I, CF_3CN

672 Sheridan, J., and Gordy, W.　*Phys. Rev. 79*, 224A　CH_3CCBr

673 Sheridan, J., and Gordy, W.　*Phys. Rev. 79*, 513　NF_3

674 Shulman, R. G., and Townes, C. H.　*Phys. Rev. 77*, 421L　OCS, HCN l-doub.

675 Shulman, R. G., and Townes, C. H.　*Phys. Rev. 77*, 500　OCS dip. mom.

676 Shulman, R. G., and Townes, C. H.　*Phys. Rev. 78*, 347A　HCN l-doub. transitions

677 Shulman, R. G.; Townes, C. H.; and Dailey, B. P.　*Phys. Rev. 78*, 145　Dipole moments

678 Simmons, J. W., and Anderson, W. E.　*Phys. Rev. 80*, 338　Cent. dist. methyl halides, BrCN, ICN

679 Simmons, J. W.; Anderson, W. E.; and Gordy, W.　*Phys. Rev. 77*, **77**; *Erratum 86*, 1055 (1952)　HCN

680 Simmons, J. W., and Swan, W. O.　*Phys. Rev. 80*, 289L　CH_3Br

681 Smith, D. F.; Tidwell, M.; and Williams, D. V. P.　*Phys. Rev. 77*, 420L　BrF

682 Smith, D. F.; Tidwell, M.; and Williams, D. V. P.　*Phys. Rev. 79*, 1007L　BrCl

683 Smith, W. V., and Howard, R. R.　*Phys. Rev. 79*, 132　Collision diam., mol. quad. moments

684 Southern, A. L.; Morgan, H. W.; Kielholtz, G. W.; and Smith, W. V.　*Phys. Rev. 78*, 639A　NH_3, isotopic analysis

685 Townes, C. H., and Dailey, B. P.　*Phys. Rev. 78*, 346A　Quad. coup. and ionic character

686 Townes, C. H., and Low, W.　*Phys. Rev. 79*, 198A　Closed shells, 20 nucleons

687 Trambarulo, R., and Gordy, W.　*Phys. Rev. 79*, 224A　CD_3NC, CD_3CN

688	Trambarulo, R., and Gordy, W.	*J. Chem. Phys. 18,* 1613	CH_3CCH
689	Unterberger, R. R.; Trambarulo, R.; and Smith, W. V.	*J. Chem. Phys. 18,* 565L	$CHCl_3$
690	Weiss, M. T.; Strandberg, M. W. P.; Lawrance, R. B.; and Loomis, C. C.	*Phys. Rev. 78,* 202	B^{10}
691	Westenberg, A. A., and Wilson, E. B., Jr.	*J. Am. Chem. Soc. 72,* 199	CHCCN
692	Whiffen, D. H.	*Quarterly Reviews 4,* 131	Review
693	Williams, J. Q., and Gordy, W.	*J. Chem. Phys. 18,* 994L	Trimethyl methyl halides
694	Williams, J. Q., and Gordy, W.	*Phys. Rev. 79,* 225A	$CHBr_3$, PBr_3
695	Wilson, E. B., Jr.	*Faraday Society Discussions 9,* 108	Molecular structures

1951

701	Amble, E.	*Phys. Rev. 83,* 210A	Trioxane
702	Amble, E., and Schawlow, A. L.	*Phys. Rev. 82,* 328A	ReO_3Cl
703	Anderson, R. S.; Johnson, C. M.; and Gordy, W.	*Phys. Rev. 83,* 1061L	O_2, 2.5 mm
704	Anderson, R. S.; Smith, W. V.; and Gordy, W.	*Phys. Rev. 82,* 264L	O_2 line breadths
705	Anderson, W. E.; Sheridan, J.; and Gordy, W.	*Phys. Rev. 81,* 819	GeF_3Cl
706	Anderson, W. E.; Trambarulo, R.; Sheridan, J.; and Gordy, W.	*Phys. Rev. 82,* 58	CF_3CCH
707	Beringer, R., and Castle, J. G., Jr.	*Phys. Rev. 81,* 82	O_2
707a	Burkhard, D. G., and Dennison, D. M.	*Phys. Rev. 84,* 408	CH_3OH theory
708	Coles, D. K.; Good, W. E.; Bragg, J. K.; and Sharbaugh, A. H.	*Phys. Rev. 82,* 877	NH_3 Stark
708a	Cornwell, C. D.	*ONR Report, Iowa State,* January 1	C_2H_3Br
709	Costain, C. C.	*Phys. Rev. 82,* 108L	NH_3
710	Crable, G. F., and Smith, W. V.	*J. Chem. Phys. 19,* 502L	SO_2
711	Cunningham, G. L., Jr.; Boyd, A. W.; Myers, R. J.; Gwinn, W. D.; and LeVan, W. I.	*J. Chem. Phys. 19,* 676	Ethylene oxide, ethylene sulfide
712	de Heer, J.	*Phys. Rev. 83,* 741	*l*-doubling sym. tops
713	Eshbach, J. R., and Strandberg, M. W. P.	*Phys. Rev. 82,* 327A	Magnetic mom. poly. mol.
714	Ewen, H. I., and Purcell, E. M.	*Phys. Rev. 83,* 881A; *Nature 168,* 356	H, interstellar radiation

715	Freymann, R.	*Physica 17*, 328	C_2H_5Cl, mod. press.
716	Geschwind, S., and Gunther-Mohr, R.	*Phys. Rev. 81*, 882L	Ge, Si, S masses
717	Geschwind, S., and Gunther-Mohr, R.	*Phys. Rev. 82*, 346A	Si, S masses
718	Geschwind, S.; Gunther-Mohr, R.; and Townes, C. H.	*Phys. Rev. 83*, 209A	O^{17} quad. mom.
718a	Gilbert, D. A.	*ONR Report, Iowa State*, January 1	Cl^{36}
719	Gokhale, B. V.; Johnson, H. R.; and Strandberg, M. W. P.	*Phys. Rev. 83*, 881A	Electronic rot. interaction
720	Gokhale, B. V., and Strandberg, M. W. P.	*Phys. Rev. 82*, 327A; *84*, 844L	O_2
721	Good, W. E.; Coles, D. K.; Gunther-Mohr, R.; Schawlow, A. L.; and Townes, C. H.	*Phys. Rev. 83*, 880A	NH_3, hyperfine
722	Gordy, W.	*J. Chem. Phys. 19*, 792L	Nucl. quad. coupling
723	Gorter, C. J.	*Physica 17*, 169	Review
724	Gunther-Mohr, R.; Geschwind, S.; and Townes, C. H.	*Phys. Rev. 81*, 288L; *82*, 343A	Cl^{35}, Cl^{37} quad. mom.
725	Gunther-Mohr, R.; Geschwind, S.; and Townes, C. H.	*Phys. Rev. 81*, 289L	Nuclear polarization
726	Hill, R. M., and Smith, W. V.	*Phys. Rev. 82*, 451L	Mol. quad. mom. collision diameters
727	Hillger, R. E., and Strandberg, M. W. P.	*Phys. Rev. 82*, 327A; *83*, 575	HDS centrifugal distortion
727a	Honerjäger, R.	*Naturwiss. 38*, 34	Review
727b	Hughes, R. H.; Good, W. E.; and Coles, D. K.	*Phys. Rev. 84*, 418	CH_3OH
728	Hurd, F. K., and Hershberger, W. D.	*Phys. Rev. 82*, 95L	CH_3SH
728a	Jen, C. K.	*Phys. Rev. 81*, 197; *Physica 17*, 378	Magnetic mom.
729	Johnson, C. M.; Trambarulo, R.; and Gordy, W.	*Phys. Rev. 84*, 1178	Centrifugal distortion, various mol.
729a	Johnson, C. M.; Gordy, W.; and Livingston, R.	*Phys. Rev. 83*, 1249L	Cl^{36}
730	Johnson, H. R.; Ingersoll, J. G.; and Strandberg, M. W. P.	*Phys. Rev. 82*, 327A	CH_2CO
731	Kisliuk, P., and Townes, C. H.	*Phys. Rev. 83*, 210A	$AsCl_3$, $SbCl_3$
732	Koch, B.	*Ergeb. exakt. Naturwiss. XXIV*, 222	Review techniques
733	Lamont, H. R. L.	*Physica 17*, 446	Freq. stab.
734	Lawrance, R. B., and Strandberg, M. W. P.	*Phys. Rev. 83*, 363	CH_2O centrifugal distortion

734a	Leslie, D. C. M.	*Phil. Mag. 42*, 37	Collision broad. theory
735	Lide, D. R., Jr.	*J. Chem. Phys. 19*, 1605	CH_3SnH_3
736	Loomis, C. C., and Strandberg, M. W. P.	*Phys. Rev. 81*, 798	Deuterated phosphine, arsine, stibine
737	Lyons, H.; Kessler, M.; Rueger, L. J.; and Nuckolls, R. G.	*Phys. Rev. 81*, 297A, 630L	Deuterated ammonia
738	Magnuson, D. W.	*Phys. Rev. 83*, 485A; *J. Chem. Phys. 19*, 1071L	NOF
739	Maier, W.	*Ergeb. exakt. Naturwiss.* XXIV, 275	Review
740	Margenau, H.	*Phys. Rev. 82*, 156	Press. broad.
741	Mays, J. M., and Townes, C. H.	*Phys. Rev. 81*, 940	Ge isotopes
742	McAfee, K. B., Jr.	*Phys. Rev. 82*, 971L	NO_2
743	Miller, S. L.; Javan, A.; and Townes, C. H.	*Phys. Rev. 82*, 454L; *83*, 209A	O^{18} spin
744	Miller, S. L.; Kraitchman, J.; Dailey, B. P.; and Townes, C. H.	*Phys. Rev. 82*, 327A	CHD_2Cl
745	Minden, H. T., and Dailey, B. P.	*Phys. Rev. 82*, 338A	CH_3CF_3, CH_3SiF_3, hindered rot.
746	Mizushima, M.	*Phys. Rev. 83*, 94; *84*, 363L; *Physica 17*, 453	Press. broad.
747	Mizushima, M., and Ito, T.	*J. Chem. Phys. 19*, 739	Quad. coupling, three nuclei
747a	Muller, C. A., and Oort, J. H.	*Nature 168*, 357	Interstellar H
748	Newell, G., Jr., and Dicke, R. H.	*Phys. Rev. 81*, 297A; *83*, 1064L	Doppler linebreadth
749	Nielsen, H. H.	*Physica 17*, 432	*l*-doubling
749a	Nielsen, H. H.	*Revs. Modern Phys. 23*, 90	Vib.-rot. energies
749b	Nuckolls, R. G.; Rueger, L. J.; and Lyons, H.	*Phys. Rev. 83*, 880A	ND_3
750	Potter, C. A.; Bushkovitch, A. V.; and Rouse, A. G.	*Phys. Rev. 82*, 323A; *83*, 987	Press. broad.
750a	Poynter, R. L.	*ONR Report, Iowa State*, January 1	C_2H_3I
750b	Ranade, J. D.	*Phil. Mag. 42*, 279	Electric quadrupole mom. and mag. mom. of bromine
751	Rogers, J. D.; Pietenpol, W. J.; and Williams, D.	*Phys. Rev. 83*, 431	NOCl
752	Rogers, J. D., and Williams, D.	*Phys. Rev. 82*, 131A	HN_3
753	Rogers, J. D., and Williams, D.	*Phys. Rev. 82*, 323A	NOCl
754	Rogers, J. D., and Williams, D.	*Phys. Rev. 83*, 210A	HCOOH
755	Rogers, T. F.	*Phys. Rev. 83*, 881A	Line shapes

756	Rueger, L. J.; Lyons, H.; and Nuckolls, R. G.	*Rev. Sci. Instr. 22*, 428L	High-temp. Stark cell
757	Schawlow, A. L., and Townes, C. H.	*Phys. Rev. 82*, 268L	Nucl. mag. mom.
758	Shaw, T. M., and Windle, J. J.	*J. Chem. Phys. 19*, 1063L	CH_3SH
759	Sheridan, J., and Gordy, W.	*J. Chem. Phys. 19*, 965	Trifluorosilane derivatives
759a	Shimoda, K., and Nishikawa, T.	*J. Phys. Soc. Japan 6*, 512	Na hyperfine structure
759b	Shimoda, K., and Nishikawa, T.	*J. Phys. Soc. Japan 6*, 516	Zeeman-mod. spectrograph
760	Shoolery, J. N., and Sharbaugh, A. H.	*Phys. Rev. 82*, 95L	Dipole mom.
760a	Shoolery, J. N.; Shulman, R. G.; Sheehan, W. F., Jr.; Schomaker, V.; and Yost, D. M.	*J. Chem. Phys. 19*, 1364	CF_3CCH
761	Shoolery, J. N., and Shulman, R. G.	*Phys. Rev. 82*, 323A	CF_3CCH
762	Shoolery, J. N.; Shulman, R. G.; and Yost, D. M.	*J. Chem. Phys. 19*, 250L	HNCO, HNCS
763	Simmons, J. W.	*Phys. Rev. 83*, 485A	CD_3Cl, CD_3Br, CD_3I
764	Sirvetz, M. H.	*J. Chem. Phys. 19*, 938	SO_2
764a	Sirvetz, M. H.	*J. Chem. Phys. 19*, 1609L	Furan
765	Smith, D. F.; Tidwell, M.; Williams, D. V. P.; and Senatore, S. J.	*Phys. Rev. 83*, 485A	CF_2O
765a	Southern, A. L.; Morgan, H. W.; Keilholtz, G. W.; and Smith, W. V.	*Analyt. Chem. 23*, 1000	Isotopic detn. of C and N
766	Talley, R. M., and Nielsen, A. H.	*J. Chem. Phys. 19*, 805L	C_2D_2 vibr.
767	Tetenbaum, S. J.	*Phys. Rev. 82*, 323A	mm region
768	Townes, C. H.	*Physica 17*, 354	Nucl. properties
768a	Townes, C. H.	*J. Appl. Phys. 22*, 1365	Freq. stabilization
769	Van Vleck, J. H.	*Revs. Modern Phys. 23*, 213	Coupling of ang. mom. vectors
769a	Van Vleck, J. H.	*Phys. Rev. 83*, 880A	NH_3, hyperfine theory
770	Ting, Y.; Weatherly, T. L.; and Williams, D.	*Phys. Rev. 83*, 210A	DCN *l*-doublet transitions
771	Weber, J.	*Phys. Rev. 83*, 881A, 1058L	Press. broad.
771a	Weber, J., and Laidler, K. J.	*J. Chem. Phys. 19*, 381L, 1089	Kinetics NH_3-D_2 exchange
772	Weiss, M. T., and Strandberg, M. W. P.	*Phys. Rev. 81*, 286L; *82*, 326A; *83*, 567	Deuterated ammonia
773	Wentink, T., Jr.; Koski, W. S.; and Cohen, V. W.	*Phys. Rev. 81*, 296A, 948	S^{35}

| 774 | Wilson, E. B., Jr. | *Ann. Rev. Phys.* *Chem. II*, 151 | Review |
| 775 | | *Landolt-Börnstein Tabellen*, Aufl. 6, B. 1, T. 2 | Tables |

1952

(Incomplete)

801	Amble, E.; Miller, S. L.; Schawlow, A. L.; and Townes, C. H.	*J. Chem. Phys. 20,* 192L	ReO_3Cl
802	Anderson, P. W.	*Phys. Rev. 86,* 809L	Press. broad. theory
803	Artman, J. O., and Gordon, J. P.	*Phys. Rev. 87,* 227A	O_2, press. broad.
804	Beringer, R., and Rawson, E. B.	*Phys. Rev. 86,* 607A	NO, lambda-doubling
805	Beringer, R., and Rawson, E. B.	*Phys. Rev. 87,* 227A	Atomic H
806	Bloom, S., and Margenau, H.	*Phys. Rev. 85,* 717A	Press. broad. theory
807	Eshbach, J. R.; Hillger, R. E.; and Strandberg, M. W. P.	*Phys. Rev. 85,* 532	S^{33}, nucl. mag. mom.
808	Eshbach, J. R., and Strandberg, M. W. P.	*Phys. Rev. 85,* 24	Rot. mag. mom.
809	Fristrom, R.	*J. Chem. Phys. 20,* 1; *Phys. Rev. 85,* 717A	SO_2F_2
810	Geschwind, S.; Gunther-Mohr, R.; and Silvey, G.	*Phys. Rev. 85,* 474	O^{17}, spin. and quad. mom.
811	Ghosh, S. N.; Trambarulo, R.; and Gordy, W.	*J. Chem. Phys. 20,* 605	CHF_3, $CHCl_3$, CH_3CCl_3
812	Gilbert, D. A.	*Phys. Rev. 85,* 716A	Cl^{36}, spin
813	Hardy, W. A.; Silvey, G.; and Townes, C. H.	*Phys. Rev. 86,* 608A	Se^{79}, spin, quad. mom.
814	Hawkins, N. J.; Cohen, V. W.; and Koski, W. S.	*J. Chem. Phys. 20,* 528L	POF_3, PSF_3
815	Hrostowski, H. J.; Myers, R. J.; and Pimentel, G. C.	*J. Chem. Phys. 20,* 518L	B_5H_9
816	Hughes, R. H.	*Phys. Rev. 85,* 717A	O_3
817	Javan, A., and Grosse, A. V.	*Phys. Rev. 87,* 227A	MnO_3F
818	Javan, A., and Townes, C. H.	*Phys. Rev. 86,* 608A	ICN anomalies
819	Jen, C. K.; Barghausen, J. W. B.; and Stanley, R. W.	*Phys. Rev. 85,* 717A	Mol. mag. moments
820	Johnson, H. R.	*Phys. Rev. 85,* 764A	Spectrograph resolution and sensitivity
821	Johnson, H. R., and Strandberg, M. W. P.	*J. Chem. Phys. 20,* 687	Ketene
822	Johnson, H. R., and Strandberg, M. W. P.	*Phys. Rev. 85,* 503L	Reduction of Doppler broadening

823 Johnson, R. H., and Strandberg, M. W. P. — *Phys. Rev. 86*, 811L — Broad. by wall collisions

824 Jones, L. C.; Bushkovitch, A. V.; Potter, C. A.; and Rouse, A. G. — *Phys. Rev. 87*, 227A — Collision diameters in mixtures

825 Kisliuk, P., and Silvey, G. A. — *J. Chem. Phys. 20*, 517 — CF_3SF_5

826 Kivelson, D., and Wilson, E. B., Jr. — *Phys. Rev. 87*, 214A — Cent. dist. in asym. rotors

827 Klein, J. A.; Loubser, J. H. N.; Nethercot, A. H., Jr.; and Townes, C. H. — *Rev. Sci. Instr. 23*, 78 — Magnetron harmonics

828 Kojima, S.; Tsukada, K.; Hagiwara, S.; Mizushima, M.; and Ito, T. — *J. Chem. Phys. 20*, 804 — $CHBr_3$

829 Lide, D. R., Jr. — *Phys. Rev. 87*, 227A — CH_2F_2

830 Massey, J. T., and Bianco, D. R. — *Phys. Rev. 85*, 717A — H_2O_2

831 Miller, S. L.; Kotani, M.; and Townes, C. H. — *Phys. Rev. 86*, 607A — O_2, mag. hyperfine structure

832 Nethercot, A. H., Jr.; Javan, A.; and Townes, C. H. — *Phys. Rev. 87*, 226A — $C_8H_{13}Br$

833 Nethercot, A. H., Jr.; Klein, J. A.; and Townes, C. H. — *Phys. Rev. 86*, 798L — HCN

834 Rogers, J. D., and Williams, D. — *Phys. Rev. 86*, 654A — HN_3

835 Schwarz, R. — *Phys. Rev. 86*, 606A — Rot. mag. mom.

836 Silvey, G.; Hardy, W. A.; and Townes, C. H. — *Phys. Rev. 87*, 236A — TeCS

837 Simmons, J. W., and Goldstein, J. H. — *J. Chem. Phys. 20*, 122 — CD_3Cl, CD_3Br_3, CD_3I

838 Sheridan, J., and Gordy, W. — *J. Chem. Phys. 20*, 591 — CF_3Br, CF_3I, CF_3CN

839 Sheridan, J., and Gordy, W. — *J. Chem. Phys. 20*, 735 — CH_3CCBr, CH_3CCI

840 Smith, D. F. — *Phys. Rev. 86*, 608A — ClF_3

841 Smith, D. F., and Magnuson, D. W. — *Phys. Rev. 87*, 226A — NO_2F

842 Sternheimer, R. — *Phys. Rev. 86*, 316; 595A — Mag. hyperfine structure, theory

843 Stitch, M. L.; Honig, A.; and Townes, C. H. — *Phys. Rev. 86*, 607A — KCl, TlCl

844 Stitch, M. L.; Honig, A.; and Townes, C. H. — *Phys. Rev. 86*, 813L — CsCl, NaCl

845 Tetenbaum, S. J. — *Phys. Rev. 86*, 440 — BrCN, 6 mm

846 Weatherly, T. L.; Manring, E. R.; and Williams, D. — *Phys. Rev. 85*, 717A — l-doubling in HCN, DCN

847 Weatherly, T. L., and Williams, D. — *J. Chem. Phys. 20*, 755L — Acetone

848 Williams, Q.; Sheridan, J.; and Gordy, W. — *J. Chem. Phys. 20*, 164 — POF_3, PSF_3, $POCl_3$, $PSCl_3$

Paramagnetic Resonance of Solids and Liquids

1945

101P	Zavoisky, E.	*J. Phys. U.S.S.R.* *9*, 245	$CuCl_2$

1946

201P	Cummerow, R. L., and Halliday, D.	*Phys. Rev. 70*, 433L	Manganous salts
202P	Zavoisky, E.	*J. Phys. U.S.S.R.* *10*, 170	$CuCl_2$, $CuSO_4$, $CrCl_3$, $MnCO_3$
203P	Zavoisky, E.	*J. Phys. U.S.S.R.* *10*, 197	$MnSO_4$, $CuCl_2$, $CrCl_3$, $MnCO_3$

1947

301P	Bagguley, D. M. S., and Griffiths, J. H. E.	*Nature 160*, 532	Chrome alum
302P	Cummerow, R. L.; Halliday, D.; and Moore, G. E.	*Phys. Rev. 72*, 173A	Iron-group salts
303P	Cummerow, R. L.; Halliday, D.; and Moore, G. E.	*Phys. Rev. 72*, 1233	Iron-group salts
304P	Gorter, C. J., and Van Vleck, J. H.	*Phys. Rev. 72*, 1128L	Theory, exchange interaction
305P	Kozuirev, B. M., and Salikov,. C. G.	*C. R. Acad. Sci. U.S.S.R. 58*, 1023	Pentaphenyl-cyclopenta-dienyl
306P	Weiss, P. R.; Whitmer, C. A.; Torrey, H. E.; and Jen Sen Hsiang	*Phys. Rev. 72*, 975L	Chromic ammo-nium alum

1948

401P	Bagguley, D. M. S., and Griffiths, J. H. E.	*Nature 162*, 538	Copper sulphate
402P	Bleaney, B., and Penrose, R. P.	*Proc. Phys. Soc. (London) 60*, 395	Chromic alum
403P	Bagguley, D. M. S.; Bleaney, B.; Griffiths, J. H. E.; Penrose, R. P., and Plumpton, B. I.	*Proc. Phys. Soc. (London) 61*, 542, 551	Survey
404P	Halliday, D., and Wheatley, J.	*Phys. Rev. 74*, 1712 1724L	Chrome alum, Mn
405P	Kittel, C., and Luttinger, J. M.	*Phys. Rev. 73*, 162	Theory
406P	Van Vleck, J. H.	*Phys. Rev. 74*, 1168	Theory, dipolar broadening
407P	Weiss, P. R.	*Phys. Rev. 73*, 470	Chromic alums
408P	Whitmer, C. A.; Weidner, R. T.; and Weiss, P. R.	*Phys. Rev. 73*, 1468L	Chrome alums
409P	Whitmer, C. A.; Weidner, R. T.; Hsiang, J. S.; and Weiss, P. R.	*Phys. Rev. 74*, 1478	Chrome alums

1949

501P Abragam, A., and Pryce, M. H. L.   *Nature 163*, 992   Theory, hyper-
                                                                     fine structure
502P Arnold, R., and Kip, A.   *Phys. Rev. 75*, 1199   Copper sulphate
503P Bleaney, B.   *Phys. Rev. 75*,   Chromic sul-
                                           1962L   phate alums
504P Bleaney, B., and Ingram, D. J. E.   *Nature 164*, 116   Hyperfine struc-
                                                                     ture in divalent
                                                                     cobalt

505P Bleaney, B.; Penrose, R. P.; and   *Proc. Roy. Soc.*   Copper Tutton
        Plumpton, B. I.   (*London*) A *198*,   salts
                                           406
507P Holden, A. N.; Kittel, C.; and   *Phys. Rev. 75*,   Nickel fluorosili-
        Yager, W. A.   1443L   cate
508P Holden, A. N.; Kittel, C.; Mer-   *Phys. Rev. 75*,   Paramagnetic or-
        ritt, F. R.; and Yager, W. A.   1614L   ganic com-
                                                                     pounds
509P Hutchison, C. A., Jr.   *Phys. Rev. 75*, 1769   Irradiated LiF
510P Ingram, D. J. E.   *Proc. Phys. Soc.*   Theory, hyper-
                                           (*London*) A *62*,   fine structure
                                           664L

511P Penrose, R. P.   *Nature 163*, 992   Hyperfine struc-
                                                                     ture
512P Pryce, M. H. L.   *Nature 164*, 117   Hyperfine struc-
                                                                     ture
513P Weidner, R. T.; Weiss, P. R.;   *Phys. Rev. 76*,   Iron ammonium
        Whitmer, C. A.; and Blosser,   1727L   alum
        D. R.
514P Wheatley, J., and Halliday, D.   *Phys. Rev. 75*, 1412   Copper sulphate
515P Yu Ting; Weidler, R.; and Wil-   *Phys. Rev. 75*, 980L   Iron-group salts
        liams, D.

1950

601P Abragam, A.   *Phys. Rev. 79*, 534L   Iron transition
                                                                     group
602P Abragam, A., and Pryce, M. H. L.   *Proc. Phys. Soc.*   Theory, copper
                                           A *63*, 409L   fluorosilicate
603P Altshuler, S. A.; Kurenev, V. Ya.;   *Doklady Akad.*   Rare-earth ele-
        and Salikhov, S. G.   *Nauk U.S.S.R.*   ments
                                           70, 201
604P Bagguley, D. M. S., and Griffiths,   *Proc. Roy. Soc.*   Copper sulphate
        J. H. E.   (*London*) A *201*,
                                           366
605P Benzie, R. J., and Cooke, A. H.   *Proc. Phys. Soc.*   Spin-lattice re-
                                           (*London*) A *63*,   laxation
                                           201
605aP Benzie, R. J., and Cooke, A. H.   *Proc. Phys. Soc.*   Copper cesium
                                           (*London*) A *63*,   sulphate
                                           1366L

606P	Bijl, D.	*Proc. Phys. Soc.* (*London*) *63*, 405L	Titanium cesium alum
607P	Bleaney, B.	*Proc. Phys. Soc.* (*London*) *63*, 407L	Titanium alum
608P	Bleaney, B., and Ingram, D. J. E.	*Proc. Phys. Soc.* (*London*) A *63*, 408L	Copper fluorosilicate
609P	Bleaney, B., and Scovil, H. E. D.	*Proc. Phys. Soc.* (*London*) A *63*, 1369L	Nuclear spin of Nd^{143} and Nd^{145}
610P	England, T. S., and Schneider, E. E.	*Nature 166*, 437	Manganese
611P	Holden, A. N.; Kittel, C.; Merritt, F. R.; and Yager, W. A.	*Phys. Rev. 77*, 147L	Organic free radicals
612P	Joynson, A. F., and Grayson-Smith, H.	*Can. J. Research 28*, 229	Iron-group salts
613P	Kikuchi, C., and Spence, R. D.	*Am. J. Phys. 18*, 167	Survey
614P	Lacroix, R. P.; Ryter, C. E.; and Extermann, C. R.	*Phys. Rev. 80*, 763L	Measuring methods
615P	Malvano, M., and Panetti, M.	*Phys. Rev. 78*, 826L	Chrome alums
616P	Penrose, R. P., and Stevens, K. W. H.	*Proc. Phys. Soc.* (*London*) *63*, 29	Nickel fluorosilicate
617P	Pryce, M. H. L.	*Proc. Phys. Soc.* (*London*) A *63*, 25	Perturbation procedure
618P	Pryce, M. H. L., and Stevens, K. W. H.	*Proc. Phys. Soc.* (*London*) *63*, 36	Line width in crystals
619P	Townes, C. H., and Turkevitch, J.	*Phys. Rev. 77*, 148L	Exchange narrowing in organic radical
620P	Ubbink, J.; Poulis, J. A.; and Gorter, C. J.	*Physica 16*, 570	Double jumps

1951

701P	Abragam, A.	*Physica 17*, 209	Iron transition group
702P	Abragam, A., and Pryce, M. H. L.	*Proc. Roy. Soc.* (*London*) A *205*, 135	Theory, nuclear hyperfine structure
703P	Abragam, A., and Pryce, M. H. L.	*Proc. Roy. Soc.* (*London*) A *206*, 164	Theory, copper Tutton salts
704P	Abragam, A., and Pryce, M. H. L.	*Proc. Roy. Soc.* (*London*) A *206*, 173	Hydrated cobalt salts
705P	Anderson, P. W.	*Phys. Rev. 82*, 342A	Line breadth in diluted xtals
706P	Benzie, R. J.	*Proc. Phys. Soc.* (*London*) A *64*, 507L	Spin-lattice relaxation

707P	Bleaney, B.	*Phil. Mag. 42*, 441	Hyperfine structure, nuclear alignment
708P	Bleaney, B.	*Physica 17*, 175	Hyperfine structure
708aP	Bleaney, B., and Bowers, K. D.	*Proc. Phys. Soc. (London)* A *64*, 1135	Cr^{53} spin
709P	Bleaney, B.; Bowers, K. D.; and Ingram, D. J. E.	*Proc. Phys. Soc. (London)* A *64*, 758L	Quadrupole moments of Cu^{63} and Cu^{65}
710P	Bleaney, B.; Elliott, R. J.; and Scovil, H. E. D.	*Proc. Phys. Soc. (London)* A *64*, 933L	Dipole-dipole interaction in rare-earth ethylsulfates
711P	Bleaney, B.; Elliott, R. J.; Scovil, H. E. D.; and Trenam, R. S.	*Phil. Mag. 42*, 1062	Gadolinium ethylsulfate
712P	Bleaney, B., and Ingram, D. J. E.	*Proc. Roy. Soc. (London)* A *205*, 336	Manganese salts
713P	Bleaney, B., and Ingram, D. J. E.	*Proc. Roy. Soc. (London)* A *208*, 143	Hyperfine structure in cobalt salts
714P	Bleaney, B.; Ingram, D. J. E.; and Scovil, H. E. D.	*Proc. Phys. Soc. (London)* A *64*, 601	$V(NH_4)_2(SO_4)_2 \cdot 6H_2O$
715P	Bleaney, B., and Scovil, H. E. D.	*Proc. Phys. Soc. (London)* A *64*, 204L	Nuclear spin of Er^{167}
716P	Bogle, G. S.; Cooke, A. H.; and Whitley, S.	*Proc. Phys. Soc. (London)* A *64*, 931L	Cerium ethylsulphate
717P	Carr, E. F., and Kikuchi, C.	*Phys. Rev. 82*, 342A	Theory, hyperfine structure
718P	Eisenstein, J.	*Phys. Rev. 82*, 342A	Ammonium chrome alums
719P	Eisenstein, J.	*Phys. Rev. 84*, 548	Relaxation theory
720P	Elliott, R. J., and Stevens, K. W. H.	*Proc. Phys. Soc. (London)* A *64*, 205L	Rare-earth ethylsulphates
721P	Elliott, R. J., and Stevens, K. W. H.	*Proc. Phys. Soc. (London)* A *64*, 932L	Cerium ethylsulphate, theory
722P	Fujimoto, M., and Itoh, J.	*Physica 17*, 266	$K_2CuCl_42H_2O$, $(NH_4)_2CuCl_4 \cdot 2H_2O$
723P	Garstens, M. A., and Ryan, A. H.	*Phys. Rev. 81*, 888L	Metal NH_3 solutions

724P	Griffiths, J. H. E., and Owen, J.	*Proc. Phys. Soc.* (*London*) A *64*, 583L	$Ni(NH_4)_2(SO_4)_2 \cdot 6H_2O$
725P	Holden, A. N.; Yager, W. A.; and Merritt, F. R.	*J. Chem. Phys. 19*, 1319L	Free radicals
726P	Hutchison, C. A., and Pastor, R. C.	*Phys. Rev. 81*, 282L	K solution in liquid NH_3
727P	Ishiguro, E.; Kambe, K.; and Usui, T.	*Phys. Rev. 82*, 680	Theory, relaxation time in chrome alum
728P	Ishiguro, E.; Kambe, K.; and Usui, T.	*Physica 17*, 310	Exchange interaction of nickel ions in nickel fluorosilicate
729P	Itoh, J.; Fujimoto, M.; and Ibamoto, H.	*Phys. Rev. 83*, 852L	Chlorides of copper
730P	Kip, A. F.; Malvano, R.; and Davis, C. F.	*Phys. Rev. 82*, 342A	Ammonium chrome alum
731P	Kumagai, H.; Ōno, K.; Hayashi, I.; Abe, H.; Shimada, J.; Shôno, H.; and Ibamoto, H.	*Phys. Rev. 83*, 1077L	Interionic dist. and line widths
732P	Kumagai, H.; Ōno, K.; Hayashi, I.; Abe, H.; Shôno, H.; Tachimori, S.; Ibamoto, H.; and Shimada, J.	*Phys. Rev. 82*, 954L	Mn sulfate
733P	Lacroix, R. P., and Extermann, R.	*Physica 17*, 427	Absorption and dispersion measurement
734P	Lancaster, F., and Gordy, W.	*J. Chem. Phys. 19*, 1181, *Errata 20*, 740 (1952)	Various organic and inorganic salts of iron and rare-earth group
735P	Levinthal, E. C.; Rogers, E. H.; and Ogg, R. A., Jr.	*Phys. Rev. 83*, 182L	Alkali-metal solutions
736P	Meijer, P. H. E.	*Physica 17*, 899	Iron-alum theory
737P	Ollom, J. F., and Van Vleck, J. H.	*Physica 17*, 205	Theory, $NiSiF_6 \cdot 6H_2O$
738P	Ramaseshan, S., and Suryan, G.	*Phys. Rev. 84*, 593L	Trivalent molybdenum cpds.
738aP	Schneider, E. E.	*Nature 168*, 645	X-ray irradiated plastics
739P	Schneider, E. E., and England, T. S.	*Physica 17*, 221	Hyperfine structure and saturation in Mn, resonance in irradiated alkali halides
740P	Ting, Y., and Williams, D.	*Phys. Rev. 82*, 507	Various salts

741P	Tinkham, M., and Kip, A.	*Phys. Rev. 83*, 657L	Absorption in crystals having color centers
742P	Tinkham, M.; Weinstein, R.; and Kip, A.	*Phys. Rev. 84*, 848L	Liquids
√743P	Ubbink, J.; Poulis, J. A.; and Gorter, C. J.	*Physica 17*, 213	Iron alums
√744P	Whitmer, C. A., and Weidner, R. T.	*Phys. Rev. 84*, 159L	Iron-alum salts

1952

(Incomplete)

801P	Bleaney, B., and Bowers, K. D.	*Phil. Mag. 43*, 372L	Anom. paramag. and exch. interaction in copper acetate
802P	Bogle, G. S., and Scovil, H. E. D.	*Proc. Phys. Soc. (London)* A 65, 368L	$Sm^{147, 149}$ spins
802aP	Bowers, K. D.	*Proc. Phys. Soc. (London)* A 65, 860	Cr^{53} mag. mom.
803P	Carr, E. F., and Kikuchi, C.	*Am. J. Phys. 20*, 110L	Demonstration model for nucl. and paramag. resonance
804P	Cohen, V. W.; Kikuchi, C.; and Turkevich, J.	*Phys. Rev. 85*, 379L; *86*, 608A	Picryl-n-amino carbazyl
805P	Elliott, R. J., and Stevens, K. W. H.	*Proc. Phys. Soc. (London)* A 65, 370L	$SmEtSO_4$, theory
806P	Garstens, M. A., and Liebson, S. H.	*Phys. Rev. 87*, 230A	$Mn(NO_3)_2$, conc. soln.
807P	Ghosh, S. N.; Gordy, W.; and Hill, D. G.	*Phys. Rev. 87*, 229A	Uranium salts
808P	Hershberger, W. D., and Leifer, H. N.	*Phys. Rev. 87*, 229A	Phosphors
809P	Hutchison, C. A., Jr.; Pastor, R. C.; and Kowalsky, A. G.	*J. Chem. Phys. 20*, 534L	Organic free radicals
809aP	Kikuchi, C.; Sirvetz, M. H.; and Cohen, V. W.	*Phys. Rev. 88*, 142	V^{50} spin
810P	Kumagai, H.; Ōno, K.; and Hayashi, I.	*Phys. Rev. 85*, 925L	Line width and exch. interaction in Mn^{++} and Fe^{+++} salts
811P	Overhauser, A. W.	*Phys. Rev. 86*, 646A	Paramag. relax. in metals
812P	Pake, G. E.; Townsend, J.; and Weissman, S. I.	*Phys. Rev. 85*, 682L	$(SO_3)_2NO^{--}$

813P	Stevens, K. W. H.	*Proc. Phys. Soc.* (*London*) A *65*, 209	Rare-earth ions, theory
814P	Wada, W. W.	*Phys. Rev. 87*, 229A	Vanadous Tutton salts, Stark and Zeeman effects, theory
815P	Weidner, R. T., and Whitmer, C. A.	*Rev. Sci. Instr. 23*, 75	Recording techniques
816P	Weidner, R. T., and Whitmer, C. A.	*J. Chem. Phys. 20*, 749L	Line shapes and dispersion

Ferromagnetic Resonance

Pre-1946

101F	Dorfmann, J.	*Z. Physik 17*, 98 (1923)	Theory
102F	Gans, R., and Loyante, R. G.	*Ann. Physik 64*, 209 (1921)	Nickel
103F	Landau, L., and Lifshitz, E.	*Physik. Z. Sowjet-union 8*, 153 (1935)	Theory, dispersion

1946

201F	Akheiser, A.	*J. Phys. U.S.S.R. 10*, 217	Theory, line widths
202F	Griffiths, J. H. E.	*Nature 158*, 670	Nickel, iron, cobalt

1947

301F	Yager, W. A., and Bozorth, R. M.	*Phys. Rev. 72*, 80	Supermalloy
302F	Kittel, C.	*Phys. Rev. 71*, 270	Theory, anomalous Larmor frequencies
303F	Snoek, J. L.	*Nature 160*, 60	Theory

1948

401F	Hewitt, W. H., Jr.	*Phys. Rev. 73*, 1118	Ferromagnetic semi-conductors
402F	Kittel, C.	*Phys. Rev. 73*, 155	Theory
403F	Luttinger, J. M., and Kittel, C.	*Helv. Phys. Acta 21*, 480	Theory
404F	Polder, D.	*Phys. Rev. 73*, 1120L	Theory
405F	Snoek, J. L.	*Physica 14*, 207	Theory

1949

501F	Beljers, H. G.	*Physica 14*, 629	Ferrites
502F	Bickford, L. R., Jr.	*Phys. Rev. 76*, 137	Magnetite
503F	Brown, W. F., Jr.	*Phys. Rev. 75*, 1959L	Theory, crystal interactions
504F	Kip, A., and Arnold, R.	*Phys. Rev. 75*, 1556	Iron single crystal
505F	Kittel, C.	*Phys. Rev. 76*, 743	Theory, spectroscopic splitting factor
506F	Kittel, C.; Yager, W. A.; and Merritt, F. R.	*Physica 15*, 256	Plane specimen, different orientations
507F	Polder, D.	*Phil. Mag. 40*, 99	Theory
508F	Polder, D.	*Physica 15*, 253	Theory
509F	Rado, G. T.	*Phys. Rev. 75*, 893; erratum *75*, 1451L	Theory, domain interactions
510F	Richardson, J. M.	*Phys. Rev. 75*, 1630A	Theory
511F	Van Vleck, J. H.	*Physica 15*, 197	Theory
512F	Yager, W. A.	*Phys. Rev. 75*, 316L	Supermalloy
513F	Yager, W. A., and Merritt, F. R.	*Phys. Rev. 75*, 318L	Heusler alloy

1950

601F	Bickford, L. R., Jr.	*Phys. Rev. 78*, 449	Magnetite single crystal
602F	Birks, J. B.	*Proc. Phys. Soc. (London)* B *63*, 65	Ferrites
603F	Bloembergen, N.	*Phys. Rev. 78*, 572	Temperature effects on g-value and line width
604F	Guillaud, C.; Yager, W. A.; Merritt, F. R.; and Kittel, C.	*Phys. Rev. 79*, 181L	Manganese ferrite, theory, ferrites
605F	Itoh, J., and Akioka, T.	*Phys. Rev. 77*, 293L	Molybdenum alloy
606F	Kittel, C., and Herring, C.	*Phys. Rev. 77*, 725L	Effect of exchange interaction
607F	Rado, G. T.; Wright, R. W.; and Emerson, W. H.	*Phys. Rev. 80*, 273	Mechanisms for dispersion in ferrites
608F	Van Vleck, J. H.	*Phys. Rev. 78*, 266	Theory
609F	Welch, A. J. E.; Nicks, P. F.; Fairweather, A.; and Roberts, F. F.	*Phys. Rev. 77*, 403L	Natural resonance in Mg ferrite

| 610F | Yager, W. A., Galt, J. K.; Merritt, F. R.; and Wood, E. A. | *Phys. Rev. 80*, 744 | Nickel ferrite |
| 611F | Trounson, E. P.; Bleil, D. F.; Wangsness, R. K.; and Maxwell, L. R. | *Phys. Rev. 79*, 542L | Magnetic resonance in antiferromagnetic materials |

1951

701F	Beljers, H. G.	*Physica 17*, 269	Induced magnetic moment
702F	Galt, J. K.	*Phys. Rev. 83*, 208A	Fe_3O_4 relaxation
703F	Galt, J. K.; Yager, W. A.; Remeika, J. P.; and Merritt, F. R.	*Phys. Rev. 81*, 470L	Zinc-manganese ferrite
704F	Griffiths, J. H. E.	*Physica 17*, 253	Thin Ni-films
705F	Kittel, C.	*J. physique et radium 12*, 291	Survey
706F	Li, Y. Y.	*Phys. Rev. 84*, 721	Anti-ferromagnetism, theory
707F	Lidiard, A. B.	*Proc. Phys. Soc. (London) A 64*, 814	Theory
708F	Macdonald, J. R.	*Phys. Rev. 81*, 312A	Ni-films
709F	Macdonald, J. R.	*Proc. Phys. Soc. (London) A 64*, 968	Theory, internal field
710F	Okamura, T.	*Nature 168*, 162	$NiOFe_2O_3$
711F	Okamura, T., and Torizuka, Y.	*Phys. Rev. 83*, 847L	$MnOFe_2O_3$
712F	Okamura, T.; Torizuka, Y.; and Kojima, Y.	*Phys. Rev. 82*, 285L	Anti-ferromagnetic resonance
713F	Okamura, T.; Torizuka, Y.; and Kojima, Y.	*Phys. Rev. 84*, 372L	Cobalt ferrite
714F	Stevens, K. W. H.	*Phys. Rev. 81*, 1058L	Theory antiferromagnetites
715F	Tsuya, N., and Ichikawa, Y.	*Phys. Rev. 83*, 1065L	Dipolar broadening
716F	Van Vleck, J. H.	*Physica 17*, 234	Theory
717F	Yager, W. A.; Merritt, F. R.; and Guillaud, C.	*Phys. Rev. 81*, 477L	Ferrites

1952

(Incomplete)

801F	Bloembergen, N., and Damon, R. W.	*Phys. Rev. 85*, 699L	Relaxation effects
802F	Keffer, F., and Kittel, C.	*Phys. Rev. 85*, 329	Theory, antiferromag.
803F	Maxwell, L. R.	*Am. J. Phys. 20*, 80	Anti-ferromag. materials
804F	Okamura, T., and Kojima, Y.	*Phys. Rev. 85*, 690L	Cobalt-zinc ferrite

805F	Okamura, T., and Kojima, Y.	*Phys. Rev. 86*, 1040L	Copper ferrite
806F	Okamura, T.; Kojima, Y.; and Torizuka, Y.	*Phys. Rev. 85*, 693L	Zinc-manganese ferrite
807F	Rado, G. T.; Wright, R. W.; Emerson, W. H.; and Terris, A.	*Phys. Rev. 86*, 599A	Ferrite, temp. depend.
808F	Stevens, K. W. H.	*Proc. Phys. Soc. (London)* A 65, 149L	Line widths
809F	Ubbink, J.	*Phys. Rev. 86*, 567L	Theory, anti-ferromag.
810F	Ubbink, J.; Poulis, J. A.; Gerritsen, H. J.; and Gorter, C. J.	*Physica 18*, 361	Anti-ferromag. resonance
811F	van Trier, A. A. Th. M.	*Phys. Rev. 87*, 227A	Anomalous wave types
812F	Wangsness, R. K.	*Phys. Rev. 86*, 146, 646A	Systems with two mag. sublattices

NAME INDEX

(Appendix and Bibliography excluded.)

435

SUBJECT INDEX

Physical
Sciences